GL copy

(this is a 2nd copy

Another exact copy in Stacks 4/2014)

this copy not in online catalog

Microphotography

PHOTOGRAPHY *AND* *PHOTOFABRICATION*
AT EXTREME RESOLUTION

Microphotography

PHOTOGRAPHY *AND PHOTOFABRICATION*
AT EXTREME RESOLUTION

G. W. W. STEVENS

M.A., Ph.D., Sc.D.(Cantab.), F.R.P.S.

JOHN WILEY & SONS, INC.

New York

Library of Congress Catalog Card Number
68–22563

To MY WIFE

Contents

List of Figures

List of Plates

Preface to Revised Edition

When writing the first edition of this book, several acquaintances doubted whether there was enough material to justify a book—or whether more than a handful of people would buy it, if it were published. The practical test confuted their misgivings. The first edition was published at a time when more advanced techniques were being rapidly developed not only in document reproduction, but also for the fabrication of long gratings and electronic and mechanical devices. Within less than a decade, the resultant mass of further information merited the preparation of this expanded edition. The great quantity and complexity of this new material has, in fact, constituted one of my greatest problems. One man could not hope to achieve an equal depth of understanding of all the matters touched on here.

To be true to myself, therefore, I decided to write from the viewpoint of a photographic scientist and, for the benefit of both myself and my readers, to explain many of the ingenious applications in as simple terms as I could contrive. In doing this, I have attempted to show what properties of microphotographic processes seemed to be of critical importance for each diverse application. By tackling my problem in this way, I hope this book may serve as a mental bridge between photographic technologists, and such people as instrument designers, electronics engineers and systems designers and data-processing engineers. When experts in these applied fields find my accounts inadequate or out-of-date, I would welcome quotable references or suggestions for improving the appropriate sections in further revisions of this book.

As when writing the first edition, I have derived countless benefits from working in the Research Laboratories of Kodak Ltd. Numerous colleagues have been most generous in helping me to interpret matters at the boundaries of my comprehension, and in drawing my attention to publications I could have missed. For discussions on the special optical and photographic problems of this work I am indebted to many, including Mr B. MacAlpine, Mr E. W. H. Selwyn, Mr T. M. Shapley and Mr N. Sherlock at Harrow and Mr J. H. Altman, Mr H. Fromm, Mr J. G. Millikan, Mr L. E. Martinson, Mr G. Rudd and

Dr J. Spence at Rochester, and Dr E. Bovey of British Scientific Instrument Research Association. Librarians Dr R. S. Schultze* and Miss M. D. Gauntlett are thanked for their alertness in directing many references to me. The form of this revised edition owes much to the suggestions of Dr Walter Clark, who also made many constructive comments when he read the complete manuscript. For the collection of a whole bundle of photographs, I am grateful to Mr G. Eaton and several other colleagues at Rochester.

Both industrial users of microphotography and manufacturers of special equipment and materials have liberally supplied me with information and photographs for this edition. In fact, I feel embarrassed by the fact that in the end I found I had collected more photographs than could possibly be used. In apologizing for not using much material so willingly offered, it should be explained that the desire to illustrate every refinement had to compromise with the need to avoid undue increase in the cost of the book. In the case of Plates 43–7, I should mention that these *do not represent* the finest or most advanced products that Texas Instruments and other manufacturers are now making. I decided to use these particular photographs because of their clarity in demonstrating integrated circuit fabrication.

For any technical author, when to stop modifications and go to press is a difficult decision, which is especially acute when fresh literature on his subject is appearing almost daily. In these circumstances, it is obvious that the complex process of book production will make the work less up-to-date than journal articles. To counter this immediate obsolescence, I have attempted to concentrate on first principles and the apparent reasons why special methods were adopted. Lessons thereby learned can frequently be applied later, even when many circumstances have changed. The preparation of this edition provided an opportunity for facing squarely some of the issues I found I had 'ducked' in the first edition. In doing this, I may have made the book more difficult to read, but I hope the end product is more useful. Some readers are likely to be disappointed in finding that important topics (such as the theory of indexing) are not mentioned at all. I believe that specialists will nevertheless soon find such topics if they follow the literature trails leading from the references I quote.

I faced a particularly formidable problem in the rewriting of the section on document microphotography (Chapter 12). It was most difficult to visualize how so many developments could usefully be

* Deceased

covered in a chapter of reasonable length, rather than in a multi-volume treatise. For this purpose, I decided to arrange the information into a rather formal framework, within which I have dealt with photographic technical matters on the basis of first principles. If this brief treatment only helps readers to ask themselves the appropriate questions before embarking on specific projects, it will have served its main purpose. Finally, I gratefully acknowledge help in proof correction from my wife, daughter (Wendy) and son (Nigel).

34 Castle Hill,   *G. W. W. Stevens*
Berkhamsted,
Herts., England

AUTHOR'S NOTE

This book is published for information only. Nothing contained herein is to be considered or construed as a recommendation of any use, manufacture or sale that may infringe or contribute to infringement of any patents now or hereafter issued.

1 · Introduction to Microphotography

This book describes the production and application of *microphotographs*. That is, photographs in which the details are reduced to a minute or even a microscopic scale. By the use of special sensitive materials and techniques microphotographic images can be made so sharp that they can be usefully viewed at magnifications requiring use of a compound microscope. The reduction factors used in making microphotographs are generally less than those employed when miles of country seen from a hill top are recorded on a negative only an inch or two wide, but such photographs can only be usefully viewed at lower magnification.

Essentially, techniques of microphotography employ all available means for delaying the loss of detail which tends to result from the use of large reduction factors. Emulsions of much reduced grain size are employed, and to offset the great exposures therefore required, only stationary objects are usually reproduced. These are illuminated very brightly and exposure times of a second or longer are usually given. Higher performances are also demanded of lens systems, and are secured by using only the axial region of certain types of high aperture objectives. With these materials it is necessary to employ refined techniques for focusing, and for the control of exposure level and degree of development. Thus, in a nut-shell, it can be said that sharpness of image, the quality of the lens, and sensitive material are prime requirements for microphotography. Matters of convenience cannot be permitted the priority they doubtless deserve in other photographic activities.

Microphotography and Photomicrography

In this book *microphotography* is used in the sense originally suggested in 1858, and is to be differentiated from *photomicrography*, which is the reverse process of producing enlarged photographs of microscopic details. Unfortunately, in English the two words have become almost hopelessly confused by careless usage or faulty translation from the German Language. Students should beware such confusions, which have been perpetrated by the most exalted authorities. However, reference to even a brief abstract usually shows in which sense the words have been used.

1

Both microphotography and the reversed technique of photomicrography are necessarily concerned with the resolution, useful flat fields and methods of using objectives. The microscopist undertaking microphotography will find other similarities, and books on photomicrography and general microscopy contain much information of use to the microphotographer. But discretion is needed in interpreting this information, in the light of the essential differences between these arts. Photographic emulsions specially suitable for microphotography have little advantage for photomicrography. For instance, when a 4 mm ($\frac{1}{6}$ in) objective giving a resolution of 2,500 lines per mm is used to project an image enlarged 500 times, the resolution of the enlarged aerial image cannot possibly exceed 5 lines/mm. The resolution of any but the very fastest emulsion should thus prove adequate, and it would be futile to use a very slow emulsion capable of giving 1,000 lines/mm, and requiring ten-thousand times greater exposure.

ORIGINS OF MICROPHOTOGRAPHY

Whether they be in the form of paintings or models or documents, miniature reproductions of familiar objects have for many centuries fascinated the human mind. Miniature inscriptions were produced by the Assyrians some 5,000 years ago. During his excavation at Ninevah, Layard found hexagonal clay cylinders inscribed with characters so small that a magnifying glass was needed to ascertain their form, and so perfect and accurately made that it seems as if they could only have been produced by an elaborate instrument. In his *Micrographia*, one of the earliest books on objects observed with the compound microscope, Robert Hooke described the appearance of minute hand writing and discussed its application to secret messages [1]. Miniature writing and the printing of miniature books, which have been practised from mediaeval times, have been reviewed by Pollard [2].

During the first half of the nineteenth century, the production of minute writings was stimulated by great improvements in the resolution obtained with the microscope. Machines were made which allowed legible characters to be written with a height of about 0·0001 in (2 microns), and dividing engines ruling as many as 50,000 lines to the inch (2,000 lines per millimetre) were constructed. The production of minute inscriptions at that time thus constituted a significant stream of human endeavour, and it is not surprising that the major (microphotographic) tributary sprang from the same period. The first recorded experiments seem to have been made in 1839 by J. B. Dancer of Manchester, within a few months of the introduction of the Daguerreotype process from France [3]; but he did not succeed in producing the image sharpness to be expected from his objective, until Scott Archer perfected the wet-collodion process in 1851 [4]. Within a few years of this date Dancer and others were selling microphotographs as curios, and Plate 1 shows a reproduction of one of his commercial results, probably made between 1860 and 1870. During the same period, French manufacturers employed the technique of mounting microphotographs on one end of a glass cylinder, so that an enlarged image could be seen without further aid when the other rounded end of the cylinder was held to the eye (Fig. 1). Microphotographs in this form were mounted in jewellery such as rings and tie-pins, and their manufacture expanded into a substantial and lucrative industry. One of the most successful operators (Dagron)

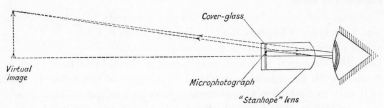

Fig. 1 *Method of viewing Microphotograph on 'Stanhope' Lens*
When the spherical end surface is placed near the eye, an enlarged virtual image is seen.

employed 150 workmen [5], and some thirty other factories were engaged in the same business.

The production of minute photographs has also been a subject for competition and record breaking. One of the smallest recorded images was made by Goldberg [6], who produced a legible image of a page of fifty lines of print within a height no greater than 0·1 mm (0·004 in). Now the area occupied by the text must have been about $\frac{1}{140}$ of a square millimetre, and it follows that no fewer than 87,500 such pages would be needed to fill a square inch. The text of rather less than two such pages is likely to be equivalent to the text of a page of the Bible, so that Goldberg's image was reduced to a scale corresponding to the production of about 50 *complete* Bibles in a square inch. 'Bibles per square inch', in fact, became the unit with which competitors exuberantly measured their achievements!

Two important developments during the last few decades merit special attention. These are the first commercial production of extreme-resolution plates in 1940 [7], and the breaking down of the apparent secrecy which surrounded techniques used in microphotography. The availability of the commercial plates made it no longer necessary for each operator to make and coat his own emulsion, and this removed an obstacle which must have hindered the wider application of microphotographic processes. Since then, the great interest of this and kindred arts has encouraged an increasing volume of publication. Many important papers are being published in connection with extreme-resolution emulsions, their application to the production of refined components for industrial tools and scientific instruments and above all their use for the reproduction of documents of many types. It is the purpose of this book to describe the technical basis of all this activity, and to demonstrate relations between the advantages and limitations of microphotographic processes and the special requirements of the numerous and varied applications.

Plan of the Book

The study of microphotography divides naturally into *basic production techniques* (Chapters 2–8), and *applications* (Chapters 9–13). The seven chapters on production techniques contain a mass of information, the digestion of which may prove a formidable task even for readers with considerable practical experience of the subject. Much of it may at first seem almost meaningless to a reader without practical experience. The present chapter is therefore concluded with a *practical exercise* permitting quite fine images to be made with a minimum of preliminary preparation. I most strongly recommend those without previous contact with this subject to work through this exercise *before* reading the remainder of the book.

Most of us would admit that great patience and skill are needed to make life-like models or produce miniatures of any kind, and in the case of microphotography it is also natural to presume that the work must be very difficult. In fact, with suitably designed materials, equipment and working methods it need not be difficult at all. It is necessary, however, to study all the factors which may influence the result, and consider how to provide conditions most likely to give successful results. For this purpose a number of chapters have been written which deal intensively with sensitive material, processing methods, objectives, focusing methods, and the camera and 'original'. These really constitute the basic 'tools' with which the microphotographer operates. To understand the way in which these tools should be operated it is desirable to have some understanding of the phenomenon of image formation. This, together with symptoms of incorrect working and the methods of control required to ensure extreme sharpness are discussed in Chapter 8. The remainder of the book deals with various applications, which are outlined below.

The Scope of Microphotography

To attempt to produce a water-tight definition dividing microphotography from other photographic techniques would be a difficult and futile exercise. In fact most of the applications are covered by the second sentence of this chapter, namely '. . . photographs in which the details are reduced to a minute or even a microscopic scale.' In some cases, however, microphotographic techniques are also used to produce images which are not really minute, but nevertheless require just as sharp an edge and the application of meticulous technique. These also are considered to fall within the scope of this book.

Microphotography constitutes an activity of great importance to our material civilization. The most extensive application is the reproduction of documents, and a very large number of cheques, invoices and other business papers are copied every day (Plate 2). By this means microphotography facilitates duplication and transport of records, saves filing space and provides a precaution against fraud and accidental loss or destruction of the original documents. The ease of transporting document microphotographs was utilized in the 'Airgraph' and 'V-mail' postal services operated by the Allies during the Second World War. Letters for overseas addresses were written on special forms and were reduced on microfilm which was sent to the country of destination. They were then enlarged to a legible size by means of automatic machines, and the enlargements were distributed by the normal postal services. Microphotographs have also been used in the transmission of secret information for espionage. In one form, copies of documents were reduced to the size of a full stop, and were implanted in the surface of an otherwise innocent document (p. 410).

Document microphotography is also important to the scholar, since it enables him to secure for private study copies of documents which could formerly only be consulted in the (sometimes distant) libraries housing the originals. The value of this development can be seen from a few examples. The Royal Society of Medicine in London operates a comprehensive and world-wide information and loan service for its members, and has collected microfilms of original papers published all over the world. From this collection, doctors, specialists or research workers can readily obtain copies pertaining to their own fields of study. An even larger service is being offered by the Microcard Foundation of Middletown, U.S.A., which was specifically established for the purpose of organizing the distribution of microphotographic copies of expensive or inaccessible books. The copies used for this purpose initially took the form of standard 5 × 3 in (12·5 × 7·5 cm) filing cards, bearing microphotographic reproductions of some fifty pages of the original text (Plate 3).[1] Thus a weighty volume of 900 pages can be compressed into 18 cards, and the cost of

---

[1] In recent years, similar copies on film (microfiche) are rapidly replacing the cards (see p. 406).

these reproductions is only a fraction of that of the original books. This service permits scholars to acquire texts hitherto beyond their reach (or purses!), and to collect the basic literature of their subject in a few boxes of filing cards.

Two other scholarly applications are worth consideration here. Teaching machines whereby students or industrial trainees may be guided most efficiently through at least part of their training, depend on the use of 'programmes' consisting of series of images on a roll of microfilm. Overloaded human teachers may hence in the future be able to concentrate their efforts to those parts of the subject where personal or individual guidance is most necessary. In addition, a bound book need no longer be considered inaccessible because it is out of print. So long as a copy is available from which a microfilm can be made, enlargement by a Xerox 'Copyflo' machine enables *single bound volumes* to be ordered at will, for a price of a few pennies or cents per page.

Document microphotography is also being actively applied to the problems of information storage and retrieval. Large government agencies, industrial firms and research institutes accumulate collections of documents numbering a million or more. For executives to make efficient use of such collections, it is necessary for them to discover which are the documents relative to their enquiry, and then to retrieve those of interest with little delay. To quote a simple but important example, collections of machine drawings are now being reproduced on 35 mm film, from which individual frames are cut and mounted over an aperture in a mechanically sorted punched card. Well proven card-sorting machines can rapidly extract any required cards from a collection, from which workable-size enlargements may be rapidly made on a reader-printer. Various systems are also beng developed for linking multi-million collections of document copies with computers for gaining access to the information they contain. It has been widely suggested that the efficient operation of such systems may be of critical significance to nations wishing to maintain the technological supremacy they now enjoy.

The dissemination of information is only one of the aids which microphotography offers the scientist (Chapters 9, 10, 11 and 13). Microphotographic processes are used for making fine graduated scales (graticules),[1] including eyepiece scales for microscopes and other scientific and military instruments, stage micrometers for measuring the magnification of microscopes, and profile graticules for the optical inspection of the form of mechanical components such as screw threads. The latter are used in precision engineering for deter-

---

[1] Throughout this book, American readers should note that *graticule* and *reticle* are considered to be synonymous.

mining whether important components comply satisfactorily with their computed form. The introduction of photographic methods for reproducing instrument scales has had an important effect on the design of such instruments as theodolites, enabling unimpaired accuracy to be obtained with instruments which are more portable and quicker to use.

Some graticules are made by straight-forward photographic processes, but when physically robust images are required to withstand mechanical shock and contamination with dust or salt spray, photomechanical processes have been used to etch images directly into glass or to etch metal plates from each side to produce apertures of accurately controlled shapes. For similar sorts of reasons, images have been made by evaporating metal through a stencil, or by making stencils on a nickel plate, followed by electrolytic deposition and stripping of the 'image'. This off-shoot of microphotographic technique really constitutes a form of micro-scale engineering production. Such methods are being used for making electron-microscope specimen grids, precision sieves, the fabrication of electronic components and 'micro-miniature' circuits, as well as semi-conductor diodes and some types of transistor. This technology is particularly important for computers, and for many electronic devices used in aircraft or rockets.

When extreme-resolution dry plate emulsions became commercially available, engineers realized that they lent themselves to the rapid production of accurate divided scales of previously unparalleled fineness, by the expedient of making series of accurately positioned 'step-and-repeat' exposures. Processes perfected for this purpose proved well adapted to the manufacture of binary-coded scales and long diffraction gratings; that is scales of a type specially adapted for automatic reading. These are now playing an essential part in systems for automation, data recording and data processing. They facilitate both the computer control of machine tools, and the recovery of information from unmanned satellites.

Thus to an increasing extent, instruments and methods made possible by applying microphotographic techniques are facilitating advanced engineering developments and scientific investigations. In some scientific research, however, microphotography plays an integral part in the experimental technique itself (Chapter 13).

For example, by the study of fine grid patterns it was possible to demonstrate that minute lateral emulsion shifts occur during the glazing of photographic prints.

The use of radioactively toned resolution-test charts permitted the orderly exploration of the optimum emulsion make-up in the early days of histological autoradiography.

Microphotographic emulsions were used to demonstrate directly that light normally reflected from a mirror forms a system of 'standing' waves parallel to the mirror.

BASIC ARRANGEMENT FOR MICROPHOTOGRAPHY

The equipment used for microphotography can vary greatly in detail, but the basic arrangement always remains the same. It is, therefore, convenient to define the various components of this basic arrangement.

The *original*, which may be a photographic transparency illuminated from behind, or a drawing or a photographic print, or occasionally a solid object, is located at the *object plane* (Fig. 2). The centre

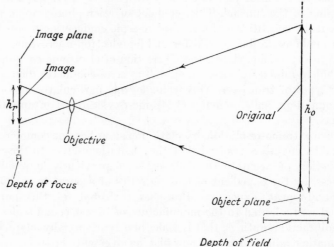

Fig. 2 *Basic Arrangement for Microphotography*

The reduction factor $\left(\dfrac{ho}{hr}\right)$ equals the objective-to-object-plane distance, divided by the objective-to-image-plane distance.

of the original is normally placed on the *axis* of the lens or objective, and the reduction factor may (if desired) be increased by an eyepiece or ocular. The emulsion of the sensitive material lies in the *image plane*. Any tolerance in the position of the object plane, within which no deterioration of image sharpness can be seen, is known as the *depth of field*. The corresponding but much smaller tolerance in the position of the image plane is known as the *depth of focus*. These definitions will be used throughout the rest of this book.

Introduction to Microphotographic Technique *a practical exercise*

By the use of commercially available extreme-resolution materials, it is possible for anyone having a camera with a tolerably good objective to obtain results far finer than the most skilled photographer can produce with more conventional emulsions.

For this exercise it will be necessary to collect:

(1) A rigid box (Fig. 3) on which the camera is held by a bolt[1]

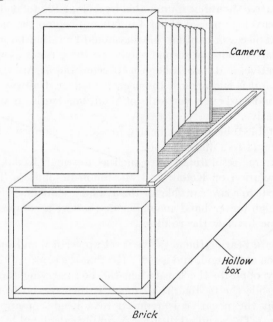

Fig. 3 *Mounting of Camera on Box*

passing up through a hole in the top of the box, and engaging with the tripod socket. The camera should be located and held square by appropriately placed wooden or hardboard battens. A brick placed inside the box will steady it and lessen the risk of accidental movement.

(2) A suitable 'negative' transparency. For this purpose an image is needed with good contrast and uniform density in the images of the lines of the inscription. A simple way to obtain the required quality is to smoke a glass plate over a candle flame, and scratch a design with a sharp point. An ideal image would be a

---

[1] The bolt should be $\frac{1}{4}$ in Whitworth for 'British' sockets or $\frac{3}{8}$ in Whitworth for 'Continental' sockets. To prevent risk of damage to the camera, the bolt should be cut so that not more than three threads can be engaged. American Standard Z/38.4.1–1942 specifies the thread as $\frac{1}{4}$–20–N.C. 1.R.H.

copy negative on a high-contrast photomechanical plate or film, with a page of up to 500 words reproduced on a negative from $1\frac{1}{2}$ in (35 mm) to 4 in (10 cm) high. A copy image on a 'fine-grain' 35 mm film developed to full contrast can also be used.

(3) A piece of hardboard in which is cut an aperture rather larger than the negative. The negative is then fixed to a piece of 'flashed' opal glass, which is mounted over the aperture. The negative should be illuminated by a No. 1 Photoflood lamp with its envelope placed about 4 in (10 cm) behind the opal.

(4) Two pieces of cardboard. One should be rather larger than the negative, but the second should be three times as wide as the negative, and long enough to obscure the negative completely when it is laid against the negative holder. Halfway across this second card cut a vertical slot about one-tenth the width of the negative.

(5) A stable table or work-bench, to which is clamped a batten 3 to 6 feet (1 to 2 metres) long.

(6) Extreme resolution plates such as Eastman Kodak Co. High-Resolution or Kodak Ltd Maximum-Resolution. These must be cut to a size suitable for the available camera.

(7) A high-power hand magnifier or (better) a compound microscope to view the results.

The board bearing the negative is set up vertical and square to the long batten at one end, and is placed so that the centre of the negative is directly opposite the lens, when the box carrying the camera is laid alongside the batten. The camera is then moved to such a distance that the negative is reduced to a height of approximately $\frac{1}{4}$ in (6 mm). The required distance is simply calculated by estimating the required reduction ratio R, then

distance from lens to negative = (approx.) $f(R + 1)$

where $\quad\quad\quad\quad\quad\quad\quad f =$ the focal length of the camera objective.

Focus the lens as accurately as possible by focusing scale, range-finder or ground-glass screen.

Now decide how the plates are to be loaded into the camera. If a plate camera is used, employ *only one plate holder* throughout, in order to ensure the best possible uniformity of registration. Roll-film cameras can usually be loaded (by safelight) by laying a suitably cut plate against the aperture which holds the film in register (Plate 4).[1] *Cautiously* close the camera-back to apply pressure on the plate.

[1] In some less expensive cameras, the film plane is deliberately curved. Such cameras cannot be readily used in this way.

If the back will not shut completely without undue force, secure the open side with adhesive tape, and drape a black cloth around the camera to exclude light.

Before making the first exposure, adjust the diaphragm to one 'stop' less than full aperture. The correct exposure has now to be determined by 'stepped' exposures, such as are used when making exposure tests in enlarging. With the camera shutter closed, turn on the lamp, cover the negative with the large card and open the camera shutter. Then expose the whole negative for 10 seconds, cover a narrow strip with the card, and expose the rest of the negative for a further 10 seconds. With the card moved in stages across the negative give further exposure times of 20, 40, 80 . . . seconds as required.

After development according to the manufacturers' instructions, the plate should be examined with the hand magnifier or microscope. If the reader is unusually fortunate, he may see quite a well defined and sharp image, but it is more usual to find that normal focusing methods prove inadequate to do justice to these emulsions. In Great Britain (and probably elsewhere), this rather disconcerting discovery sometimes befalls photographers attempting to make their first graticule!

Now the interpretation of exposure tests depends on just how unsharp the image is seen to be. The less sharp the image is, the greater will be the area of plate over which light will have been vainly spilt, and the greater will be the increase of density produced by focusing correctly. As a guide for the next test, the exposure might be reduced threefold if the image is 'very unsharp' halved if it is 'markedly unsharp', and be reduced by one-third if it is only 'rather unsharp'.

The next operation is to focus with extreme delicacy. The method to be used depends on the fact that small changes in the camera-to-negative distance alter the objective-to-image distance by the small movement *divided by the square of the linear degree of reduction*. For instance, if a reduction ratio of ten is used, a change of 1 mm (0·04 in) in the camera distance will change the objective-to-image distance by one-hundredth of this amount, or 0·01 mm (0·0004 in). For this purpose make a narrow index mark on the side of the box supporting the camera, and on the batten opposite fix a ruler with the middle of its millimetre scale opposite the index mark.

The reader is now equipped to make a *photographic focusing* test, in which images of separate parts of the negative are successively photographed on a single plate, with small changes of focus made between each exposure. *Do not* alter the focusing adjustment of the camera itself, but move the camera *away* from the negative by exactly 1 cm. Now place the slotted cardboard in front of the negative, so that one side of the negative is seen through the slot. To indicate that this is the first exposure of the test, hold a pencil horizontally across the slit, *and expose for the time indicated by the previous test.* Move the camera closer to the negative by exactly 5 mm, move the slotted cardboard across the negative by rather more than the width of the slot, and make another exposure. Repeat this cycle of operations three times more, by which time the camera will have been moved 1 cm closer to the negative, than its original position. The processed images can be inspected while wet, and after only a brief rinse.

When viewed with sufficient magnification the images may show a gradual improvement of sharpness, followed by a gradual deterioration. This is a satisfactory result, since it indicates that the range of positions included the optimum focus. The test may, however, show sharpness progressively improving up to the last image. In this case it is better to make a further test, starting with the positions giving the sharpest images in the first test, and extending the range of positions further.

By this time it is possible that the reader will have already found conditions giving quite creditable results, but two further series of test are desirable to ensure the best quality his camera is capable of giving. Firstly it is possible that the approximate exposure indicated by the initial test may be seen not to give the best result, once a focusing position closer to the optimum has been found. A further exposure test may therefore be desirable, with the camera moved to the estimated position of best focus. Exposure times may then be usefully selected from a closer graduated series of times: 10, 14, 20, 28, 40, 56 . . . seconds. The best exposure time indicated by this test may then be used for another focusing test around the best position, with the camera distance now adjusted by increments of only 2 mm or even 1 mm.

LESSONS OF THE EXERCISE

Although the description of this exercise is rather lengthy, the whole operation should not take longer than two evenings to do. If the reader has chosen to use a photograph of a book page as an original, this procedure should have given quite a legible copy. Although the images are not particularly small by microphotographic standards, they are nevertheless equivalent to reproducing more than 20 pages of the book in a square inch, or more than 1,500 pages in the area of a 10 × 8 in (25 × 20 cm) sheet of typing paper. By proceeding calmly and methodically it is hoped that he will have convinced himself that there is nothing intrinsically very difficult about this work. It is hoped that he will also have learnt:

(1) Some basic impressions of microphotographic technique, which should assist comprehension of subsequent chapters.

(2) That the improvement of image sharpness is gained at the expense of relatively massive exposures, the use of only the axial region of the lens and the application of meticulous care at all stages.

(3) Techniques for photographic exposure and focusing tests, which must be closely integrated with each other.

(4) Perhaps also he will be encouraged to study the matter further, and hence acquire the organized body of knowledge required to control these processes and produce the finest results.

UNITS FOR MEASURING SMALL DIMENSIONS

In concluding the chapter, mention should be made of the units conveniently used for measuring the dimensions of microphotographic images. These are the thousandth part of an inch, (often called a '*thou*' in Great Britain and a '*mil*' in the United States of America) and written as 0·001 in, and the thousandth part of a millimetre, which is called a 'micron' and is represented by the symbol 'μ'. The size of these units can be appreciated by comparing them to a human hair, whose thickness is about 2 'thou' or 50μ. It is interesting to note that the micron is not much greater than the wavelength of visible light, which ranges from 0·4 μ (in the violet) to 0·7 μ (in the red); but wavelengths are more commonly measured by the Ångstrom Unit (written Å), which equals one ten-thousandth of a micron. The visible spectrum thus extends from 4,000 to 7,000 Å.

Some years ago, the British Standard Institute indicated a preference for *micrometre* and μm instead of micron and μ. Many Journals however, continue to use the older forms, a practice which will be observed throughout this book.

REFERENCES

[1] Hooke, Robert, *Micrographia* (London, 1664).

[2] Pollard, A. F. C., 'Miniature and Microscopic Documents', *Proc. Brit. Soc. Int. Bibl.*, 5, 43, 1943.

[3] Sidebotham, J., 'On Micro-photography', *Liverpool Phot. J.* (now *Brit. J. Phot.*), 6, 91, 1859.

[4] Scott-Archer, F., 'On the Use of Collodion in Photography', *The Chemist*, March, 1851.

[5] Luther, F., *Microfilm. A History. 1839–1900*, National Microfilm Association and Barre Publishing Co., Barre (Massachusetts, 1959), p. 35. See also Dagron, R. P. P., *Traité de Photographie Microscopique* (Paris, 1864).

[6] Goldberg, E., 'A New Process for Microphotography', *Brit. J. Phot.*, **73**, 462, 1926: translation taken from *6th Int. Congress. Phot.* (Paris, 1926), p. 236.

[7] Anon, 'Maximum Resolution Plate', *J. Sci. Instruments*, **18**, 66, 1941.

2 · The Sensitive Material

The choice of a sensitive material tends to be confused by the fact that microphotography comprises a number of related but essentially different arts. In most of these the ability to record very fine detail is the dominant requirement, and photographic speed is quite a secondary consideration. This is because the 'originals' take the form of transparencies, with which contact or projection printing permits the use of illuminating systems providing sufficient light for tolerably brief exposures even with very slow materials.

Emulsions for Document Microphotography

In document microphotography, however, the originals are opaque documents which are photographed by reflected light. Much of the light leaving the document never enters the objective, and the volume of work precludes the use for each image of an exposure longer than a few seconds. With most available illuminating systems, these restrictions demand the use of an emulsion whose speed is approximately equivalent to that of a 'bromide' enlarging paper. This necessity for specifying a minimum practicable level of speed constitutes an essential difference between commercial document microphotography and most other applications. The setting of the speed at this relatively high level indicates that the sensitive materials used must be those whose development gives a large effective amplification factor, with an associated limit to the fineness of image structure which can be achieved. Until recently only silver-halide 'dry-plate' emulsions were used, and many photographic manufacturers produce films specially designed for this purpose (Burroughs 'Microfilm', Gevaert 'Duplo', Ilford 'Microneg', Kodak 'Micro-file', and so on). These are all designed to provide relatively high resolution combined with the necessary speed (Chapter 12, p. 375). Their emulsions have grain diameters lying mainly in the range from 0·1 to 0·4 microns, and give fairly high contrast. Recordak Direct Duplicating Film (Type S.O. 156) gives duplicate negatives with archival silver images by direct printing from original microfilm negatives. The use of cellulose-nitrate film bases is undesirable because of fire hazard and the deterioration of the base on storage. For these reasons the use of 'safety' base for document microphotography is obligatory in most countries.

In recent years it has been shown that electrophotographic materials developed in special conditions can give the resolution needed for document microphotography, and they also have the required photographic sensitivity.

Whilst this speed requirement sets a limit to the sensitive materials that can be used for the initial generation of microfilm document images, many of the much slower materials can be used in high-intensity contact copiers for making subsequent copies. Transparent film sensitized with a diazonium salt and 'Kalvar' bubble film in particular are being used for this purpose (pp. 407 and 429).

Materials for Extreme Resolution

A much wider range of sensitive materials can be used for the extreme-resolution applications, since this work permits even the slowest photographic emulsions to be exposed adequately without great inconvenience. Silver-halide–gelatin emulsions can be used with grain sizes down to the lowest limit it is practicable to make.

The concentrated Lippmann emulsions, for instance, have grain diameters in the range 0·01 to 0·1 μ (Plate 5). An impression of the improved resolution this permits is given in Plate 6. Other materials which have been used are:

(i) 'wet' collodion,
(ii) silver salts imbibed into 'Cellophane',
(iii) silver albuminate,
(iv) silver-halide print-out emulsions,
(v) bichromated colloids,
(vi) photopolymerizing resins,
(vii) diazonium salts used on their own or incorporated with a mercury salt
(viii) photo-sensitive glass.

In spite of this wide variety, these materials suitable for extreme resolution all have certain essential properties in common.

Properties of Importance for Extreme Resolution

THE SUPPORT

The support, whether it be glass, paper or film, can do much to hinder or assist the potential resolution of any microphotographic emulsion layer. The surface of a coated emulsion normally follows the contours of the surface on which it is coated, although it may partly fill in the hollows. Roughness of the emulsion surface produced by any cause will tend to have a disruptive effect on the image, which becomes increasingly objectionable as progressively smaller images are produced. The surface of the base should therefore be smooth— if it is 'glass' smooth so much the better. Paper bases should be coated with baryta or another smooth white pigment, and should have a 'glossy' finish. The surface finish of transparent film or glass plates is usually satisfactory for most purposes.

The bulk optical properties of the support are important. With transparent substances such as glass or film, the light transmitted by the emulsion can travel sideways as a result of internal reflection from

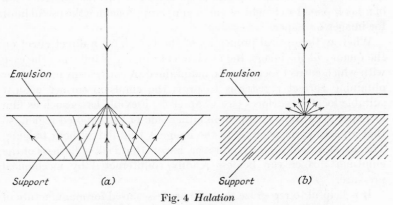

Fig. 4 *Halation*

(*a*) With slightly scattering emulsion on transparent support.
(*b*) With transparent emulsion on light scattering support.

the back surface of the support [Fig. 4(*a*)]. This is the cause of ordinary halation, and is normally prevented by application of a light-absorbing layer (or backing) in optical contact with the back of the support [1]. The necessity for a backing depends markedly on the type of image to be formed, and it can usually be dispensed with when only a very small proportion of the emulsion surface needs to be exposed. In fact Kodak Limited have found that unbacked Maximum-Resolution plates tend to be cleaner, and recommend customers not to use backed plates unless their work really requires them.

Paper and other light-scattering bases cause halation in a different way, by providing a diffuse reflector just below the emulsion surface [Fig. 4(*b*)]. The cure is to apply a light-absorbing layer containing a bleachable dye or pigment between the emulsion and the base, and this method can also be used with film (p. 376). Either type of halation is most likely to prove harmful with emulsions whose unexposed layer has a low opacity for actinic light, and may not be troublesome if the layer absorbs so strongly that the image is confined to the emulsion surface.

Minute images are best viewed by a beam of transmitted light, focused by a condenser so that the cones of light from each point of the image just fill the objective. To permit these conditions to be achieved, the base should be transparent, and of a thickness permitting correct focusing of the sub-stage condenser of a microscope. Plates used for producing images whose height is equal to or less than 0·5 mm (0·02 in) should for this reason not be much thicker than 1 mm (0·04 in). With paper or other opaque and light-scattering supports, these ideal conditions cannot be met, and achieving adequate brightness is also a problem (p. 406). For this reason, reduction of a book page to a height of ¼in (6 mm) is approaching the useful limit for images on paper.

Whereas the optical properties of the base have a direct effect on the quality of the image, the mechanical properties influence the ease with which correct focus can be maintained. A convenient method for obtaining correct register is to press the emulsion surface against suitable locating surfaces (see Chapter 5). Flexible bases such as film or paper need to be clamped on either side of the exposed region, so that an area corresponding to the image is held flat without bulging. The use of a rigid support, however, means that lack of flatness of the emulsion surface can be less readily counteracted by mechanical pressure.

It is helpful to recognize that the processes used for manufacture of glass for photographic plates do not give perfect flatness, but glass of improved quality can be obtained by sensitive methods of inspection and subsequent selection. The Eastman Kodak Co., for example, describe three specifications of flatness, giving surfaces departing from true flatness by not more than 0·001 in, 0·0005 in and 0·0002 in (25, 12 and 5 μ) per inch of plate for 'Normal', 'Ultra-flat' and 'Microflat' plates respectively [2].

The unevenness often consists of a bowing or a series of waves, but the curvature of the plate surface is normally so gentle that little trouble is likely to be experienced when the emulsion is pressed against locating surfaces within 1/2 in (12 mm) of the image (p. 139). Difficulties due to unevenness mainly arise when contact printing, or when images are made on larger plates which have been registered at points an inch or more from the image. In such cases superior results should be obtained with 'plate' glass, since this is ground and polished. In extreme cases optically worked glass, which should have a surface flat to a quarter of a wavelength of light (say 0·15 μ), can be used. The maximum possible error is then well within the depth of focus of a 1/6th in (4 mm) microscope objective (Chapter 4). When other requirements do not require images to be formed on a rigid support, satisfactory contact prints are more easily made on film or paper.

The choice of a support will also be influenced by such factors as dimensional stability and stiffness, freedom from flaws and resistance to damage and breaking, and convenience in storing and viewing the images. While some readers may have special reasons for preferring film or paper, the beginner is advised to use glass plates. They are easy to coat in small quantities, and the images do not tend to go out of focus when viewing them with a microscope.

Emulsions

The light-sensitive systems used in microphotography mostly consist of a photosensitive compound contained by an inert colloid medium. Although it is chemically incorrect, silver-halide gelatin systems have universally and for many years been called 'emulsions'. For convenience, this word will be used for all photosensitive systems described in this book.

THE COLLOID BINDING MEDIUM

The colloid binding medium must be capable of giving a substantially flat, glass-clear layer, having no visible discrete structure. Such layers are most usually produced by applying a solution of the colloid (which solution also often contains the photosensitive substance) to the support, and then allowing the solvent to evaporate, with or without previous gelling of the colloid. The conditions must be adjusted to prevent the upper surface forming a semi-rigid skin, while the lower layers are still quite fluid. The skin may otherwise crumple to form a net-like 'reticulation' pattern, with a disastrous effect on the appearance of the image. With gelatin emulsions the layer 'sets' or gels as a result of chilling, and skin formation is prevented by standing the plates on a chilled level slab, after coating with warm emulsion, so that the lower layers set first. In collodion 'emulsions', skin formation is avoided by use of a suitable mixture of high-boiling and low-boiling solvents. The solvents must also be blended so as to avoid too rapid cooling by evaporation, since this can lead to condensation of water accompanied by formation of a milky layer ('blushing') harmful to extreme resolution. Disruption of the image can also be caused by crystallization of the soluble salts left in a silver-salt emulsion after precipitation of the silver halides (Plate 7). This is avoided by washing the set emulsion either after precipitation, or after the plates have been coated but not dried. In collodion emulsions the trouble has been avoided by using deliquescent salts showing less tendency to crystallize. Thus Goldberg [3] chose lithium salts for his print-out emulsions, since these salts are not only soluble in alcohol–ether mixtures, but show less tendency to crystallize when the layer dries.

In several cases, the surface layer of the support itself constitutes the binding medium. Elvegård and Sjöstedt produced very fine-grain silver-halide materials by successively bathing 'Cellophane' in solutions of potassium iodide, followed by silver nitrate and potassium bromide [4]. Diazo films are sensitized by imbibition of the photosensitive diazonium salt into the base, and in some variants the surface of the base is hydrolysed by alkali to increase its permeability. Images have been produced on glass without the use of any binding medium at all. Burmistrov [5] described a process depending on the 'adsorption' of silver compounds, but the published record does not seem to indicate that this got beyond the experimental stage.

In an increasingly important group of processes, the colloid layer or the support itself may be photosensitive. Photosensitive resins such as those produced from polyvinyl cinnamate produce stencil images with valuable resist properties. Glass and nylon can also be made photosensitive, and a thermoplastic film base has been made effectively photosensitive by an electrophotographic procedure.

THE THICKNESS OF THE EMULSION LAYER

In recent years, the sharpness given by high-speed negative emulsions has been substantially improved by decreasing the thickness of the emulsion layer. The improvement was obtained by the resultant restriction of the sideways spread of scattered light in the emulsion. It would be reasonable to suppose that extreme-resolution work also requires a very thin layer, but this is not always true. As will be shown later, the light scatter in microphotographic emulsions is reduced to negligible proportions. Thus one reason for the improvement of high-speed emulsions (by reduction of thickness) has vanished. With truly transparent emulsions, lenses should be able to produce an almost equally sharp image of a point source at any depth in the layer. The thickness of the emulsion layer could then add to the useful depth of focus.

In practice the matter is usually decided by the degree of convergence of the cones of rays from the lens to form the image. If a small lens aperture is used, the convergence within the thickness of a conventional emulsion may be negligible, and the emulsion thickness is relatively unimportant. With the larger apertures needed to secure high resolution figures (p. 105), convergence strongly influences the vertical light distribution within the emulsion layer (pp. 200–204). When the transparency being reduced consists of widely separated narrow transparent lines on a dark background, a high-contrast negative-forming emulsion (i.e. giving reversed tone values) may only produce blackening at the focal plane.[1] Sharp images can then indeed be formed at different depths in the layer, and a relatively thick emulsion (say 7–10 μ, 0·0003–0·0004 in) can be an advantage (Plates 17 and 65). This is because the lens is being employed in such a way, that it can only utilize a small proportion of the emulsion thickness.

In all other cases a much larger proportion of the emulsion layer is used in image formation. This applies when clear narrow lines in the transparency are crowded close together, or when the transparency has fine dark lines on a clear background. It also applies when the image is produced by a 'direct-positive' process, in which the action of the light is to inhibit subsequent blackening on development.

In all these instances, it follows that a really sharp fine line can only be produced if the effective emulsion thickness is no greater than the depth of focus of the objective used to form the image (p. 204). Examples of direct-positive processes are the reversal of silver-halide emulsions by bleaching and reblackening after development of a negative image, and the diazotype process in which the dye is formed from the diazonium salt which has not been decomposed by the action of light.

The emulsion thickness is also of critical importance in processes where the image is formed by the light action producing a change in the solubility of the colloid medium. This is because of the mechanical behaviour of the areas forming the image during and after the washing out of the more soluble areas.

If we take a cube of an unswollen colloid, and allow it to swell in a solvent, it will tend to expand uniformly; so that all three dimensions are increased to the same extent [Fig. 5(a)]. A thin layer of colloid coated on a rigid support behaves quite differently, since, so long as it adheres to the support, it can only expand upwards [Fig. 5(b)]. The swollen layer is, in fact, in a stressed condition, because its tendency to swell laterally is prevented by adhesion to the support. With the relatively thick coating applied to commercial plates this stress sometimes causes wrinkling of the emulsion, or 'reticulation'. Consider what happens during the washing out of a stencil image in such a stressed layer. In the case of a thin clear line in a blackened

---

[1] These apparently restricted conditions apply in important classes of work, such as the production of many types of graticule or instrument scale.

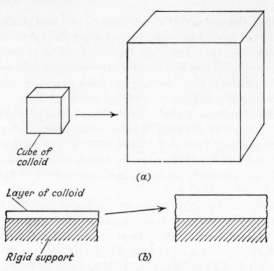

Fig. 5 *Swelling of Colloid Layers*

(*a*) Cube swells uniformly in all directions.
(*b*) Constraint of coated layer by rigid support only allows vertical swell to occur.

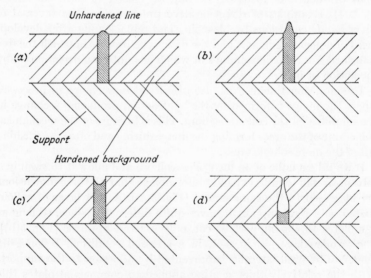

Fig. 6 *Washing-out of Narrow Lines*

(*a*) At first, unhardened colloid in the lines swells slightly more than background.
(*b*) The difference of swelling increases.
(*c*) Colloid washes from the surface layers of the line.
(*d*) Internal pressure in the hardened (but swollen) colloid causes it to bulge inwards, and hinder further washing-out.

(or hardened) background, the washing out of part of the material of the line will allow the edges of the adjacent hardened areas to lean inwards [Fig. (6)]. This may sometimes be so pronounced that opposite sides touch, and no further washing out can occur. A different result is observed when the stencil image consists of fine lines. Before washing off, the internal stress in the material of the lines is balanced by the stress in the surrounding background, so that the image of the lines is supported by the neighbouring areas and serious distortion cannot occur. When these neighbouring areas are washed away their supporting effect is also removed, and the internal stress in the line can be released by bending of the image. In some cases the lines may fall into sets of waves (Plate 8).

These undesirable effects occur mainly when the thickness of the swollen emulsion layer is too great in comparison with the width of the lines. They occur less (or not at all) when the emulsion is used to produce stencil images with lines whose width is several times the thickness of the swollen layer, and such wide lines are also more likely to resist mechanical damage. Really fine lines can be produced with stencil processes either by using an extremely thin emulsion layer or by using an emulsion which strongly absorbs the exposing light, so that the image is confined to a very thin layer. This latter method introduces difficulties, in that it necessitates exposure through the support, which therefore needs to have a high degree of flatness and optical uniformity. Projection printing through the support is also likely to introduce spherical aberration, and may need the use of a specially corrected objective.

STRUCTURE OF THE PHOTOSENSITIVE COMPOUND

The physical condition of the photosensitive compound is of paramount importance for microphotography, since it controls not only the structure of the final image but also influences the optical properties of the unexposed layer. In some emulsions the sensitive compound has no discrete structure, and is probably molecularly dispersed or dissolved in the colloid. Examples are diazotype, bichromated colloids, photosensitive resins and silver albuminate. In these the sensitive unit is virtually the individual molecule, and such processes should be inherently unrivalled for the highest resolution. The major part of the photographic industry is, however, based on silver-salt emulsions which consist of minute crystals of silver halide embedded in a colloid (usually gelatin). When exposed and developed, these crystals (or grains) are usually developed completely. Thus the structure of the image and the size of the silver grains is initially determined by the size of the crystals from which they are formed, and the emulsions behave as if the crystals are the photosensitive units. They range in diameter from about 0·01 μ to 2 or 3 μ, but only emulsions in which the majority of the grains are smaller than 0·1 μ are likely to give extreme resolution.

OPTICAL PROPERTIES OF THE EMULSION

The exquisite sharpness required for microphotography can only be obtained by forming an immaculate image inside the emulsion layer. The sharp aerial image produced by the objective must not be spoilt by refraction or scatter when the light enters the emulsion. We shall therefore consider how the energy distribution in an aerial image may be modified once the light enters an emulsion.

When light strikes an emulsion it will tend to be refracted at the

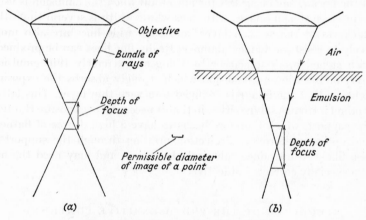

Fig. 7 *Refraction at the Emulsion Surface*
The angle of the cone of rays from the objective is decreased by refraction, thus increasing the depth of focus *inside* the emulsion layer.

emulsion/air interface, absorbed in the body of the emulsion, and often also scattered at the surface of the silver-halide grains. The main effect of refraction at the emulsion surface is to reduce the angle of convergence of the bundle of rays forming the image, so that the depth of focus inside the emulsion is actually greater than in air (Fig. 7). Refraction at a rough emulsion surface will obviously tend to disrupt an image.

All emulsions useful for extreme-resolution work scatter very little light, and are practically non-turbid for light of wavelengths to which they are normally exposed. The proportion of the incident light absorbed by a given small thickness of an emulsion is independent of the incident intensity, and is practically independent of the position within the emulsion layer. Thus if the first micron thickness halves the intensity, the second will reduce it to one quarter, and so on. The proportion of incident light absorbed by each unit layer of an emulsion is an important property, since it controls both the depth below the surface at which an image can be formed, as well as the distance which any scattered light can travel sideways in an emulsion.

Such materials as the print-out emulsions, wet-collodion and concentrated Lippmann emulsions have a relatively low absorption: the last material may absorb only 50 per cent of the incident actinic light in a layer 7 μ thick (Chapter 8). Other emulsions such as bichromated colloids and diazotype absorb more heavily, and Dippel [6] showed that the layer produced by impregnating 'Cellophane' with the mixture of mercury and diazonium salts absorbed practically all the incident actinic light in the first few microns.

According to their size, the grains of silver-salt emulsions tend to scatter more or less of the light which strikes them. Thus the relatively large grains of high-speed emulsions (from 0·5 to 2 μ in diameter) scatter heavily, and this is the reason for the 'milkiness' or turbidity of ordinary photographic films. The scatter can be reduced to very small proportions if the grains are made with a diameter only a fraction of the wavelength of the exposing light, and this is why Lippmann emulsions are so transparent. Even in these emulsions scatter is not completely eliminated, and the residual scatter is of the Rayleigh type, in which the intensity of the scattered light is inversely proportional to the fourth power of the wavelength.

The low light scatter of microphotographic emulsions makes it difficult to see which side of a plate is coated with emulsion, but with emulsions based on such colloids as gelatin and glue, the emulsion side can be identified by breathing on the back of the plate. A mist readily forms on a resin backing layer or on bare glass, but gelatin or glue layers prevent mist formation. Some operators have found that blemishes may be produced by projection of saliva droplets, and breathing on the emulsion surface is to be avoided so far as possible. With commercially coated plates this can be done by noting that plates are usually packed in fours, in which the central pair are placed emulsion outwards between separators. The outer two plates are packed emulsion side inwards against the separators.[1]

Interaction of absorption, scatter and the sensitometric properties of an emulsion determines the image spread or turbidity. This property can be examined by Mees's 'tadpole' test, in which an objective

[1] With the increasing demand for clear unblemished plates, more extreme-resolution plates are packed in individual slots in special boxes. The emulsion side of all plates then faces the same way.

was used to project a reduced image of a slit on the emulsion surface [7]. An optical step wedge with the steps separated by opaque bands was placed behind the slit, so that the image was divided into rectangles increasing in brightness from one end to the other. As Mees originally showed with a Lippmann emulsion, in the absence of turbidity this arrangement gave a series of images of nearly uniform size, and with density increasing with exposure. With commercial emulsions, increasing exposure usually resulted in a more or less

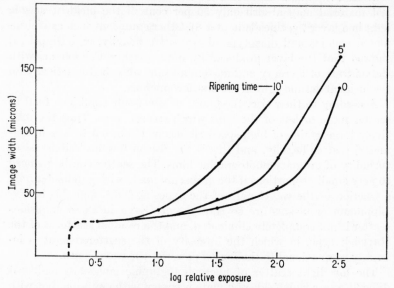

Fig. 8 *Image Spread and Effect of Ripening*
After H. Frieser, Bull. Res. *Council of Israel*, 5C, 285, 1957.

pronounced widening of the image, and this widening was an indication of the turbidity. Normal silver-halide emulsions are very turbid and thus show pronounced widening at quite moderate densities, but microphotographic emulsions suitable for extreme resolution only show serious spread at exposure values greater than those needed to give adequate density (Plate 9). This test is a direct method for determining whether an emulsion is suitable for extreme resolution, since the reduced width of the slit can be made equal to the line width it is desired to reproduce. It should, however, be noted that the aerial image given by an objective is unlikely to be so immaculate that no widening at all occurs with over-exposure, even on a perfectly non-scattering emulsion.

Frieser examined the image spread of fine-grain emulsions by projecting a reduced image of a narrow slit, and recording this at a series of increasing exposures on the emulsion to be tested [8]. The effective image widths were measured from microdensitometer traces, and the widths were plotted against log relative exposure. Fig. 8 shows that the image reproduced by an unripened emulsion only widened very gradually with exposure, but only a small amount of ripening resulted in markedly increased image spread.

While all emulsions giving extreme resolution should give adequate density before serious widening is observed, those in which the sensitive compound is molecularly dispersed should show the least turbidity. The turbidity of the concentrated Lippmann emulsions tends to be very wavelength-dependent as a result of Rayleigh scatter. Kodak

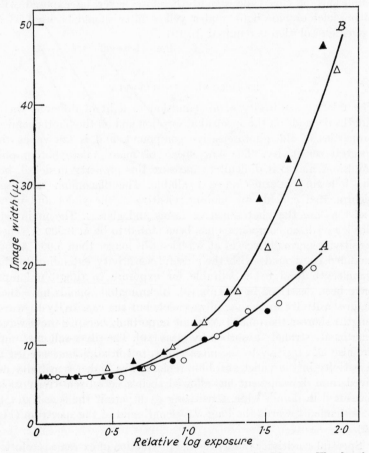

Fig. 9 *Dependence of Turbidity of Maximum Resolution Plates on Wavelength*
(a) Exposures made with deep yellow filter.
(b) With blue filter.
Hollow and solid points represent separate determinations.

Maximum-Resolution plates, for instance, have been found to give substantially less sharp images when exposed with a blue instead of a yellow filter. To eliminate any possible effect of chromatic aberration in an objective, this result was checked by contact printing through a negative with lines 7 μ wide. The contact-printing test demonstrated conclusively that the sharpness difference was due to increased turbidity on exposure with the blue filter (Fig. 9). As was to be expected with the fourth-power wavelength dependence of Rayleigh scattering, the increase of turbidity with decreasing wavelength was very abrupt. In such circumstances the small increase of lens performance obtainable by use of short wavelengths is useless. Emulsions of this type should therefore never be exposed with ultra-violet or blue light, and a yellow filter should be used when extreme resolution is required (p. 191).

SPECTRAL SENSITIVITY

The relative sensitivity of an emulsion to light of different wavelengths depends on the spectral absorption and on the photochemical properties of the photosensitive compound, and is known as the spectral sensitivity. The low speed of many microphotographic emulsions makes it difficult to measure this property in detail, but the following information is available. The diazonium salts and bichromated colloids are mainly sensitive in the violet and ultraviolet as are the photosensitive resins and glasses. The main sensitivity of diazo compounds has been stated to be at 3,900 Å. Their sensitivity normally ceases at wavelengths longer than 5,000 Å, but modified compounds with their useful sensitivity extending to this wavelength (and hence suitable for exposure to tungsten lamps) have been described in patents [9]. Bichromated colloids have their main sensitivity in the far ultra-violet, but the sensitivity to wavelengths shorter than 3,500 Å is not important, because these wavelengths are strongly absorbed by glass [10]. The silver-salt materials are also all sensitive to the ultra-violet, but in addition have useful sensitivity in the violet and blue regions. The higher sensitivity derived from development has allowed their spectral sensitivity to be measured in detail, while sensitizing dyes permit the sensitivity to be extended towards the long-wavelength end of the spectrum (Fig. 10).

Spectral sensitivity influences the production of extreme resolution in several ways. The resolution limit of a 'perfect' objective of given aperture increases with decreasing wavelength, so that it should be possible to make even finer images by exposing with ultra-violet light. This possibility could only be realized by using an objective corrected for spherical aberration in the ultra-violet, together with an emulsion which does not scatter even ultra-violet light. The performance of the objective can depend on the spectral sensitivity of the emulsion in another way, since this property determines the width of the band of wavelengths from a given illuminant which is effective in forming the image. The narrower the band of effective wavelengths, the less will the sharpness tend to be spoiled by residual chromatic aberration of the objective. Recently high-performance objectives have been designed specifically for use with the Maximum-

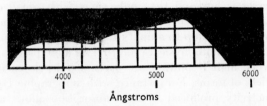

4000   5000   6000

Ångstroms

Fig. 10   *Spectral Sensitivity of 'Kodak' Maximum-Resolution Plates.*
Similar basic emulsions have been sensitized to even longer wavelengths, particularly for holography.

Resolution plate, with freedom from spherical aberration computed for the mercury 5,461 Å line (p. 111).

When visual focusing methods are used, it is an advantage for the effective spectral sensitivity of the emulsion to match that of the eye, since chromatic aberration of the objective can cause the 'photographic' focus to differ from the visual focus.

It has already been noted that the turbidity of concentrated Lippmann emulsions is strongly wavelength-dependent, and that they should not be exposed to blue light if the maximum sharpness is required. Since these emulsions are strongly dye-sensitized to the green, they can be exposed to tungsten light through a yellow filter, with little loss of speed. The spectral sensitivity always influences the effective speed of emulsions, since it determines the proportion of the energy emitted by the illuminant which is actually used in image formation. The maximum emission of incandescent lamps, for instance, is in the infra-red and the emission falls off progressively towards shorter wavelengths. Extension of the sensitivity of silver-salt emulsions towards longer wavelengths is an effective method for increasing their speed to this type of source, but possible adverse effects on lens performance needs to be considered (see p. 100).

SPEED

Although relatively low levels of photographic sensitivity or speed can be obtained when extreme resolution is required, this property is important in determining the convenience of any process. The speed is a complex property depending on many variables, and the influence of spectral sensitivity has just been noted.

In some materials, such as bichromated-colloid, some types of photosensitive resin, diazotype, dye-bleach and silver-salt 'print-out' processes, the final image is built up directly by the light action in units of individual atoms or molecules. The speed of all these processes is low and they only show fairly small differences between each other. In other processes the speed can be increased by using a development step to amplify the light-stopping power of the photochemical or photophysical products. As more processes capable of giving very high resolution are invented, development takes a greater variety of forms. For instance, with xerographic layers, local photoconductivity produced by light absorption allows an electro-static charge to leak away. High resolution can then be obtained by immersing in an insulating solvent, in which is suspended finely divided pigment particles bearing the opposite charge to the selenium plate. In this case a large amplification results from the fact that relatively few absorbed quanta are needed to produce the loss of an electrostatic charge capable of holding a large number of pigment molecules. In another form of electro-photographic process, the image-wise distribution of charge resulting from initial electrostatic charging and exposure results in local wrinkling of the film surface when it is softened by warming. This wrinkling greatly decreases light transmission in a Schlieren-type optical system, thus producing a large effective amplification (see p. 51).

More typically, however, development is achieved by allowing the primary photochemical product to catalyse reduction of a metal salt (usually silver). Amplification factors of many hundreds or thousands can be achieved in this way, so that a high density can be obtained from a quantity of photochemical product so small as to be invisible by itself. In such cases the primary photochemical product is called the *latent image*, and it is believed that development can only proceed when the latent image consists of nuclei having a minimum critical size. The speed can therefore be increased by allowing the photochemical product to coagulate, and this almost certainly occurs in the Philips'-Dippel mercury-diazonium process [6].

The silver-halide–gelatin emulsions provide a more familiar example of amplification by development. Since they behave as if the crystals (or grains) are the photosensitive units, their sensitivity generally increases with the grain size. This is thought to arise in the following way [11]. The absorption of a light quantum at any point in a grain causes the eventual deposition of silver as specks at a few preferred places in the grain. As soon as any single speck reaches the minimum critical size, it enables the whole mass of the grain to be converted to silver when the emulsion is treated in a 'chemical' developer (Chapter 3). The critical size is thought to be independent of the size of the grain, but the amount of light absorbed by each grain with a given exposure as well as the mass of silver produced on development of the grain both increase with grain size. The photographic speed of silver-halide emulsions thus increases with grain size. Increasing grain size, unfortunately, inevitably means reduced resolution, so that speed and resolution are intrinsically antagonistic properties. This has been strikingly illustrated by Brock, who plotted the logarithms of the resolving powers of a number of modern aero emulsions against the logarithms of their speeds [12]. The points fell practically on a straight line, whose slope showed that the resolving power was inversely proportional to the square root of the speed. Thus a sixteen-fold reduction of speed would be needed to give about four times the resolution. Speed comparisons published by Dippel [6] suggest that these differences may be even greater for very fine grain materials. He found Maximum-Resolution plates, which have almost ten times the resolution of 'Micro-file' panchromatic film, to be some 10,000 times slower. There is thus much data to show that improved resolution is only likely to be obtained at the expense of a large loss of speed. The importance of this antagonism is not restricted to microphotography, but extends to motion-picture and aerial photography.

The emulsions which can be used for extreme resolution have different spectral sensitivities, and with some the speed is not constant for all exposure times, but depends on the actual duration of the exposure. This means that a speed comparison may be valid for only one set of exposure conditions. Direct comparisons are, nevertheless, useful for showing the order of magnitude of speed differences. With tungsten-arc ('Pointolite') illumination a wet-collodion plate was found to have practically the same speed as a concentrated Lippmann emulsion, but silver-chloride print-out emulsions in collodion or gelatin were slower by a factor of 10,000. A bichromated-gelatin layer had a speed slightly less than the print-out emulsions. On exposure to a high-pressure mercury-vapour lamp, the mercury-diazonium process gave one-eightieth of the speed of a commercial concentrated Lippman emulsion [6]. The difference is likely to have been greater if it had been measured with a tungsten source.

CONTRAST

The emulsion speed mainly concerns the convenience of a process, but the contrast—or rate of change of blackening with increasing exposure—has a direct effect on the tone reproduction and sharpness of the image. Contrast is usually evaluated from the characteristic curve obtained by giving a graduated series of exposures, measuring the resulting densities, and plotting the densities against the logarithm

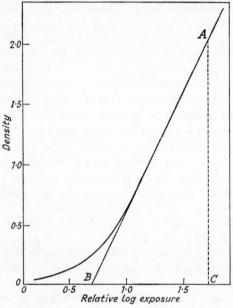

Fig. 11 *Characteristic Curve of Silver-Halide Emulsion*

The contrast is described by the 'gamma', i.e. the slope of the tangent to the straight line $= \dfrac{AC}{BC}$.

of the exposures (Fig. 11). One convenient method of giving a graduated series of exposures is to expose the emulsion behind a film bearing a series of uniformly blackened bands (i.e. a step-wedge). The relative log exposure behind each band can then be found by subtracting the optical density of each band from an arbitrary constant. (A more convenient procedure is to plot the abscissae as step-wedge densities increasing from *right to left*, and this is equivalent to a scale of exposures increasing from left to right.) It therefore follows that the characteristic curve shows how any emulsion will reproduce the tones of a transparency. If the slope of the tangent to the curve (this quantity is known as the gamma) is greater than unity the contrast of the image will be increased, and if it is less than unity the contrast will be decreased. In some materials, such as diazotype or the print-out emulsions, the gamma has practically a fixed value close to unity, but in other high-resolution materials treated in a metal-forming developer, the gamma may be five or more. The actual value then obtained depends also on the composition of the solution and the duration of development (pp. 69–73).

For practical purposes the factors determining the gamma required are much the same as in other fields of photography. With continuous-tone pictures the gamma should be suited to the density range of the original, and values less than 2 will usually be required. This must be accompanied by an adequate exposure scale, since a low gamma obtained by drastic under-development of a high-contrast emulsion merely results in a poor density range (p. 90). Emulsions with higher gammas will normally be used for making line images, and really high values can be beneficial when working close to the resolution limit of the objective. In such cases the aerial image of a line has a flat intensity profile (see p. 106), which can be reproduced as a steep density profile when recorded on a high-contrast emulsion (Fig. 12). This can result in improved sharpness of the line, and in a reduced line width for any given density. These advantages are obtained at the expense of a decrease in exposure latitude, and the full benefit can only be ensured by accurate exposure control (see p. 207).

The useful contrast range of any one type of extreme-resolution microphotographic emulsion is usually narrow. Contrast is thus an important factor in deciding not only which emulsion, but also what process is needed for any application. This point is well illustrated by the concentrated Lippmann emulsions. Their method of preparation seems to lead naturally to the production of high contrast values, but in their 'Minicard' materials Eastman Kodak have succeeded in producing a Lippmann-type emulsion with an effective gamma value of about one. This was considered to be important for a number of reasons. When originals with lines of different width or blackness are greatly reduced, the effective brightness of different parts of the image can vary greatly, so that the image characteristics tend to approach those of a continuous tone image. If such an image is copied with a high-contrast emulsion, detail is likely to be lost at either high densities or low densities. These losses become progressively worse if the high-contrast emulsion is used to make one or more further generations of copies by contact printing.

Because the contrast range given by individual extreme-resolution emulsions is generally narrow, the operator either has to choose a process which suits the density range of the transparency, or else adjust the density range of the transparency to suit an available

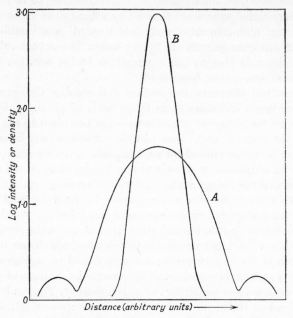

Fig. 12 *Steepening of Line Profile by High-contrast Emulsion*

Curve (*A*). Logarithmic intensity profile of line image. Curve (*B*). Density profile obtained by recording the same intensities on high-contrast emulsion. [See curve for 2 minutes' development: Figure 15(a), p. 70.]

emulsion. The Phillips'-Dippel mercury-diazonium processes provide an exception, since the gamma can be adjusted over an exceptionally large range by changing exposing or processing conditions.

Properties of the Developed Image

IMAGE STRUCTURE

Whatever process is used to obtain extreme resolution, the developed image must have a structure which will not hinder the recognition of fine detail. When the image consists of a molecularly dispersed colouring material, its texture will appear quite uniform under the microscope, but satisfactory resolution will only be obtained if the image shows no tendency to 'bleed'. Sideways diffusion in the emulsion layer by the photochemical reaction product or by the colouring material formed by development may spoil the sharpness of the image.

In processes producing a metallic deposit, the image usually consists of small discrete particles of metal dispersed in the colloid layer. The diameter of these should only be a small proportion of the width of the finest detail it is wished to record. According to the quality required, the minimum ratio of the width of the finest detail to the developed grain diameter should be five or ten, or even twenty to one. In this connection it should be noted that continuous-tone pictures require finer grain than 'line' images for a given width of detail. Line images are normally made with a high density and a very steep density gradient at the edge of the line. This means that any granular structure in the body of the line is relatively unobtrusive, or is virtually invisible. In such cases the granular structure of the image can only be seen from the slightly 'gritty' appearance of the edge (see Plate 6). With continuous-tone pictures, however, the lower contrast and density of the image readily allow any granular structure to be seen, even in the centre of most elements of the image.

As we have already noted, the image structure given by bichromated colloids or photosensitive resins depends on factors influencing the distortion at the edge of each element of the image during washing-off and drying. These factors include the thickness of the colloid, the degree of swelling of the hardened areas during the washing-off process and the firmness of adhesion of the hardened colloid to the support.

LIGHT ABSORPTION BY THE DEVELOPED LAYER

A further requirement for extreme resolution is that the final image should give the necessary contrast in a thin layer. This is because the full sharpness of really fine microphotographic images can only be observed by viewing them with high-aperture microscope objectives, having a small depth of focus. This means that only a thin layer of emulsion can be in focus at any one time, and that the image will only show optimum sharpness if sufficient density is contained in such a thin layer of the developed emulsion. The image should, ideally, also be confined to this thin layer, since the presence of a perfectly sharp photographic image outside the depth of focus of the viewing microscope will make the image appear less sharp. This is a matter in which the concentrated Lippmann emulsions score over the old dilute emulsions (see p. 41). The finer grain of the latter should give their images greater sharpness, but with chemical development much of this advantage was lost by inadequate light absorption in the developed layer.

Normally the satisfaction of this requirement demands the concentration of a sufficient amount of light-absorbing image material in a very thin layer, but processes have recently appeared in which the same result is achieved by refraction of light. Images are formed which consist of minute gas bubbles in the colloid, or of minute wrinkles, in the surface of the colloid, either of which refract light. In both cases, projection of an image of satisfactory contrast depends on the use of an illuminating system giving highly collimated light (see p. 407).

Resolution of the Developed Image

FORMAL METHODS OF ASSESSING RESOLUTION

The most important property of a microphotographic emulsion is its ability to reproduce fine details sharply. In recent years several methods for assessing this property have first found favour, and then lost it. *Resolving power* was measured by photographing a test chart usually consisting of a series of sets of parallel lines of decreasing size (see Plates 58 and 62). The smallest image size at which the component lines of the image could *just be visually separated* was used to estimate the resolving power. The resultant numerical figure therefore indicated the *absolute limit* of the ability of the system to separate small details. Some caution was always needed in interpreting the significance of resolving-power figures, because the assessment depended on subjective judgement, and the figure obtained also depended on extraneous factors such as test chart design and contrast. With extreme-resolution emulsions the matter is particularly difficult, since the figures are usually limited by the available optical systems at least as much as by the emulsion performance. For this reason, additional caution is needed in interpreting very high published figures for emulsion resolving power (say 500 lines/mm or more). In order to demonstrate the potentialities of the emulsion, the test is likely to have been made with an extreme-aperture objective covering only a minute field, or by forming interference fringes in the emulsion to give a distribution of light seldom met in actual use.

Another objection to the wider use of resolving power tests was presented by Higgins and Jones [13], who showed that it was possible to obtain pairs of images in which that giving the higher measured resolving power definitely looked less sharp. Such cases are relatively unusual, but they nevertheless demonstrate that the correlation between resolving power and sharpness is far from perfect. They pointed out that sharpness is a psycho-physical concept, associated with the shape of the density gradient across the edge of an image. They proposed to measure sharpness by evaluating a quantity called 'acutance', which was computed from microdensitometer traces across the edge of an image reproduced by the emulsion under test.

The present trend is for theoretical workers to abandon both of these methods in favour of concepts stemming from electronics as well as from optics. Consider a microdensitometer trace made from a reduced image of a series of parallel lines with decreasing width and spaces (Plate 10). The widest lines are reproduced with high contrast and a square-edged profile, and as line width is reduced, rounding of the lines first sets in. Further reduction of line width causes the image contrast to be reduced, until the existence of separate lines can no longer be recognized. Now it had been noted

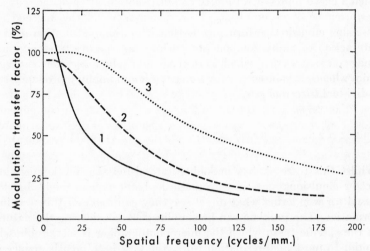

Fig. 13 *Modulation-Transfer-Function Curves for Emulsions*
1. Fast pictorial negative, 2. fine-grain pictorial negative, 3. fine-grain duplicate positive.
From Mees, C. E. K., *Theory of the Photographic Process* (3rd edition). Courtesy of the Macmillan Co.

that once the contrast started to be reduced, the line-intensity profiles in the emulsion became sinusoidal. When this happened, it was convenient to use a resolution-test chart in which the transmission profiles of the lines were themselves sinusoidal. The use of sinusoidal test charts reduced assessment of the reproduction of all line widths to the same basis. This method of study now approached closely the concepts of electronics engineers, who were interested in finding how the relative amplitudes of electrical signals of different frequency were reproduced by their circuits.

From such considerations grew the idea of imaging a sinusoidal test chart on an emulsion layer, and observing the quality of the image so produced by making a microdensitometer trace. By the use of a relatively long slit, the effect of graininess is minimized, and the use of an instrument reduces the dependence of the measurements on subjective judgements. From the microdensitometer trace and the emulsion's characteristic curve, it is possible to calculate the amplitudes of the sinusoidal light distribution in the emulsion layer for every line frequency. The amplitudes so obtained are expressed as a percentage of the amplitude of the sinusoidal images incident on the emulsion surface [14]. The resulting so-called *modulation-transfer function* curves show the proportional recording of the initial amplitude plotted against the line frequencies of the test chart (Fig. 13). Such a curve represents a pretty complete specification of the optical performance of an emulsion. A particular merit of this method of assessing emulsion performance is that it permits calculation of the interaction of many components, such as an *objective* producing an image on an *emulsion*, which in turn is scanned by a *television camera*, from whence it is broadcast by *transmitters* and finally reproduced by individual *television sets*.

PRACTICAL INTERPRETATION OF QUANTITATIVE RESOLU-
TION INFORMATION

Whilst this research has undoubtedly assisted the development of better emulsions and lenses, practical photographers might be excused for wondering what direct use they can make of this new information. The problem can be simplified by considering the nature of the specific tasks which the microphotographer is setting himself to do. In most high-resolution work, the task is to greatly reduce a line image, while preserving sharp lines with a minimum distortion of relative line widths or rounding of corners and intersections. Of the different types of numerical data of emulsion performance so far published, there is no doubt that the modulation-transfer function is the most complete. The following argument shows how this information can be used.

The main hindrance the microphotographer has to combat is loss of image contrast resulting from light dispersal by the emulsion and lens. The modulation-transfer function curve for an emulsion shows how successful an emulsion is in avoiding this loss at different line frequencies. If an image has to be produced with lines of minimum width x microns, it approximately corresponds to a frequency of $1/2x$ lines per millimetre. Hence the probable performance of different emulsions can be compared from the magnitude of their modulation transfer functions at the chosen frequency. The functions for higher frequencies are also important for two reasons. Firstly they demonstrate the potential reserve capacity of the system, should it be required to produce even finer lines. Secondly it can be shown that the intensity profiles of the square-edged lines, which are mainly required in practice, can be analysed into a fundamental frequency and many harmonics of higher frequency. The ability of an emulsion to reproduce these higher harmonics indicates its potential for producing something sharper than a sinusoidal line profile. For this sort of reason, the ultimate interpretation of this *numerical* data to predict the *quality* to be anticipated in a particular practical situation is not straight-forward.

In considering the figures for modulation-transfer function given by any emulsion, it should not be forgotten that lenses were needed both to form the image and to measure the density profile on a microdensitometer. With line frequencies up to 200–400 per millimetre, there is little problem in finding lenses whose own limitations will not seriously distort the information they give about the emulsion under test. Hence the method is excellent for evaluating emulsions in the speed range from 'process' materials to high-speed negative film. With extreme-resolution materials, the limitations of available lenses are significant, and any quantitative measurement becomes a pretty blunt instrument for comparing the desirable properties of different emulsions.

QUALITATIVE USE OF RESOLUTION-TEST CHARTS

The circumstances described above mean that there is no really satisfactory quantitative measurement from which the quality of image to be anticipated by use of a particular extreme-resolution emulsion can be reliably predicted. In this dilemma there is one simple method of self-help open to the microphotographer. From resolution test-chart images which are commercially available, he can produce a series of reduced images *with his own equipment*. Although square-edged (as opposed to sinusoidal) test charts are less frequently used for fundamental work, they still provide an excellent method for making qualitative comparisons of different microphotographic materials. In interpreting the results, the microphotographer should pay less attention to the finest images, but should rather attempt to estimate the finest lines reproduced with a quality satisfactory to the ultimate user of the images. This represents a *practical resolution limit* observed with this particular emulsion and equipment, and is more immediately relevant than the *physically measured resolving power* shown by the smallest decipherable images.

The distinction between these quantities is one the practical man cannot afford to forget. The practical resolution limit is necessarily a quantity which will tend to vary from one use to another, and it therefore has no generally valid meaning. For control of the manufacture of extreme-resolution emulsions, however, observation of the finest separated images in a resolution test is still useful. The author found that estimations of the resolution limit obtained in fixed conditions with a 4 mm (1/6th in) microscope objective were suitable for the batch control of concentrated-Lippmann plates. Reasonable correlation was observed between the resolution limit and the image quality obtained with any batch.[1]

SUBSIDIARY EMULSION PROPERTIES

A number of emulsion properties have no direct influence on the image quality of the final microphotographs, but largely control the convenience with which acceptable results can be obtained. Foreign bodies in the emulsion, so small as to be of little consequence for ordinary photographic work, can completely spoil a microphotograph.

The keeping properties of the coated plates are also important. In the wet-collodion or the original form of mercury-diazonium processes, for instance, the layers had to be sensitized shortly before use, while layers of bichromated colloids can only be kept a day or two before exposure. Silver-halide–gelatin 'dry' plates, by contrast, can be stored in a temperate climate for years. This is not only very convenient but also assists systematic working with standardized exposures. The superior keeping properties of coated layers of photosensitive resins is an important reason for their increasing popularity.

The ability to give reproducible results is most desirable, particularly when the exposure latitude is small, or when large numbers of similar images have to be made. It is clear that the quality of the images can only be satisfactorily controlled with a process capable of giving consistent results. In some processes, for instance with silver-halide dry plates, control for any one batch is achieved simply by adhering to a definite set of exposure and development conditions. In others, such as the wet-collodion process, success cannot be assured by automatically following a prescribed routine, and personal skill is also needed. This was probably one of the reasons that operators at the Möller graticule factory were considered to need at least six months' preliminary training (see p. 44).

Emulsions Suitable for Extreme Resolution

We have so far considered emulsion properties in general terms. This approach provides the basic information for deciding how suitable any emulsion is for obtaining extreme resolution, but is no substitute for an examination of individual emulsions. The remainder of this chapter will therefore be devoted to a review of the more notable processes which can be used.

---

[1] For further enlightenment, see Brock [47].

SILVER-HALIDE—GELATIN EMULSIONS

The advantages which permitted silver-halide–gelatin 'dry' plate emulsions to displace earlier photographic materials for general photography, should also appeal to most workers in microphotography. We have already noted that emulsions for extreme resolution must have grain diameters of less than 0·1 μ, and this automatically eliminates the vast majority of commercial dry-plate emulsions. Probably the first silver-halide–gelatin emulsions with an average grain size below this limit were made for the Lippmann interference process of colour photography (Chapter 13). The successful operation of this process involved the reproduction of images of interference fringes at frequencies up to 6,000 per millimetre (p. 465).

Lippmann emulsions were made by using exceptionally dilute solutions of halides and silver nitrate, and by precipitating the silver halide in the presence of a relatively high concentration of gelatin [15]. Both these conditions were considered to favour the production of very fine grain. The emulsion was coated immediately after precipitation and washed as soon as the layer had set: a procedure giving the least possible opportunity for grain growth to occur. Emulsions made in this way had a very low silver-halide/gelatin ratio, so that only low densities (0·5 or less) were obtained by chemical development of coatings having a normal thickness for dry-plate emulsions. The extreme fineness of grain, however, meant that the image consisted of a vast multitude of minute silver particles, which served as excellent nuclei for physical intensification. Very high densities can thus be obtained by physical intensification of such an image (Fig. 14), or by developing directly in a physical developer.

In 1941 methods were discovered for increasing the silver content of Lippmann emulsions without unduly increasing their grain size [16], and several manufacturers have produced plates which give densities of three or more by direct chemical development, accompanied by a resolution of over 1,000 lines/mm and a speed that is not impractically low for many purposes. Materials of this type are the Kodak High-Resolution and Spectroscopic 649-GH plates, and the Maximum-Resolution plate made by Kodak Limited in Great Britain. The emulsions used on all these materials are conveniently described as extreme-resolution Lippmann emulsions. The fact that sufficient density can be obtained by direct chemical development means that the results can be methodically controlled by time and temperature, and the images need not be watched during development. This property makes these materials suitable for the production of large batches of microphotographs, or for building up large images by the successive exposure of many very small areas.

Like the majority of commercial silver-halide emulsions, extreme-resolution materials do not necessarily give the same result if the same exposure (i.e. the product of time and intensity) is given with very different exposure durations. Two aspects of this *reciprocity failure* may cause some concern. With exposures shorter than 1/500th of a second, speed and contrast may be reduced. It is, therefore, prudent to check that acceptable results can be obtained when designing microphotographic equipment. Loss of speed and contrast

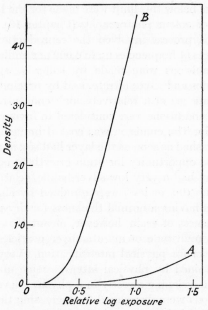

Fig. 14 *Physical Intensification of Lippmann Plate*
(A) Curve produced by chemical development. 3 minutes at 70° F in D.158.
(B) Intensified image resulting from physical intensification of developed image.

can also occur with long duration exposures. Exposures longer than 15 minutes are likely both to waste time and to give disappointing results, and should be avoided by increasing the light intensity.

Since concentrated Lippmann extreme-resolution emulsions became commercially available, a number of procedures for making emulsions of the required very small grain-size have been published. These include papers by Crawford, who worked at the National Physical Laboratory on emulsions for recording stationary light waves [17] and by Perfilov, Novikova and Prokofyeva, who developed very fine-grain and silver-rich emulsions for recording nuclear particles [18]. The physical-chemical conditions needed for the production of very fine grain and uniform grain size have been demonstrated with penetrating studies by Berriman [19] and Demers [20].

While this published literature means that information required for making very fine-grain emulsions is available, setting up the equipment and training the staff to achieve the consistent results required for industrial or commercial applications is a formidable undertaking. It is an enterprise that can not be lightly initiated.

Until recently, users of extreme-resolution emulsions have either had to employ factory-coated plates or blanks, or else to *make* and *coat* their own emulsion. In Great Britain, some graticule manufacturers have for many years wanted to coat their own blanks with M-R emulsion, but it was not clear how this could be conveniently arranged. To satisfy this demand, it would have been necessary to store the uncoated wet emulsion for considerable periods, and such fine-grain emulsions are completely spoilt by even a small amount of spontaneous grain growth. The emulsion was also required in such small quantities that the handling costs of making and *testing* a special batch were uneconomically high. However, the stability of the dry coated emulsion is excellent, and to meet this special requirement, Kodak Limited introduced the 'Pre-Stripping' M-R plate. M-R emulsion was thickly coated on 'stripping' glass, so that about 1·8 grams of dry emulsion could be readily stripped from a 10 in × 8 in plate. A 10 per cent solution was obtained by soaking the emulsion from each plate in about 18 cc of cold water. The emulsion was melted by gently warming to about 40° C (104° F) with stirring.

By this method the user was provided with a means for obtaining small amounts of liquid emulsion at very short notice. If correctly handled, each melt from a single batch of coated plates should have identical photographic properties. To secure similar consistency from successive emulsion precipitations would be both difficult and expensive. In fact, this apparently preposterous method involving two successive coatings and dryings of the same bulk of emulsion is seen to have real advantages.

THE WET-COLLODION PROCESS

The wet-collodion process has been used for making microphotographs ever since its invention by Scott-Archer in 1851 [21]. It enabled Dancer to perform his pioneering experiments, and Dagron used a variation for the operation of the Paris Pigeon Post in 1870–1 (p. 363). Advantages of this process for the industrial production of graticules at the Möller factory have been described by Bovey [22].

In essentials the process consists of the following steps. After cleaning the glass, and applying a 'sub' coating to secure adhesion, the operator coats the glass by flowing over a collodion solution containing soluble iodides. As soon as sufficient solvent has evaporated to let the layer set, the plate is sensitized by bathing in a silver-nitrate solution containing dissolved silver iodide. This results in the precipitation of a fine-grain deposit of silver iodide in the layer, and the plate is exposed and developed before the emulsion can dry completely. This procedure ensures that the layer is still sufficiently permeable for the processing solutions to penetrate. The emulsion layer becomes impermeable to aqueous solutions if it is allowed to dry right out.

It is important to realize that the wet-collodion 'process' is not one standardized method, but a whole group of procedures among which may be found great variations in the composition of the sensitizing solutions and developing methods. The form most widely known until recently (but now largely superseded by silver-halide–gelatin emulsions) was that used for making photo-mechanical negatives for half-tone blocks; but the methods used by photo-engravers can give a coarse developed grain, which is useless for extreme resolution. Precise working details of the original methods used by Dancer and Dagron never seem to have been published. It is believed that the latter used a variation originated by Taupenot in 1855, in which the sensitized collodion plate is covered with an iodized-albumen layer. The resultant almost insensitive plates can be stored for several months, and the plates are re-sensitized in a silver bath immediately before exposure. The reader wishing to operate a collodion process is advised to consult published accounts of methods which have been specifically worked out for extreme resolution. Even these differ amongst themselves. Lehmann and Miethe, for instance, used the Taupenot process, and developed the plates first in a mercury and then in a silver physical developer [23]. In another variation of this process used by the firm of Zeiss for making graticules, all the constituent solutions were different from those used by Lehmann and Miethe, and a silver physical developer containing pyrogallol was used [24]. The Möller factory employed still another procedure of the type introduced by Russell in 1861; in which the sensitized plates were treated with tannin before exposure, and this was stated to act both as a sensitizer and anti-foggant [22].

In addition to the employment of appropriate solutions and a suitable variety of collodion, the success of the wet-collodion process depends on the skill and experience of the operator. There seems to be little question of being able to obtain the desired result immediately by rigorously following a prescribed drill. This is the reason why photo-engraving wet-plate operators require considerable training, and why the firm of Möller insist on plates being exposed and processed by the operator who sensitized them. The reader would, therefore, seem to be well advised not to use this process unless he is prepared to devote the time needed to master the art.

In spite of these disadvantages the wet-collodion process has many attractive features. The very thin layer assists high resolution, dimensional accuracy and rapid processing. The effective speed is comparable with that of the concentrated Lippmann emulsions, and changes in the development procedure can be used to give the high contrast needed for line images, or the low contrast required for continuous-tone pictures. The fact that the entire process from coating the emulsion to producing the images can be completed in about 30 minutes in a single room is convenient, in addition to the ease with which glass blanks of any size or shape can be sensitized. An outstanding advantage of the procedure operated at the Möller factory was the ability to remove individual images from the original plate on which many are made, and transfer them without distortion to the final graticule blanks. It must be for reasons such as this that the firm used wet collodion as a large-scale production method for many years.

CELLOPHANE IMPREGNATED WITH SILVER HALIDE

In 1939 Elvegård and Sjöstedt described the preparation and properties of a sensitive material produced by successively bathing Cellophane in solutions of bromide or iodide, followed by silver nitrate and a final acid bath to remove fog or stain nuclei formed in the silver bath [4]. The silver halide in the sensitized Cellophane formed a latent image, which was developed by a metol–potassium-carbonate developer. The silver halide was found to lie within a zone 9 μ (0·0004 in) thick at each surface of the Cellophane, but a cross section of an exposed and developed layer showed a densely packed zone of silver restricted to the top 3 μ (0·00013 in) of the side facing the exposing light. Clearly, heavy light absorption had confined the image to the emulsion surface. The authors commented on the great fineness of grain of their material, and photomicrographs of developed layers certainly showed a structure definitely finer than a cine-positive emulsion of that date. Parshin [25] examined the optimum conditions for producing a very fine-grain emulsion by their method, and used a photo-electric cell to follow the increased light absorption as the silver salt was precipitated in the Cellophane. On the material so made, he compared its resolving power with that of a Lippmann emulsion and with Goldberg's print-out material (see below). All materials gave high resolution figures limited by the performance of the lens, indicating that the sensitized Cellophane must have had a very high resolution indeed.

SILVER SALT 'PRINT-OUT' PROCESSES

All processes giving a silver image have the advantage that the image is very stable to light, while its resistance to chemical attack can be readily increased by conversion to gold or platinum. With all silver processes using a development stage, however, Goldberg realized that coarsening of the image structure is a necessary consequence of the large amplification factor [3]. This drawback was avoided by use of a collodion–silver-chloride print-out emulsion, such as G. Wharton Simpson evolved in 1865 for the making of contact prints [26]. Stock collodion solutions containing respectively an alcohol-soluble chloride and silver nitrate were mixed to give a fine-grain silver-chloride emulsion, and citric acid was added as a halogen acceptor. When thinly coated, the material gave adequate contrast and density directly by printing out.

Although it was later stated that Simpson's emulsion resolved 2,000 lines per millimetre [27], the literature of his own period seems to give no more than a vague hint that it might be suitable for microphotography. In Goldberg's modification of this process, lithium chloride was used because of its alcohol solubility and the lesser tendency of lithium salts subsequently to crystallize in the dry layer [3]. The three stock collodion solutions, containing respectively silver nitrate, lithium chloride and citric acid, kept indefinitely if tightly stoppered, and the emulsion was made by mixing them shortly before coating. After coating, the plates were exposed until sufficient density was obtained, and the image was fixed and gold toned. The fact that the image became directly visible simplified exposure control, and Goldberg interrupted his exposure at intervals, so that the density could be judged on examination by non-actinic light (Chapter 5). In addition, the low speed of the emulsion allowed it to be handled by ordinary tungsten illumination, but condenser illumination in the camera was needed to ensure tolerably brief exposures.

With this process Goldberg produced images whose fineness has been a challenge to all subsequent workers. He made legible copies of a page of fifty lines of print reduced to a height of 0·004 in (0·1 mm) so that individual letters were only one micron (0·00004 in) high.

Silver-chloride print-out emulsions in gelatin have also been used for extreme resolution [28], but are now of no more than historical interest.

THE SILVER–ALBUMEN PROCESS

The use of a silver-sensitized albumen layer for making contact copies from mechanically ruled scales has been described by Burmistrov [29]. An exceedingly thin layer of egg albumen (0·5 microns (0·00002 in) thick) was coated on plates by whirling, and after drying was sensitized in a 5 per cent silver-nitrate solution. The excess silver salts were washed-out in running water. After drying, the plates were exposed behind a master negative for 20 minutes at 3 ft from a 20-ampere arc, and were developed in a physical developer. The sensitive compound probably consists of molecularly dispersed 'silver-albuminate', and there is every reason to suppose that this material should give extreme resolution.

Processes using Photosensitive Organic Compounds

Many dyes and organic compounds are unstable to light, and chemists have considered the use of such compounds for photography, and in particular for the copying of colour photographs [30]. In some of these experimental processes an addition agent was used to increase the light-sensitivity of the dye, and it is desirable that the removal of the addition agent should leave a reasonably stable dye image. The optical properties of a colloid layer impregnated with such a dye would be admirably suited for making minute images. An important additional requirement is that the un-decomposed dye should not diffuse after exposure. Dye-bleach processes using several dyes appear to offer the best hope for the production of multi-coloured images of truly microscopic proportions.

The National Cash Register Company have described particularly interesting applications of so-called photochromic organic compounds. These are mostly colourless, and on absorbing ultra-violet the electronic state of the molecules is excited, so that they absorb visible light and appear coloured. The excited molecules do not decompose, and can be 'switched back' to their original colourless state by longer wavelengths of visible or infra-red radiation or by the ambient temperature.

In the layers used for extreme-resolution work, the photochromic compound was in an amorphous form dispersed in the coating vehicle, to give a transparent layer which became coloured on exposure to ultra-violet [31]. The resolution was naturally very high, and excellent results were obtained when microfilm negatives of documents were further reduced to give an over-all reduction factor of 150 (p. 411).

Because the photochromic compound can be switched back to its colourless state by exposure to infra-red, images or even small parts of an image could be erased. Many cycles of image formation and erasure could follow each other on one area, without a change of sensitivity being observable. The images only had a life of a few hours at room temperature, and the entire camera for producing the

c

reduced images was therefore enclosed in cold dry air. The exposed material was stored in a deep-freeze where it was stated to be stable for many years. No loss of information was caused by printing from the photochromic images on to an extreme-resolution silver-halide emulsion.

DIAZO PROCESSES

Processes employing diazonium salts are of great interest because they have not only been extensively used in the photographic copying of plans and drawings, but in recent years they have also been employed for making duplicate copies and enlargements of existing silver-image microfilms (p. 419). The diazo films have been shown to resolve well over 1,000 lines/mm [32].

Diazonium salts absorb mainly in the blue and ultra-violet, and are thereby decomposed with the evolution of nitrogen. Because the diazo salts only absorb feebly in the visible, the unprocessed images look pale and are of poor visual contrast, but can be developed in several ways.

(i) The un-decomposed diazonium salt can be converted to a deeply coloured dye by coupling with a suitable phenol, and this gives a direct-positive image in which the unexposed areas are heavily coloured.

(ii) The decomposition product (usually a phenol) can be coupled with another diazonium salt to form a negative dye image heavily coloured in the exposed areas.

(iii) The decomposition product can be allowed to react with a metal salt (usually mercury), resulting in the formation of nuclei for physical development.

The first method is that used for dye-line photocopying papers, and for diazo films used in making duplicates of microfilms (p. 407). The dyes formed are highly substantive to the medium: probably an important factor in preventing diffusion and ensuring high image resolution.

MERCURY-DIAZONIUM PROCESSES

The third of these methods forms the basis of a most interesting group of extreme-resolution processes described by C. J. Dippel and his colleagues in the Philips' Laboratories at Eindhoven [6]. In the earlier processes called 'M.D.' (mercury–diazonium), a base such as 'Cellophane' was impregnated with a diazonium salt and a mercurous salt. On exposure, the decomposition product of the diazonium salt sequestered the mercuric ions always present in solutions of mercurous salts.

$$2Hg^+ \rightleftharpoons Hg^{++} + Hg_{metal}.$$

Equilibrium displaced to the right by sequestering Hg^{++}

The mercury atoms so formed condensed to form metallic nuclei, which could act as a latent image. The exposed layer was subsequently developed by 'plating' of silver or mercury from solution ('physical' development, see p. 67).

In spite of its obvious potentialities and very high resolution, little commercial use was made of this form of the process. This may have been because the life of the coated material was brief, so that extra preparative steps were involved each time images had to be made.

This disadvantage seems to have been overcome in later variants. Aryl diazo-sulphonates (such as p. methoxy-benzene diazosulphonate) were imbibed into the surface of base materials such as 'Cellophane', cellulose esters, polystyrene, 'Perspex', 'Estar', polycarbonates and anodized aluminium [33]. In some cases the surface layer of the support may be hydrolysed or coated with a thin layer of another colloid. On exposure, the diazosulphonate decomposed into diazonium and sulphite ions. When the exposed layer was briefly treated in a solution of mercurous and silver salts, complexing of mercuric ions by the sulphite resulted in the formation of nuclei effectively consisting of a silver–mercury amalgam. Because this stage occurred after exposure, the process has been called 'P.D.' for 'post-disproportionation', (but the same initials serve for Philips'-Dippel). The latent images consisting of the nuclei were similarly developed physically.

A cellulose-triacetate film sensitized with this type of compound was found to have a shelf life of at least two years. The opacity of the sensitive layer to ultra-violet (3,650 Å) gave 90 per cent absorption in a layer 5 μ thick, and the layer must have had a very low light scatter. Special means were used to counteract regression of the sulphite ions, and no latent-image fading was detected in 30 hours. There also seemed to be negligible lateral displacement of the sulphite ions, and the contrast of the process could be increased at will by increasing the proportion of silver to mercurous ions in the nucleating solution. Throughout their work on these processes, Dippel and his colleagues have been introducing means for circumventing the disadvantages of physical developers, and in the latest forms used solutions of remarkable stability and activity (p. 68).

The latest forms of the process gave images with very high resolution and edge sharpness. A twentieth-generation copy of a hundred-diameters reduction of a book page was still legible, whereas a similar eight-generation copy on a Lippmann emulsion was illegible. This achievement demonstrated that P.D. images can be contact printed with exceptionally little loss of sharpness, and the process is being used to achieve the rigorous tolerances required in micro-electronics manufacture. In concluding this section on application of diazo compounds, the process used in 'Kalvar' vesicular film should also be mentioned. On heating a thermoplastic polymer containing a recently exposed diazonium compound, the nitrogen released by exposure produces an image consisting of minute bubbles. The fact that the bubbles need to be large enough to scatter light limits the potentiality of this process for extreme resolution. Its application to the duplication of microfilm images is described in Chapter 12.

PHOTORESISTS

When thin layers of glue, gelatin or certain other colloids containing a dichromate are exposed to blue or ultra-violet light, the dichromate is reduced and the resultant product combines with the colloid and makes it insoluble. The unexposed areas are then washed out with a solvent, and the remaining exposed and 'hardened' or 'tanned' areas constitute a stencil image. In the printing industry, such images are used to protect metal plates bathed in acid etching baths: a process still widely employed for making half-tone blocks. As discussed earlier in this chapter, a very thin layer is needed to ensure high resolution, but bichromated-glue layers have, nevertheless, been used extensively for the production of graticules and stage micrometers (p. 261).

The bichromated-glue process is the forerunner of an important group of extreme-resolution methods. Intrinsically, stencil images can be employed to effect image-wise etching or incorporation of dyes or other materials in the support as well as image-wise deposition of materials on the surface of the support. Practical applications of these potentialities are described in Chapters 9 and 11.

In spite of their wide-spread use, bichromated-colloids suffered from quite serious disadvantages. The coated layer was liable to harden in the dark, so that coatings could not be safely stored for more than a day or two. Their sensitivity tended to be influenced by atmospheric humidity. The most serious limitation, however, was the indifferent resistance of the stencil to the aqueous solutions usually required for etching of the substrate. Even when the stencils had been fortified after washing-out (for instance by subsequent tanning or partial carbonizing by heating at temperatures up to 300° C (600° F), they lacked the resistance needed for some modern processes.

In a recent review, Hepher ascribed most of these deficiencies to the fact that a relatively hydrophilic colloid seems to be required to give satisfactory tanning on exposure with dichromate, or even to allow the water-soluble dichromates to be incorporated in the layer [34]. He described a variety of methods which have been employed to by-pass these limitations. One solution was the use of two-layer pro-cesses, in which the bichromated-colloid was coated on a thin layer of more resistant material such as 'Bakelite', bitumen or silver. The bichromated stencil was then used to control the image-wise erosion of this underlayer, employing conditions causing a minimum of undercutting.

A more fundamental approach was the organic chemists' search for methods of sensitizing hydrophobic colloids so as to endow them with the ability to undergo photolytic cross-linking: the reaction respon-sible for insolubilization of the bichromated colloids. An early form was described by Davis and Pope of the United States National Bureau of Standards [35]. They used a partly polymerized mixture of phenol-formaldehyde or resorcinol-formaldehyde resins, which were dissolved with iodoform in a ketone solvent. Glass blanks were coated thinly and uniformly by pulling them vertically and at a controlled rate through the surface of the solution held in an accumulator jar. With this method the coating thickness was controlled with con-siderable precision, since it depended only on the rate of withdrawal through the meniscus and on the viscosity and specific gravity of the solution. In their conditions, a withdrawal rate of 1 in (2·5 cm) in $6\frac{3}{4}$ seconds gave a dried-down layer 0·000038 in (0·95 μ) thick. As with bichromated colloids, the photosensitive compound (iodoform) was molecularly dispersed and the dry layer substantially non-scattering. On exposure to violet and ultra-violet light, photochemical decomposition of the iodoform resulted in further polymerization and insolubilization of the colloid. After washing-out with an appropriate solvent mixture, simple baking gave stencils with adequate resistance to the hydrofluoric acid solution used to etch glass. Their photo-micrographs indicated that duplicate divided circles made by this process were of high quality. These improved photosensitive layers, however, still did not meet all desired requirements, since the coated layer hardened in the dark and had a relatively short storage life.

Sustained efforts by organic chemists are now producing a variety of products with fewer of the original defects, and with properties better suited to particular photomechanical applications. An impor-tant group has been based on cinnamic acid and its derivatives, which dimerize or produce cross-linking on exposure to light. Particular attention has been given to cinnamic-acid esters of polyvinyl alcohol or cellulose. The cinnamate residues form side chains on the polyvinyl backbone, and exposure is likely to produce extensive cross-linked networks. It would appear from the literature [36] that Kodak

Photo Resist and its variants [37] are commercial products resulting from such developments.

Products of this type can be sensitized by quinones and nitro-compounds, and give layers several times faster than the bichromated colloids. The coated layers are stable for about a year, and since exposure to light makes the polymer completely insoluble in most common solvents, development latitude is excellent. When coated at a thickness permitting the formation of very sharp image elements about 0·001 in (25 μ) wide, the layers have excellent resistance to solutions having a strong etching action on many metals or glass. The industrial applications of these properties (discussed in Chapter 11) tends to make increasingly strenuous demands on the materials. They are, for instance, being used as resists on resistant substrates such as silicon or molybdenum. These require the use of drastic oxidizing solutions such as strong chromic acid, and securing the desired resistance in a thin layer of inherently oxidizable organic matter still constitutes a problem [34]. The sensitivity of these materials allows them to be used conveniently for contact printing with a mercury arc. With condenser optics behind a transparency, convenient exposure times are also achieved by optical projection, particularly when high reduction ratios are obtained with large aperture microscope objectives.

From Hepher's review, it is clear that numerous other compositions giving rather similar properties are being studied and tested on the market. For instance, on addition to a colloid and exposure to light, organic azides decompose to form a free radical which can produce cross-linking. In particular, bis-azides soluble in hydrophobic solvents are added to solutions of natural or synthetic rubbers, and produce a reaction analogous to vulcanization. From the photo-chemical standpoint such preparations are capable of giving high resolution, but in some, a tendency for nitrogen bubbles to form in the exposed layer limits the minimum satisfactory line width.

All the layers so far described in this section are 'negative-working', in that the exposed areas are hardened by the light action. Hydrophobic layers with satisfactory resistance to etching solutions have been made from materials based on orthoquinone-diazides or diazo-oxide structures. On exposure to light, nitrogen is released with the formation of carboxyl groups, and the solubility so conferred permits the stencil to be washed-out in aqueous alkali. Thus a positive stencil is formed, in which the hardened areas correspond to the opaque areas of the image behind which the layer was exposed. Other reactions giving such 'direct-positive' stencils have been proposed, and all such processes would seem to offer two advantages. Firstly there is the obvious point that formation of a direct-positive stencil can in appropriate conditions offer the most convenient method of producing an image structure of a desired configuration. Secondly it should be noted that the insoluble areas of the resist are formed merely by coating without the intervention of the exposure. It therefore seems likely that they will tend to be relatively free from 'pinholes' caused by dust shadows (but, see p. 82).

THREE-DIMENSIONAL STRUCTURES FROM A SINGLE PHOTOSENSITIVE LAYER

In processes where exposure results in a difference of solubility, use of an optically clear layer not absorbing the exposing radiation too heavily permits the direct photochemical production of quite thick images. Such are exemplified by the Corning Photosensitive glasses and by Du Pont's light-sensitized nylon 'Dycril' and 'Templex' photosensitive plastics.

CORNING PHOTOSENSITIVE GLASS

A typical composition for a photosensitive glass has been stated to be: SiO_2, 81·5; Li_2O, 12·0; K_2O, 3·5; Al_2O_3, 3·0; CeO_2, 0·03 and Ag, 0·02 all in weight per cent. The cerium and silver compounds confer photosensitivity, and on exposure to light the released photo-electrons are believed to be trapped in the silicate-glass network [38]. When the exposed glass was heated to around 500° C (930° F), silver ions were reduced by the photo-electrons and the silver atoms aggregated. In one form of the glass they gave a dark colour, and in another form silver particles reaching a critical size served as nuclei for the production of lithium metasilicate crystals. On complete development, these crystals can grow to 4 μ (0·00016 in) diameter and form an opalescent image. Most important of all, such exposed and heat-treated glass is etched by hydrofluoric acid at about fifteen times the rate of etching of the unexposed glass.

As a result of this differential solubility, etching in a stirred aqueous hydrofluoric acid solution (2–10 per cent) removed glass in a pattern determined by the exposure. The shape of the apertures so formed was modified by the slower etching of the unexposed glass. As a result of etching at the side-walls of etched cavities, holes were experimentally found to have a taper of 4 degrees. Thus 1·4 mm (0·055 in) thick glass can be etched right through to give a structure with more than 12,000 holes per square inch. The results obtained are discussed more fully on p. 323.

LIGHT-SENSITIZED NYLON

Layers of an alcohol-soluble nylon can be made photo-sensitive by adding potential cross-linking agents such as methylene bis-acrylamide with an activator such as benzophenone. On exposure to ultra-violet, the benzophenone forms free radicals, which react with both the other compounds and hence insolubilizes the nylon. The benzophenone is used at about 5 per cent by weight of the other solids, giving a layer with a relatively low absorption coefficient. As a result, layers 0·005 in (127 μ) thick or more can be insolubilized throughout their thickness and the unexposed areas are dissolved. The method was first exploited for the production of relief printing plates.

Once again it seems that stencil processes first developed for the printing industry are potentially useful for extreme resolution processes. In a study of the potentialities of the process, Lohse and Bruins showed that a 0·001 in (25 μ) etch of a 0·001 in (25 μ) wide line had virtually parallel sides with no detectable signs of undercutting [39]. They suggested that such stencils should be used to control deposition of metals (see p. 326). Du Pont 'Templex' photosensitive plastic allows stencils with vertical sidewalls to be produced in thicknesses up to 0·042 in (approx. 1 mm). Suggested applications are for the fabrication of tooling jigs, alignment fixtures and fluid state components [39(b)].

EXPOSING TECHNIQUE FOR THREE-DIMENSIONAL LIGHT-FORMED STRUCTURES

Since the exposure of these materials necessarily involved photo-chemical production of a difference of solubility in quite a thick layer, simple optical projection of images with high-aperture objectives was out of the question. Neither the reduction of sharpness nor the reduction of the intensity in narrow exposed lines in out-of-focus planes would be tolerable. As the photosensitive layers were essentially non-scattering, exposure behind a 'pattern' to parallel light should permit quite a sharp image to be produced at considerable depths (and considerable distances) from the 'pattern'. So long as the parallelism of the transmitted light was not spoilt by refraction at the surface of the photographic master negative used as a pattern, the sharpness at different depths should be limited mainly by diffraction. In these circumstances, the form of the edge profile of an element of an image or the vertical angle of different parts of the image can be modified by altering the angle of incidence of the exposing beam. An interesting example of the potentialities of such processes concerned the experimental production of prototype aperture plates for the R.C.A. colour television system. Because of the etching properties of photosensitive glass, the perforations were truncated cones of 0·009 in (0·225 mm) diameter at the small end. The cones for each colour record were required to have all their axes directed towards a common focal point. Such a structure would result by placing a small enough exposing source in the position that each electron gun would ultimately occupy.

'THERMOPLASTIC' RECORDING

It is well known that an electrostatic charge on a film of oil can cause the surface to ripple. In the Eidophor process of colour television the ripples locally disrupt a reflected beam which can subsequently be projected on a large screen. Glenn used a similar phenomenon to form high resolution images in a thin layer of low melting point thermoplastic polymer [40].

A high-melting-point film base was coated with a transparent conducting coating and then with the thermoplastic layer. Since the film was to be exposed directly to a beam of electrons from a cathode-ray tube, the entire equipment was continuously evacuated to about 0·1 μ of mercury. By using continuous motion of the film to provide vertical sweep and causing the electron beam to sweep horizontally across the film, television-type rasters of charge were laid down. After receiving its image-wise electrostatic charge, the film passed through a radio-frequency heater. This induced current in the transparent conducting coating for about 0·01 sec, which produced heat right underneath the top thermoplastic surface and allowed ample time for the ripples to form. Because the heating was very localized, the surface cooled rapidly by diffusion of heat into the base, and the ripples were thereby fixed or frozen. Schlieren-type optical systems were used to project the images, and in one form gave colour projection of recorded television programmes.

For monochrome projection, a series of linear light sources were imaged on a set of opaque bars by the condensing lens. Where the film is smooth because it received no charge, no light entered the projection lens and the screen appeared black. Refraction of light by the ripples resulting from the image-wise deposition of charge deflected light from the bars, so that the rippled areas appeared light. The resolution was high, since two-micron spots on centres separated by four microns have been recorded, and television pictures 2 × 2·5 mm (0·08 × 0·1 in) were stated to be fully resolved.

If the thermoplastic layer was heated well above its melting point, it became sufficiently conducting for the charge to leak away, and surface tension smoothed out the ripples. On cooling, the film was then ready for re-use. By confining the radio-frequency heating field, erasure could be restricted to an area a few 'thous' or 'mils' square (a small fraction of a square millimetre).

Although purists could object to the description of this process as photographic, Thermoplastic Recording can produce results comparable with those given by a number of microphotographic systems. It has the limitation that relatively elaborate equipment is needed for recording, but the film can be used several times, and the development process is rapid and dry.

PHOTOPLASTIC RECORDING

Although other methods of producing the image-wise distribution of charge were considered, it is obvious that the inventors considered that an electron beam in a vacuum was by far the most practical for Thermoplastic Recording. Thus the images had to be formed by electron optics, and the film had to be inserted into and extracted from a high vacuum. The necessity for these restrictive conditions has been avoided by making a similar layer photoconductive. The pattern of electrostatic charge was then produced by uniform electrification in the dark, followed by image-wise 'xerographic' discharge on exposure. In one form of such a process, Gaynor and Aftergut [41] coated glass firstly with a stannic-oxide conductive layer, and then with a thermoplastic and photoconductive layer from 0·0005 to 0·002 in (12–50 μ) thick. The photoconductive layer could consist of a polymerized photosensitive aromatic hydrocarbon, or a thermoplastic polymer made photoconductive by the addition of phenazine, phenothiazine, β-carotene, carbazole or finely divided cadmium sulphide. The organic compounds were mainly ultra-violet sensitive, but could be sensitized to the visible by dyes such as Rhodamine B and Rose Bengal.

In principle, the method of developing and fixing was the same as for Thermoplastic Recording. The images were also likewise projected by a Schlieren optical system, which caused the smooth areas to appear dark on the screen. Since these smooth areas were produced as a result of the exposure permitting the charge to leak away, it follows that an effectively negative image was formed. Illustrations in Gaynor and Aftergut's paper demonstrated that the resolution was similar to that given by Thermoplastic Recording. Images could also be erased and the layer re-used. Thus both these processes and the N.C.R. Photochromic Micro-image Memory share the facility for erasure or modification of or addition to large assemblies of images at a later date.

FROST XEROGRAPHY

The usefulness of the above described form of the Photoplastic process was clearly limited by the rigid glass support, but an apparently similar process called Frost Xerography and employing flexible film was described by Claus and Sullivan [42]. Mylar base 0·1 mm (0·004 in) thick was vacuum-coated with aluminium, to give a layer 0·1 μ thick, and having an optical density of 0·18 and a resistance of 4,000 ohms/square. On this was coated a 10 μ layer of vinyl plastic incorporating a heterocyclic photoconductor, and a 2 μ layer of a thermoplastic rosin ester.

The exposure required to discharge the electrostatic charge corresponded to an equivalent A.S.A. speed of 0·2, and a photomicrograph of the developed reticulation pattern ('Frost Image') indicated a unit cell size of 2–4 μ. The layer would be optically structureless during exposure, and the resultant measured resolution was 100 l/mm for exposure to 'positive' images and 200 l/mm on exposure to 'negative' images.

The advantages of the process were seen to be the use of relatively simple equipment, rapid (15 seconds) processing, and the ability to alter contrast and tonal direction by modifying projection conditions.

The main disadvantages are connected with the special optical properties of the developed image. If light transmitted by the image is collected over a large solid angle, virtually no contrast is obtained. Thus the images cannot be copied by contact printing. Furthermore, the top surface is more easily abraded than the surface of conventional microfilm, and the necessity for projection by collimated light means that every surface blemish shows.

POLYMERIZATION BY ELECTRON BOMBARDMENT

In all microphotographic processes using image formation by light, the resolution is limited by diffraction according to the wavelength of light used (p. 105). Thus even with an oil-immersion objective of N.A. 1·3 and exposure to ultra-violet of wavelength 3,600 Å (0·36 μ), the theoretical limit of line separation is about 0·14 μ. The minimum width of lines showing satisfactory sharpness would be considerably greater than this. For certain advanced proposals in computer construction, really sharp lines 0·1 μ wide were required, and consideration has been given to their formation by electron optics [43].

The proposed image recording system was derived from observations on specimen contamination in the electron microscope. If the vacuum of an electron microscope contains low pressures (0·1μ of mercury) of certain hydrocarbons or tetraethoxysilane, a monolayer was adsorbed on cool surfaces. Electron bombardment of this mono-layer caused formation of free radicals and consequent polymeriza-tion in the layer. Further adsorption could then occur, and the process was automatically repeated so that layers of thickness many tens or hundreds of Ångstrom units were built up. By using a scanning electron microprobe whose movements are controlled by a computer, or by exposing a photocathode behind a negative and using elec-tronic lenses to reduce the resultant image-wise electron emission, it was proposed to form stencil images by this polymerization process.

The feasibility of the chemical stages of such a process was examined by vacuum deposition of a molybdenum layer 800 Å thick. A 400-mesh-to-the-inch copper specimen screen was laid on the molybdenum layer, which was bombarded with 1·2 KV electrons after tetraethoxy-silane vapour at 0·1 μ of mercury had been admitted to the vacuum. After removing the specimen screen, the molybdenum was etched through the stencil so formed, by heating the layer to 300° C and admitting chlorine at a low pressure to the vacuum. In such a process of vapour etching, formation of a volatile compound from the etched metal means that the entire etching process can be completed in the vacuum.

In this experiment, image-wise etching of the areas of molybdenum, which had been shielded from stencil formation by the specimen screen, was demonstrated. The edge sharpness was considered to correspond to the formation of lines finer than a micron wide. As in other processes where emulsions are exposed to electrons, such as in autoradiography and secondary electrons in microradiography, one factor limiting resolution is the path length of highly scattered low-energy electrons when they enter a solid. For this reason the accelera-ting voltage was maintained at 2 KV or less. In an experiment where minute polystyrene spheres were used to cast shadows, the sharpness of the edge suggested that stencils with a 70 Ångstrom unit resolution could be obtained.

THERMAL RECORDING BY LASER

The range of physical methods known to be applicable to high-resolu-tion recording has been extended by work in the laboratories of the National Cash Register Co. to include 'heat-mode' recording [45]. The beam from a helium-neon laser emitting at 6,328 Å was focused by a lens of N.A. 0·4 to form a spot of diameter effectively 1·8 μ, and power density $1·5 \times 10^6$ watts/cm². At such high intensities, absorption of the light was accompanied by such rapid rises of tem-perature that transparent spots could be produced rapidly in a 500 Å thick layer of tantalum. In spite of a melting point around 2,800° C, this action occurred in about 10^{-5} s. With such violent heating, a great variety of other materials could be used as thermally sensitive layers. A 500 Å thick layer of lead became transparent in 10^{-6} s, and a 1 μ layer of plastic with a tri-phenylmethane dye was decolourized in about 10^{-6} s.

The image-forming potentialities of such systems were demonstrated in two types of experiment. By causing the spots to scan the recording surfaces rapidly, high-contrast lines 2·5 μ or less wide were produced in the tantalum, lead and dyed-plastic layers. To produce two dimensional images, a document was scanned photoelectrically, and the signals were used to modulate the intensity of the synchronized scan of the laser beam. Thus by a process analogous to facsimile teletransmission, and with overlapping of the scan lines [46], a very (and immediately) legible copy of the document was produced directly with a reduction factor of 128.

Myers [46] noted that such recordings were compatible with the high-reduction N.C.R. microfiche produced by means of the Photochromic Microimage Memory (p. 410). He also stated that the input information could be fed into the laser recorder directly from a computer or transmission line. Production of masks for large scale integration of microelectronic circuits has also been effected by programmed movements of a laser beam focused on a thin metal film (p. 352).

SELECTION OF A SENSITIVE MATERIAL

Before studying the matter, it seemed reasonable to suppose that sensitized layers suitable for extreme resolution might be rare or extraordinarily difficult to make. This chapter demonstrates the reverse, and shows that a potentiality for extreme resolution can be regarded as almost commonplace. The point has been emphasized by the developments of the last decade. We thus find a situation met with regard to other photographic tasks. Many materials can be used, so that the basic properties can almost be taken for granted. In such circumstances it is the subsidiary properties which determine what material a particular user selects. This chapter has attempted to present facts needed for making a choice, and will conclude with some suggestions for restricting the number of materials the reader need consider seriously.

The choice can conveniently be divided into several stages.

(i) *Consideration of required result* with respect to special optical or physical properties demanded of the final images, and their chemical, physical and dimensional stability.

For some purposes stencil images are needed, and resistance to etchants, behaviour in high vacuum or three-dimensional properties may be important. Other factors to be considered are freedom from defects in the image or background, suitability for use with multi-generation printing procedures or whether the processing of the layer destroys the sensitivity of unexposed areas. In some applications, the capability for add-on exposures or for erasure and re-use are important.

(ii) *Consideration of apparatus required* for forming images with the processes selected in stage 1. In some circumstances the user will consider which processes are well adapted for use with available equipment with respect to specific focusing mechanisms, objectives and illuminants. With this would also have to be considered the production rate desired, and whether the sensitivity of the emulsions otherwise suitable permits short enough exposures with available illumination systems.

(iii) *Convenience and cost* then constitute the factors determining the final decision. Under these headings should be considered not only the purchase price of sensitized materials, but the availability of synthetic compounds, the preparative work required before each exposure, and the keeping properties of the coated layer. Other relevant factors are the amounts of skill and training required for successful operation, whether the emulsion can be handled by room lights, and consistent emulsion response which can be critically important when large numbers of images have to be made.

Different users will have to contend with such different circumstances, that no simple guidance is possible. Many users (and above all beginners) are likely to decide that commercially available extreme-resolution plates fill their requirements. Certainly the convenience of these materials will largely tend to offset advantages that some of the other processes offer. In any case they can often be most conveniently used for initial adjustment and focusing of apparatus, even if special requirements indicate a different ultimate solution.

The amateur is, of course, entirely free to follow his own inclination. Some might wish to explore the potentialities of several processes, while others could experiment with new emulsions. Microphotographic processes are capable of producing very decorative results, with a visual appeal that could be applied to jewellery. Another fascinating field which is virtually untouched is the possibility of producing really microscopic colour photographs. If these could be made small enough to be mounted on a Stanhope lens, the results could have a wide-spread appeal. The production of such colour microphotographs is a task to challenge the skill of the most ambitious worker.

REFERENCES

[1] Wall, E. J., *Photographic Facts and Formulas*, Chapman and Hall (London, 1937), p. 31.

[2] Kodak Photographic Plates. Glass Specification. *Tech-bits* (Eastman Kodak Periodical, p. 3) 1966, No. 1.

[3] (a) Goldberg, E., *Brit. J. Phot.*, **73**, 462, 1926, (see reference [6], Chapter 1).
(b) Fergg, B., 'Untersuchungen über den Einfluss der verschieden Komponenten vom photographischer Auskopieremulsionen auf die Bildenenstehung', *Z. Wiss. Phot.*, **52**, 24, 1957.

[4] Elvegård, E. and Sjöstedt, G., 'Halogensilberfilme aus Hydratzellulose', *Z. Wiss. Phot.*, Part I, **38**, 157, 1939. Part II, **38**, 229, 1939. Part III, **39**, 25, 1940.

[5] Burmistrov, F. L., 'Adsorption Photography', *Phot. J.*, **76**, 452, 1936.

[6] Dippel, C. J., 'The Metal-Diazonium Process', *Phot. J.*, **90B**, 34, 1950.

[7] Mees, C. E. K., 'On the Resolving Power of Photographic Plates', *Proc. Roy. Soc.*, **83A**, 10, 1909.

[8] Frieser, H., 'On some properties of Photographic Layers for the Production of Mikrats', *Bulletin Research Council Israel*, **5C**, 285, 1957. See also *Z. angew. Photogr.*, **3**, 57, 1941.

[9] (a) Süs, O., Schmidt, M. P., Werner, G. and von Poser, G., German Patent 763, 721.
(b) Kosar, J., *Light-Sensitive Systems*, John Wiley (New York, 1965), p. 198.

[10] Koch, R. W., and Rossell, R. E., 'The Spectral Sensitivity of Dichromated Albumin', *Penrose Annual*, **47**, 122, 1953.

[11] See such standard works as: Mees, C. E. K., *The Theory of the Photographic Process* (any edition).

[12] Brock, G. C., 'Problems and Progress in Air Photography', *Photogrammetric Record*, **9**, 169, 1957.

[13] Higgins, G. C. and Jones, L. A., 'Evaluation of Image Sharpness', *J. Soc. Mot. Pict. Tel. Eng.*, **58**, 277, 1952.

[14] See for example: Lamberts, R. L., 'The Production and Use of Variable-Transmittance Sinusoidal Test Objects', *Applied Optics*, **2**, 273, 1962.

[15] (a) Ives, H. E., Formula quoted by: Wood, R. W., *Physical Optics*, Macmillan (New York, 3rd Edition, 1947), p. 215.
(b) Denisyuk, Y. N., and Protas, I. R., *Optics and Spectroscopy*, **14**, 381, 1963.

[16] Anon, 'Maximum Resolution Plate', *J. Sci. Inst.*, **18**, 66, 1941.

[17] (a) Crawford, B. H., 'The Preparation of Ultra-fine Grain Photographic Emulsions', *J. Sci. Inst.*, **31**, 333, 1954.
(b) Crawford, B. H., *Small-scale Preparation of Fine-Grain Colloidal*

Photographic Emulsions, National Physical Laboratory Notes on Applied Science, No. 20, H.M. Stationery Office (London, 1960).

[18] Perfilov, N. A., Novikova, N. R. and Prokofyeva, E. I., 'Very Fine-Grained Emulsions for Nuclear Research', Paper presented to 1957 UNESCO Conference on the use of Isotopes in Scientific Research, Unseco/NS/RIC/7. Also, *Trav. Inst. Rad. Chlopin*, **7**, 257, 1956.

[19] Berriman, R. W., 'Crystal Growth during the Formation of a Silver-Bromide Dispersion in Gelatin', *J. Phot. Sci.*, **12**, 121, 1964.

[20] Demers, P., 'New Photographic Emulsions showing Improved Tracks of Ionizing Particles', *Canadian J. Research*, **25A**, 223, 1947.

[21] Scott-Archer, F., *The Chemist*, March 1951 (see reference [4], Chapter 1).

[22] Bovey, E., *Methods of Graticule Production at J. D. Möller*, H. M. Stationery Office, 1947, B.I.O.S. report 1552, p. 100.

[23] Miethe, A. and Lehmann, E., 'Fine-Grain Photographic Plates', *Brit. J. Phot.*, **49**, 707, 1912.

[24] Bovey, E., as reference [22], p. 88.

[25] Parshin, E. D., 'Influence of Optical Properties of Base on Resolution of Fine-Grain Emulsions', *Zh. nauch. Priklad. Fotogr. Kinematogr.*, **3**, 267, 1958.

[26] Simpson, G. Wharton, 'Collodio-chloride of silver on Opal Glass', *Brit. J. Phot.*, **12**, 244, 1865.

[27] Gundlach, K. and Rzymkowski, J., 'Die Herstellung optischer Gitter auf Photographischer Wege', *Z. Wiss. Phot.*, **45**, 8, 1945. (This paper contains a review of many extreme-resolution materials.)

[28] Weigert, F., 'Effect of Polarized Light on Light-sensitive Substances', *Ann. d. Phys.*, **63**, 681, 1920.

[29] Burmistrov, F. L., 'The Photographic Production of Large Precision Scales and Graticules', *Tech. Phys. U.S.S.R.*, **5**, 43, 1938.

[30] Friedman, J. S., *History of Colour Photography*, American Photographic Publishing Co. (Boston, 1944), Chapter 28.

[31] Tauber A. S. and Myers, W. C., 'Photochromic Micro-Images: A Key to Practical Microdocument Storage and Dissemination', *Proc. Ann. M. Nat. Microfilm Assoc.*, **11**, 256, 1962. Reprinted in *Am. Doc.*, **13**, 403, 1962.

[32] Alfaya, R., 'Diazotype Systems for High Acuity Continuous Tone Reproduction', *Phot. Sci. Eng.*, **6**, 258, 1962.

[33] Dippel, C. J. and Jonker, H., *in:* O. Helwich (Ed.). *Reprographie*, 1st Int. Congress of Reprography, Verlag Helwich (Darmstadt, 1964), p. 187, 'Ein Neues Reproduktionsverfahren Mittels Metall-keim-Introduktion'.

[34] Hepher, M., 'The Photo-Resist Story—from Niépce to the Modern Polymer Chemist', *J. Phot. Sci.*, **12**, 181, 1964.

[35] Davis, R. and Pope, C. I., 'Techniques for Ruling and Etching Precise Scales in Glass and their Reproduction by Photoetching with a New Light-Sensitive Resist', *National Bureau of Standards, Circular*, **565**, August, 1955.

[36] (a) Kosar, J. as Reference [9(b)], p. 141.
(b) Minsk, L. M., Smith, J. G., Van Deusen, W. P. and Wright, J. F., 'Photosensitive Polymers. I Cinnamate Esters of Poly(vinyl Alcohol) and Cellulose', *J. Applied Polymer Science*, **2**, 302, 1959.

(c) Robertson, E. M., Van Deusen, W. P., and Minsk, L. M., 'Photosensitive Polymers. II Sensitization of Poly(vinyl Cinnamate)', *ibid.*, **2**, 308, 1959.

[37] Eastman Kodak Co., 'Photosensitive Resists for Industry', *Industrial Data Book*, p. 7. First published 1962.

[38] (a) Stookey, S. D., 'Photosensitive Glass', *Ind. Eng. Chem.*, **41**, 856, 1949.
(b) Stookey, S. D., 'Chemical Machining of Photosensitive Glass', *Ind. Eng. Chem.*, **45**, 115, 1953.

[39] (*a*) Lohse, J. M. and Bruins, P. F., 'Etching of Microfine Patterns in Nylon Photopolymer', *Phot. Sci. Eng.*, **7**, 238, 1963.
(b) See also ' "Templex" a photosensitive plastic', E. I. Du Pont de Nemours and Co. Industrial Bulletin No. 1, April 1965.

[40] Glenn, W. E., 'Thermoplastic Recording', *J. Appl. Phys.*, **30**, 1870, 1959, and *J. Soc. Mot. Pic. Tel. Eng.*, **69**, 577, 1960.

[41] Gaynor, J. and Aftergut, S., 'Photoplastic Recording', *Phot. Sci. Eng.*, **7**, 209, 1963.

[42] Claus, C. J. and Sullivan, S. A., 'Micro-Images by Frost Xerography', *Proc. Ann. Conv. Nat. Microfilm. Assoc.*, **14**, 87, 1965.

[43] Buck, D. A. and Shoulders, K. R., 'An Approach to Microminiature Printed Systems', *Proc. Eastern Joint Computer Conference*, Special Publication T-114, December 1958.

[44] Mester, H., 'Einige Eigenschaften Ultrafeinkörniger Photographischer Emulsionen unter besonderer Berücksichtigung des Weigert-Effektes', *Z. Wiss. Phot.*, **49**, 137, 1954. (Contains extensive bibliography on early fine-grain emulsions).

[45] Carlson, C. O., Stone, E., Bernstein, H. L., Tomita, W. K. and Myers, W. C., 'Helium-Neon Laser: Thermal High-Resolution Recording', *Science*, **154**, 1550, 1966.

[46] Myers, W. C., Private Communication.

[47] Brock, G. C., 'Reflections on Thirty Years of Image Evaluation', *Phot. Sci. Eng.*, **11**, 356, 1967.
Discusses the relative usefulness of resolving power and other criteria for assessing performance of emulsions.

3 · The Processing of Microphotographs

All photographic materials require treatment after exposure, either to make the image permanent or to increase the blackness, or even to make the image visible at all. The appearance of ordinary photographs can be modified by adjusting the processing conditions, but the quality of microphotographs tends to be exceptionally sensitive to changes in processing. The precise conditions may influence:

the microscopical structure of the image,
the effective emulsion speed,
lateral spread of the image or movement of the layer,
the cleanliness of the final pictures.

The ways in which these properties are influenced depend on the nature of the emulsion and processing operations. The interaction of these factors is the main subject of this chapter, which is chiefly concerned with extreme-resolution microphotography. Processing of commercial document microphotographs, which are often on long lengths of film, is discussed separately in Chapter 12.

CLASSIFICATION OF PROCESSING OPERATIONS

Processing operations can be divided into a few main types. *Development* is a general term applied to treatments which increase the visibility of the image in an exposed emulsion: often it signifies the production of a visible picture from an invisible (latent) image. *Fixation* consists in the removal or modification of the residue of the light-sensitive substance, so that the image is stabilized against further light action. Images in silver-salt emulsions may also be subjected to after-treatments to decrease or increase the blackening (reduction or intensification), or to modify some property such as the colour of the image (toning). The processed images often also have to be washed to remove harmful constituents of the processing solutions, and finally have to be dried.

DEVELOPMENT

In Chapter 2 the reader will have noticed that some emulsions (notably the 'print-out' and photochromic materials) require no development at all, whereas the development of other emulsions can take a variety of forms.

DEVELOPMENT OF DIAZOTYPE LAYERS

As we have already seen, photolytic breakdown of diazotype layers has three consequences: namely the decomposition of diazonium salt, the release of nitrogen and the formation of a phenolic breakdown product. All three consequences have now been harnessed for image formation. In the best known use of diazo materials, the undecomposed diazonium salt is coupled with a phenol in an alkaline environment, to produce a strongly coloured dye. This may be accomplished by bathing in an alkaline solution of the coupler; or the coupler may already be incorporated in the layer, and development is then effected by fuming with ammonia vapour. In this form, diazo materials are direct-positive working, giving a positive from a positive.

Three other diazotype variants are negative-positive working and are distinguished by different modes of development. The breakdown product itself can be coupled with a diazo salt supplied from solution. Although the process has been known for many years, it has not been extensively used. In the original form of the Philips'-Dippel metal-diazonium process, the breakdown product reacted with a mercury salt already in the layer, resulting in the formation of an invisible deposit of minute mercury droplets [1]. This latent image was developed by the process of physical development, which is described later.

An intriguing variant is Kalvar development, in which heating of the thermoplastic colloid of the emulsion permits the nitrogen released by previous exposure to form minute light-scattering gas bubbles (p. 50).

DEVELOPMENT OF BICHROMATED COLLOIDS AND OTHER STENCIL-FORMING LAYERS

Since the image produced directly by stencil formation is often of no direct use, 'development' of stencil-forming layers sometimes consists of two or more stages. The first is the 'washing-out' process whereby the soluble (usually unexposed) areas of the layer are dissolved by a solvent which does not significantly attack the insoluble exposed areas. The solvent may be cold or hot water, or an organic solvent, according to the solubility of the colloid constituting the layer. It may be used in a dish with rocking, or a gentle stream of solvent or a spray may be allowed to play over the layer. When only narrow lines have to be washed out, some operators assist the process by judicious swabbing, but with fine lines this is clearly an operation requiring great caution.

A particularly elegant method of washing-out stencils formed in some synthetic organic materials (such as Kodak Photo Resist) is by use of commercial vapour degreasing equipment. A suitable solvent such as trichlorethylene is boiled steadily in the bottom of a fairly deep pot. When boiling starts, the vapour rises until it reaches the level of a cooling coil wound round the inside of the pot near the top. The volume reduction on condensation at the coil is so rapid, that the vapour level does not rise much above the level of the coil. When a work-piece at room temperature is suspended in the vapour, the solvent condenses on its surface and washes out the unhardened areas. Thus the work-piece is always developed in freshly distilled and pure hot solvent.[1] The dissolved resist immediately runs back into the sump and cannot therefore contaminate the work, and because the surface of the work-piece is rapidly raised to the boiling point of the solvent, it dries almost as soon as it is lifted from the degreaser.

A second stage in the processing of some stencils is a chemical bath or a heat treatment to increase the resistance of the thin colloid layer to etching baths. Bichromated glue or gelatin stencils have been treated with chrome-alum solutions after washing out, or are 'burnt-in' by heating to temperatures around 300° C (570° F).

As we have already seen, stencil-forming layers have to be coated very thinly if extreme resolution is required: thicknesses of at most only a micron or two are often used. In exceptional cases, the stencil image itself may have the properties desired of the end-product, but additional chemical treatments are often given. Stencils have been blackened by bathing alternately in a solution of a lead salt and of sodium sulphide, so that a dense deposit of lead sulphide is built up [2.] In some cases such as in the S.I.R.A. glue–silver process (p. 261), nuclei for physical development have been added to the colloid before coating, so that the washed-out stencil can conveniently be blackened by physical development. Washed-out stencil images can also be made visible by dyeing. They are then subsequently used as a physical barrier against the deposition of fresh material on the support, or against the etching of the support itself, or of a special under-layer. Such processes are used in the making of graticules, etched-metal grids and microelectronic devices (Chapters 9 and 11).

---

[1] For industrial use, appropriate precautions should be taken against escape of toxic or semi-toxic vapours.

Processing by 'wash-off' methods is potentially capable of giving exceptionally clean images, since the colloid should be completely removed from the non-image areas, together with its own population of dirt particles. Stencil images can also be obtained by special treatments of silver-halide dry-plate emulsions, but the resolution and chemical resistance of the stencils is likely to be inferior to those obtained from the much thinner layers of photosensitive resins.

PHYSICAL DEVELOPMENT OF METALLIC NUCLEI

The exposure of silver-salt emulsions and of metal-diazonium layers is believed to cause the deposition of minute particles of metal (see Chapter 2). These may remain in the layer after all the photosensitive compound has been removed by washing or by fixing in a suitable solvent; but they can still act as centres for the deposition of silver or mercury from special 'plating' baths. It was at one time thought that the mechanism of this type of development was simply physical condensation, such as occurs on dust nuclei in a cloud, and the process was therefore called 'physical' development. The present view is that it is caused by heterogeneous catalysis [3], but the original name is still used.

Physical developers resemble mirror-coating solutions in that they contain both a metal salt and a reducing agent; but the conditions in physical developers are adjusted so that deposition from the solution is slow in the absence of an external stimulus. Deposition is accelerated when the solution comes into contact with catalytically-acting metal nuclei, and the consequent growth of the nuclei makes the image visible. Physical development continued for a sufficient time can produce metal particles 1 μ or more in diameter: in fact comparable with the developed grains of high-speed negative emulsions. For extreme-resolution work, therefore, it is essential that the process is not carried too far, since it will produce a ruinous coarsening of the image (Plate 11). It is interesting to note that the prevention of this defect in microphotographs was discussed in the literature before 1860.

For our purpose it is important to note that most of the metal in the developed image comes from the solution, so that there is no automatic proportionality between the total mass of the exposed grains and the eventual mass of the developed image. Changes in the degree of development can thus lead to exceptionally large variations in the contrast and density of the image. The process of physical development requires considerable care. The working solutions are metastable, since both components of a reacting system are present, and the reaction can easily be initiated by influences other than a latent image. As a result, metal may be deposited on the walls of measuring vessels or dishes, or in the bulk of the solution. This usually results in rapid exhaustion of the solution and poor or irreproducible development.

These difficulties have been combated in two ways. Firstly, several hygienic precautions are taken to avoid parasitic nucleation. The two active components (metal salt and developing agent) are usually stored in separate stock solutions, which are only mixed together *just* before use. All solutions are handled in unblemished porcelain or glass vessels, which are effectively cleaned *every time* before use by nitric-acid or chromic-acid cleaning baths. (Both these solutions are *dangerously corrosive*, and should be handled carefully.) The working physical-development solution is used only once, and after discarding, chemical cleaning of all vessels is repeated. The solutions are preferably prepared with distilled water, and particular care should be given to the metal-salt solution. Since these are potentially light sensitive, it is advantageous to compound them in a dim light and store in brown-glass bottles. It has been found that silver-nitrate solutions give less trouble if kept as a strong stock solution (10 per cent or more).

The second approach has been to add substances to the solution to inhibit or retard spontaneous deposition of metal. Lüppo-Cramer added gum arabic to an acid-metol physical developer for this purpose [4]. This addition only appears to be partially effective, and seems to produce no improvement of alkaline physical developers. Many suggestions for improving the process of physical development have been published by Dippel and his colleagues of the Philips Research Laboratories [5]. An effective means was the addition of an ionic surface-active agent to the solution. This adsorbed on the surface of any unprotected nuclei, and prevented their further growth. It probably also inhibited spontaneous nucleation in the bulk of the solution. The micelle size of the surface-active agents used was so large that they could not penetrate the colloid layers used as binders for photographic emulsions. Thus development of a latent image in the colloid was not retarded, and the process required only a few minutes; but the life of the bath was extended from minutes to days.

Another improvement was achieved by using a mixture of a ferrous salt (developing agent) and ferric salt (metal bleaching agent). Such solutions constitute buffered redox systems, and with suitable proportions of ferrous and ferric salt, they can be made to develop latent image centres larger than a critical size, but actively bleaching all centres below this size. As a result of these refinements, it was claimed that solutions could be made which were stable for 3 months but developed a latent image in 1 minute, or were stable for 6 hours and developed in 1 second.

Some emulsions such as wet-collodion and silver-albuminate have always been developed in a physical developer. Physical developers can be used to intensify chemically developed microphotographic images, and this application is discussed later in this chapter.

CHEMICAL DEVELOPMENT

The minute crystals (grains) of silver-halide emulsions react only slowly when the unexposed emulsion is bathed in suitable solutions of a reducing agent. Grains on which traces of silver have been released by exposure are, however, rapidly and completely reduced to silver. This process is known as 'chemical' development, and in its purest form is distinguished from physical development by the fact that all the metal in the developed grains is provided by the exposed grains themselves, rather than by the solution.

The effective emulsion speed given by chemical development depends primarily on the ability of the developer to distinguish between unexposed grains, and those having received only a small exposure. The general experience is that the speed is mainly a characteristic of the emulsion, and is dependent to a relatively minor extent on the composition of the developer [6]. With extreme-resolution emulsions, however, this simple picture is only a part of the story. One would, for instance, expect that the minute size and large specific surface of the grains in an extreme-resolution emulsion should permit them to be reduced so quickly, that development ought to be completed more rapidly than in coarser-grained emulsions. The reverse is in fact true.

The density and speed given by Maximum-Resolution plates, for example, continues to grow with development time long after a 'process' emulsion would have completed its development. The density increase on extreme-resolution emulsions in such cases is accompanied by an increase in the size of the silver particles until they are much larger than the grains of the unexposed emulsion. This effect is particularly marked at lower densities, and is accompanied by striking changes in the image colour. The increases in developed grain size and in density are influenced by silver-halide solvents such as thiosulphate, or a high concentration of potassium bromide. Thus it can be shown that the special action of Kodak developers D.8 or D.178 in giving high contrast on these emulsions is connected with their high concentration of potassium bromide. (See Appendix 1A for solution formulae.) Reducing the concentration of bromide, which with normal emulsions would be expected to increase the activity of the developer, substantially lowers it. The influence of the grain growth on speed and contrast is illustrated in Fig. 15, showing

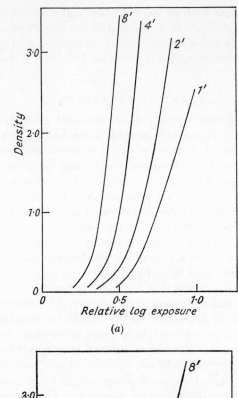

(a)

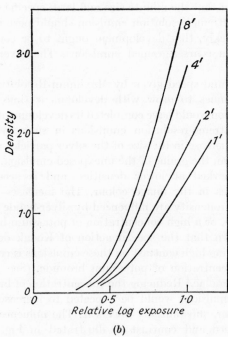

(b)

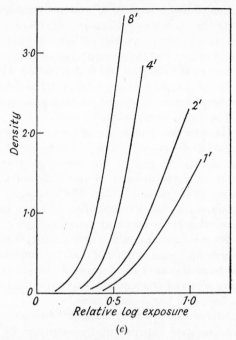

(c)

Fig. 15 *Growth of Density on Maximum-Resolution Plate*

(a) With development for a series of times (figures denote minutes development at 70° F.) in Kodak D.178 (2 parts plus 1 part water).

(b) as (a) but with Kodak D.158 (1 part plus 1 part water).

(c) as (b), but with 2·5 grams/litre sodium thiosulphate added to working solution.

characteristic curves of Kodak Maximum-Resolution plates developed for increasing times in D.178 and in a conventional 'Elon-' hydroquinone developer (Kodak developer D.158). Although 2 minutes' development in D.178 gives about the same speed and contrast as 8 minutes in D.158, increasing the time to 4 minutes in D.178 produces a greater increase in density than was obtained by extending the development in D.158 from 4 to 8 minutes. It might be supposed that this result was due to the caustic alkali in D.178, but a similar behaviour can be obtained by adding $2\frac{1}{2}$ grams of hypo per litre to D.158 [Fig. 15(c)]. It is interesting to contrast these observations with the behaviour of high-speed emulsions, which suffer a reduction of speed and graininess when silver-halide solvents are added to the developer [7]. On chemical development, extreme-resolution emulsions give an image of green or brown tone by transmitted light. Addition of thiosulphate to the developer has been recommended for obtaining a neutral image tone [8].

The explanation of this behaviour of extreme-resolution emulsions is connected with the enormous surface area of the silver halide. One gram of silver halide in Maximum-Resolution emulsion has a surface area of about 500 square feet (50 square metres), or about 200 times the superficial area of the plate on which it is coated. This allows the silver halide to dissolve rapidly in any solvent in the developer, which is thereby transformed into a physical developer as soon as it enters the emulsion. The small silver particles produced by chemical development of the exposed grains are effective nuclei for physical development, and the developed grains will thus tend to grow at the expense of the unexposed grains. The chemical processes are, in principle, similar to those utilized in the Polaroid Camera or in document copying by chemical transfer. The local drop in the silver-salt concentration which follows deposition of silver on the nuclei, permits the dissolution of the adjacent unexposed grains to continue. As a result of this mechanism it is clear that the greatest increase of grain size will occur where the number of nuclei is small and the supply of silver halide from the unexposed grains is large; namely, in the areas which have received the smallest exposures, and at the boundaries between high and low density areas.

These speculations on the development behaviour of extreme-resolution emulsions were experimentally confirmed by Solman [9]. By using the electron microscope to demonstrate the increase in size and change in habit of the developed silver, he proved that physical development was responsible. In addition, no such image build-up occurred in a 'non-solvent' developer, in which the conditions required for silver transfer were relatively absent. Since the silver ions for the physical development were provided by the least sensitive emulsion grains, these contributed to the developed density without, in effect, having been themselves exposed. In consequence, the effective sensitivity spread of the emulsion was reduced and its contrast increased.

The effects of this complex chemical and physical development process are of importance for the processing technique of many fine-grain emulsions. In nuclear-particle emulsions, for instance, it results in the grains developing to a diameter substantially greater than that of the undeveloped grains. This enables the tracks of weakly-ionizing particles to be seen more easily, but can cause tracks of strongly-ionizing particles to become 'clogged' so that less detailed information can be obtained from them. So long as it is not allowed to go too far, this grain growth is useful in microphotography. The effective increase in emulsion speed is particularly valuable when extreme-resolution plates are used for making intermediate negatives by direct reduction from an original drawing by reflected light (Chapter 7).

Any gain in speed to counteract the long exposure required is valuable, while the resolution needed in an intermediate negative is not so great that some coarsening of the image structure is likely to be harmful. The increase of contrast derived from grain growth can be used to improve the apparent sharpness of line images, with which it is relatively difficult to detect the granular structure of the image (Plate 6). It also seems likely that this sort of grain growth makes it possible to obtain sufficient density when the image is confined to a small proportion of the emulsion thickness by optical sectioning (Chapter 8). In this case the grains in the exposed layer of the emulsion can acquire silver obtained from the unexposed emulsion layers.

Care to avoid excessive grain growth is particularly necessary when making continuous-tone images, and when extreme-resolution emulsions are used for microradiography (Chapter 13). Grain growth is also likely to be obtrusive when line images are made with an optical system which fails to produce a really sharp edge. Unsharp lines always show a fringe with a low density, and the greatest effect of grain growth tends to be seen at the edge of the fringe. This results in a displeasing line having a central black core flanked with a ragged fringe of coarse grains. The physical development accompanying the use of a solvent developer may also permit some stain to form. This consists of exceedingly minute silver particles giving a yellow or orange colour, which has sometimes been mistaken for residues of the sensitizing dye. Stain can be hindered by not pushing the development too far, and techniques for removing it are described later in this chapter.

It is thus apparent that physical development in *chemical* developers may have both good and bad effects. The influence of physical development grows progressively with time, so that a brief development may give an image of fine structure and moderate contrast produced entirely by chemical development, and lengthening the time gives more and more grain growth. With moderate degrees of physical development the adverse effect of coarsening of image structure is often cancelled by improved contrast. Numerous resolution tests on Kodak Maximum-Resolution plates have shown that 3–4 minutes' development at 68° F (20° C) in D.178 (two parts of developer stock to one part of water) gives optimum sharpness for line images. Although the developers D.178 and D.158 have been recommended for these plates, there is little doubt that equivalent results could be obtained with other formulae.[1] The fine grain and high resolution are primarily properties of the emulsion, and only grossly

[1] In fact, to eliminate an extra dust hazard, liquid developers are now recommended for Kodak High-Resolution and Maximum-Resolution plates (see Appendix I).

inappropriate treatment would be expected to spoil the results completely. The reader would, nevertheless, be well advised to use the recommended developers, since their suitability has been confirmed by experience extending over many years.

SPECIAL CONDITIONS IN THE DEVELOPMENT OF
MICROPHOTOGRAPHS

Certain conditions not usually found in normal photography occur during the development of truly microscopic images. The images may, for instance, often occupy only a small proportion of the area of the plate, and often consist of lines narrower than the thickness of the dry emulsion layer. During processing, the width of such lines will only be a small fraction of the thickness of the swollen emulsion, and sideways diffusion of development-reaction products out of, and fresh developer into, the image of the line will be more important

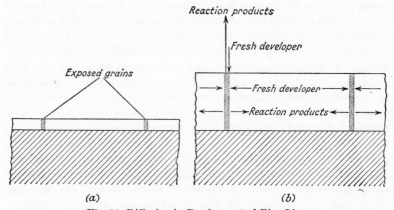

(a) (b)

Fig. 16 *Diffusion in Development of Fine Lines*

(a) Dry emulsion layer with exposed lines narrower than emulsion thickness.
(b) Diffusion processes during development of swollen emulsion layer.

than diffusion between the solution and the emulsion layer as a whole (Fig. 16). Agitation of the solution, however, mainly influences diffusion between the solution and the emulsion, and can therefore be expected to have little effect on the development of such fine lines.

The small size of the exposed areas means that the passage of a number of plates through the developer will produce relatively little exhaustion of the solution. Under these conditions atmospheric oxidation may consume more developer than reduction of silver halide, and it should prove economical to develop in a deep vessel such as a beaker or a small accumulator jar. The reduction of the ratio of surface area to volume of the solution lessens the rate of atmospheric oxidation. This implies that it should be safe to use a given volume of developer longer, but whether this is wise depends on the circumstances. Frequent changes of developer, even to the point of using a fresh volume of developer every time, may be considered prudent when developing racks of graticule images, or when many hours of work have been used to expose different parts of a plate surface to different components of a large image (see Chapters 9–11).

Control of the development process plays an important part in microphotographic technique, since small differences in the exposure or in the effective emulsion speed given by development can produce a marked change in the quality of the image (see Chapter 8). The necessity for control is increased by the exceptional development characteristics of extreme-resolution emulsions already described. Unlike most silver-halide–gelatin emulsions, which initially develop their density rapidly and thereafter show a much slower density increase, the density increase on extreme-resolution emulsions, shows no signs of ceasing within a convenient development time (Fig. 15). It is, therefore, not possible to obtain reproducible results by developing practically to completion, so that small changes in development time or temperature make little difference to the image.

The small size of the images generally prevents convenient control of development by inspection, and control by the time-and-temperature method should be used. Satisfactory reproducibility for most purposes should be obtained by maintaining the temperature within half a degree Fahrenheit (a quarter of a degree Centigrade) of the set value, and by timing development to within 5 seconds for a time of 2 minutes or longer. The aim should be to handle each plate (or rack-full of plates) *exactly* alike. With normal development temperatures one can assume that the development process continues at much the same rate during transfer from the developer to the acid-stop bath. The instant of actual immersion in the acid stop may, therefore, be considered to terminate development.

ACID-STOP TREATMENT

The precision and cleanliness essential for the processing of microphotographs is assisted by the use of an inexpensive and easily compounded acid-stop bath (see Appendix I). This type of solution rapidly neutralizes the alkali carried over from the developer, with the following beneficial results:

(i) development is terminated with great abruptness, which is conducive to reproducible processing,

    (ii) the effective 'killing' of the developer before the emulsion enters the fixing bath removes a potential source of stain and streaks,

    (iii) formation of scum is hindered and

    (iv) the working life of the fixing bath is prolonged.

The influence of stop baths on dimensional stability of images is discussed on p. 83.

FIXATION

Silver-salt emulsions are normally fixed in a solution of sodium or ammonium thiosulphate, which readily dissolves any undeveloped silver salt. Fixing baths are usually acidified to counteract stain, and contain a gelatin hardener to inhibit excessive swelling of the emulsion during washing (see Appendix I). The fine grain of micro-photographic emulsions permits any slight milkness of the layer to clear very rapidly, but the time taken for the hardener to react with the gelatin is the same as for other emulsions. The full fixing time recommended for extreme-resolution emulsions should therefore be given; but should not be greatly exceeded, because of the risk of a gradual reduction of density of the fine-grain image, especially with modern ammonium thiosulphate rapid fixers (see Appendix I).

WASHING AND DRYING AND PRESERVATION OF CLEANLINESS

Microphotographic images are particularly easily spoiled by contamination of the emulsion surface during exposure or processing. A piece of dirt only large enough to have a trivial effect on a 35 mm negative can completely spoil an eyepiece–micrometer scale. The contamination may come from the atmosphere, or from any of the processing baths, or from the wash water. Washing and drying are particularly critical operations for preserving cleanliness, and the whole subject of cleanliness in handling is appropriately discussed in the present section.

The problem of obtaining clean microphotographic images can be attacked in two quite different ways. One theoretically effective method is to handle the emulsions in solutions and in an atmosphere free from all dirt particles with a diameter of more than a micron or so. The alternative, which we shall consider first, is to concentrate the precautions at the stages which are really critical for the cleanliness of the images.

The presence of dirt is most damaging during exposure and during drying, and if dirt can be effectively removed at both these stages, much less trouble is likely to be produced by its presence during processing itself. Dirt on the emulsion surface during exposure can spoil the image either by casting shadows, or by refracting light so that some areas receive too much light and others receive too little. Knocking the edge of the plate firmly on the bench just before exposure, or brushing softly with a clean camel-hair brush have been proposed. Such cleaning of emulsion surfaces just before exposure is important for a number of critical photographic tasks, and the Eastman Kodak Co. have published a detailed memorandum on the subject [10]. In addition to information on how to keep brushes for this purpose clean, other methods discussed are brushing in an anti-static ionizing environment, cleaning by jets of compressed gas, and cleaning by ultrasonic vibrations in a tank of clean and photographically inert solvent. Holthaus [11] has described a particularly stringent routine for ultra-sonic cleaning of plates before making microelectronic masks. An entire box-full of plates was loaded into a slide-tray, which was lowered into a first bath of filtered methyl alcohol. After agitation, the slide-tray was withdrawn, and then again agitated in two further methyl alcohol baths. The last bath used for each tray full of plates was freshly filtered.

Another method of minimizing the effect of dirt during exposing, resembles the technique used to conceal scratches when printing motion-picture film [12]. The negative film is immersed in a liquid with a refractive index intermediate between those of gelatin and film base. By cancelling the refractive disturbances produced by the scratches, it renders them effectively invisible. Now many of the small dirt particles in (or on) emulsion layers are transparent and spoil the image by refracting, rather than by absorbing light. Their refractive index is usually close to that of gelatin, so that their harmful effects can be counteracted by immersing in a liquid with a similar refractive index. For projection printing, a liquid (such as xylene) may be used behind a cover-glass,[1] or with contact printing the immersion liquid is placed between the negative and the unexposed emulsion. Although rather messy, this method is well worth trying if dirt has proved a major obstacle to success. With contact printing it can also improve the sharpness of the prints (p. 221).

Finger-prints can result in local variations of density having a bad effect on microphotographic images. This damage is most likely to result from touching the dry emulsion surface with greasy or damp fingers, or fingers bearing traces of processing chemicals. Their incidence can be greatly reduced by reasonable care, and should be completely eliminated by wearing clean dry cotton gloves until the plates

---

[1] This may involve use of an appropriately corrected objective with some modification of registration procedure.

are loaded in the processing equipment. Damage is less likely to result from touching the emulsion once it has swollen in a processing bath, nor should contact with small insoluble dirt particles in itself be harmful during processing. Serious trouble is, however, caused by leaving dirt on the emulsion during drying: the dirt may then adhere so firmly that it cannot be removed without leaving a scar. The cure is, therefore, to remove dirt from the emulsion just before drying, but it is also prudent to minimize any contamination of the emulsion during processing.

Access of dirt to the emulsion surface during processing can be reduced by preparing the developer so as to prevent formation of lime scum (see Appendix I), by filtering all solutions and the wash water [13] and (perhaps most important of all) by holding the emulsion surface vertical or facing downwards throughout processing [14]. Most dirt reaches the emulsion surface by simple sedimentation, and an astonishing improvement can result from this last simple precaution.

At the end of washing, dirt on the emulsion surface is only loosely held, and can be removed by wiping gently. The problem is how to remove the dirt with the minimum risk of scratching the emulsion surface. Much of the lime deposit from hard water can be removed by soaking the plates (after a brief wash) in a 5 per cent solution of acetic acid, but the remainder of the dirt has to be removed mechanically. The success of this final stage of processing is assisted by handling the emulsion throughout processing so as to avoid excessive swelling. For this reason the temperature of all the processing solutions should be no higher than is necessary, the emulsion should be thoroughly hardened during fixation, and the washing should not be needlessly prolonged. Another useful precaution is to soak the emulsion for a few minutes in a mixture of three parts of 'industrial' spirit to one part of water. This causes the emulsion to shrink and become mechanically tougher.

Some of the loose dirt can be removed from the emulsion surface by a powerful jet of liquid, but a more effective method is to wipe down with a chamois leather or a viscose sponge. The author has found the following method to be relatively safe. At the end of washing, the plates are left in the alcohol solution for at least 10 minutes—they can safely be left in this solution for hours. The wiping is then done in two stages. In the first stage, the plates are held emulsion-side down in the alcohol solution, and the fully saturated wiping material is passed gently over the emulsion surface. This treatment should disperse most of the dirt into the bulk of the solution, or into the pockets of solution contained by the wiping material. The wiping material is then wrung out, and is held so that it makes contact with the top edge of the plate to be wiped and is held against the emulsion surface only by its own natural springiness. It is then pulled smoothly down over the emulsion surface, when necessary using a number of overlapping strokes until the whole area is covered. The aim of the second stage of wiping should be to remove as much as possible of the surface liquid, and with it the last traces of dirt. The removal of the liquid during wiping should be watched by holding the plate at such an angle that the eye sees an image of the room light specularly reflected at the emulsion surface. The same method of inspection can be used to examine the surface when the small residual beads of liquid have evaporated, a few minutes after wiping. The surface should then appear smooth, with very few bumps. If it is obviously still dirty, the plate may be returned to the alcohol solution, and the wiping repeated.

The success of this wiping procedure depends on skill and on the cleanliness of the wiping material. After each use the wiping material should be squeezed out in several changes of clean water, and then left in a dust-free cupboard to dry. The necessary skill can only be obtained by practice, but it is not necessary to use exposed and developed plates for this purpose. Excellent practice can be obtained by wiping an unexposed plate which has been fixed and washed.

Dirt reaching the surface of a gelatin emulsion during drying is likely to be trapped by the tacky surface, and may then stick almost as firmly as dirt left on the emulsion at the end of the washing. It is important to remember, however, that the only particles to be trapped in this way are those which actually *touch* the emulsion surface, and the number of these can be greatly reduced by drying the plates emulsion side downwards. Dirt which falls on the back of the plates is harmless, as it can all be polished off when the plates are dry. When the plates are dried in this position, dirt can only reach the emulsion as a result of air currents. It is therefore advantageous for the workroom to be free from draughts, and a high level of cleanliness must also lessen the risk of dirt reaching the emulsion.

Another method for drying with freedom from dirt is to support the plates face downwards over a dish containing a desiccant such as silica gel or anhydrous calcium chloride. For convenient action the emulsion surface should be no more than $\frac{2}{5}$ in (1 cm) from the surface of the desiccant, and the dish should be covered so that the air-space between the emulsion and the desiccant is shut off from the outside atmosphere. This method also has the interesting advantage that the volume of air and consequently the population of dust particles which might ever gain access to the emulsion surface are drastically reduced. Whatever method of drying is used, the hazards of this stage are terminated as soon as the emulsion has passed beyond the tacky

D

condition. Dry dirt reaching it after this can be safely removed by methods described (p. 77) for cleaning plates before exposure.

The methods described above are analogous to antisepsis, in that they are devised to control the harmful effects of dirt rather than to eliminate dirt completely. The rigour with which these precautions should be applied depends on the circumstances in which the work is undertaken. The amateur making relatively few images for his own satisfaction can either adopt most of the suggested precautions, or can make more images but with less care, and then select the cleanest when the work is completed. The choice for commercial operators will be determined by the combination of precautions giving the lowest cost per satisfactory image. When a very high standard is required, as in the case of scales to be viewed in the focal plane of an optical instrument or in the manufacture of large divided scales or micro-electronic masks, 'antisepsis' alone may prove insufficient: precautions analogous to asepsis may be needed. It may be necessary to construct tiled darkrooms which can be regularly hosed down, and are supplied with filtered air passed through an electrostatic precipi-tator and maintained at a pressure slightly in excess of the atmos-phere. The operators may have to wear dust-proof clothing, and enter the work-rooms through a 'dust-lock'. In recent years, techniques for securing high standards of cleanliness have been extensively applied in connection with the assembly of electronic devices and gyroscopes for the guidance of missiles [15].

The provision of 'aseptic' conditions can be divided into three topics.

(a) The provision of clean working spaces.
(b) The monitoring of the cleanliness standards achieved.
(c) The cleaning of fluids used in manufacturing processes.

The industrial demand for clean working conditions has been met by firms offering special air-filtration equipment, often coupled to special clean work-benches which do not restrict operators' freedom of movement [16]. This has been achieved by the use of laminar-air-flow benches. In one form, the wall facing the operator (i.e. behind the work-bench) was replaced by a large diffusion panel, through which passed a non-turbulent low-velocity (about 1 m.p.h.) flow of filtered air directed towards the operator. Thus dust particles which tend to be shed even by operators in protective clothing were con-tinuously swept away from the work space. The cleaning effect of the air stream was supplemented by a narrow and more rapid down-ward stream directed from the top front lip of the bench [16(b)].

For an introduction to the monitoring of clean rooms, readers can be referred to a pamphlet produced by the Millipore Filter Corporation, which markets special kits for the purpose [17]. This contains descriptions of the monitoring of air and work spaces, and of protective garments and liquids by observing the particles trapped on appropriate Millipore filters. The methods are coupled to procedures approved by standards issued by American armed services and the American Society for Testing Materials. Another method favoured for checking the freedom of liquids from particles is to observe the rate of decrease of flow due to clogging of a filter, and special equipment for this Silting Index Test is supplied.

The Millipore Corporation has also provided for the filtration of liquids to various standards, including the removal of all particles down to sub-micron size, and the methods employed are discussed in other pamphlets [18].[1] One described the design of filtration systems for both 'open-end' systems delivering liquids, and for re-circulation systems. Illustrations were given of good and bad practice, and the following principles for delivering clean liquids were advanced.

(1) Place the Millipore (membrane) filter at the last possible point in the system.
(2) Place a generously sized and highly retentive depth filter upstream of the membrane (final) filter.
(3) Place all valves upstream of the final membrane filter.
(4) Conduct the fluid from the membrane filter directly to the critical point of application without re-handling.
(5) Keep the system simple.

The filtration procedures described were clearly applicable to all processing solutions and liquids used in the handling of emulsions or photoresists for producing extreme-resolution images, and equipment for various stages of handling was illustrated. Particularly noteworthy was the attachment of membrane filters to hypodermic or micro-syringes used for the dispensing of photoresist solutions. By this means, every drop of solution was re-filtered to the required limits immediately before application. Solvents and washing fluids could likewise be re-filtered immediately before use by employment of a Solvent Filtering Dispenser comprising a wash-bottle with built-in membrane filter.

'Aseptic' precautions are obviously expensive, and are most likely to prove successful when combined with the antiseptic strategy described above. Whatever precautions are taken, it would be naïve to expect the best results as soon as special precautions have been put into operation. The highest standard is only likely to be achieved by operators who have refined their technique and developed their

[1] The topic has also been more extensively treated by Dwyer [27].

morale by progressive improvements introduced over a period of many weeks or months.

DEFECT MINIMIZING PROCEDURES

In some projects, and especially in the fabrication of complex electronic devices, control of dirt and defects has tended to be the most pressing single problem that production technicians may be required to tackle. In an analysis of this problem, Plough, Crevier and Danley [19] suggest that the outcome may be influenced by the fact that there are often *critical pattern areas* in which defects must be minimized. They quote an example in silicon-wafer processing (see p. 332) in which defects in the washed-out areas of the stencil are critically important, whereas the electrical consequence of pinholes in the stencil itself are less serious. For other structures in microelectronic circuits, the reverse applies.

Now there are several photomechanical routes by which desired image configurations may be reached by differently combining positive- and negative-working photosensitive resists, and by alternatively using the stencils to control etching of a deposit from, or to prevent local deposition on the substrate (lifting). For instance, production of narrow lines of deposit on a background can be achieved by the methods shown in Table 1.

Table 1. Alternative methods for production of narrow lines of deposit

Transparency lines	Background	Stencil formation by photoresist	Stencil appearance	Control of deposition
Clear	Dark	Negative-working	On lines	Etch
Clear	Dark	Positive-working	Background	Lift
Dark	Clear	Negative-working	Background	Lift
Dark	Clear	Positive-working	On lines	Etch

The extent of the mischief from different types of defect is then influenced by whether the individual stages in each route are negative- or positive-working. For example, with negative-working resists and etching, pinholes in the original transparency allow islands of resist to be hardened, whereas dirt in the lines of the transparency results in pinholes in the lines of the resist. Light divergence during printing on the resist tends to increase the size of the islands but to decrease the size of the pinholes in the lines. Over-etching through the stencil has the reverse effects.

By this type of analysis applied to all possible routes for making each required structure, the authors developed a strategy for minimizing the crop of defects.

PREVENTION OF DISTORTION OF GELATIN
EMULSIONS

Silver-halide–gelatin emulsions coated on glass have a well-deserved reputation for preserving the dimensions of an image with minimum distortion. Nevertheless, the literature contains a number of investigations of residual shifts on glass plates, and such shifts are promoted by unsuitable processing conditions. The dimensional accuracy given by a gelatin emulsion is only achieved as a result of firm adhesion to a rigid support, and it is clear that excessive swelling will tend to promote shifts. For the less critical purposes this can be avoided by keeping the temperature of all solutions down to the recommended values, by using rinse and wash waters at a relatively low temperature (say below 60° F or 15° C) and by using a hardening fixing bath for a sufficient time to harden the emulsion adequately.

There are additional precautions which might be considered when the dimensional stability of the image is particularly important. Cooksey and Cooksey considered that one source of emulsion shifts was a state of strain present in the emulsion layer of factory-dried plates [20]. This caused shifts as soon as the emulsion entered the developer. They released the strain by swelling the emulsion slightly in an aqueous-alcohol solution, and drying slowly before exposure. This treatment was reported to lessen distortions substantially, but the risk of contaminating the emulsion surface makes such bathing treatments inadvisable for microphotography. Essentially the same result should be obtained without this risk by supporting the unexposed plates (emulsion-side down) over a dish of water for an hour or two. This permits the emulsion to swell enough to become quite plastic, without any liquid actually touching the emulsion surface. The emulsion is likely to be tacky after this humidification, and should be re-dried before use.

It seems likely that emulsion shifts may be promoted by the rinse bath between development and fixation. The tendency of emulsions to swell greatly in alkaline developers is usually checked by their high concentration of carbonate or sulphite salts. In the rinse water, however, the salt content drops rapidly while the emulsion is still quite alkaline, and it is known that the emulsion swells very rapidly at this stage. This could result in forces producing emulsion shifts, a hazard which can be reduced by using a swelling-depressant stop-bath [21], such as Kodak formula SB-4 (p. 479).

Finally distortion could occur during the last, drying operation. The emulsion at the edges of the plate dries first, and inspection of partly dried plates usually shows a fairly abrupt transition between the dry area and the wet area in which the emulsion is still heavily swollen.

This transition zone creeps across the emulsion surface, and is almost certainly associated with severe local stresses. A safer drying procedure for special purposes should be to extract water at the same rate from every point of the emulsion surface, by soaking the plate for about 5 minutes in spirit solutions of ascending concentration. Such a technique is used for the dehydration of biological tissue sections and concentrations of 50 per cent, 75 per cent and 90 per cent by volume of industrial spirit in water are suggested. At the final stage the emulsion will have shrunk nearly to its dry thickness, and very little distortion should occur during the final drying.

AFTER-TREATMENT OF DEVELOPED IMAGES

In many branches of photography, developed silver images are submitted to chemical after-treatments. The density and contrast of the image can be decreased by reduction or increased by intensification. These processes are used to compensate for errors in exposure, or to give a contrast or line sharpness or density unobtainable by simple development. The image can also be converted to some other form in order to modify its colour or permanence, or to give it other desired properties, without substantially altering the density. Special care is needed in the application of these techniques to microphotographs, since the images can so easily be spoiled by coarsening of the grain structure, or by dispersing the material of the image sideways, or by attacking images of lines of different widths at relatively different rates. Because of these pitfalls the reader is advised to apply these methods only when they are essential for obtaining a desired result. Errors in exposure should preferably be corrected by making fresh images, rather than by reduction and intensification which are quite likely to give inferior results and waste time. The following two sections, therefore, are only intended for guidance in the small proportion of cases in which a modified exposure or development cannot give the desired result.

REDUCTION (AND REMOVAL OF SILVER STAINS)

Reduction can be used to remove silver stain, or to clean the edges of ragged lines, or to prepare images for subsequent intensification.

Silver stain consists of very minute particles of silver, and Henn, Crabtree and Russell have shown that slow-acting reducing solutions, such as an acidified ammonium-thiosulphate solution can attack the stain image substantially more rapidly than an ordinary developed image (Appendix I) [22]. This method should be useful when development has been forced to increase emulsion speed with a resultant formation of stain, or when stain is seen on a valuable image (or batch of images) after the work is almost complete.

The ammonium-thiosulphate reducer contains a high concentration of a feebly acting silver-bleaching agent, but it is often also useful to employ a low concentration of an active agent. Such solutions can be compounded by adding 0·2 per cent (or less) of potassium ferricyanide to 1 per cent potassium bromide or 10 per cent sodium-thiosulphate solution (Appendix I). The solution tends to become locally exhausted as soon as it reaches an area with a high silver content, but will tend to continue acting in low-density areas where the rate of consumption of ferricyanide is not much greater than the rate of replacement by diffusion from the bulk of the solution. The proportion of the silver removed from a low density may, therefore, be much higher than that removed from a high density, and the edge of a blackened area may be attacked more rapidly than the centre. This is the mode of operation of the 'cutting' reducers which are used to sharpen the dots in half-tone photomechanical negatives. They can be used in the same way to sharpen the lines in microphotographs, but there is a danger that they may spoil the images by rounding-off corners, by attacking the ends of lines preferentially and by producing proportionally greater reductions in the widths of fine lines. Whenever possible, reduction should therefore first be tried on a waste image. It is also prudent to interrupt the process at frequent intervals so that the influence on line quality can be assessed by examination at a suitably high magnification. Another precaution is to effect the reduction in two stages, by treating first in the ferricyanine–bromide solution. This does not remove silver from the layer as thiosulphate–ferricyanide solutions do, but merely bleaches it to lightly coloured silver bromide. The extent of the bleaching can be followed with the microscope, and when the desired action is achieved the silver bromide is simply removed by re-fixing the plate. If the bleaching is accidentally carried too far, however, the original image can be restored by treating in a developer in the light until all the silver bromide is blackened. A tentative procedure of this type has much to recommend it when dealing with these delicate and chemically-fragile images.

For reasons which are explained in the next section, cutting reducers are useful for ensuring complete absence of nuclei between the lines when the images are to be subsequently intensified.

INTENSIFICATION

Developed silver images can readily be intensified by bleaching them to an insoluble silver salt, using a solution which also causes the simultaneous precipitation of the reduced bleaching agent, formed by reaction with the silver as a by-product. Such processes involve the risk that the reduced bleaching agent may diffuse sideways in the gelatin before precipitation, and hence spoil the sharpness of the images. This difficulty is avoided by choosing processes giving very insoluble by-products, and by balancing the solution so that the rate of precipitation of the by-product is at least as rapid as the bleaching of silver which causes its formation. The required balance is achieved by using an adequate concentration of the precipitating ion with a suitably low concentration of the silver-oxidizing ion, whose reduced form is subsequently precipitated.

Of the many intensification processes known, the mercury intensifier (Appendix I) was found particularly suitable for treating microphotographs. The silver image is first bleached in a solution of mercuric bromide:[1]

$$Ag + HgBr_2 \rightarrow (AgBr)(HgBr)$$

giving a white deposit of the mixed mercurous-silver bromide. After removing unreacted mercury salts by rinsing in dilute hydrochloric acid and thorough washing, the mixed salt is blackened in a non-staining developer, forming a mixture of metallic silver and mercury. Further intensification can be obtained by repeating the whole process.

An especially powerful method for intensifying microphotographic silver images is provided by physical development, in which the extra material added to the image is selectively deposited on the centres produced by the preliminary development. This process avoids any risk of sideways spreading of the image as a result of diffusion of reaction products. Now Arens [23] showed that the density obtained on physical development is determined mainly by the number of nuclei present, and not on their original size. The highly-dispersed silver image formed by chemical development of extreme-resolution emulsions is thus in a more favourable condition for physical intensification than the coarser deposit formed by faster emulsions. Extraordinary increases of density can, in fact, be obtained by physical intensification of these emulsions (Fig. 14, p. 42).

The very potency of this method means that it should be handled with care and discretion. The standard of cleanliness of apparatus required is the same as for the physical development of latent images (see p. 68). If carried to completion, physical intensification can give very coarse grain (Plate 11), and sufficient intensification of microphotographic images is usually obtained when the process is stopped at an early stage. The density obtained by a curtailed treatment is

---

[1] This is a very poisonous compound.

likely to be limited by the rate of supply of metal ions from the solution, rather than by the number of nuclei present. In these circumstances, a chemically developed microphotographic image having a relatively low density may already contain sufficient nuclei to achieve deposition of all the metal that the solution can supply; and the proportional rate of increase of density is likely to be greatest for the lowest densities of the original image. It is therefore important that the images to be intensified should have absolutely no fog grains or stain nuclei in the background, as the background density may otherwise build up from a previously imperceptible deposit. Plates to be physically intensified should therefore, when possible, be processed with special care. Only a brief development (1 to 2 minutes in D.158) is needed, and this should be followed by an acid-stop bath before fixation. Application of a 'cutting' reducer, such as the ferricyanide–bromide or ferricyanide–thiosulphate solutions described previously, can be used to remove stain or background grains resulting from light scatter or development fog. As the increases of density obtainable are so great, an image of satisfactory density can be obtained even after the chemically-developed image has been reduced until the lines are quite faint. The more drastic the reduction, the less likely are nuclei to be left in the background, but the reduction should be carefully controlled to prevent excessive rounding of the corners of the image.

Since physical intensification consists of the continued growth of the silver particle from each exposed grain until sufficient density is obtained, the structure of the image is inevitably coarsened. The final result will, nevertheless, be much sharper than an image of the same grain size produced by chemical development of a coarser-grained emulsion [compare Plates 6(b) and 11]. The spatial relationships of the grains to each other still depend on the optical properties of the emulsion at the instant of exposure, and the light scatter of the coarser-grain emulsion causes the edges of the lines to be far more ragged, even though the image is built up from developed grains equal in size to those of the intensified extreme-resolution emulsion [Plate 6(b)].

Intensification by physical development is worth considering when exceptionally difficult images have to be made, such as those in which fine clear lines are required in the middle of a large dark background. With images of this type, the minimum exposure giving adequate density by direct development is often sufficient to cause lens flare or light scatter in the emulsion to veil over the lines. This can be avoided by using a lesser exposure, which reduces the intensity of the flare and scattered light below the threshold at which the grains show any latent image. The resultant 'ghost' image shows less image spread, and can be brought up to a useful density by physical development. Strongly physically intensified images on microphotographic emulsions are much more neutral in colour than chemically developed images, a property which may be exploited for special purposes, such as in making resolution test images. Another feature of physical intensification is that it enables the image to be directly strengthened by metals other than silver. Thus physical intensification in a mercury physical developer gave an image with a higher opacity to X-rays than could be obtained from a silver image (Chapter 13).

TONING

Oxidation of a silver image followed by precipitation of a silver salt or of the reduced oxidizing agent can be used to modify such properties as the colour and durability of microphotographic images. As with intensification, the solution must be compounded to give minimum sideways diffusion of the image. The following uses have been found for toning processes in microphotography. Goldberg [24] treated the images produced in his print-out emulsion with a gold toner of the type which used to be employed with printing-out (daylight) papers. This method gives a pleasing cold-blue tone, and the image is very permanent. The same process might be used with other emulsions with which plain development gives a silver image of unpleasant colour. There are many other ways of modifying the colour of silver images, of which bleaching and redevelopment in a dye-coupling developer is noteworthy. A process for making coloured microphotographs might be based on this principle, but the couplers would have to be selected to deposit the dye very close to the developed silver particles.

In their graticule factory the firm of Möller preserved valuable master negatives by bleaching the silver image to silver iodide, and it was found that the images were still in perfect condition after storing for many decades [25]. The same firm also converted graticule images from silver to platinum, so that they could be burned into the surface of the glass on heating nearly to the softening point of the glass. Conversion of microphotographic images to silver compounds has also been carried out in the presence of different radioactive compounds, to give radioactive images suitable for testing the resolution of autoradiographic emulsions (p. 455). Finally, the brightness of Lippmann colour photographs and reconstructions from Holograms has been improved by bleaching developed silver images to a colourless light-stable form.

When microphotographic images have to be printed in very accurate register with details previously formed by photomechanical processes on silicon wafers (p. 342), the high opacity of silver images hinders microscopic observation of register. Ables [26] avoided this difficulty by using the mercuric bromide solution to bleach the silver image, but then darkened it in a sulphite solution. Although this is normally considered an intensification process, when applied to the fine-grain image on a Kodak H.R. plate, it gave an image which was quite transparent to red light. Thus registration could be readily observed through the darkest part of an image, which still had a high density to the shorter wavelengths used for printing on photoresist.

MISCELLANEOUS PROCESSES

(i) PRODUCTION OF STENCIL IMAGES FROM SILVER-HALIDE GELATIN LAYERS

If silver-halide–gelatin emulsions are coated without hardener, and are protected from unintentional hardening, stencil images can result from the image-wise hardening produced by a tanning developer or a tanning bleach. Stencil images from hardened emulsion layers can also be made by bleaching a developed silver image in an 'etch-bleach' solution containing a cupric salt and hydrogen peroxide. The cuprous salt formed as a result of reaction with the silver image is thought to catalyse destruction of gelatin by the peroxide.

As with other stencil processes, a very thin layer is required to produce high-resolution stencils (see p. 21). The emulsions would therefore have to be specially coated for this purpose, and even then the process would still be beset with the disadvantages of hydrophilic stencils discussed on p. 50. Thus at the present stage of the art, production of extreme-resolution stencils from silver-halide–gelatin emulsions seems to have little advantage.

Note, however, that use of stencil processes with thin glue layers proved most important for production of graticules with completely clear backgrounds (p. 261).

(ii) DEVELOPMENT FOR REDUCED CONTRAST ON EXTREME-RESOLUTION EMULSIONS

Extreme-resolution emulsions commercially coated for such purposes as graticule production have intrinsically high contrast and small latitude. The high contrast is normally an advantage, since much extreme-resolution photography involves the production of 'line' images, and high contrast assists by sharpening the edges of the lines (p. 34). Lower contrast can certainly be obtained on such emulsions by incomplete development in an active solution with a low concentration of developing agent, but such methods reduce contrast merely by depressing the maximum density (curve B, Fig. 17). They cannot produce the desired result: namely an extension of latitude without loss of maximum density (Curve C, Fig. 17). Continuous-tone images can be made more satisfactorily by using emul-

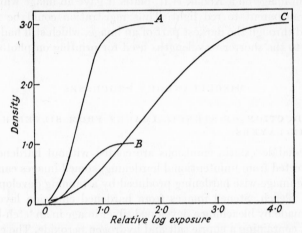

Fig. 17 *Tone Reproduction by Extreme-Resolution Emulsion*

(A) Curve produced by moderate-contrast developer. (B) Reduced contrast and maximum density produced by dilute developer. (C) Result required for continuous-time work.

sions of lower intrinsic contrast, such as 'Minicard' emulsion (p. 33), wet-collodion or collodion print-out, or by using an extreme-resolution emulsion with a low-contrast intermediate negative. For the last purpose, a soft-gradation developer (Appendix I) is definitely useful for producing low-contrast images on 'negative' emulsions having moderate or high latitude.

(iii) REVERSAL PROCESSING OF SILVER-HALIDE EMULSIONS

Extreme-resolution emulsions, like other silver-halide–gelatin materials, can be processed to give a direct-positive image by the operations of developing, bleaching-out the developed silver, fogging and re-developing (Appendix I). The reversed image is formed from the silver halide which is not blackened by the first development, and the resolution obtainable is impaired in two ways. In the first place the reversed image is necessarily formed throughout the whole emulsion thickness, so that the advantage derived from focusing very high-aperture objectives right in the surface of the emulsion can no longer be obtained (see Chapter 8). Reversed images are, moreover, only considered satisfactory when the transparent parts are completely clear. This condition is only achieved when the first exposure and development are sufficient to cause the reduction of substantially all the silver halide throughout the entire thickness of the emulsion. The exposures needed are therefore greater than the minimum required to give an adequate density by direct development, and are likely to be accompanied by greater image spread. The part of the image spread due to light scatter in the emulsion can, in materials such as Maximum-Resolution plates, be minimized by exposing to the longest wavelengths to which the emulsion is sensitive. With tungsten or mercury-vapour illumination, a Wratten No. 8 or No. 16 filter is suitable.

The wisdom of producing images by a route demanding reversal processing depends on factors such as the aperture of the objective (and hence the degree of convergence of the bundle of rays forming a point image), and on the relative widths and positions of the dark and light areas in the transparency (pp. 21 and 204). On Maximum-Resolution plates, reversal processing has been found by some users to give satisfactory line quality down to line widths of about 3 μ (0·0001 in). Reversal processing may lead to improved results when a reduced image is required with fine clear lines on a dark background, since a 'negative' transparency can be used with resultant decrease in light flare in the lens.

Reversal processing has proved particularly useful to graticule manufacturers, for building images of large scales by many successive exposures to unit elements of the image, with the extreme-resolution plate moved by a dividing engine before each exposure. Because of the limited useful field of existing lenses, only an area of about a square millimetre (0·04 × 0·04 in) can be exposed at once (see p. 246). For example, 360 exposures (one for each degree of a circle), will give a continuous circle of about 10 cm (4 in) diameter, consisting of an annular ring of thickness 1 mm (0·04 in). Normal processing of this would give a positive image, but reversal processing gives a negative directly, thus eliminating one stage of contact printing in the production of the final scales.

REFERENCES

[1] Dippel, C. J., *Phot. J.*, **90B**, 34, 1950 (see reference [6], Chapter 2).
[2] Bull, A. J. and Cartwright, H. M., 'The Production of Graticules', *Phot. J.*, **87B**, 43, 1947.
[3] James, T. H., 'The Reduction of Silver Ions by Hydroxylamine', *J. Am. Chem. Soc.*, **61**, 2379, 1939.
[4] Lüppo-Cramer, H., 'Schwellenwert und Physikalischer Entwicklung', *Phot. Ind.*, **797**, 1921.

[5] Dippel, C. J. and Jonker, H., in: O. Helwich (Ed.). *Reprographie.* *1st Int. Congress of Reprography*, Verlag Helwich (Darmstadt, 1964), p. 187 (see reference [33], Chapter 2), *also* N.V. Philips Gloeilampen-fabrieken. British Patent 936,609.

[6] James, T. H., 'Maximum Emulsion Speed in Relation to the Developing Agent', *J. Frank. Inst.*, **239**, 41, 1945.

[7] Crabtree, J. I. and Henn, R. W., 'An Improved Fine Grain Developer Formula', *Phot. J.*, **79**, 17, 1939.

[8] Altman, J. H. and Lamberts, R. L., 'Neutral Images with Kodak High Resolution Plates', *Phot. Sci. Eng.*, **2**, 160, 1958.

[9] Solman, L. R., 'The Role of Physical Development in determining the Sensitometric Response of Maximum-Resolution Emulsion', *J. Phot. Sci.*, **14**, 171, 1966.

[10] 'How to have the cleanest plates on your block', *Tech-bits* (Eastman Kodak Periodical, p- 3), 1964, No. 1.

[11] Holthaus, D. J., 'The basic ABC's of Photo Mask making' in *2nd Kodak Seminar on Microminiaturization*, Kodak Pamphlet No. P-89 (Rochester, N.Y., 1967).

[12] (a) Stott, J. G., Cummins, G. C. and Breton, H. E., 'Printing Motion-Picture Films Immersed in Liquid. Part I. Contact Printing', *J. Soc. Mot. Pict. Tel. Eng.*, **66**, 607, 1957.

(b) Turner, J. R., Grant, D. E. and Breton, H. E., 'Part II. Optical Printing', *ibid.*, 612, 1957.

[13] Lawson, J. C., 'KMER Techniques used in Mesa Transistor Manufacture' in *Kodak Seminar on Microminiaturization*, June 1965, Kodak Pamphlet No. P-77 (Rochester, N.Y., 1966). On p. 25 are discussed filtration techniques using products and procedures recommended by the Millipore Filter Corporation.

[14] Farnell, G. C., 'An improvement in the Technique of Washing Photographic Plates', *Brit. J. Phot.*, **101**, 295, 1954.

[15] The following are a few references on dust control.

(a) Jenkins, D. E. P., 'Clean Rooms for Special Valve Assembly', *Instrument Practice*, 8, 1085, 1954.

(b) Eirich C., 'Super White Rooms', *Instruments and Automation*', **31**, 1207, 1958.

(c) *Clean Rooms*. Trade leaflet of South London Electrical Equipment Co. Ltd., Hither Green Lane, London.

(d) Contamination Control Inc., Kulpsville, Pennsylvania, U.S.A.

(e) Anon. 'Clean-Room Installation for Precision Assembly', *The Engineer*, March 4, 351, 1966.

[16] (a) Contamination Control Inc., Kulpsville, Pennsylvania, U.S.A.

(b) *Clean Rooms* and *Lamina Flow Benches*. Trade leaflets of South London Electrical Equipment Co. Ltd, Hither Green Lane, London.

[17] Millipore Filter Corporation, *Detection and Analysis of Particulate Contamination*, Pamphlet ADM. 30, Millipore Corp. (Bedford, Massachusetts, October 1966).

[18] Millipore Filter Corporation, *Ultracleaning of Fluids and Systems*, Pamphlet ADM 60, and *Microfiltration Procedure: Photosensitive Resists*, Pamphlet MPF-2, Millipore Corp. (Bedford, Massachusetts, 1966).

[19] Plough, C. T., Crevier, W. F. and Danley, L. W., 'Photoresist

Process Optimization for Production of Planar Devices', in *2nd Kodak Seminar on Microminiaturization*, Kodak Pamphlet No. P-89 (Rochester, N.Y., 1967).

[20] Cooksey, C. D. and D., 'Unreliability of Photographic Emulsions on Glass for Recording Distances and a Method for Minimizing this Defect', *Phys. Rev.*, **36**, 80, 1930.

[21] Gollnaw, H. and Hagemann, G., 'Displacement of Photographic Emulsions and a Method of Processing to Minimize this Effect', *Astronomical Journal*, **61**, 399, 1956.

[22] Henn, R. W., Crabtree, J. I. and Russell, H. D., 'An Ammonium Hypo Reducer', *Phot. Soc. Am. J. (Phot. Sci. Tech.)*, **17B**, 110, 1951.

[23] Arens, H., 'Uber die Natur des Latenten Bildes bei Physikalischer Entwicklung', *Z. Wiss. Phot.*, **32**, 65, 1933.

[24] Goldberg, E., *Brit. J. Phot.*, **73**, 462, 1926 (see reference [6], Chapter 1).

[25] Bovey, E., B.I.O.S. Report 1552, p. 37 (see reference [22], Chapter 2).

[26] Ables, B. D., 'A study of Transparent Microphotographic Masks and their Application using Lippmann Emulsion', *Phot. Sci. Eng.*, **10**, 229, 1966.

[27] Dwyer, J. L., *Contamination Analysis and Control*, Reinhold (New York, 1966).

This book considers control of particulate contamination as a technology in its own right, rather than as a minor aspect of other technologies. It is particularly recommended to readers involved in microphotographic projects for which dirt control is important.

[28] Agnew, B., 'Application of Aerospace Clean Room Techniques in Photographic Laboratories', *J. Soc. Mot. Pict. Tel. Eng.*, **76**, 111, 1967.

4 · The Objective

It is convenient to consider microphotography as being concerned with the production of three types of images: namely microscopic images up to a millimetre or two in diameter (say 0·1 in), instrument scales and other relatively large articles requiring exceedingly sharp lines, and finally commercial document copies. The last type is distinguished from the others by the different criteria used for selecting the objective. Although there is a trend towards the use of ever greater reduction ratios, the bulk of commercial document copying is still done at reduction ratios from 15 : 1 to 40 : 1. Lens-to-copyboard distances may hence need to be as large as forty-one times the focal length of the objective. For commercial operation it is important that the equipment should be compact enough for easy transportation and installation in available offices and work-rooms, and it is therefore the practice to use objectives of relatively short focal length. The diagonals of the negatives made range from one-third up to well over one-half of the focal length of the objective used, which means that the angular fields of view are not much less than those used for 'pictorial' photography. In document copying the legibility of the characters in the extreme corners of the field is just as important as on the axis, whereas the conventional concentration of interest of pictorial photographs well away from the corners means that reduced sharpness in the corners can often pass unnoticed. For this reason manufacturers of document-copying equipment have given special attention to the provision of objectives giving satisfactory sharpness right up to the corners of the negative. Lenses designed for pictorial photography often prove less satisfactory in this respect.

Since the essential quality of objectives for document microphotography is *uniformity* of sharpness over the field, there is little point in demanding extreme resolution on the axis. The usefulness of high axial resolution is also restricted by the fact that the emulsions used must have a minimum level of speed, which in practice often sets an upper limit to the resolution obtainable (see Chapter 2). These emulsions are, in fact, generally incapable of detecting small residual aberrations which might be intolerable for extreme-resolution photography.

Because of the economic importance of document microphotography, the problem of providing objectives for the commonly used reduction ratios and the techniques for using them to the best advantage have already been largely worked out. A reader proposing to carry out this work is thus likely to obtain satisfactory results with the minimum of effort by obtaining good equipment and following the manufacturer's instructions (see Chapter 12, p. 376). He may, therefore, find that the remainder of this chapter does not directly concern him, since it deals with objectives for making extreme-resolution microphotographic images, for which the choice of objective is much less 'cut and dried'.

OBJECTIVES FOR EXTREME RESOLUTION

While lens designers are only too well aware of the shortcomings of photographic objectives, the performance obtained is commonly adequate for most photographic tasks. In practice, the limitations imposed by the objective often prove relatively unimportant compared with the effects of graininess and light scatter in fast negative emulsions, even if unaccompanied by camera-shake or incorrect focus. It is probably true to say that the resolution given by high-quality photographic objectives is, for most purposes, sufficient to provide a reasonable margin for safety. Quite acceptable results can, therefore, be obtained even by an operator with but a rudimentary knowledge of their properties. In extreme-resolution microphotography, however, one is forced to work much closer to the limit of performance of the objective; and it is advisable to consider the objective as a working tool with its own qualities and limitations, rather than as a piece of equipment whose properties can be taken for granted.

The remainder of this chapter therefore deals with those properties of importance for extreme-resolution work, with the types of objective which may be used, with means for testing and selecting an individual objective and with the practical precautions needed to secure extreme resolution. While reading these sections, the reader should remember that the standard of sharpness demanded by extreme-resolution microphotography is completely beyond ordinary photographic requirements. He should, therefore, not be unduly disturbed if some of the tests cause him to detect deficiencies in the lens of his own camera. Defects which are serious for microphotography are often not detectable in ordinary use.

The Properties of Objectives

FOCAL LENGTH

When an objective is focused on an object at a distance u, a real image is formed at a distance v from the objective. The object and image are then said to be at conjugate foci, and the distances u and v are related to each other by the equation:

$$\frac{1}{v} + \frac{1}{u} = \frac{1}{f}$$

where f is the focal length of the objective.[1]

The focal length is an important quantity characterizing each individual objective, and is equal to the effective distance at which an image is formed when the object is at infinity. In conjunction with variations of the above formula, it allows many useful quantities to be calculated [1]. The reduction factor, for instance, is equal to the object distance divided by the image distance, and this quantity can be evaluated by the formula:

$$\text{Reduction Factor } (R) = \frac{u}{v} = \frac{u - f}{f}.$$

This shows how the reduction factor is increased by increasing the object distance, or by using an objective of shorter focal length. The use of this simple lens formula for calculating reduction factors is complicated by the fact that it assumes that the lens is of negligible thickness. With thick lenses, u and v should be measured from *nodal points*, which are inside the lens and are separated by a finite distance. Determination of the position of nodal points requires special equipment not available to most users, and they are, therefore of mainly theoretical interest. In fact with compound lenses, measurement of the image distance v with the accuracy required for reduction factor calculations is impracticable. The total object-to-image distance (i.e. $u + v$), however, is a larger quantity which can be measured reasonably accurately; and because the distance will be relatively great, the distance between the nodal points only represents a small error. Reduction factors can then be calculated from an alternative approximate formula:

$$\text{Reduction factor } (R) = \frac{D - 2f}{f}$$

---

[1] In this version of the formula, the distances are measured from the objective. In formal optics it is more usual to relate the distances to the direction of the incident light, so that u becomes negative and the formula then becomes:

$$\frac{1}{v} - \frac{1}{u} = \frac{1}{f}$$

where D is the object-to-image distance. Apart from the production of precision scales such as graticules, this formula gives sufficiently accurate results with reduction factors of twenty or more. More precise results can be obtained for any lens by interpolating from observed values for R obtained at different values of the object-to-image distance D.

Although it is difficult to measure the effective values of u and v directly, it is fairly simple to measure changes in these distances with reasonable precision. The lens formula is, therefore, useful for computing the changes in image distance resulting from a given change in object distance. This information is useful when focusing a distance piece, or when focusing an objective by altering the distance of the object plane (Chapter 5). Values calculated for a series of nominal focal lengths are tabulated in Appendix IIA.

More precise figures can be obtained by substituting the object distance (u) and the exact focal length (f) in the formula:

$$\text{Image distance } (v) = \frac{fu}{u - f}.$$

The calculations can be simplified by computing the figures for a focal length of unity, when this takes the form:

$$v = \frac{u}{u - 1}.$$

The values for an objective of any focal length are simply obtained by multiplying the results by the focal length of the objective. Values of the ratio $\dfrac{u}{u - 1}$ for a range of reduction factors are tabulated in Appendix IIB.

Consideration of the focal length provides a useful preliminary guide to the selection of an objective for any particular job. Microscope objectives of the same focal length made by different manufacturers frequently have much the same aperture, and are likely to give approximately the same resolving power. With decreasing focal length, the degree of reduction at a given distance, the angular aperture and the resolving power are all increased, but the useful field is decreased.

THE APERTURE

The aperture, or the relationship between the focal length and the effective opening of an objective, is a quantity of great importance. In the case of a single thin lens an approximate value for this ratio can be found by focusing the objective on an object at infinity, and then dividing the image-to-lens distance by the diameter of the lens

(Fig. 18). With thick, complex lenses, however, the aperture has to be described with regard to the physics of image formation [2]. When a lens is corrected for coma and spherical aberration (see below), as all satisfactory photographic objectives must be, all rays entering the lens parallel to the axis converge to a focal point on the axis. It can be shown that the points at which they appear to change direction, if the rays entering and leaving the objective are projected forward

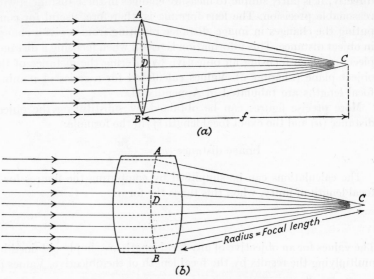

Fig. 18 *Apertures of Thin and Thick Lenses*

(a) For thin lens, F-number $= \dfrac{CD}{AB}$.

(b) For thick lens, F-number $= \dfrac{CD}{AB}$, since $CD = CA =$ focal length.

and backward respectively, lie on a sphere with its centre at the focus, and of radius equal to the focal length [Fig. 18(b)]. Now photographic objectives are described by their 'F-number', or the ratio of the focal length to the effective diameter of the aperture. If θ is half the angle which this diameter subtends an image on the axis, it follows that:

$$\text{F-number} = \frac{f}{AB} = \frac{f}{2AD}$$

but

$$\frac{AD}{f} = \sin\theta$$

hence

$$\text{F-number} = \frac{1}{2\sin\theta}$$

The angular aperture of an objective is thus inversely proportional to its F-number.

The aperture of microscope objectives is usually defined by the numerical aperture:

$$\text{Numerical aperture (N.A.)} = n \sin \theta,$$

where n is the refractive index of the medium in which the objective is used.

In the case of 'dry' objectives working in air, n is unity, the N.A. therefore equals $\sin \theta$, and from the formula for the F-number it follows that:

$$\text{Numerical aperture} = \frac{1}{2 \times \text{F-number}}$$

Since both the numerical aperture and the F-number are simple functions of the angle θ, equivalent values can be readily calculated.

Table 2. Connection between numerical aperture and F-number

Numerical aperture	Equivalent F-number
0·15	3·3
0·20	2·5
0·25	2·0
0·30	1·7
0·40	1·25
0·50	1·0
0·60	0·83
0·70	0·71
0·80	0·63
0·90	0·56

Table 2 shows that a low-power microscope objective, with a moderate N.A. of 0·3, already has a greater aperture than the majority of camera lenses.

When diffuse illumination is used (Chapter 7), the brightness of the image is proportional to the square of the N.A. of the objective used, or inversely proportional to the square of the F-number. The aperture of a lens in addition influences the depth of focus and the useful flat field, and not infrequently also the aberrations shown. As will be shown later, the resolving power of microscope objectives

Table 3. Dependence of depth of focus on aperture

Numerical aperture	Depth of focus	
0·25	7·9 microns	
0·50	1·9 ,,	
0·75	0·8 ,,	
1·25 (oil immersion)	0·4 ,,	(in medium with $n = 1·5$)

increases with N.A., but the depth of focus and useful flat field are decreased by increasing the aperture. Martin and Johnson [3] give, in Table 3, the depth of focus of microscope objectives of different aperture.

COLOUR CORRECTION

The refractive index of glass decreases with increasing wavelength, so that a simple positive lens will have a longer focal length for red light than for blue [Fig. 19(a)]. The rate of change of refractive index with wavelength (dispersion) is an important property of glasses, and generally increases with increasing refractive index. Lens designers use this fact to produce compound lenses, in which the dispersion of a strong positive component made from a glass of low dispersion is balanced against that of a weak negative component made from a glass of high dispersion. This combination gives a positive lens of longer focal length than the positive component itself, but with greatly reduced variation of focal length with wavelength. In the case of 'achromatic' objectives, corrections of this type result in red and blue images being focused at the same distance. This correction is only complete for two specific wavelengths, and residual chromatic aberration will still be shown both between and outside these wavelengths. One practical consequence of chromatic aberration becomes apparent when an image is focused visually by non-actinic light of a longer wavelength than that used for producing the image on a blue or ultra-violet sensitive emulsion. Such differences of focal length at different wavelengths were a source of trouble to the early microphotographers [4] who found that they had to compensate for the difference between the visual focus observed by white light, and the photographic focus when using wet-collodion plates. The same trouble has been experienced by modern workers operating the collodion process, but was alleviated by focusing through a blue filter so that the spectral regions used for focusing and image formation were brought closer together.

Chromatic aberration is a property which has quite different effects on the image quality of photomicrographs and microphotographs. In photomicrography the emulsion is often required to record the whole visible spectrum in order to give a satisfactory reproduction of coloured specimens; and chromatic aberrations can result in loss of sharpness, or actual colour fringes at the edge of the image may be recorded on colour film. A minimum of chromatic aberration is thus of real importance for photomicrography. In fact 'apochromatic' objectives recommended for this purpose are corrected so that three wavelengths are brought to the same focus.

For most microphotographic tasks, however, there is no need to use a broad band of wavelengths.[1] In fact, sharper images should result from the use of monochromatic light, because of the elimination of the effect of residual chromatic aberration. Effectively mono-chromatic rendering can be readily obtained by exposing green-sensitized extreme-resolution emulsions with mercury or tungsten lamps (p. 191). Lens designers have now appreciated this fact, and a number of objectives have been specially designed for using in these conditions (p. 111).

For extreme-resolution microphotographic work, therefore, the reader need regard chromatic aberration only as a slightly incon-venient property, whose effects can be circumvented by suitable focusing and illumination methods. No special advantage is to be expected from the use of expensive apochromatic objectives, but some users [5] have found the Carl Zeiss Planapochromats (such as the x10, N.A. 0·32) to be very well corrected and to give fine micro-photographic images over a relatively large field.

DISTORTION

Most objectives give an image which is not completely free from distortion. Images of rectangular ruled grids may be produced with lines curved, or with angles changed or with different spacings in different parts of the field. Distortion may be defined as variation of magnification over the field. So long as these effects are not present to an immediately obvious extent they are not of serious consequence for some types of microscopic images, nor for document microphoto-graphy. Distortion may, however, be critically important for the production of precision scales and graticules (Chapter 9). Thus at the Möller graticule factory it was the practice to test several objectives of the same make for distortion, and only use those which survived the most rigorous examination [6]. It is, perhaps, also worth noticing that distortion is a serious problem in aerial survey (photogrammetry). If their other properties are satisfactory, lenses used for aerial survey might therefore prove suitable for some purposes in microphoto-graphy. The presence of minimal distortion is frequently quoted as one of the features of the new generation of objectives specifically developed for microphotographic tasks (p. 112).

[1] The rare exception is when multi-coloured microphotographs are to be pro-duced at extreme resolution.

SPHERICAL ABERRATION

Diagrams illustrating ideal image formation by a lens show all zones of the lens collecting light from a point on the object, and then focusing this light to form a point in the image plane. In fact, this ideal situation only occurs with so-called 'perfect' objectives when both the object and the image lie close to the axis of the lens, and are situated at special positions known as the *aplanatic points*, so that a definite reduction factor is obtained. When the degree of reduction is altered, or with practically all photographic objectives, light passing through the outer zones of the objective tends to be focused on a different plane from the focus of the central zone [Fig. 19(b)]. This

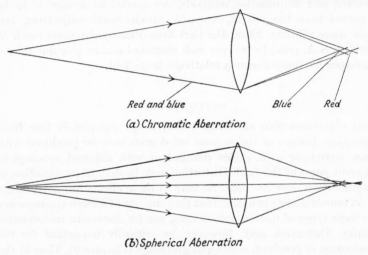

Red and blue   *Blue*   *Red*

(a) Chromatic Aberration

(b) Spherical Aberration

Fig. 19 *Aberrations*

Images are formed at different distances: (a) by light of different wavelengths in the case of *chromatic aberration*, and (b) by light from different zones of the lens in the case of spherical aberration.

defect is known as spherical aberration, and is of crucial importance for the sharpness of microphotographs.

Lenses are frequently classed as 'perfect' or otherwise according to their spherical aberration. The perfect lenses are those designed to show a minimum of coma and of spherical aberration on the axis. They are mainly used in instruments such as microscopes or telescopes, in which the objective is used to cover a small angular field while working at a practically constant magnification. Perfect lenses are so well corrected that they can be used at full aperture without loss of resolution, and the resolution is actually decreased by stopping down (see p. 123). It cannot be too strongly emphasized, however, that their full resolution is only obtained quite close to the axis, so that these objectives cover a very restricted field.

The objectives used in photographic cameras are, on the other hand, required to cover a much larger field and to give acceptable results at a range of reductions. The designer meets these requirements by compromises giving greater flexibility in use at the expense of some axial resolution. Photographic objectives normally show appreciable spherical aberration even on the axis, and some consequences of this have been discussed by G. H. Cook [7]. The correct focus in these objectives is defined not so much by a point but rather by the smallest disc through which rays from all zones of the lens pass. As a result of spherical aberration, photographic objectives tend to give their best resolution at one or two stops below full aperture, and the position of best focus may alter as the aperture is changed. This change of focus has a detrimental effect when an objective is focused at its full aperture and is stopped down for making the exposure. Objectives intended for photomechanical work (so-called 'Process' lenses) are usually designed to reduce such changes of focus to a minimum.

The spherical aberration shown by an objective is not a constant property, but changes with the conditions of use. Thus it may be increased when an objective is used at an unsuitable reduction, or when part of the light path between the objective and the image is occupied by an unsuitable thickness of a medium of high refractive index, such as a cover-glass. As we shall see later, therefore, one aim of the microphotographer is to ensure maximum sharpness by choosing conditions which minimize the influence of spherical aberration.

Lenses show other aberrations such as astigmatism and coma, when the image is formed further away from the axis. Except for specially designed large-field objectives, these are of relatively little practical consequence for extreme-resolution microphotography, as their influence tends to be overwhelmed by field curvature.

FIELD CURVATURE AND FIELD SIZE

The size of the flat field over which a lens will give satisfactory resolution is strictly limited. Objectives normally reproduce a flat original as a saucer-shaped surface with its concave side towards the objective (Fig. 20). The useful area of the field is then determined by the portion of this saucer whose depth is just contained within the depth of focus of the objective.

In microscope objectives the diameter of the useful field is usually less than one-tenth (or even one-twentieth) of the focal length of the objective. This limitation of the area of the field has proved a serious handicap in photomicrography, and microscope manufacturers have devoted much attention to the improvement of this property. Larger useful fields can be obtained by the use of 'Planachromat' or 'Plana-pochromat' objectives specially designed for this property, or by using such eyepieces as the 'Periplan' or 'Homal' which flatten the field by using their own field curvature to cancel that of the objective.

In any case the microphotographer using microscope objectives has to seek the best compromise for his purpose. The alternatives are to use either a high-power objective giving a high resolving power over a very small field, or else use an objective of lower aperture and resolution for the sake of its increased field. With any given objective a somewhat larger field can be obtained by inserting a 'stop' against

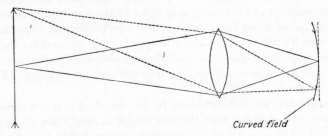

Curved field

Fig. 20 *Field Curvature*

The image of a flat original projected by an uncorrected objective often lies on a spherical surface.

the back component, but this reduction of aperture will also reduce the resolution obtainable.

Photographic objectives are more thoroughly corrected for field curvature, and as we have already seen are normally used to cover a plate whose diagonal approaches the focal length. When used with extreme-resolution emulsions, however, such objectives are only likely to give their sharpest image over a field whose diameter is at most one-fifth of the focal length, and may be substantially less. In this connection it is interesting to note an important difference between the properties required in objectives used for making docu-ment copies and such articles as instrument scales or microelectronic masks. In the latter application small size and portability of the reducing apparatus are much less essential, so that it is practicable to employ objectives of longer focal length, and use only the central part of the field for making the images.

The effective size of the field obtained with any objective can also be increased by arranging the image so that it tends to conceal the reduced sharpness of the outer parts of the field. Thus resolution-test images can be laid out in a roughly spiral pattern, with the finest images in the centre of the field (see Plate 58). A degree of unsharpness which would spoil the smaller images may hardly be detected on the larger images at the edge of the field. It is also useful to remember that the loss of sharpness due to astigmatism in areas off the axis tends to be greater for lines running tangentially with respect to the axis, than for those running radially. Thus on moving out from the axis, 'cross-wires' in a graticule image are likely to show loss of sharpness later than lines placed at right angles to them.

FLARE AND GHOST IMAGES

It has long been recognized that light can reach an emulsion from directions not intended by camera or lens designers, and can give rise to such phenomena as ghost images, flare spots or a general loss of contrast. Even when all the elements of a lens are quite clean, such straying of light may be the result of reflection at air–glass interfaces, at the internal surfaces of lens mounts or by scatter at the ground edges of individual glass elements of the lens.

The nearer a task approaches the resolution limit of any lens design, the less tolerable will any resultant degradation of image quality by stray light seem to be. Such problems can be combated in two ways. Firstly, the stray light can be minimized at its origin by coating free glass surfaces with anti-reflection coatings, and by fitting the interior of lens barrels with adequately blackened knife-edge diaphragms [2]. Secondly, harmful consequences of stray light can certainly be reduced by judicious choice of working conditions. It is advantageous to arrange the processes so that transparencies to be reduced through an objective have a large part of the field black. Flooding of light into small unexposed areas from adjacent large exposed areas is a more serious menace than loss of a proportion of the light entering the objective from small exposed areas.

RESOLUTION AND SHARPNESS

The ability of an objective to give a sharp image of fine detail is (for microphotography) the most important property of all. In practice, the resolving power of any objective is controlled by its aperture and by any aberration which may be present. Most books on microscopy describe how resolution is limited by diffraction resulting from the wave nature of light. For aberration-free lenses, it has been calculated that the minimum distance between a pair of lines which can just be separated, is given approximately by the expression

$$d = \frac{\lambda}{2(\text{N.A.})}$$

where λ is the wavelength of the light used.

Thus the larger the aperture and the shorter the wavelength of the light, the smaller will be the distance d, and the higher will be the resolving power of the optical image. The observed axial resolution of telescope and microscope objectives is usually close to the figure given by this formula, but the axial resolution of photographic objectives is generally reduced by residual aberrations. In such cases, it can often be improved by stopping down, and so cutting out the marginal zones of the lens which show the worst aberration. The improvement obtained by stopping down by one or two increments (e.g. from F/3·5 to F/4·5 or F/5·6), may more than compensate for any theoretical loss caused by the reduced aperture. Stopping down more than this usually leads to loss of resolution by diffraction.

In recent years, ideas about the measurement of resolution of lenses have gone through the same sort of changes as for the measurement of the image sharpness given by emulsions (pp. 36–40). The time-honoured method was to judge this ability by measuring the *resolving power* of the objective. For this purpose the objective was used to reduce a test-chart image, consisting of sets of lines of decreasing width and spacing (Plate 58). The reduced aerial image was either inspected directly with a microscope, or it was recorded photographically on a suitable emulsion and the resultant image was examined microscopically (p. 451). The smallest image in which the component lines could *just* be separated indicated the resolving power. It is important to note that the measured figure indicated only the *limit* of resolution, and told us nothing about the sharpness of larger images.

The physical reasons for the existence of a resolving power limit have been explained by Selwyn and Tearle [8] in the following way. Consider the intensity distribution across the lines of a test image with lines of progressively decreasing width and separation (Plate 10). The objective at first reproduces the wide lines with only slight degradation; but, with decreasing line width, the edges become rounded until the contrast of the entire image starts to decrease. The limit of resolving power is then determined by the line width at which just enough contrast remains for the image to be recognizable.

As with figures for the resolution of emulsions (Chapter 2), caution is needed in assessing the significance of the resolution figure of an objective in terms of the eventual image sharpness likely to be obtained. The observed resolving power depends not only on the properties of the lens but also on the conditions used to observe the image. This is well illustrated by a figure in Selwyn and Tearle's paper, which shows that the aperture of aero objectives giving the optimum resolution was strongly dependent on the emulsion used. Such results are due to the interplay between aberrations and emulsion properties. Another example was provided by Perrin and Altman [9], who determined the connection between the measured resolving power of photographic emulsions and the apertures of the 'perfect' lenses used to form the images. Kodak 548 GH Spectroscopic plates gave figures increasing up to the highest aperture used (N.A. 0·85), whereas the resolution measured on high-speed emulsions actually decreased with apertures above N.A. 0·25. It should also be remembered that the resolution obtained with objectives showing chromatic aberration will depend on the spectral distribution given by the illuminant and the spectral sensitivity of the emulsion. Furthermore, Higgins and Jones's paper on sharpness (p. 36) showed that the correlation of sharpness with resolution measurements is no better with objectives than with emulsions [10]. An instance was shown where images made with an objective focused to give optimum resolution were notably less sharp than others made with the focus altered by $\frac{1}{25}$ in (1 mm). In the former case the objective recorded a point source as a small dot surrounded by a diffuse aberration patch, and in the latter the image was a compact dot about three times the diameter of the first.

The test-chart images originally used (and many still employed today) have square-edged line-intensity profiles, but as the line frequency approached the resolution limit, the intensity distributions were degraded to sinusoidal profiles. As with measurement of the resolution performance of emulsions, lens performance has been investigated by using test images with sinusoidal profiles and measuring the percentage of the original intensity amplitude reproduced by a lens at different line frequencies. The results are depicted by plotting the so-called *modulation-transfer function* (as a percentage) against the spatial frequency of the reduced image (Fig. 21). Such a curve gives a complete description of the performance of the part of the field of the lens at which the measurements were made. Because the modulation-transfer function is also measured for the lower frequencies corresponding to the practically useful resolving power, the curve can be used to predict the range of light intensities which will be obtained in the image at these frequencies. It should, of course, be remembered that the curves only apply to the reproduction of sinusoidal test images, but it can be shown that the intensity profile of a square-wave test-chart can be synthesized by integrating the effects of the fundamental sine wave with a series of harmonics [11]. In fact, the higher the modulation-transfer function for the higher frequencies, the sharper should a lens be capable of reproducing square-edged lines.

These newer methods of assessing lens performance were originally applied by the research worker and systems designer. The actual tests need both specialized apparatus and skills, and the detailed interpretation of results to predict the photographic line quality to be expected at different line widths on a particular emulsion is a none too simple matter. The practical man will, nevertheless, have to contend with the probability that lens manufacturers will increasingly use this method to describe the performance of their products. To his

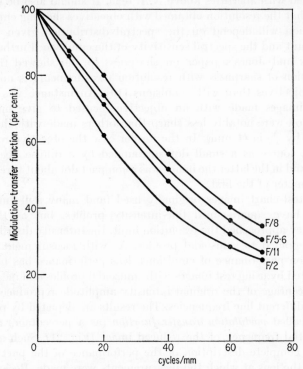

Fig. 21 *Modulation-Transfer-Function Curves for Lens*
Performance of F/2 miniature-camera lens focused for optimum resolution.
Courtesy of L. R. Baker, B. J. Biddles, R. A. Lane, P. Welsh and Director of British Scientific Instrument Research Association.

advantage, is the fact that organizations such as the British Scientific Instrument Research Association have developed equipment permitting the modulation-transfer curve of a lens to be displayed immediately on an oscilloscope [12]. By manipulating the controls, the results of changing focus or stopping down ('on' or 'off' axis) can be demonstrated in a few minutes. For the larger organization or institution, the commercial availability of equipment for such tests is worth noting [13]. Furthermore, the B.S.I.R.A. has undertaken to inspect individual lenses at least as a service to member firms.

Fromm has suggested that modulation-transfer function information should be applied to the selection of a lens for a particular task [14]. For this purpose, he calculated the line frequencies at which given values of modulation-transfer function would be obtained for perfect lenses used at different apertures to reproduce images on Kodak High-Resolution film at a wavelength of 5,250 Å. If contours corresponding to each value of modulation-transfer function were then drawn on a graph with logarithmic scales for line frequency and lens aperture, they appeared as parallel straight lines (Fig. 22). Such

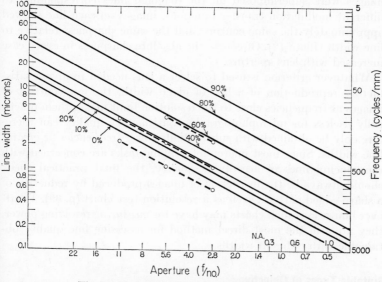

Fig. 22 *Modulation-Transfer-Function Contours*
By following the contour for the required modulation-transfer function, the aperture needed to obtain the required reproduction for a specified line frequency (or width) can be read off.
Courtesy of H. J. Fromm and Journal of Photographic Science.

diagrams can be used to predict the relative line contrast and sharpness to be anticipated in different conditions. To a reasonable approximation, line width can be considered to equal the reciprocal of *twice* the frequency; i.e. 5 μ equals one millimetre (1,000 μ) divided by twice a frequency of 100 lines/mm. Thus the figure can be used to estimate the *mimimum* aperture needed to give a required modulation-transfer function for a given line width. It can also be used to indicate the smallest line width of an acceptable quality which is likely to be obtained with a lens of a given aperture. As would be expected from the resolution formula given above, increasing the aperture of a perfect lens by a given ratio increases the acceptable line frequency or *divides* the acceptable line width by the same ratio.

Fromm emphasized that Fig. 22 only shows the best possible result, and aberrations will decrease the quality, particularly for the larger apertures of photographic objectives. Nevertheless, he was able to produce a striking demonstration of the validity of this method. A set of lines was reduced with the lens diaphragm adjusted to $F/2 \cdot 8$, $F/5 \cdot 6$ and $F/11$, so that the geometrical widths were $17 \cdot 6$, $8 \cdot 8$ and $4 \cdot 4$ μ respectively. When photomicrographs of the different reduced images were superimposed on the diagonal lines corresponding to different modulation transfer functions, images on each line showed approximately the same contrast and the same sharpness relative to line width (Plate 12). Of course the absolute sharpness in every case increased with lens aperture.

Whatever criterion is used to select a lens needed to give a satisfactory reproduction of a line of given width, the low contrast of images at frequencies close to the resolution limit makes them practically useless for microphotography. Satisfactory quality can therefore only be obtained with substantially lower frequencies or greater line widths. Since most microphotographic tasks are concerned with reproducing lines of acceptable quality, the final practical check should always be the inspection of images produced by reduction of a sharp-edged pattern, such as a resolution-test chart (p. 39). Whatever limitations such charts may have for *measuring* resolving power, they are still the most direct method for assessing line quality obtainable with different widths.

Suitable Types of Objective

The crux of the problem in selecting an objective is to find a lens providing *both* the required resolution and a flat field of adequate size. We have already seen that these properties are related reciprocally. Extreme resolution even in so-called perfect lenses is usually only obtained over a very limited field, and the limited resolution of most field-flattened photographic objectives is shown up remorselessly by extreme-resolution emulsions.

Lenses Specially Designed for Extreme-resolution Microphotography

Until 1962, industrial microphotographers (particularly graticule makers) have tended to bemoan the fact that there were no lenses specifically designed for their work. The historical reasons for this are simple. Until a few decades ago, microphotographers had not only to learn the special techniques of *using* their emulsions, but also had to *make* and *coat* the emulsions themselves. The difficulties of this work therefore seemed so great that there were only a small number of production units in the world making such images as graticules. It would have been surprising if such a sparse and scattered market had seemed worth the attention of lens designers. As will be apparent from the later chapters of this book, the advent of commercially available emulsions has now made industrial use of microphotographic processes attractive for a wide variety of purposes. Since the introduction and wide-spread use of extreme-resolution emulsions, both the need for special objectives and features of existing objectives which could be sacrificed to gain a degree of freedom in design became apparent. As we have already noted, there is no intrinsic need for lenses to be achromatized when they are to be used with emulsion/illumination systems employing a narrow band of wavelengths for image formation. Furthermore, the designer can discard some hampering restrictions if the lenses are designed and used to give optimum sharpness at one specific reduction ratio. The design of lenses for such narrowly specified conditions has constituted a departure from previous practice, and many workers now use a computer to optimize the designs.

To the business men financing such projects, it must still seem that the market is small compared with the market for lenses for mass-produced cameras. The matter has been further complicated by the diverse opinions of different industrial users as to the lens specification they wished. *Such difficulties can be minimized if users were to realize that the choice of a suitable objective is the most difficult single decision for the making of microphotographic images.* In these circumstances, a sensible policy is to choose the objective *first*, and adapt the size of the original, the reduction factor and the wavelengths used for image formation to secure the best performance of the chosen objective-emulsion combination. If users prove willing to co-operate in this fashion, fewer modifications will be called for, which should assist designers and manufacturers to meet the need.

A number of lens manufacturers are now offering objectives designed to be used in strictly specified conditions. For example, the Wray Optical Co. have produced an F/4 3-in (75 mm) 'Special Copying Lens' designed for use with M-R plates exposed to the mercury 5,461 Å green line. Alternative forms were designed to be used at reduction ratios of 25 or 10, and virtually diffraction-limited resolution over a circle of $1\frac{1}{2}$ in (38 mm) diameter has been claimed. The Wray Optical Co. have further increased field sizes by the use of similar methods to produce objectives of focal lengths 5 and 10 in (12·5 and 25 cm). In 1966, W. Watson and Sons introduced a special reduction lens of focal length 25 mm, N.A. 0·23 and covering 8 mm ($\frac{1}{3}$ in) field diameter. An interesting feature was the equipment of this

E

Table 4 Ultra-Micro NIKKOR family of objectives

Aperture at standard reduction ratio	Focal length	Reduction ratio	Object-to-image distance	Aerial resolving power lines/mm	Diameter of field at full resolution	Distortion at image corners	Date available
F/4	155 mm	10	1,821 mm	300 at F/4·5	42 mm	− 0·05% at 42 mm	In preparation
				250 at F/5·6	56 mm	− 0·12% at 56 mm	
F/2·8	125 mm	25	3,364 mm	400	28 mm	− 0·3%	1965
F/2·8	105 mm	30	3,352 mm	400	24 mm	− 0·45%	1962
F/2	55 mm	4	315 mm	500	10 mm	− 0·00%	In preparation
F/1·8	28 mm	10	315 mm	650	4 mm	− 0·06%	In preparation
F/1·2	30 mm	25	810 mm	1,200	2 mm	− 1·3%	1964

objective with its own pneumatic gauge for monitoring focus (p. 340).

The greatest efforts in this direction seem to have been made in Japan. Z. Koana of Tokyo University and Z. Wakimoto of Nippon Kogaku K.K. [15] discussed the design, application and testing of a range of special lenses for microelectronics (see also p. 338). This work culminated in the production of the family of Ultra-Micro NIKKOR lenses by the Nippon Kogaku Co. (Table 4).

There have been published few independent accounts of the performance of these objectives, but an idea of their potentialities can be

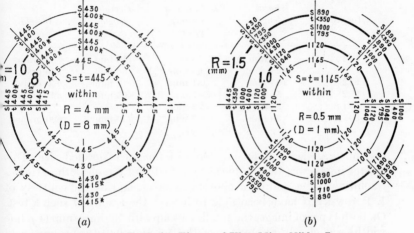

(a)   (b)

Fig. 23 *Measured Resolution Figures of Ultra-Micro Nikkor Lenses*

(a) Aeriel image of 105 mm lens formed at F/3·2. The asterisk denotes a slight 'halo' of no practical consequence.

(b) Photographic image produced on Kodak High-Resolution plate by 30 mm lens at F/1·2.

Courtesy of Z. Koana and Z. Wakimoto.

obtained from results of the originator's tests. Figure 23 shows measured sagittal and tangential resolution observations for two of the lenses. A photomicrograph reproduced in Koana and Wakimoto's paper substantiates these figures, which refer to physically measured resolving power and not to practical resolution limit (p. 39).

A notable feature of the design of the Ultra-Micro NIKKOR objectives is their large size resulting from combining large aperture and relatively large focal length. For example, the nominal aperture of the 125-mm F/2·8 is 2·4 times that of the Wray F/4 3-in objective.

In relation to the minute images they are designed to produce, their size and weight is also remarkable (Table 5). A practical consequence of their focal lengths and reduction ratios is that rather long optical benches or 'cameras' are required (Table 4).

Another interesting development is the proposal by Spectra-Physics to use the same objective either for the production of masks on extreme-resolution plates, or for direct exposure of a photoresist layer by projection. For this purpose, they have produced a Model 500 Copy lens of aperture F/1·5 and focal length 45·5 mm (1¾ in) corrected for image formation at 4,360 Å [20]. To demonstrate the performance of this lens, they produced a master image 6·3 mm (2½ in) square containing an array of more than 3,600 complete resolution

Table 5. Some dimensions of the Ultra-Micro NIKKOR lenses

Aperture	Focal length	Diameter of entrance pupil	Overall length	Weight
F/4	155 mm	56 mm	118 mm	785 grams
F/2·8	125 mm	60 mm	86 mm	700 grams
F/2·8	105 mm	51 mm	71 mm	450 grams
F/2	55 mm	29·7 mm	65 mm	325 grams
F/1·8	28 mm	22 mm	70 mm	—
F/1·2	30 mm	34·5 mm	230 mm	800 grams

test images, each comprising ten test images of graded size. This master image was then reduced by a factor of ten on both extreme-resolution plates and on a photoresist layer, and by the courtesy of I. Barowsky, I have been able to inspect the results of such a test. On both types of image, the smallest group with 500 lines/mm (1 μ line width) was clearly resolved over the 5·5 mm (0·216 in) square field [diagonal more than 7 mm (¼ in)]. In my opinion, the quality constituted 'useful' resolution, and indicated that the physical resolution limit was probably 1,000 or more lines/mm. It was stated that similar test plates would be supplied to purchasers of this lens.

SELECTION FROM LENSES PRODUCED FOR OTHER PURPOSES

Prior to 1962, all extreme-resolution microphotographs were made with lenses designed primarily for other purposes. In spite of this, much excellent work has been done, and the remainder of this section will therefore review types of objective amongst which the reader might profitably search.

General-purpose objectives may suffice when the finest lines to be produced are not less than 10 microns (0·0004 in) wide. Their performance is often described by the ratio of the 'circle of confusion' to the focal length, which implies that the actual size of this circle may decrease with decreasing focal length. It is possibly for this reason that Allen [16] suggested the use of objectives designed for narrow-gauge ciné work, and those used on 'sub-miniature' cameras might be considered for the same reason.

In fact, some modern ciné objectives are made with an aperture large enough to merit consideration for the making of even finer lines. For example, Plate 12 shows images made with an F/1·4 Kodak Ciné-Ektar of 25 mm focal length, used at F/2·8 with a 15 mm converter. It is apparent that tolerable line quality was obtained at a width of 4·4 μ (less than 0·0002 in). The Ferranti Company have used a Kern 12·5 mm, F/0·9 Switar Ciné lens for making micro-electronic masks (p. 340). By the courtesy of R. Freestone, the author had the opportunity to compare one of these lenses with a 16-mm microscope objective of N.A. 0·28. On M-R plates the axial image quality at a line width of 1–2 μ (0·00004–0·00008 in) was indistinguishable from that given by the microscope objective, and the field of undiminished resolution was substantially larger.

The price or age of a photographic objective may give little indication of its suitability for this work. Some simple and less costly objectives, such as portrait lenses, may be found to give excellent sharpness over a restricted field. The century-old 'Petzval' design[1] is in particular reputed to show a high axial resolution, and such a lens may be acquired (second-hand) for a modest sum. Another early type of potential interest is the Dallmeyer Triple Achromatic lens shown in the International Exhibition of 1862. This was stated to have an exceptional flat field, and was chosen by Dagron for the exacting task of producing the pellicles for the Paris Pigeon Post in 1871 [17]. No fewer than 16 printed newspaper sheets were copied at a single exposure [18]; and although the maximum aperture was only F/10, readily legible copies of text were reproduced at about 45 diameters reduction right out to the corner of the field (Plate 49). Good results should also be obtained with objectives designed for more critical photographic tasks, such as in photomechanical work. 'Process' objectives, for instance, tend to have reduced spherical aberration and should show no change of focus on stopping down. An interesting catalogue of objectives used in the Möller graticule works was given by Bovey [6]. A few of these are listed in Table 6.

The Leitz Summar and Goerz Hypar objectives were singled out as being particularly good. The latter objective was used for making scales 5 mm long divided into 500 divisions by 3 micron lines: a most meritorious performance. The interest of this list depends on the fact that it describes objectives which have been found suitable for the industrial production of graticules. It should, however, be noted that each lens was a specially picked individual, and thus cannot be assumed to represent the ordinary commercial standard. It is likely that

[1] This design is still used for some high aperture (F/1·9) ciné lenses.

equally suitable objectives could be selected from lenses of similar types produced by non-German manufacturers.

While images with a diagonal of 0·2 in (5 mm) or larger are conveniently made with photographic objectives, the resolution is unlikely to be satisfactory for much smaller images. Really fine lines over a restricted field are more readily obtained with microscope objectives. 'Achromats', representing the less-expensive objectives made by modern manufacturers, are corrected for spherical aberration for only one colour, usually the yellow-green. They thus give satisfactory results on the usual types of commercial extreme-resolution emulsion, which have a pronounced sensitivity peak in this region of the spectrum. Chromatic aberration in achromats is normally corrected for two wavelengths, one in the blue (4,861 Å) and the other in the red (6,563 Å), and these objectives show small changes of focal length between these limits. They are, however, prone to show a rapid

Table 6. Some objectives used in the Möller graticule factory

Manufacture	Name of objective	Focal length in.	Focal length mm.	Aperture
Goerz	Artar	23½	600	F/11
,,	Hypar	1¼	30	F/4·5
Voigtländer	Apo-Collinear	39	1,000	F/12·5
,,	Dinar	4⅔	120	F/6
,,	Altin	1½	35	F/4·5
Leitz	Periplan	6	150	F/10
,,	,,	3½	90	F/3
,,	Summar	3	80	F/4·5
Winkel	Mikroluminar	2	50	Not stated
Zeiss	Mikrotar	1¾	45	F/4·5

change of focal length at shorter wavelengths (violet and ultra-violet), which makes them less suitable for emulsions having most of their sensitivity in this region.

The more expensive 'fluorite' and 'apochromatic' objectives are better corrected for use with a wide band of wavelengths, but cover a smaller field and have to be used with a compensating eyepiece. If they have any advantage, it should be for the making of multi-colour microphotographs.

Some objectives are corrected to bring the near ultra-violet (3,650 Å) and the green (5,461 Å) wavelengths to the same focus, so that they can be focused visually by green light and then used for image formation on ultra-violet-sensitive emulsions. We have already noted that certain combinations of objective and eyepiece have been used to give an increased field in photomicrography, and these may also be valuable for microphotography.

Practical Testing of Objectives

No two objectives have completely identical properties, and the stringent requirements of microphotography may reveal differences of little significance for their ordinary use. The critical user, therefore, has not only to choose a suitable type, but also to select an individual objective. The importance of such a selection is accentuated by the dearth of precise published information on lenses for this work, and by the unusual working conditions and the especially critical performance required. It is, in this connection, interesting to note that Möller's graticule factory made a standard practice of obtaining a number of objectives of a given type, and subjecting them all to a rigorous inspection to select the best [6]. This was done by using the objectives to photograph an image comprising five copies of a fine grid, with one copy in the centre and the others at the corners of the field. The resulting image was closely scrutinized for resolution and image distortion.

The following sections describe tests, requiring no elaborate equipment, which the reader can himself use to determine the suitability of any objective for extreme-resolution work. These tests will also show the conditions giving the best image quality with any particular objective.

EXAMINATION OF IMAGE CONTRAST

While nothing short of actual use for producing photographic images will give a completely reliable indication of the effective resolution of an objective, a valuable preliminary opinion can be obtained by visual inspection of the enlarged image projected on the object plane, when a test object is placed in the image plane. Resolution test images giving line frequencies of 200 lines/mm or more after reduction are now commercially available, and these can be used to examine the contrast and sharpness of the image of lines of different widths projected by the lens. Different lenses could be compared by noting the minimum line widths at which a certain subjective line quality was obtained. Used in this way, a resolution-chart will help to systematize the test. This method of using resolution test-charts is limited by the small area of field which can be examined at any one time, and by available line frequencies which may not be high enough for examination of large-aperture microscope objectives.

In any case, another test object permitting the whole field of the objective to be scanned at one time is also required. For this purpose the objective should be focused on a target whose structure is so fine that differences of image quality between lenses will be clearly apparent. The graininess pattern of a modern high-speed monochrome film uniformly exposed and developed to give a density around 0·5 is excellent for the examination of photographic objectives. For microscope objectives a conventional emulsion layer is too thick. A suitable object is a single-grain layer of photographic-emulsion grains, which can be made from an undeveloped high-speed photographic plate by gently washing most of the emulsion off with hot water. It may be necessary firstly to soften the emulsion by soaking it in equal parts of concentrated nitric acid and water (*an extremely corrosive solution*). So long as the washing is done gently, and no solid is allowed to touch the surface of the plate, it will be found to have retained a very thin film of emulsion grains which provide an ideal test object for our purpose (Plate 13).

Whatever test object is placed in the image plane, it should be illuminated with a condenser or opal screen so that the objective is 'filled' by the cone of light from each point of the object. The enlarged image projected by the objective is inspected with the aid of a ground-glass screen or a focusing magnifier. In the case of microscope objectives this test is particular easy to carry out, since the objective and the test-chart can be mounted on a microscope, and the sub-stage condenser is used to illuminate the target.

Inspection of the projected image will reveal the relative contrast and sharpness of the images of different-sized emulsion grains, and the presence of colour fringes due to chromatic aberration. The same method can be used to examine the alteration of image quality likely to result from such changes as reduction of aperture, use of an eye-piece, change of reduction factor or use of a restricted band of wave-lengths for forming the image. Thus this type of test both enables a suitable objective to be chosen for use in given conditions, and indicates the best working conditions for any one objective. Inspection of the changes of sharpness on moving out from the centre of the field are also easily observed, so that it can be used to show the size of the useful flat field and the approximate position of the axis of the objective (Plate 13).

Assessment of the results of this test must necessarily be subjective, and depends on the judgement of the observer. The beginner may, therefore, feel bewildered and doubt his ability to derive any useful information from it, but experience has to be obtained by practice. The fortunate reader having access to several objectives of similar focal length can soon learn by comparing them with each other. Skill can also be gained by comparing the image quality on and off the axis, refocusing to obtain the greatest sharpness in each zone. It is also most instructive to compare the results given on the axis by one objective used in different conditions. Thus the image, formed by a $\frac{2}{3}$ in (16 mm) objective at a distance of 39 in (99 cm), can be compared with that produced at approximately the same magnification at 10 in (25 cm) from a ×6 eyepiece used with the same objective. The relative image quality given by each of a pair of objectives may be reversed by these changed conditions.

Visual inspection of the enlarged projected image is most likely to give useful information when the objective is to be used for the formation of images by light in the blue-green to red regions of the spectrum. Clearly the method is useless for predicting an objective's performance with ultra-violet sensitive emulsions, and with blue-sensitive emulsions it is less effective because visual acuity to blue light is markedly reduced. In such cases photographic testing must be employed, and the obvious method is to use the objective directly to make microphotographic test images. This is, in any case, the ideal method for confirming the preliminary indications of the visual method.

DETERMINATION OF FOCAL LENGTH AND PREDICTION OF IMAGE SIZE

The focal length of objectives is seldom exactly equal to the nominal figure, and may differ from this by as much as 10 per cent. The error can be quite serious when it is desired to calculate the object-to-image distance required to give a certain image size. A closer approximation to the effective focal length can be found by using the objective to make a microphotograph, or more easily, to project an enlarged image of a stage-micrometer scale. The reduction factor (or enlargement) and the object-to-image distance are then measured as accurately as possible and the values obtained substituted in the formula:

$$f = \frac{D \times R}{(R + 1)^2}$$

where D equals the object-to-image distance
and R equals the reduction factor.

With increasing values of R this formula approximates more and more closely to the simplified form:

$$f = \frac{D}{R + 2}$$

In fact, with reduction factors of 20 or more the error due to the use of the approximate formula is likely to be less than the experimental errors in determining D and R.

When focal lengths are determined in this way, the figures obtained should enable any desired image size to be obtained with an accuracy of about 1 per cent by direct calculation. It is a good plan to measure the reduction factor each time an objective is used at a different distance and plot the measured factors against the object-to-image distance. The reproducibility of this method depends on the precision with which values of D can be repeated. Even with the simple negative holder and optical bench described in Chapter 6, it is possible to produce the required image size straight away, with an accuracy chiefly limited by the image distortion of the lens.

METHOD OF USE

We have, in this chapter, discussed a number of ways in which the performance of objectives departs from the ideal. The effect of these deficiencies can be kept to a minimum by selecting the best conditions for high resolution. This is done mainly by avoiding conditions which tend to increase the aberrations shown by the objective.

DIRECTION OF OBJECTIVE

Among opticians it is common knowledge that a lens can only be completely corrected for one distance. This means that the greatest freedom from aberrations, and hence the sharpest image, will only be obtained with one fixed pair of conjugate foci for each objective. Since the initial production of microphotographic images is always achieved by producing a reduced image, the emulsion-to-lens distance will always be less than the object distance, and the ratio of the distances (i.e. the reduction factor) should theoretically have a fixed value for each lens. In addition most lenses are asymmetrical about a plane at right angles to the axis, and only give the best result when facing the right way. *It is most important to ensure that the correct end of the objective faces the nearer conjugate focus (i.e. the emulsion); and this rule must be observed whatever the direction in which the objective is customarily used.* Thus microscope objectives are normally employed to form an enlarged image of a small object, and the R.M.S. thread (see Fig. 42) points towards the large image. When used for microphotography the thread must still point towards the further conjugate focus. It is immaterial that a large object is now placed there, and that a reduced image is formed at the nearer focus. Similarly the short focal-length objectives used with narrow-gauge ciné cameras are used with the engraved side of the mount facing the further conjugate focus, while the thread faces the emulsion. If used with a microscope for microphotography, such a lens must be mounted so that the engraved side points up the microscope tube, and thus still faces the original placed at the further conjugate focus. The fact that the thread normally used for mounting the objective cannot conveniently be used is a necessary but inconvenient fact.

REDUCTION FACTOR PERMISSIBLE WITH DIFFERENT OBJECTIVES

Although the best resolution obtainable with any objective is in theory only secured at one reduction factor, some departure from the ideal conditions may in practice give satisfactory results. In fact the production of microphotographic images with lenses designed for other purposes sometimes involves discovering what liberties can be taken without incurring too serious a loss of image quality.

Lenses used in general-purpose and hand-held cameras are often designed for use at object distances from 25 feet (8 metres) to infinity, and might be expected to show increased aberrations when used to reproduce objects at the smaller distances necessitated by the limited space in most work-rooms. Enlarging and photomechanical 'process' lenses, on the other hand, are generally computed to give their best results at working distances of 10 feet or less, with correspondingly smaller reduction factors. Since they were never intended for the rigorous test involved in microphotographic work, a fixed reduction for the best performance is usually not specified. In the case of objectives like the special Wray F/4 3-in Copying Lens or the Ultra-Micro Nikkor's, however, the designs were specifically computed for one reduction factor. With such lenses it would be silly to depart appreciably from the manufacturer's recommendation.[1]

The high aperture and exact corrections of microscope objectives makes them sensitive to any departure from the optimum conditions. In fact, for microscopy, an objective should ideally be used at only one magnification, normally corresponding to the formation of the primary enlarged image at the end of a tube of length $6\frac{1}{2}$ in (160 mm). Moreover, most microscope objectives are designed for the inspection of specimens mounted under a cover-glass. Appreciable departure from either of these conditions introduces spherical aberration. Martin and Johnson [19] show how spherical aberration can be recognized by the uneven appearance of the patches of light formed by projecting an enlarged image of a 'pinhole' in a silver mirror, and adjusting the focus to positions slightly inside or outside the correct focus.

The production of the primary image at a distance of 160 mm ($6\frac{1}{2}$ in) as demanded by orthodox microscopic practice is often

[1] The designer of the Wray Lens has, however, said that a change of ±5 per cent, with respect to the designed reduction factor, would not be expected to produce a detectable decline in performance.

inconvenient for microphotography, since it involves small reduction factors and the consequent use of inconveniently small transparencies. Thus if a 1 in (25 mm) objective is required to make an image 1 mm (0·04 in) high, the reduction at 6½ in will only be about six diameters, and the transparency must be only ¼ in (6 mm) high. Such an image is too small, since exceptional care would be needed to produce the perfection desirable in an intermediate transparency for microphotography (Chapter 7).

Experience has shown that surprisingly good resolution can be obtained with suitably chosen microscope objectives used at distances at least up to 39 in (1 metre). The image quality given by 'low-power' objectives of focal length greater than ½ in (12 mm) does not seem to suffer too severe degradation from the use of these 'incorrect' conditions. The author has even obtained images resolving more than 1,500 lines per millimetre by using a ⅙ in (4 mm) achromatic objective of N.A. 0·85 at a distance of 26 in (65 cm). This excellent performance under 'incorrect' conditions was probably due to two facts. Martin and Johnson [19] point out that longer tube lengths may be used to compensate for the absence of a cover-glass. In fact, the error due to excessive working distance is at least partly compensated by the absence of a cover-glass. Moreover, the objective was an individual specimen specially chosen for use with these greater distances. It was found that a pair of 4 mm (⅙ in) objectives by the same reputable manufacturer gave very different image quality when examined by projection of the enlarged image of emulsion grains. When tested by making microphotographs, corresponding differences were found, although both objectives gave excellent images when they were used correctly with an eyepiece. The explanation is that microscope objectives are still largely hand-made articles. Hence no two individuals are absolutely identical, and some must therefore be better suited for use in microphotographic conditions. It is just this sort of fact which makes a rapid visual method so useful for assessing probable suitability for microphotography.

USE OF AN EYEPIECE

We have, so far, assumed that microscope objectives will be used without an eyepiece; but many microphotographers prefer to use one. The arguments for using or omitting it do not yet seem to have been resolved. With an eyepiece, the length of bench required to achieve a given reduction factor is substantially lessened. This simplifies the task of constructing and mounting an adequately rigid bench (see p. 159), and is particularly desirable for use with a vertical bench. In addition some modern photomicrographic objectives are designed for use with field-flattening eyepieces. When it is essential to obtain the largest possible field containing lines of a given width, use of a suitable objective-eyepiece combination would seem to be indicated.

In spite of all this, there is no doubt that excellent images have been (and can be) made by using a microscope objective without an eyepiece. The longer working distance diminishes the need to employ an objective adjusted for use without a cover-glass. Use of an eyepiece also complicates the precise calculation of the working distance needed to obtain a given image size. Another difficulty is that eye-pieces contain glass/air surfaces which are very close to the longer conjugate focus of the objective. Because of this, out-of-focus images of diffraction patterns from dirt in an eyepiece can be imaged near the microphotographic object plane. This phenomenon can be readily seen when using a microscope for visual observation of an object, such as a stage-micrometer, having large clear areas. Unless the eyepiece has been cleaned with extreme care, unsharp images of dirt are recognizable when the eyepiece is rotated. It can be argued that avoidance of this trouble is an everyday feature of photomicrographic technique; but if the usual high-contrast extreme-resolution emulsion is used for making microphotographs, the results of residual dirt will be exaggerated. Working without an eyepiece means complete free-dom from this particular difficulty.

ADJUSTMENT OF APERTURE

In the section on resolving power, we saw that the resolution limit of a perfect lens is determined by its aperture. From the approximate formula (p. 105), one can calculate that a lens of aperture F/2·8 should be able to separate lines 1·54 μ apart, and give a resolution of around 650 lines/mm. When stopped down to F/5·6, F/11 and F/22, resolution limits of about 320, 160 and 80 lines/mm should be res-pectively obtained. Even the lowest of these figures is adequate for many photographic purposes, since the resultant negative should give very satisfactory sharpness when enlarged five diameters. In these circumstances it is natural that little thought need be given to the effect of stopping down on resolution. In fact, with modern automatic 'snapshot' cameras, control of the aperture is delegated to a photocell, and is decided solely on the amount of light and the shutter speed to be used.

For microphotography, of course, any reduction of resolution pro-duced by stopping down will be detected by the extreme-resolution emulsion and will decrease the sharpness of the final image. With photographic objectives, however, the greatest aberrations generally come from the marginal zones of the lens; and the initial reduction of aberrations by stopping down one or two stops more than compensates for the reduction of theoretical resolving power. It follows that the objective's best performance will be given by an aperture which reduces aberrations without too great a loss of resolution. The best results with photographic objectives are usually given by an aperture between 1 and 2 stops (on the 'F' scale) smaller than the maximum. To guard against changes of focus resulting from spherical aberration (see above), objectives used for extreme-resolution work should always be focused at the aperture used for actual image formation. This differs from the common photographic practice of focusing at full aperture, and stopping down before exposure.

Appreciable stopping down of correctly-used microscope objectives should always result in a loss of resolution; but a small reduction of aperture may improve the image contrast by reducing the intensity of the flare light. Reduction of the aperture may also be used to increase the area of the useful field obtainable with any objective. Few microscope objectives are fitted with an iris diaphragm, but their aperture can be reduced by placing a disc of black paper with a carefully centered hole of suitable size on top of the back component of the objective.

REFERENCES

[1] *The British Journal Photographic Almanac*, 'Appendix on Optical Calculations'. This information is reprinted year after year.

[2] Kingslake, R., *Lenses in Photography*, A. S. Barnes and Co. Inc. (New York, revised edition, 1963).

[3] Martin, L. C. and Johnson, B. K., *Practical Microscopy*, Blackie and Son (Glasgow, 1931), p. 39.

[4] Shadbolt, G., 'On the Mode of Producing Extremely Minute Photographs for Microscopical Examination', *Phot. J.*, 4, 79, 1857.

[5] Altman, J. H. Private Communication.

[6] Bovey, E., B.I.O.S. report 1552, p. 46 (see reference [22], Chapter 2).

[7] Cook, G. H., 'Miniature Camera Lenses', *Phot. J.*, 89A, 219, 1949.

[8] Selwyn, E. W. H. and Tearle, J. L., 'The Performance of Aircraft Camera Lenses', *Proc. Phys. Soc.*, 43, 496, 1946.

[9] Perrin, F. H. and Altman, J. H., 'Studies in the Resolving Power of Photographic Emulsions. III. The Effect of the Relative Aperture of the Camera Lens on the Measured Value', *J. Opt. Soc. Am.*, 41, 1038, 1949.

[10] Higgins, G. C. and Jones, L. A., *J. Soc. Mot. Pict. Tel. Eng.*, 58, 277, 1952 (see reference [13], Chapter 2).

[11] Frieser, H., 'Die Photographischer Auflösung von Strichrastern in Abhängigkeit von der Beschaffenheit der Raster', *Z. Wiss. Phot.*, 37, 261, 1938.

[12] Baker, L. R., 'How Good can a Lens be', *Perspective*, 6, 133, 1964.

[13] (a) Bates, W. J., 'S.I.R.A./Beck Equipment for Measuring Optical Transfer Functions', *J. Sci. Instruments*, **42**, 538, 1965.
(b) *Equipment for Measuring the Response of Optical Systems*, pamphlet issued by R. and J. Beck Ltd, Watford, England.

[14] Fromm, H. J., 'Factors Influencing Microimage Quality', *J. Phot. Sci.*, **10**, 147, 1962.

[15] Koana, Z. and Wakimoto, Z., 'Lenses for Ultra-Microphotography', *Jap. J. Appl. Opt.*, **4** (Supplement 1), 113, 1965.

[16] Allen, R. M., *Photomicrography*, D. Van Nostrand (New York, 2nd edition, 1958), page 319.

[17] Angers, G. W., Translation of, *Memoir on the Photographic and Administrative section on the Service of Dispatching by Carrier Pigeons*, by De La Follye, 1871. Published G. W. Angers (Springfield, Massachusetts, 1952).

[18] Stevens, G. W. W., 'Microphotography since 1839', *Phot. J.*, **90B**, 150, 1950.

[19] Martin, L. C. and Johnson, B. K., as reference [3], page 21.

[20] Spectra-Physics, *Data Sheet. Model 500 Copy Lens* (Mountain View, California, U.S.A.).

5 · Establishment and Maintenance of Focus

One of the essential problems to be solved when making extreme-resolution microphotographs is that of establishing and maintaining the exact focus. Methods which are normally used successfully, even in an exacting field such as 'miniature' photography, are of comparatively little use. The difficulty can be readily understood, when one realizes that the 'circle of confusion' which has to be specified for microphotography is necessarily much smaller than that required for any other type of photographic work. Let us take a numerical example. With a camera lens of focal length 2 in (50 mm), a circle of confusion of one two-thousandth of the focal length (i.e. 0·001 in or 25μ) would be considered reasonably satisfactory. This is equivalent to a resolution figure of less than 40 lines/mm. With an extreme-resolution emulsion, however, a good miniature-camera objective should be found to give an axial resolution approaching 300 lines/mm. This is equivalent to a circle of confusion about eight times smaller than the previous figure. A number of practical consequences can be deduced from this example:

(a) The depth of focus at the emulsion surface will necessarily be much shallower than when the same lens is used with less critical emulsions (Fig. 24).

(b) The structure of even the finest ground-glass screen is so coarse that it can only be employed for making preliminary rough adjustments.

(c) The registration by which the emulsion is repeatedly located in a predetermined plane has to be effected with greater precision.

For reasons such as these, refined methods of focusing are essential for microphotography. In spite of this, success can be easily achieved by a careful analysis of the problem followed by adoption of adequately designed procedures. The problem of ensuring sharp focus can then be conveniently divided into the optical problem of establishing focus and the mechanical problem of maintaining it. Several solutions of each problem are available. The matter is so vital for this work that

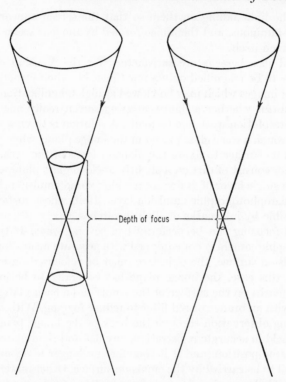

Fig. 24 *Reduction of Depth of Focus in Microphotography*
Depth of focus is reduced in proportion to smaller 'circle of confusion' recordable by extreme-resolution emulsion.

no apology need be made for describing these methods, and their merits, in some detail.

Establishing Focus

The focus (or plane of sharpest image formation) should be placed at or just below the emulsion surface (Chapter 8). This adjustment can only be made with certainty when sufficiently sensitive means are used both for observing the results of focusing adjustments, and for moving the plane of the aerial image relative to the emulsion layer.

DIRECT VISUAL OBSERVATION OF THE FOCUSING OPERATION

An easy and convenient method of observing the focusing operation in normal photography is to employ a ground-glass screen in which one side of a glass plate is covered with innumerable glass pits. These scatter the light falling on them so that the screen appears as if it were self-luminous, and the image formed by the lens seems to reside in the screen itself.

Ground-glass screens are satisfactory for the focusing of images which are to be magnified only a few times, but their structure is too coarse for images which may be viewed at high magnifications. In fact it is doubtful whether a light-scattering screen really adequate for extreme-resolution work can be made. A solution is to view the aerial image through a clear glass placed in the image plane, while using fine detail on its surface to fixate the plane of focus of the eyes. The fine detail may consist of dirt on a slightly unclean glass plate, or a plate bearing a single layer of grains from a high-speed emulsion (Plate 13), or the microphotographic emulsion layer itself, whose surface can be made visible by ink marks or slight scratches.

Visual focusing can be performed in several ways. If the microphotographic camera is not equipped with accurate means for locating the emulsion surface, the objective must be refocused on each plate used. In this case, the image plane has generally to be located by viewing marks on the surface of the emulsion on each plate, and this is done with an orange or red filter to reduce fogging. With apparatus permitting observation through the back of the image plane while a plate is held in accurate registration, any flat and rigid plate will take up the same position, and it is therefore no longer necessary for the fine detail to be carried by the emulsion surface. Other materials, such as the single layer of grains or a fogged plate, can be used for fixing the focus of the eyes, and plenty of light of any suitable visible wavelength can then be used without risk of fogging the sensitive plates. Whatever type of layer is used to fixate the focus of the eyes, an effective method must be employed to magnify the fine detail, so that focusing can be accomplished with the necessary accuracy.

OBSERVATION THROUGH THE BACK OF THE PLATE

A microscope directed at the back of the plate may be used to observe the focusing operation. For this purpose the aperture of the viewing objective must be at least as great as that of the image-forming objective. If it is smaller the focusing operation will be relatively uncritical and less able to allow for any residual aberrations in the image-forming objective (Fig. 25). It is also desirable to employ a magnification rather greater than that likely to be used for inspecting the final microphotographs, so that small errors of focusing are less likely to show in the final result.

The viewing microscope must be held quite rigidly and steady relative to the image plane. For this reason the use of a separate microscope involves some elaboration of the apparatus, and may only prove profitable in large-scale commercial work. The Möller graticule factory, for instance, employed focusing microscopes not only for focusing but for checking the size of the reduced aerial images as well [1].

A simpler method, described by Shadbolt as early as 1857 [2], was

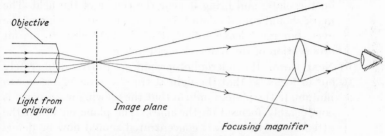

Fig. 25 *Visual Focusing at the Image Plane*

The magnifier shown will only accept light from the central zones of the objective, and focusing will tend to be inaccurate.

to mount the image-forming objective in the condenser holder of a microscope, and lay the emulsion-coated plate face downwards on the stage. The ordinary objective and eyepiece of the same microscope was then used to examine the focus. This method should allow the owner of a microscope to commence making microphotographs with a minimum of preparation, so long as the microphotographic objective is aligned and centred with sufficient care (see Chapter 6).

THE TECHNIQUE OF VISUAL FOCUSING

During infancy, we learn to adjust the focus of our eyes according to the distance of the object viewed, and the resultant accommodation of focus becomes automatic and involuntary. For microphotography this skill can be an embarrassing acquisition. As an example, the difficulty experienced by an engineer starting to make graticules can be quoted. His method was to select a glass plate of exactly the same thickness as an emulsion-coated plate. With the glass plate in position a microscope was focused carefully on the image plane occupied by the front surface of this plate. The glass plate was then replaced by the emulsion-coated plate, and the image-forming objective was focused until a sharp aerial image was seen through the microscope objective. Not only was this method clumsy, but it overlooked the fact that the eyes will automatically accommodate for small errors of focus when viewing an aerial image. It is for this reason that suitable details, such as ink lines, which are visible throughout the focusing operation, must be provided to fixate the focus of the eyes. Even then, the accuracy can be seriously reduced if the focus of the eyes is allowed to jump alternately between the emulsion surface and the aerial image. With a little practice, the following technique should overcome this difficulty.

(i) First use the viewing microscope to locate a focusing mark on the plate, and bring it near the centre of the field. The mark should contain detail requiring critical focusing of the eyes, but must leave sufficient of the field clear to permit observation of the reduced aerial image.

(ii) Next throw the microphotographic objective deliberately out of focus, so that the light it transmits merely serves to illuminate the plate. Confirm that the viewing microscope is comfortably focused on the mark. The plane on which the attention of the eyes is concentrated should now be determined only by the position of the plate surface.

(iii) Adjust the microphotographic objective until the aerial image appears sharp, in the meantime keeping the focus of the eyes locked on the emulsion surface. The focus should now be correct.

An alternative method is to proceed as above, and when both the image and emulsion surface can be clearly seen, move the eye a small distance sideways. The focus will be correctly adjusted when there is no apparent movement of the aerial image relative to the emulsion surface. This method, known as 'focusing by parallax', is frequently described in works on optics and photomicrography. In the author's experience it is no more accurate and definitely more tiring than the procedure described above. It also has the additional disadvantage that small relative movements of the images may be caused by errors in the optical system, and these tend to confuse and lessen the sensitivity of the parallax test for critical focus.

OBSERVATION FROM THE FRONT OF THE PLATE

The use of a separate microscope for inspecting the emulsion surface is by no means essential. Most optical systems are reversible, and the objective used to form the minute images can also be used to project an enlarged image of the emulsion surface back on the object plane (Fig. 26). When this enlarged image is in focus at the object plane, the object plane will in turn be correctly focused at the emulsion surface. Even with this method the author prefers to use a transparent screen at the object plane, viewing the aerial image as described in the preceding section. This is because the depth of field at the object plane

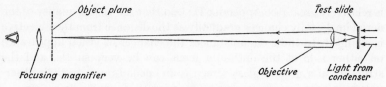

Fig. 26 *Focusing by projecting the Image Plane back on the Object Plane*

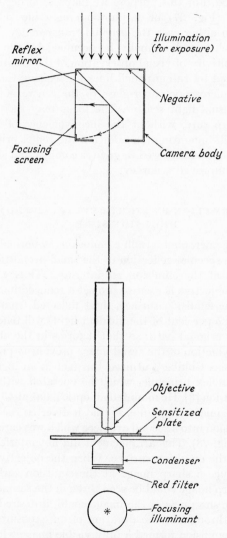

Fig. 27 *Reflex Focusing Method*

Use of body of reflex camera to hold negative and focus by back projection.

is relatively great (see Appendix IIA), so that the visible quality of the aerial image only changes gradually as the distance from the objective is changed. In these circumstances the changes of visual appearance on either side of the optimum focus can be very subtle, and the structure of a ground-glass screen is an encumbrance to their observation.

The principle of the reflex camera can be used to facilitate this focusing method. For this purpose we may use either the body of a reflex camera (Fig. 27) or a photomicrographic side-tube reflex attachment. In either case the original transparency is mounted in the plane which would normally be occupied by the photographic plate. The sensitivity of visual observation of the ground-glass screen can be improved by ruling pencil lines for fixating the visual focus, and oiling a microscope cover-glass to the centre of the screen to suppress the usual light scatter. The focus may then be inspected before each exposure, without the inconvenience of removing the original from its mounting. In addition the reflex principle usually allows the screen to be viewed in greater comfort and should thereby contribute to improved accuracy.

OBSERVATION BY LIGHT REFLECTED FROM THE EMULSION SURFACE

The surface of microphotographic emulsions is normally sufficiently perfect to give specular reflection of the small proportion of incident light reflected at the emulsion/air interface. Thus when a microphotographic objective is used to project a reduced image of a transparency on the emulsion surface, light reflected from the emulsion (usually about 5 per cent of the incident light) will tend to be turned back along its original path, so that it forms in the object plane an enlarged reproduction of the aerial image previously projected on the emulsion surface. Goldberg utilized this fact in an ingenious modification of the reflex principle, which he operated with his collodion print-out emulsion [3]. He mounted an optical flat at 45 degrees to the axis across the microscope tube, so that it diverted the light reflected from the emulsion into a second eyepiece which was carefully matched to the first (Fig. 28). This arrangement did not interfere with image formation at the emulsion surface. When the objective was focused so as to produce a sharp image at the emulsion surface, a correspondingly sharp image could be seen through the second eyepiece. By this means the sharpness of the image could, if desired, be inspected continuously throughout the duration of an exposure. In addition, the print-out emulsion formed a fully visible image without development, so that its density could be inspected at any stage by interrupting the exposure and using the condenser of the microscope to illuminate the emulsion with red light.

Goldberg pointed out that this system could not be used with oil- or water-immersion objectives, since insufficient reflection would

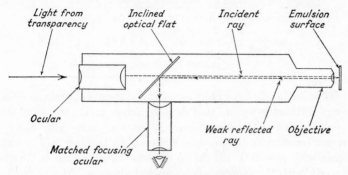

Fig. 28 *Goldberg's Reflex Method*

An optical flat mounted in the microscope tube diverted light reflected at the emulsion/air interface.

occur at an emulsion surface in contact with these liquids, and no image would therefore be seen through the viewing eyepiece. The method of focusing by the small proportion of the image-forming light reflected from the emulsion surface can also be used with split-beam photomicrographic cameras of the type which are mounted directly on the tube of the microscope.

PHOTOGRAPHIC-FOCUSING TESTS

Although the visual methods described above provide direct means for observing the changes in the aerial image produced by the focusing operation, only photographic tests can demonstrate precisely how these changes will affect the final image. The most reliable method is to inspect a series of photographic images produced with different focus settings, but this can only be done with equipment allowing the emulsion to be placed repeatedly with great precision at a fixed distance from the objective (see below). The equipment must also be designed and manipulated so that the emulsion-to-objective distance can be reproducibly altered by very small amounts. These should be sufficiently small to allow two or three settings around the correct focus to give almost equally sharp images, but yet large enough to enable changes of image quality to be observed on each side of the focus without having to make too many images in any one series. The increments of distance shown in Table 7 are intended to serve as a rough guide.

Table 7. Size of increments for photographic-focusing tests

| Objective | Focal length | Suggested focusing increment | |
		Thousandths of an inch	Microns
Photographic	4 in (100 mm)	1·0	25
,,	2 in (50 mm)	0·5	12
Microscope	2 in (50 mm)	0·5–0·25	12–6
,,	1 in (25 mm)	0·2–0·1	5–2
,,	⅙ in (4 mm)	0·2–0·04	5–1

It is important that the photographic test should contain a sufficient range of settings to ensure that definite deterioration can be detected on each side of the correct focus. A series of images in which the sharpness continues to improve right up to the last image cannot indicate with certainty whether optimum sharpness has in fact been achieved. With the increments suggested above a series of from five to ten images should prove adequate.

A photographic-focusing test made in this way provides a permanent record not only of the position of sharpest focus but also of the variation on each side. It is thus possible to set the focus to the position giving the greatest working latitude. In addition, it shows how the effective field covered can be influenced by the focus, and is particularly useful in cases where the field covered by the objective is barely sufficient. Careful study of a focusing test may permit the selection of a compromise setting effectively covering a slightly larger field. Examination of focusing tests also enables the operator to visualize the consequences of any adjustments made. They are thus an invaluable aid to the improvement of microphotographic technique (see Chapter 8, pp. 209–14).

APPLICATION OF VISUAL AND PHOTOGRAPHIC OBSERVATIONS

It should not be thought that the visual and photographic methods for observing the focusing operation are mutually exclusive. In all visual methods, focusing should, as far as possible, be effected with light of the colour to be used for image formation. Residual chromatic aberration of the objective may otherwise cause a significant separation between the planes of visual and photographic focus (see Chapter 4). When visual focusing is observed by the light used for exposing the emulsion, fogging of the emulsion can be prevented in various ways. With Goldberg's method, an approximate focus could be found by using the microscope condenser to illuminate the plate with red light [3]. The sensitivity of his emulsion was so low, that he could then adjust the focus with the exposing light before a significant image could be formed by the out-of-focus beam. With the faster micro-photographic emulsions this is not possible, and fogging of the emulsion in the area selected for image formation can be avoided by focusing at one end of the plate and moving a fresh area of emulsion into position before exposure. This method is subject to errors arising from the imperfect flatness of the glass. These difficulties vanish when equipment is available for locating the emulsion surface at a precisely fixed distance from the objective: the emulsion-coated plate is then simply replaced by any convenient focusing target.

When measures have been taken to avoid the above mentioned pitfalls, visual focusing is undeniably quick and convenient. To obtain the finest results, however, certainly demands considerable skill. Photographic focusing, on the other hand, substitutes methodical operation for personal skill, and has the advantage of permitting the focus to be judged by observation of the finally desired result. Thus it can be seen that visual focusing will save much time if used to obtain a provisional adjustment before making a photographic test. Photographic focusing can provide the ultimate precision of control, which is so necessary when working tolerances are reduced by the fineness of the required image, or the size of the field to be covered.

ADJUSTMENT OF FOCUS

The present chapter has, so far, dealt with the methods used for observing the focusing adjustment, since without sufficiently sensitive observation the finest microphotographic camera would be of little use. We must now consider how the actual focusing adjustment can be performed with the necessary smoothness and sensitivity.

ADJUSTMENT OF THE OBJECT DISTANCE

Exact focusing in many optical instruments depends on the employment of mechanisms designed for making sufficiently small adjustments of the objective-to-image-plane distance. For instance, double-extension plate cameras were commonly fitted with rack-and-pinion motions which could be adjusted to a series of discrete positions by pushing in the focusing knob. The increments of focus so provided were adequately small, even when such a camera was used with 'Process' plates, but the motion was definitely too coarse when extreme-resolution plates were used. In microscopes the coarse rack-and-pinion movement is only adequate for the lower power objectives, and much attention has been given to the design of fine-focusing mechanisms giving small movements very smoothly. In our case, however, the problem is more difficult, since the ultimate success of the focusing operation can only be judged when the microphotographs themselves are inspected; whereas with visual use of a microscope, changes in image quality resulting from focusing are immediately apparent.

In microphotography the adjustment of the focus can be made directly by altering the emulsion-to-objective distance, or indirectly by moving the original to or from the camera, as described in Chapter 1. The variations of emulsion-to-objective distance need to be so small that the direct method can only be used with apparatus having a good micrometer-focusing movement. In contrast to this, relatively large alterations in the distance from the original to the camera can, as Nicholls showed in 1860 [4], easily give the precision needed. The table in Appendix IIA shows how minute are the changes in emulsion-to-objective distance following quite substantial changes in the distance of the original transparency.

The success of this method depends on the fact that, for small movements of the original, the change in the image-to-objective distance equals the movement of the original divided by the square of the degree of reduction. Thus if an image is being reduced thirty diameters, a small movement of the original will change the objective-to-image by one-nine-hundredth of the distance moved: 0·5 in (12·5 mm) movements (for example) will alter the focus by just over 0·0005 in (12μ). This method of calculating approximate changes of objective-to-image distance is simple enough for mental arithmetic, and is extreme useful.

As already indicated, the focusing mechanism of ordinary photographic cameras may be found insufficiently sensitive for use with extreme-resolution emulsions. With such equipment, a convenient method is to use the focusing mechanism *only* for rough focusing. The correct focus can then be found with any desired degree of precision by changing the distance of the original. With this procedure it is not generally possible to secure sharp focus with the transparency placed at the exact position calculated to give a desired image size, and exact image size should therefore be adjusted by altering the size of the transparency.

ADDITIONAL LIMITATIONS OF 'ORDINARY' PHOTOGRAPHIC CAMERAS

While fairly fine images can be obtained by the careful use of ordinary photographic equipment, the reader should realize that extreme-resolution work demands a standard of precision for which conventional cameras are never designed. Such precision would, in fact, be largely wasted on the relatively low-resolution high-speed emulsions normally used in such cameras.

Our special requirements may show that the rigidity of folding cameras is unsatisfactory, particularly if the camera has been worn by much use. Difficulty from this source can be minimized by leaving the camera open throughout any one set of exposures. Care should also be taken to avoid shifting the camera-front while adjusting the diaphragm or setting the shutter. With plate cameras the registration between the focusing screen and the plate-holders, and even between successive plate-holders, may, for our purpose, not be sufficiently accurate. An obvious precaution is therefore to use a single plate-holder for all photographic-focusing tests as well as for making the final exposures. Moreover, the objective normally fitted will only be found to cover a small area in the centre of the plate while giving the resolution needed for extreme-resolution work. The important part of the image will thus be formed well away from the edges of the plate, where the emulsion surface is usually registered. Lack of flatness of photographic glass plates can, in these conditions, cause a random variation in sharpness. This trouble has been avoided with the wet-collodion process by coating the emulsion on plate glass, and stripping the processed images for transfer to their final support [5].

The use of flexible film instead of glass plates introduces further problems caused by bending and buckling of the film. Cures are to fix extra registration supports in the camera, so that the film is supported as close as possible around the region of image formation; or to hold the film flat with a vacuum back.

Maintenance of Focus

Although some workers may prefer to adjust the focus visually just before each exposure, this can only be done at all conveniently if a reflex-focusing device is used. This method is even then wasteful of effort and time. It is generally more satisfactory to construct apparatus which will maintain the focus within fine limits, so that many exposures can be made without readjustment of the instrument. Although the permissible tolerances are small, correct design allows accurate results to be obtained with simple, and sometimes apparently crude equipment.

The reader wishing either to make large numbers of extreme-resolution images, or to explore the potentialities of microphotography to the limit, should obtain apparatus capable:

(i) of locating the emulsion surface in a given plane with a precision of at least 2 microns (0·00008 in), and

(ii) of allowing reproducible variations of the emulsion-to-objective distance to be made in increments of 10 microns (0·0004 in) down to 1 micron (0·00004 in), according to the depth of focus of the objective used.

To meet these specifications it is necessary to consider such factors as the lack of flatness of glass plates, and the influences of dust, thermal expansion and the bending of apparently rigid structures under quite small loads [6]. In spite of these formidable requirements, the following sections will show how the necessary performance can be simply obtained by adapting existing equipment or construction of special apparatus. The important thing to notice is that the necessary precision is obtained more by attention to certain critical factors in the design, than by demanding exceptional skill from the constructor.

SPECIALLY DESIGNED APPARATUS

In the following sections we shall consider apparatus which has been designed to overcome these limitations. It is not difficult to make equipment whereby the emulsion surface can be repeatedly located in a fixed plane relative to the objective with a precision of plus or

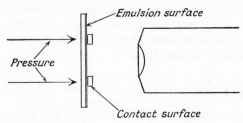

Fig. 29 *Basic Method for Accurate Location of Emulsion Surface*

minus a micron. A general form of such apparatus is diagrammatically described by Fig. 29. The plane of focus is fixed by a contact surface situated as close as possible to the axis of the objective. The emulsion is pressed against this surface by a force ideally acting only opposite the contact surface. This basic arrangement is suitable for obtaining both rapid working and extreme precision. One overriding advantage is that it permits uncontrolled variations of register to be eliminated almost completely. Thus when determining the best conditions for making an image, variations of image quality are likely to be due to differences in emulsion properties or exposure level or development, but the interpretation of the results cannot be confused by random and unexpected changes of focus.

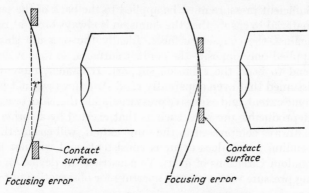

Fig. 30 *Spacing of Contact Surfaces*

The closer are the contact surfaces to the point of image formation, the less will be the focusing error produced by curvature of the emulsion.

The following points should be considered when working out details in the design of apparatus of this general form:

(1) The contact surfaces should be located as close as practicable to the site of image formation. Fig. 30 shows how this minimizes errors due to lack of flatness in the emulsion support, whether it be glass or film. With objectives having sufficient working distance between the objective and the emulsion, the contact surface can be brought very close to the image. In other cases, where the working distance is too small to admit the structure supporting the contact surfaces, a space has to be left between the surfaces to allow the objective to be brought sufficiently close to the emulsion. This is, unfortunately, mainly necessary with high-power objectives, with which the greatest precision of focus is needed.

(2) The contact surfaces should be large enough to prevent serious damage to the emulsion surface (i.e. they should not be 'pinpoints'), but if too large will unnecessarily increase the danger of trapping dust. Either a small circle close to the axis of the objective, or three small surfaces equidistant from the axis and spaced at 120°, are convenient arrangements. The edges should be rounded so that the emulsion is not scratched when the sensitive material is moved laterally. In the most advanced apparatus, damage is completely avoided by pneumatic gauging (see below).

(3) The structure supporting the contact surfaces, and hence determining its distance from the objective, must be sufficiently rigid to prevent appreciable distortion when the emulsion is pressed against the surfaces.

(4) Sufficient pressure must be applied to the back of the sensitive material to ensure that the emulsion is always brought right up against the contact surfaces. Ideally the pressure should be applied only opposite the contact surfaces, so that it does not tend to bend the emulsion support. It cannot, moreover, be assumed that even apparently rigid structures will not bend to some extent, and excessive pressure should therefore be avoided. Reproducible pressure, such as that exerted by a spring which is always compressed to the same extent, will ensure that any bending which does occur is consistent, and will not lead to random variations of focus. To construct the device for applying pressure with a central aperture for observation of focus, is a useful refinement.

(5) The emulsion should be kept away from the contact surfaces when the plate is moved laterally between exposures, or on insertion of a new plate. This precaution lessens the risk of the focus being changed by debris from the emulsion surface piling up on the contact surface, and also prevents damage to both the contact surfaces and the emulsion. The sensitive material generally has to be supported so that the plates can be moved laterally in order to bring any desired area of the emulsion surface opposite the objective. This has to be done in such a way that the plate is still quite free to move up against the contact surfaces. If this movement is not perfectly free, the plate (or other support) may be held back, so that the emulsion surface is able to touch only one side of the contact surface. This can cause intermittent trouble, and since failure to satisfy this requirement can lead to perplexing (and time-consuming) variations of image sharpness, it merits particularly careful attention.

By complying with the conditions listed above, errors of registration will have been eradicated at their source. Descriptions of some actual working systems will now show how these principles can be put into practice.

DISTANCE PIECES GIVING A FIXED EMULSION-TO-OBJECTIVE SEPARATION

Goldberg fitted a microscope objective with an accurately made tube of such a length that an object at a fixed distance was brought into focus when the emulsion was pressed against the contact surface on the lower end of the tube [3]. Such tubes are known as distance pieces, and represent a simple and effective means for converting any microscope into a microphotographic camera.

The end of the tube facing the objective has to be located against some suitable reference surface on the outside of the objective mount: fortunately most objectives bear a flange conveniently placed for this purpose (Fig. 31). It is clear that the distance piece can only give precise location of the emulsion surface, if its top surface and the flange on the objective are kept absolutely free from dust. Any dirt is likely to produce a significant increase in the distance from the objective to the plane of the contact surfaces. There is, therefore, a definite risk that the focus will be slightly altered every time the distance piece is removed from the objective. Experience has shown

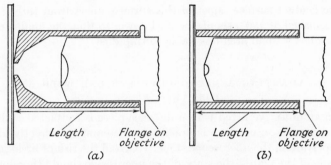

Fig. 31 *Designs for Distance Pieces*

(a) 'Salt-cellar' distance piece for medium-power objectives with adequate working distances.

(b) Tubular construction necessitated by small working distance of high-power objectives.

that this risk is not serious with objectives down to $\frac{2}{3}$ in (16 mm) focal length, or with N.A. values up to 0·30. In such cases the distance piece may be made to give a smooth sliding fit over the outside of the objective, and may be removed and replaced with little fear of disturbing the focus. With objectives of shorter focal length and higher numerical aperture, frequent removal of the distance piece is most inadvisable. In such cases it may be protected against accidental disturbance by moistening the inside surface of the distance piece with a shellac solution before it is finally pressed into position on the objective. A more drastic but most effective method is to cut a thread on the outside of the barrel of the objective mount and on the inside of the distance piece, so that the distance piece can be firmly screwed into position. An objective, permanently fitted with such a distance piece for microphotography without an eyepiece, can still be used for ordinary microscopy. The working distance of the objective, when used with an ocular for visual microscopy, is substantially greater than for microphotography with 'tube-lengths' much longer than $6\frac{1}{2}$ in

(160 mm). The distance piece does not, therefore, prevent the objective from being focused on the specimen.

The working distance of long focal-length objectives (down to $\frac{1}{2}$ in or 12 mm) leaves plenty of room for the insertion of a fairly substantial structure between the front of the objective and the emulsion surface. The distance piece can then be made rather after the pattern of the top of a salt-cellar, so that the contact surface is placed very close to the site of image formation (Fig. 31). The smaller working distance of higher-power and shorter focal-length objectives leaves insufficient space for this type of construction. The distance piece must then take the form of a straight tube with the lower end acting as the contact surface. Most of this surface, apart from three small facets spaced at 120°, should be filed down, so that the final contact surface has a small area less liable to trap dust.

ADAPTING A MICROSCOPE FOR USE WITH A DISTANCE PIECE

When an objective fitted with a distance piece is contacted with the emulsion surface, pressure is applied to the emulsion directly above the aperture in the microscope stage. To avoid the risk of breaking or bending of the plates, the stage of the microscope should therefore be fitted with a rigid sheet of glass or metal to support the emulsion-coated plate. Glass is to be preferred, since it allows a test specimen to be illuminated by transmitted light during the focusing of the distance piece, and should be at least $\frac{1}{8}$ in (3 mm) thick. The top surface of this supporting glass should, in theory, lie in a plane exactly parallel to the contact surface of the distance piece. Then if the emulsion is coated on glass of which both sides are flat and parallel, the emulsion surface will also lie in a plane parallel to that of the contact surface. In fact, with the 'salt-cellar' distance piece, the tolerances are sufficient to prevent the focus from being spoiled by quite an appreciable lack of parallelism (Fig. 30). Emulsions can be used coated on the glass ordinarily used for photographic plates, and need only be laid flat against the supporting glass fitted to the microscope stage. Film can, for the same reasons, be used satisfactorily under these conditions. While the film almost certainly bows slightly inwards when the distance piece is lowered against it, the displacement of focus seems to be too small to affect the image sharpness.

Greater precision is needed with shorter focal-length objectives both on account of the reduced depth of focus and because of the impracticability of placing the contact surfaces so close to the site of image formation. The emulsion surface must therefore be allowed to orientate itself until it is lying accurately in the plane of the contact surfaces. This can be done by mounting a ring of resilient material on the supporting glass opposite the contact surfaces. For this purpose it is preferable to use a firm sponge rubber, of the type which still feels resilient when compressed between the thumb and first finger. The plate is laid with its back against this ring. When the distance piece is gently lowered, the first contact-surface facet to touch the emulsion presses the plate down, and forces generated by compression of the rubber ring cause the plate to roll until all three contact-surface facets are pressed against the emulsion. This arrangement permits great precision to be obtained with glass plates, even when coated on glass of ordinary photographic quality. This is because errors, introduced by any lack of flatness over small areas of one side of a plate, are likely to be much smaller than the lack of flatness or of parallelism between the two surfaces observable over a plate as a whole.

A similar system can also be used with emulsions coated on film, provided the film is itself held flat against a rigid support. The author has used supporting microscope slides made permanently 'tacky' with a highly-plasticized lacquer such as 'Kodaflat', but this method does not seem readily to give the extreme precision needed. It should, however, be possible to hold film quite flat by placing it against a perforated plate connected to a vacuum pump.

However solidly a distance piece is made, it is unwise to assume that it will not deform slightly under load. Such small deformations are quite harmless if reproducible, and may in practice completely evade detection. The deformation of the apparatus under load will always be the same, if the same moderate pressure is always used to press the emulsion surface against the distance piece. The fine-focusing mechanism of a microscope can be used to obtain reproducible pressure in the following way. In most microscopes of the type focused by movement of the tube, this mechanism operates by raising the tube against both gravity and the downwards force of a compressed spring. In this type of movement the downwards motion is obtained by allowing the tube to follow the movement produced by the focusing knob. If the fine-focusing knob is turned until the tube is in its lowest position, the tube can be lifted against the force of the spring by raising it with the hand. The tube will be similarly lifted when the coarse-focusing knob is used to lower the distance piece against the emulsion surface, until the upwards force on the distance piece is sufficient to compress the spring in the fine-focusing mechanism. This spring can be relied on to provide a reproducible pressure, so long as the downwards movement of the coarse-focusing adjustment is stopped immediately compression of the fine-focusing spring is felt to start.

F

CONSTRUCTION AND FOCUSING OF DISTANCE PIECES

Adjusting a distance piece to form a sharp image at a convienient distance is, as Goldberg modestly described it, 'an operation requiring dexterity and patience' [3]. It can, in fact, be a quite formidable task if the image has to be focused at a pre-determined distance, since it may finally be necessary to shorten the distance piece a micron (0·00004 in) at a time. In this instance, above all others, is it more convenient to effect the final fine focusing by altering the object distance, so that the distance piece need only be made to focus an image at approximately the required distance.

The focusing operation is carried out by decreasing the length of the distance piece, until the original is sharply focused at a convenient distance. It is thus essentially an operation involving the gradual removal of metal from one end of the distance piece. Appendix IIA shows that this may entail the removal of very small thicknesses, particularly at the end of the operation. Under such circumstances it is only too easy to 'overshoot' and completely ruin the work. It is theoretically possible to compensate for such errors by the insertion of shims (very thin sheets of metal) between the end of the distance piece and the bearing surface on the objective, but this method is unsatisfactory for such fine work, since the shims never seem to seat down with the precision required. The reader must therefore use a procedure which makes such accidents least likely. The following method has been found suitable, even for the critical task of focusing a distance piece to be used on a 4 mm ($\frac{1}{6}$ in) objective of N.A. 0·65.

The first operation is to determine the approximate length the distance piece should have. To do this, the objective is fitted to the microscope, and is used to project an enlarged image of a suitable test layer (Plate 13) on a screen placed in the plane to be occupied by the original. When the enlarged image seen on the screen is sharply focused, the distance from the flange on the objective to the test layer indicates the length the distance piece should have (Fig. 31). This distance can be measured fairly accurately with calipers, but it is nevertheless advisable to start by making the distance piece rather too long.

The main body of the distance piece may now be made from an easily-worked and rustless metal such as brass, and the overall length should be at least 0·01 in (0·25 mm) greater than the distance measured in the preliminary test. The internal diameter should be made so that the distance piece either fits smoothly over the objective barrel just in front of the flange, or can be screwed on a thread cut on the barrel of the objective. In the former case the back of the tube of the distance piece may be slit with a fine saw, so that the tube can be bent in slightly to give it a 'springy' fit over the objective barrel.

The second operation consists of the gradual removal of metal from one end of the distance piece, until the plane at which the enlarged image of the test layer is focused moves out to the required distance. The rough distance piece should first be fitted on the objective and lowered on the test layer, and the plane of focus ascertained by placing a small magnifier up against the microscope tube and then moving it backwards until an image can be seen. (If no image can be found, it is probably because the distance piece is so long that the enlarged image is right inside the microscope tube, out of reach of the magnifier.) The focusing tables in Appendix IIA are then used to find how much the distance piece should be shortened to bring the image to the required distance. The distance piece is next turned on a lathe to shorten it by perhaps two-thirds of the calculated amount. It is usually more convenient to remove the metal at this stage from the end which is eventually to bear on the emulsion. The shortened distance piece should again be tested on the microscope. By alternating the removal of less than the required amount, and testing to follow the progressive increase in the distance of the plane of focus, the distance piece should be shortened until it is apparent from the tables that its length exceeds the required figure by not more than 0·001 in (25 microns). This lathe-work requires frequent checking of the length with a micrometer to ensure that too much metal is not removed at any stage.

With very careful use of the lathe, so that only about 0·0001 in (2·5 microns) is removed at a time, the final adjustment of distance pieces for objectives with focal lengths of $\frac{1}{2}$ in (12 mm) or more can be done directly on the lathe; but the adjustment of distance pieces for shorter focal-length lenses should be completed by hand working. Very small amounts of metal can be removed by rubbing the distance piece on a sheet of 'Perspex' moistened with a paste of jeweller's rouge. These final adjustments should also be made gradually in several stages, checking the distance of the plane of focus at each stage. At this juncture an ordinary hand micrometer hardly gives the sensitivity needed, and in any case it only offers an indirect indication of the progress of the work. For the final stage, therefore, it is better to rely entirely on direct optical checking on the objective.

In this way, it is not too difficult to adjust a distance piece so that it focuses at a distance within 10 per cent of the designed figure. The final precise focusing may then be done photographically with the negative-holder placed at a series of distances along the bench. The intervals should be selected to give appropriate movements of the focal plane with respect to the emulsion surface, and can be readily calculated by multiplying a suitable distance, such as 1 micron or 1 'thou' ('mil'), by the square of the approximate reduction factor at which the objective is to be used.

Table 8. Approximate movements of negative-holder needed to alter objective-to-image distance by 1 micron

Focal length of objective	Working distance	Reduction factor R	R^2	Movement needed to alter focus by 1 micron
16 mm	640 mm	40	1,600	1·6 mm
8 mm	640 mm	80	6,400	6·4 mm
4 mm	640 mm	160	25,600	25·6 mm
16 mm	320 mm	20	400	0·4 mm
8 mm	320 mm	40	1,600	1·6 mm
4 mm	320 mm	80	6,400	6·4 mm

This table shows that the longer is the focal length and the less the working distance, the smaller will the focusing intervals need to be.

EXPLOITATION OF DISTANCE PIECES

Distance pieces offer a convenient method for converting any microscope[1] into a precision camera for making microphotographs. Once the necessary care has been devoted to their construction and calibration, production of images can be commenced with a minimum of delay. For example, within 30 minutes of unloading apparatus from a car, the author was able to start making 0·2 mm (approximately 0·008 in) stage micrometers divided into 100 parts in front of an audience in an exhibition hall. Distance pieces are also particularly convenient when images have to be made at irregular intervals. For this reason they are most useful for such routine operations as the resolution testing of photographic emulsions (Chapter 13). They have proved satisfactory in resolution cameras constructed in the Kodak Research Laboratories at Harrow (England) and Rochester (U.S.A.) [7], and permit images showing well over 1,000 lines per millimetre to be produced reliably by operators with no previous special skill in microphotography. Because the method is so simple, there is very little that can go wrong, and use of distance pieces is therefore also appropriate if large numbers of images with extreme resolution have to be made.

Distance pieces have two disadvantages. Since plate emulsions are rarely protected with a supercoat, the necessary firm contact at the emulsion surface may result in the development of an abrasion mark. These undoubtedly constitute a blemish, but are of low density and

[1] If the fine-focusing mechanism does not include a suitably resilient spring, it is advisable to fit a sprung extension piece between the objective and the microscope tube.

rarely matter if only a single image or one row of images has to be made. An objective fitted with a distance piece also constitutes an inflexible system, which is not to be recommended if a variety of work, involving the use of several objectives at different distances, is to be undertaken.

FIXED-FOCUS CAMERAS

Still simpler apparatus can be used if the reader decides only to employ one objective at one distance for making microphotographs. In such cases the distance piece may also constitute the support for the objective. A spring-operated plunger bearing the pressure pad completes the camera. A simple design for equipment of this type is shown in Fig. 32. An internally threaded metal tube, shaped at one end to form the contact surfaces, has a smaller tube carrying the objective screwed inside it. Focusing is effected once and for all by

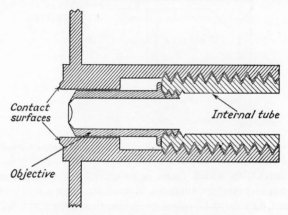

Fig. 32 *Simple Microphotographic Camera*

rotating the inner tube in its thread, until a sharp image of a focusing-test layer is projected at the required distance. Once the objective has been focused, the inner tube is locked in place with set-screws or with a locking-nut and shellac.

The front of the plunger should be made so that the emulsion surface is forced to orientate itself and lie accurately in the plane of the contact surfaces. One method is to use a sponge-rubber pad, but this should not be allowed to rest against the contact surfaces when the apparatus is not in use. Great trouble was at one time experienced by the author as a result of the focus being altered by the contact surfaces becoming contaminated with traces of rubber, but this difficulty was cured by attaching a disc of sheet 'Bakelite' to the front of the rubber pad. Correct orientation of the emulsion surface was achieved in a different way in a German camera made for copying espionage documents [8]. The pressure was applied by a hinged arm bearing a loose hollow stud, whose back spherical surface fitted into a conical socket. When the hinged arm was allowed to swing against the back of the film, the stud rotated in its socket until perfect orientation of the film against the contact surfaces was achieved (Fig. 33).

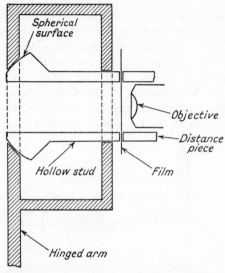

Fig. 33 *Rotatable Stud for holding Film against Distance Piece*

If equipment, in which focus is secured by a spring forcing the emulsion against contact surfaces, is used to make a series of images on one plate, care must be taken to ensure that the plate is withdrawn from the contact surfaces before moving it laterally for another exposure. Weak springs, for instance, may be fitted to press the emulsion near the edge of the plate, so that the plate falls back as soon as the plunger is withdrawn.

Apparatus of this type is suitable for routine work, either when a few images have to be made at intervals or when large numbers of similar images are required. It can also be fitted with a repeating back, so that a single row containing any required number of images can be made.

PNEUMATIC GAUGING

The disadvantages of locating the emulsion surface by pressing it physically against contact surfaces have been overcome by pneumatic gauging. Consider a distance piece which has been hermetically sealed to the objective, and which has air flowing into it through a side tube (Fig. 34). Before the distance piece approaches the emulsion, air escapes without restriction through the front of the distance piece. When the distance piece is lowered on the emulsion, free escape of air is progressively hampered as the gap between emulsion and distance piece is closed, and a back-pressure starts to build up. The magnitude of this back-pressure is inversely proportional to the cube of the gap, and a manometer or pressure gauge thus provides a sensitive indication of the position of the distance piece relative to the emulsion. By

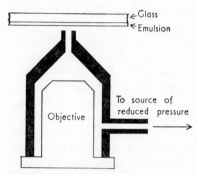

Fig. 34 *Distance Piece adapted to form Pneumatic Gauge*
Courtesy of F. R. Padgham, F. C. Bird and E. Bovey
and 'Journal of Photographic Science'.

suitable adjustment of the rate of air flow and the size of the orifice, reproducible setting with a precision of one micron (0·00004 in) can be achieved.

The use of pneumatic gauging for this purpose was first described by Padgham, Bird and Bovey [9], who employed a 16 mm microscope objective. To provide the necessary constant pressure difference between the atmosphere and the tube connected to the distance piece, they used a simple water-operated 'filter' pump and a side tube connected to a constant-pressure bottle. This was a water-filled bottle fitted with a side tube, and with the top closed by a rubber stopper holding a glass tube having a sintered glass bubbler at the bottom. The bubbler was 10 in (25 cm) below the water surface, and as soon as the filter pump reduced the pressure by more than 10 inches of water, air started to enter the system through this side tube. By use of a sufficient pumping speed, this equipment ensured a constant air flow into the distance piece, and focusing was effected by observing the reduction of pressure. The authors found this an effective method of focusing a $\frac{2}{3}$ in (16 mm) objective, and used it to produce more than 30 resolution-test images distributed over the area of a $1\frac{1}{2} \times 1$ in (38 × 26 mm) test slide. Bovey has also stated that they made other distance pieces with three nozzles, and satisfactorily focused a $\frac{1}{6}$ in (4 mm) objective [10]. In this instance, it is clear that reduced pressure was used because of the simplicity of the required pumping equipment. The authors noted, however, that it caused dust to build up on the surface of the objective, and for this reason it would have been better to use positive pressure.

The technique of pneumatic gauging clearly has several virtues. Above all it avoids the need for any mechanical contact with the emulsion surface, and abrasion marks from the focusing operation are therefore completely avoided. The force needed to produce the necessary manometer reading is so small, that practically no distortion of film should be caused, and it probably presents the best method of maintaining focus for images on film. The method is also more flexible than the use of a rigid distance piece, since with a pneumatic gauge there will be a range of distances with which the apparatus gives the necessary sensitivity. So long as the objective's performance is not compromised, it is therefore practicable to calibrate a distance piece by determining the pressure readings required to focus on a negative placed at different distances.

For efficient use of a pneumatic gauge, it must be positioned on the lens so that the indicated pressure is in a sensitive part of the pressure range when the objective is in focus. To establish this desirable condition rapidly, Altman [12] equipped his microscope with an extension piece between the objective and the body of the microscope. The objective was then surrounded by the gauging head, consisting of a hollow annular air chamber fitted with small nozzles. The gauging head was connected by rigid struts to a solid brass collar sliding on the extension piece. When an objective was first attached to the extension piece, the apparatus was visually focused by back projection (p. 130). With the pneumatic gauge operating, the collar was then moved towards the emulsion until the gauging head occupied a position causing a pressure in the sensitive range to be indicated, and the collar was clamped with set screws. Final focusing was established by a series of trial exposures with the gauge adjusted to give a convenient range of pressure (and hence focus) values. By this means, a single pneumatic gauge could be rapidly adjusted to any objective.

Equipment for pneumatic gauging is commercially available (for example from Solex Gauges Ltd, 72 High Road, Chiswick, London). One unit comprises a manometer about 30 in (75 cm) high, together with its own unit for stabilizing the incoming air pressure. So long as the input air pressure was between 25 and 40 p.s.i., stable readings were obtained. W. Watson and Sons Ltd connected this unit to the pneumatic gauge on the objectives of their step-and-repeat camera designed for microelectronics (p. 340).

The greatest advantage from pneumatic gauging is likely to be obtained when a substantial proportion of the emulsion surface has to be practically filled with very high resolution images, for instance in the manufacture of binary-coded discs (p. 274), multi-image microelectronic masks (p. 336) or the production of thousands of document copies on one emulsion surface (p. 411).

To ensure adequate sharpness of all the images for this type of application, it was previously usual to coat emulsion on optical flats and traverse the plate under the objective by a mechanism ensuring that the objective-to-emulsion distance was practically constant. With pneumatic gauging the same level of mechanical precision is no longer essential, since the objective can be rapidly adjusted to the emulsion surface before each exposure. Moreover, it should not be forgotten that pneumatic devices are adaptable to servo operation, so that the adjustment of focus could be made both rapid and completely automatic.

VARIABLE-FOCUS APPARATUS WITH THE PLATE REGISTERED BY THE EMULSION SURFACE

Possibly the most satisfying apparatus for experimenters to construct and operate is that which allows any suitable objective to be focused at the required distance in a reasonably short time, and yet will enable a number of identical images to be produced once correct focus has been established. An essential requirement of such apparatus is that it should have a focusing mechanism giving distances reproducible to a precision of one micron (0·00004 in) when the instrument is reset to the same position as before. This condition is adequately fulfilled by the fine-focusing adjustment of most microscopes satisfactory for use with high-power objectives. The rest of this section will show how such a microscope can be adapted for this purpose.

As registration must be effected from the emulsion surface (in view of the lack of flatness and non-uniformity of thickness of most ordinary photographic base materials), the plates are placed, emulsion side upwards, against contact surfaces fitted on the under-side of the microscope stage. A stout metal plate, at least $\frac{1}{4}$ in (6 mm) thick, should be fitted with contact surfaces around an aperture of sufficient size to allow the objective to focus the image, and should be firmly bolted or clamped to the under-side of the microscope stage. Pressure can then be applied to the back of the plate by raising a rubber pad attached to the condenser-holder of the sub-stage.

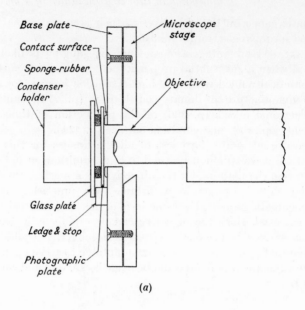

(a)

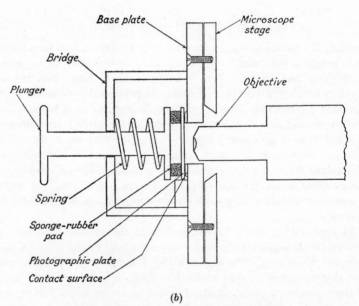

(b)

Fig. 35 *Methods for converting Microscope*

(a) Unit, for attaching beneath microscope stage, whereby pressure is applied with the condenser holder. Note how the ledge supporting plate also serves as stop for limiting movement of pressure pad.

(b) More elaborate unit, complete with bridge and plunger bearing pressure pad.

Random variations of focus were at first experienced by the author with this form of apparatus, but these were traced to variations in the bending of the stage when different pressures were applied to the rubber pad. This difficulty was cured by fitting a stop, so that the pad could only be raised to a fixed position, thus applying reproducible compression and causing consistent bending [Fig. 35(a)]. Since the same pressure was applied both when focusing and exposing plates, the consistent bending was automatically compensated by a small shift in the focus.

A disadvantage of this method for applying pressure is that the pressure on the stage is applied well away from the point at which the stage is anchored to the microscope, thus increasing the probability that significant bending will occur. This tendency can be lessened by applying the pressure from a bridge, which is attached not to the stage but to the metal plate fixed underneath the stage [Fig. 35(b)]. The bridge should be attached as close to the point of image formation, as the width of the plates to be used permits. Pressure can be applied by a spring-loaded and hollow plunger, through which light may be shone for visual focusing.

Since the coarse-focusing movement of the microscope may not permit the tube to be lowered far enough for the objective to be focused on a plate placed at the back of the stage, it may be necessary to fit an extension tube between the objective and the microscope tube. Tubes with an R.M.S. thread at each end are commercially available.

FOCUSING OF VARIABLE-FOCUS APPARATUS

Variable-focus apparatus embodying means for really accurate registration of the emulsion surface can be focused by any of the visual methods described in the earlier sections of this chapter, but the most cunningly devised methods for visual focusing inevitably involve sources of error and uncertainty which can be eliminated by photographic-focusing tests. We have already noted that photographic-focusing tests can only be used successfully if the equipment is designed and manipulated so that the emulsion-to-objective distance can be reproducibly varied by very small increments. The design of the equipment has already been discussed, and we must now consider the refinements of manipulation needed to ensure the utmost accuracy.

It is first necessary to consider the process of fine focusing with a microscope in some detail. As has already been described, the tubes of many microscopes are forced downwards by a compressed spring. Thus if the fine-focusing knob is turned so that it raises the tube, the mechanism will directly drive the tube against the force of the spring and gravity, and the motion should be very reproducible; but when the knob is turned the other way the tube may only move as a result of the spring (or gravity) causing it to follow the motion of the fine-focusing mechanism. Any slight 'stickiness' in the slides bearing the tube may cause the control when lowering the tube to be less perfect than when raising it.

It is also important to realize that the driving mechanism tends to be in a greater state of compression when the tube is raised, than when it is lowered. This may cause a small but appreciable difference between the planes of focus obtained by setting the fine-focusing knob to the same position from opposite directions. Such 'back-lash' is the source of lack of precision in many mechanisms: the steering gear of motor-cars being a familiar example. For our present purpose its consequences can be practically eliminated by always approaching a desired position by *raising* the tube away from the stage. If the tube has to be lowered, the fine-focusing mechanism should first be moved to take the plane of focus well below the desired position, so that the final approach is still made by raising the tube. The great accuracy obtainable by this method can be demonstrated by using an oil-immersion objective and a $\times 12$ (or higher magnification) eyepiece to view a processed image on an extreme-resolution emulsion. In the clear areas there will always be a small number of minute developed 'fog' grains, which provide a sensitive indication of the focus setting. Once the focus for one particular grain in the emulsion has been found by using the fine-focusing mechanism to raise the tube, it should be possible to re-focus on this grain without looking down the microscope, by lowering the tube with the fine-focusing knob and then re-setting this knob to the scale position it occupied when the objective was focused visually.

Photographic-focusing tests are conveniently carried out in the following way. The fine-focusing mechanism of the microscope is first adjusted to a half-way position, so that there is plenty of room for both downward and upward movements, and the focus is then found approximately by one of the visual methods. Really critical focus is established by lowering the objective a small distance, and raising it by a number of suitably small increments (Table 7), while making an exposure at each position. To obtain the greatest possible sensitivity from this test, allowance must be made for the fact that the density as well as the sharpness of really fine lines alters with changes of focus. The best conditions for exposure and focus can, therefore, only be established with certainty by adjusting both the focus and the exposure, until the best combination has been found. This necessitates tests in which successive corrections are made separately to the exposure and the focus, and the methods used are described in detail in Chapter 8.

REFERENCES

[1] Bovey, E., B.I.O.S. report 1552, p. 24 (see reference [22], Chapter 2).

[2] Shadbolt, G., *Phot. J.*, **4**, 79, 1857 (see reference [4], Chapter 4).

[3] Goldberg, E., *Brit. J. Phot.*, **73**, 462, 1926 (see reference [6], Chapter 1).

[4] Nicholls, J., *Microscopic Photography: its Art and Mystery*, F. J. Cox (London, 1860).

[5] Bovey, E., as reference [1], page 8.

[6] Martin, L. C. and Johnson, B. K., 'Simplified Apparatus for Ultra-Violet Microscopy', *J. Sci. Inst.*, **7**, 1, 1930. (In this paper the authors show how the bending of the stage of a microscope under small loads can be used to give ultra-fine focusing.)

[7] Perrin, F. H. and Altman, J. H., 'Resolving-power Cameras in the Kodak Research Laboratories', *J. Opt. Soc. Am.*, **41**, 265, 1951.

[8] Editors of *Look*, *The Story of the F.B.I.*, E. P. Dutton (New York, 1947).

[9] Padgham, Mrs F. R., Bird, F. C. and Bovey, E., 'A Method of Preparing Projection-Lens Resolution Test Slides', *J. Phot. Sci.*, **4**, 25, 1956.

[10] Bovey, E., 'Graticules and fine scales: their production and application in modern measuring systems', *J. Scientific Instruments*, **39**, 405, 1962.

[11] Crick, H. R., 'Air Gauging', *Metalworking Equipment News*, 14, August, 1966. This article contains a review of general applications of pneumatic gauging.

[12] Altman, J. H., 'Some current work in Microphotography', *Third Kodak Seminar on Microminiaturization* (in the press).

6 · The Work-Room, Camera and Optical Bench

Although extreme-resolution photography subjects most of the materials used to a searching test, the work-room may require less elaborate installation than is wanted for most other photographic processes. The emulsions used for making really minute images have such a low speed that exclusion of all extraneous light, for example, is not a serious problem. Some, such as print-out emulsions and the mercury-diazonium material, can safely be operated in rooms lighted by diffuse daylight or by tungsten lamps. Quite bright safelights such as the 'Wratten' Series 1 (red), or the Series OB (amber-yellow), may be used even with extreme-resolution silver-halide or wet-collodion materials respectively, which are typical of the fastest emulsions suitable for really fine work (Chapter 2).

Processing is often simplified by the fact that the area of plate handled may often be so small that it is quite practicable to work in a room without running water. Individual small plates can be processed in from six to eight small tumblers, one each for developing and fixing, and the others for successive changes of wash water. Results of permanent interest can then, if desired, be re-fixed and re-washed later. Most elaborate installations are, of course, needed when high standards of cleanliness have to be achieved, as in the production of graticules and allied articles (Chapters 9–11).

The Camera

For microphotography, a camera has to fulfil several functions. It has to allow a restricted area of the emulsion to be exposed to a projected image without fogging the remainder of the plate. Since microphotographic emulsions necessarily have low speed (Chapter 2), relatively large amounts of stray light can reach the emulsion without producing fog. It is therefore not essential to use a 'camera' in the sense of a totally light-excluding box bearing a lens at one end, although the body of an available camera may prove convenient. When the apparatus is used in a darkened room, it is generally only necessary to insert the plate and drape a black cloth over the top, and around the back and sides of the apparatus, before turning on the exposing light. Objectives used on a microscope should carry a 5 × 3 in (12·5 × 7·5 cm), or larger, opaque card, with a tightly fitting aperture in the middle, pressed on to the barrel of the objective or distance piece.

The camera has to permit successive plates to be placed in a predetermined plane, so that a precise lens-to-emulsion distance is reproduced with very high precision. Many small cameras will give the desired precision by dark-room loading of single plates (Chapter 1). Principles for achieving the required perfection of register in specially constructed apparatus have been described in Chapter 5.

A mechanical shutter is unnecessary when the light intensity in the image can be adjusted to require an exposure duration of at least 10 seconds, which can be timed with sufficient accuracy by manipulating a lens cap. When shorter exposures are needed to secure a desired rate of output of images, a mechanically operated shutter or a 'process' timer controlling switching of the exposing light should be used.

CAMERAS FOR PRODUCING MANY IMAGES ON A SINGLE EMULSION SURFACE

The minute overall dimensions of individual extreme-resolution microphotographic images has prompted the idea of placing many images on one plate. Thus, early French workers producing images for mounting on 'Stanhope' lenses fitted their cameras with a sliding plate holder, so that a whole row of images could be produced on a single plate (Fig. 36). By fitting the lens or plate in a vertical slide, two or more rows of images can be made on a single plate. In recent years, mechanisms for moving a plate controllably, so that its entire area could be filled with images, have acquired increased importance. For the production of semi-conductor devices these arrangements are desirable both to achieve economic output and to assist production of circuit elements with adequately consistent properties (p. 335). Since the manufacturing processes may include several stages, each requiring its own different photographic image, the spatial register of the many images in each negative of the set has to be reproduced with great accuracy. High-reduction document-copying systems, such as the National Cash Register Company's Photochromic Micro-Image Memory, use what is essentially a mechanical stage to enable several thousand images of separate pages to be reproduced in the area of a normal filing card (p. 412). The greatest accuracy in moving the plate between successive exposures is needed when elements of an image produced by separate exposures constitute the divisions of a precision scale. For this purpose, nothing less than a dividing-engine can provide sufficiently accurate movements, and the equipment for projecting the images then becomes a minor component of the system (Chapters 9 and 10). Thus, a multiplicity of component images may need to be produced on one plate for a variety of reasons. Different standards of precision can be required for each application, and the

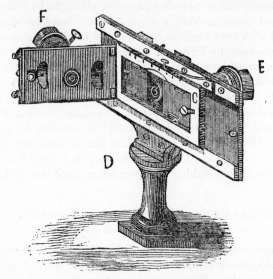

Fig. 36 *Willemin's Century-Old Photorepeater for Micro-images*

Sliding plate holder gives horizontal row of 8 images. Three rows were produced on each plate by moving the lens vertically.

H. Willemin, *British Journal of Photography*, March 24, 1865.

design of appropriate equipment for some applications is a problem in applied metrology.

While mechanical shutters and plate-shifting mechanisms may be essential for the production of the numerous images required by these special applications, they do little to improve the quality of individual images. In fact, by introducing possible sources of vibration and change of focus, they may actually add to the difficulties. For the production of a few extreme-resolution images the experimenter or amateur can obtain quite as good results as the commercial worker, since the latter's chief advantage is in the arrangements provided for mass production.

The Optical Bench

A micro-reduction apparatus consists essentially of the illuminating system, the 'original' (normally a transparency: see Chapter 7), the objective and a means for locating the sensitive emulsions. These components must be correctly positioned relative to each other, before making any images. The preparations made to ensure correct positioning influence the convenience of working, the speed with which the apparatus can be set up and the dimensional accuracy of the images. Makeshift arrangements in the long run waste more time than they at first appear to save. It is much better to use equipment holding all components of the system positively in their correct relative positions. In some cases the original, the illuminant and objective have all been mounted in one tube, to make a unit rather like the projection head of an enlarger. Such a unit is convenient for mounting on a dividing engine (see p. 246), but is too inflexible for some applications. Many workers prefer to use an optical bench, which according to requirements can be made more or less elaborate. The primary function of an optical bench is to ensure that the original and the emulsion surface lie in parallel planes normal to the axis of the lens: an ordinary requirement of any photographic copying apparatus. It must also support the camera and original so that vibration causes them to move as one unit rather than to move relative to each other. Further desirable features are that it should

(i) allow the distance of the original to be varied, while ensuring that its centre always lies on the axis of the lens,

(ii) permit the illuminant to be placed at a reproducible distance from the original,

(iii) provide for the convenient adjustment of the illuminant, when condenser illumination is used.

CHOICE BETWEEN HORIZONTAL AND VERTICAL BENCHES

The optical bench may be either vertical or horizontal. Vertical apparatus has the advantage that parallelism of the original and the emulsion planes can be readily checked with a spirit level. This procedure was employed by Koana and Wakimoto [1] who mounted their transparencies on an illuminator on one floor with the camera pointing through a hole in the floor above. With this arrangement, alignment was further checked by hanging a plumb-line from the centre of the lens mount to indicate the position of the axis of the lens. Furthermore, they were using lenses weighing one pound or more and up to 9 in (23 cm) in length, and supporting these with sufficient stiffness must have been simplified by mounting with the axis vertical. A factor to be considered in constructing vertical apparatus is whether the image should be projected upwards or downwards. With upwards projection, the emulsion surface is horizontal and faces down, and is therefore in the best position for preventing dirt from settling on it during a long run of exposures. Upwards projection is also convenient if observation through the back of the plate is used to check the focus or the location of the images. For example, Padgham, Bird and Bovey made a positioning plate indicating the desired position at which thirty-three separate images were to be made on a single plate [2]. The positioning plate was temporarily fixed to the back of an M-R plate with 'Plasticine', and a red filter was placed in front of the objective. The plate carriage was then moved before each exposure until the appropriate numbered rectangle neatly framed the slightly out-of-focus image of the original. Vertical apparatus for microelectronics manufacture has been built around

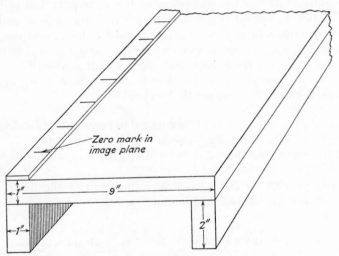

Fig. 37 *Simple Microphotographic bench*
Construction of base.

the vertical column of an enlarger or a drilling machine, which provides the means for holding the different components horizontal in their required positions.

With a horizontal bench there is no need to provide clamps to hold the components in position. So long as the components are supported at three points, are not top-heavy and are heavy enough to stand still, they can just be laid on the bench and held by gravity. Thus horizontal apparatus is simpler to construct, and it is certainly easier to adjust components of a horizontal bench to the exact positions indicated by photographic focusing tests.

Once the essential requirements have been satisfied, the optical bench can be as elaborate or simple as the circumstances demand. When images are to be made on an industrial scale to fine tolerances, their ultimate value, and the probable saving of operator's time, is likely to justify purchase or construction of an expensive bench. Clamps to hold all components exactly in position are an obvious precaution. For amateur or experimental, or early-stage development work, however, the essentials can be provided by 'do-it-yourself' carpentry. The following sections describe the construction and adjustment of a bench of this type used by the author. To some readers it may seem crude to the point of quaintness, but it embodies all essential features, and its construction and operation has provided much valuable experience. Its effectiveness can be judged from the fact that only a few minutes were needed to assemble the equipment and start the production of images at a public microscopy exhibition (see also, p. 146).

A SIMPLE HORIZONTAL BENCH FOR USE WITH A MICROSCOPE

The bench, on which all the other components were supported, was made from a well-seasoned plank 1 in (25 mm) thick, 9 in (22 cm) wide and 4 ft (120 cm) long. This was stiffened with 2×1 in (50×25 mm) battens underneath its entire length (Fig. 37). A lath having a straight edge bearing a metre scale was attached to one side of the top surface, and was used both to position the components at suitable distances along the bench and to ensure their squareness.

A microscope stand, with its tube in the horizontal position, was placed on one end of the bench, so that the tube pointed to the other end of the bench and the stage was approximately opposite the start of the scale. Thus the approximate distance of the original transparency from the image plane ($u + v$, see Chapter 4) could be read off directly by noting its position relative to the scale.

The negative-holder consisted of a baseboard 12 in (30 cm) long, 8 in (20 cm) wide and $\frac{1}{2}$ in (12 mm) thick, holding an upright firmly and accurately square at one end. A 4 in (10 cm) square aperture, with its centre the same height as the axis of the microscope tube, was cut in the upright, and slots to hold the transparency and any light-diffusing screen or filter were fitted around this aperture on either side of the upright. It was convenient to mount the original on the front surface shown in Fig. 38, and mount the diffusion screen or negative-holder at the back. Three dome castors were fitted to the under-side of the negative-holder to allow it to slide smoothly along the bench, and its baseboard was fitted with an index line to indicate the position of the original relative to the metre scale. From Table 8,

(p. 146) it is apparent that positioning of the negative-holder to the nearest millimetre was in most cases sufficiently sensitive for accurate focusing. Greater sensitivity in positioning could be obtained by mounting a 9 mm scale divided into 10 parts instead of the index line. Such a small scale can be made accurately enough by photographic reduction. When the small scale was laid against the metre scale it

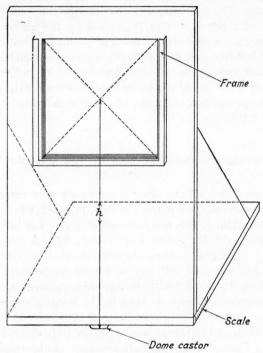

Fig. 38 *Negative-holder*
The height *h* equals the height of the axis of the objective.

acted as a vernier, allowing small changes in the distance of the transparency to be measured to $\frac{1}{10}$ millimetre. The ability to measure such small movements was valuable when images had to be adjusted exactly to a certain size, even if the absolute distance from the original to the emulsion was only measured approximately. Small movements of the transparency may also be needed when focusing longer focal-length microscope objectives used with small degrees of reduction (Table 8, p. 146).

When an objective is focused by changing the distance of the negative-holder from the camera (and particularly if photographic focusing tests are being made with this method), it is desirable to be able to change the distance with the minimum possible disturbance of the illuminating system. It would, in fact, be convenient to be able to make satisfactory exposures after each movement without having to adjust the illuminating system at all. For this reason, a convenient arrangement is to support the illuminating system entirely on the

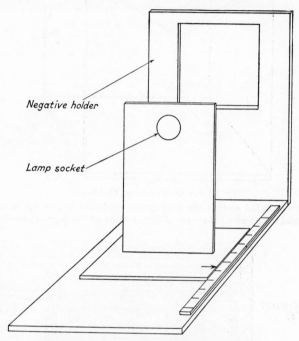

Fig. 39 *Lamp-holder mounted on negative-holder*
This form is convenient for diffuse illumination.

negative-holder, so that the transparency and its illuminant can be moved as a single unit (Fig. 39).

If a condenser is used, it may be supported on V-shaped uprights (Fig. 40), so that its axis lies on the axis of the objective and passes through the centre of the square aperture. The position of the illuminant has to be adjusted quite critically in relation to the condenser to give uniform illumination, and it is therefore advisable to construct a lamp-holder with vertical and horizontal slides (Fig. 41). The base of this lamp-holder itself may run in slides on the base of the negative-holder, and should be clamped in position once the correct distance has been found (Chapter 7). A laboratory retort stand can be used as a lamp-holder, but is unsatisfactory since the position of the lamp always seems to move as the clamps are finally tightened.

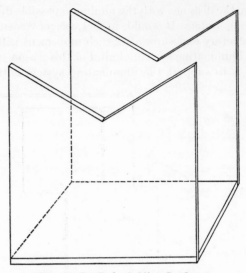

Fig. 40 *Cradle for holding Condenser*

This is constructed so that the axis of the condenser lies on the axis of the objective, and is opposite the centre of the aperture of the negative-holder.

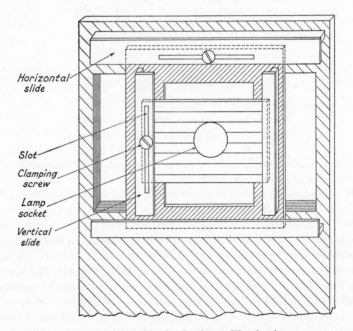

Horizontal
slide

Slot

Clamping
screw

Lamp
socket

Vertical
slide

Fig. 41 *Lamp-holder for Condenser Illumination*

To enable the lamp to be centred with respect to the condenser, the lamp-holder is fitted with vertical and cross slides.

ALIGNING THE MICROSCOPE WITHOUT AN OBJECTIVE

The microscope has to be placed on one end of the bench with the axis of the objective parallel to the straight edge on the lath, and passing through the centre of the aperture in the negative-holder. The centre of the transparency will then lie on the axis of the objective at all distances along the bench.

The first step in making this adjustment is to confirm that the tube of the microscope is truly horizontal. Stand the microscope on a previously levelled surface and use a spirit level to check whether the tube is horizontal. Some microscopes have a small adjustable 'stop' screw for making this adjustment. It will, for the moment, be assumed that this inspection is sufficient to ensure that the axis of an objective fitted to the microscope will lie in a horizontal plane parallel to the bench, when the microscope is stood on the bench.

There are several ways of aligning the microscope. Allen [3] described a method for aligning photomicrographic apparatus which should be equally effective for microphotography. The sub-stage condenser was centred to the objective in accordance with ordinary microscopic practice, and the optical parts of the condenser and the eyepiece and objective were all removed from the microscope. The condenser-diaphragm was then closed down to a pinhole, and a disc of card with a pinhole exactly in the centre was inserted in the eyepiece end of the microscope tube. Now these two pinhole apertures should lie on the axis of any objective used with the microscope, which could therefore be aligned by placing a lamp behind the condenser-diaphragm, and screening off all stray light. The alignment could then be judged by observing the spot of light projected through the diaphragm and pinhole. The microscope was moved until this spot of light fell on the centre of the aperture in the negative-holder, when this was placed at its nearest and furthest distances on the bench. The centre of the original should then lie on the axis of the objective at all distances along the bench.

Another method depends on the facts that a line from the eye to the position of its reflection in a mirror is exactly normal to the mirror, and that microscope objectives are centred during manufacture so that the axis is normal to the plane of the flange at the base of the R.M.S. thread (Fig. 42). The corresponding flange on the microscope at the base of the tube will, therefore, also be normal to the axis when the objective is screwed right home. The microscope can thus be aligned by holding a piece of mirror flat against this latter flange, and observing the reflections seen from the negative-holder. A white card having a pinhole in the centre surrounded by several

concentric circles should be inserted in the negative-holder and
brightly illuminated. The microscope is then moved until the eye
placed behind the pinhole sees an image of the pinhole reflected from

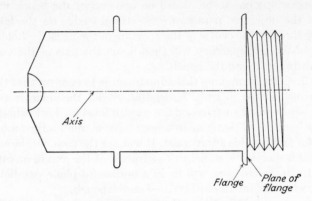

Fig. 42 *Diagram of Microscope Objective*

In manufacture, the lenses of objectives are centred so that their axes are
normal to the plane of the flange, and hence to any surface on which the flange is
seated.

the centre of the small circle of mirror visible through the microscope
tube (Fig. 43). This adjustment is facilitated by the concentric circles
drawn on the card. The alignment should again be tested in this way

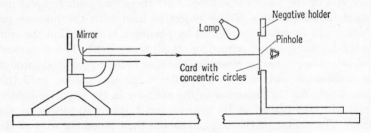

Fig. 43 *Use of Mirror for aligning Microscope Tube*

with the negative-holder placed at both its nearest and furthest distances.

This method is sensitive and easy to carry out, and a mirror placed
in the emulsion plane can, in the same way, be used to confirm that this
too is normal to the axis. In addition, the squareness of the negative-
holder can likewise be tested by fitting a mirror in the plane of the
original, and viewing this through a pinhole in the centre of a card
mounted over the aperture in the microscope stage. This last test also
provides a further check on the alignment of the microscope, since

the reflection of the card should be mirrored in the centre of the negative aperture.

Williams has described another most sensitive method for testing the parallelism of two surfaces [4], which should be especially suitable when absence of distortion in the image is important, or for aligning equipment for use with lenses such as the Wray Special Copying lens giving high resolution over an exceptionally large field.

Williams placed a mirror on the copy-board, and with the lens removed from the camera, viewed the first mirror through a small hole scratched in the middle of another mirror placed in the position of the focusing screen. When the two mirrors were parallel, the eye saw a series of concentric images of the lens mount produced by successive reflections. For our purpose, two variants of this test can be used, according to the ease with which the eye can be placed behind a mirror in the object plane. With the bench already described, one small mirror can be placed in the image plane (Fig. 44), and a second larger mirror with a small hole cut in the silvered layer at the centre is mounted in the negative-holder. On the front surface of this larger mirror there should be stuck an annular ring of white paper with its centre coincident with the hole, and this paper ring should be illuminated obliquely. When the mirrors are correctly aligned, the eye

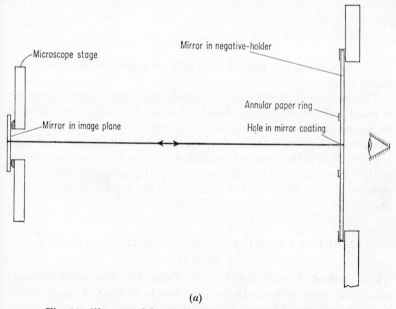

(a)

Fig. 44 *Alignment of Image and Transparency Planes by Mirrors*

By observation (a) through mirror in negative-holder and (b) through mirror in ·image plane (see overleaf).

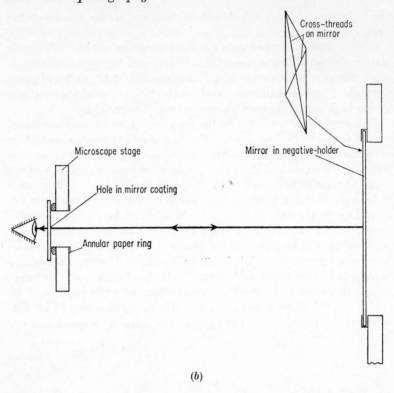

(*b*)

placed behind the hole should see a series of concentric images of the paper ring.

This method of observation is inconvenient when the transparency is usually illuminated by a closed light-box. The alternative is then to mount an unmarked mirror in the centre of the screen of the illuminator, and indicate the centre of the field by diagonally stretched threads. This is then viewed through a small hole in a mirror placed in the image plane. To facilitate observation, an obliquely illuminated annular ring of white card is attached to the top of the microscope stage.

ALIGNING THE MICROSCOPE WITH THE OBJECTIVE IN POSITION

These methods for aligning the axis of the objective are all indirect, since with none of them is the objective itself used. A more direct test is to use the objective to project an enlarged image of a single-grain focusing-test layer on a card placed in the negative-holder (Chapter 4). The projected image usually shows a fairly distinguishable boundary between the axial zone where the grains are sharply imaged, and the outer zones which are unsharp as a result of field curvature. This boundary should be a circle whose centre lies on the axis (Plate 13). A more precise way of locating the axis is to examine the apparent movement of individual grains when the magnification is altered. A grain lying right on the axis will not appear to move at all, while those off-axis will appear to move by an amount propor-

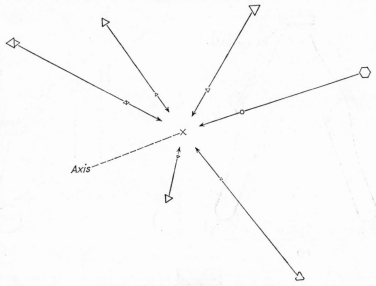

Fig. 45 *Locating the Axis of the Objective*
Relative positions of several grains when projected at two different magnifications.

tional to their distance from the axis. To carry out the test, focus the image of the test plate on the card when the negative-holder is in a near position, and mark the position of one particular grain close to the centre of the field. Shift the holder to a more distant position, re-focus and mark the new position of the grain. If it is off-axis, a line passing from the second point through the first should go through the axis. In fact, lines drawn similarly for a number of grains should all intersect at the axis (Fig. 45).

MOUNTING THE MICROSCOPE

When the microscope has been aligned, locating blocks should be fitted so that it can always be replaced in the same position without losing its alignment. They may be made from a hard wood such as oak or beech, and in their simplest form constitute a straight edge against which the microscope is pushed, and a point to limit its movement when the microscope is slid along in contact with the edge (Fig. 46). These blocks must of course, be fitted without moving the microscope at all. A good precaution is to fix the microscope temporarily by wedging small pieces of 'Plasticine' against the inside of the stand. The blocks may then be stuck in position with liquid glue, and finally screwed down after the glue has dried.

However the locating blocks are constructed, it is important to

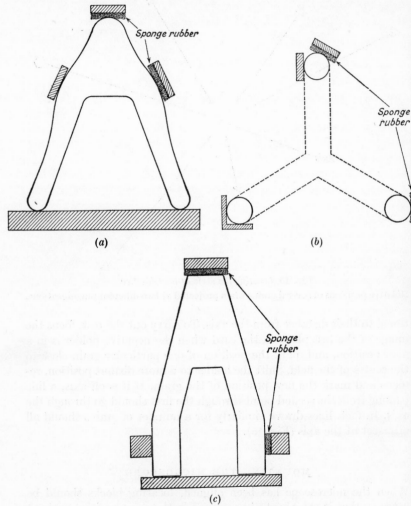

(a)

(b)

Sponge rubber

Sponge rubber

Sponge rubber

(c)

Fig. 46 *Methods for Locating Microscopes*

The positions of the blocks and pressure pads have to be adapted to different designs of microscope foot.

ensure that the microscope cannot move at all during use, and it is a good plan to provide sponge-rubber pads to wedge the microscope firmly against the blocks (Fig. 46).

If the microscope stand does not include a screw for levelling the tube in the horizontal position, the alignment tests may have indicated that the tube is not strictly horizontal. This can be corrected by making a small depression or building the bench up, underneath the 'heel' of the microscope stand. The result of this adjustment can be observed by the same methods used for testing horizontal alignment.

VIBRATION

However perfect the other arrangements may be, really sharp images can never be ensured if vibration is allowed to cause a movement of the negative-holder relative to the microscope. Such movements will cause the aerial image to move over the emulsion surface during exposure, thus blurring the image. Vibration is caused by the movements of traffic, people or machinery which shake the building and submit the apparatus to a rapid series of accelerations and decelerations. In the author's experience this trouble is much more likely to occur in a rigid building with a concrete and steel frame, than in an old and 'flabby' building. The former is more effective in transmitting high frequencies, which approximate to the natural frequency of vibration of the apparatus itself, and are thus more likely to produce movements of one part of the apparatus relative to another.

The movement of a point of the image over the emulsion surface resulting from vibration may describe a circle, or an ellipse or a straight line, but the most likely motion is a straight line in either a vertical or horizontal direction. The motion is also likely to resemble that of a pendulum, in that it is most rapid when the point is at its central position, and slows down and reverses its direction of movement at the extreme positions. The appearance of an image affected by vibration depends on the total proportion of the exposure time during which the image of a line is projected on each element of the emulsion surface; and hence on the relation between the width of the line and the amplitude of the vibration. If the amplitude is relatively small, the edges of the total exposed area will receive less light than the centre, thus giving a line with a fuzzy edge on each side. With a large and constant amplitude, a single line may be recorded as a pair, corresponding to the extreme positions receiving the greatest exposure as a result of the slow movement of the image at the ends of its swing, and the space between will have a lower density. Vibration can also result in the complete disappearance of fine lines, if the area over which the light is spread is so large that no density can be produced. Another feature of images spoilt by vibration is that their appearance depends greatly on the angle between a line and the direction of swing, since no deterioration of the sharpness of a line will result when the direction of a linear vibration is parallel to the line (Plate 14). The resulting apparent astigmatism will be uniform over the whole area of the field, as contrasted with astigmatism of an objective which tends to be negligible on the axis but becomes worse in marginal zones.

If unsharp images are produced as a result of vibration, the cause of the trouble may be obvious from the symptoms described above, but vibration should always be suspected if images of very variable quality are being produced in the absence of any obvious defect in the mechanism for maintaining focus.

The problem of eliminating the effects of vibration is precisely the same as in photomicrography. The various parts of the equipment must all be mounted so that they have no tendency to rock or wobble, but move with the bench as a single unit. The bench should be so stiff that any vibrations allowed to reach it cannot result in appreciable whip or torsional vibration of the bench itself. These elementary precautions will already do much to lessen the harmful effects of vibration. It is also usually advantageous to weight the bench with bricks or other weights, so that a large force is needed to produce a given acceleration, and to mount the bench on resilient supports which will only transmit vibrations very sluggishly. Under these conditions only the low frequency 'soft' components of vibration are likely to be transmitted to the bench, and it is improbable that these will cause blurring of the image.

Sponge-rubber is an excellent material for combating vibration, so long as it is firm enough to retain appreciable resilience when the load is applied. It may be used to support both the optical bench and the table on which the bench is laid. For photomicrography Allen suggested placing pieces of 1 in (2·5 cm) thick sponge-rubber under the legs of the table, with a metal plate between the leg and the rubber to distribute the load over the entire area of the pads [5]. The area of the rubber should be sufficient to allow the table to sway gently when pushed hard. This method cannot be used when working on built-in laboratory benches, and the optical bench itself must be resiliently mounted. Sponge-rubber pads fixed at intervals along the stiffening battens of the bench proved a satisfactory precaution against vibration, even when working next to a busy passage in a building which was also vibrating from machinery.

Isolation of apparatus from the effects of external vibrations is a relatively simple matter, but the problem can become more difficult when the apparatus is provided with automatic mechanisms for moving the plate or changing the negative between successive exposures. Vibration can then be a more serious problem, and in these circumstances all components (including the plate-holder) may need to be firmly mounted to a tube or similarly rigid structure. The apparatus may also be mounted on a heavy concrete block, which is itself isolated from vibration.

REFERENCES

[1] Koana, Z. and Wakimoto, Z., *Jap. J. Appl. Opt.*, **4** (Supplement 1), 113, 1965 (see reference [15], Chapter 4).

[2] Padgham, Mrs F. R., Bird, F. C. and Bovey, E., *J. Phot. Sci.*, **4**, 25, 1956 (see reference [9], Chapter 5).

[3] Allen, R. M., *Photomicrography*, Van Nostrand (New York, 2nd edition, 1958), p. 124.

[4] (a) Williams, L., 'Optical Method for Squaring Cameras and Enlargers', *Photo Technique*, **1**, 30, July 1939.

(b) Southey, R., 'Squaring the Camera to the Copy', *Brit. J. Phot.*, **97**, 585, 1950.

[5] Allen, R. M., as reference [3], p. 116.

7 · The 'Original' and its Illumination

The successful production of microphotographs depends on many factors, some of which at first appear to merit but little thought. The choice of the 'original' for the final stage of reduction, for instance, can exert a profound influence on the subsequent task. The present chapter deals with the factors to be considered when choosing an original, and the methods used to illuminate it.

The Form of the 'Original'

The original used for the final reduction may consist of solid objects or opaque pictures, or of a transparency or intermediate negative. As no photographic process yet appears to have been worked out for making truly microscopic coloured photographs[1] (Chapter 2), there seems little point in using a coloured original. In view of the low photographic speed of extreme-resolution emulsions, transparent originals are generally to be preferred, since they facilitate the production of a really bright image at the emulsion surface and hence avoid the necessity for inconveniently long exposures. In fact, only the fastest extreme-resolution emulsions (such as concentrated Lippmann or wet-collodion) are suitable for photographing opaque originals by reflected light, and these emulsions will usually give tolerably well-exposed images of objects illuminated by direct sunlight with an exposure of less than 1 minute at F/2. A distant scene photographed with a 2 in (50 mm) microscope objective on Maximum Resolution plate is shown in Plate 15. Comparison of this enlargement with photographs to the same scale, made with an ordinary camera at shorter distances, shows that the microphotograph possesses the foreshortening so characteristic of telephotographs.

The Characteristics of Transparencies

Since transparencies are the most usual and useful originals, their properties will be considered in some detail. The first important decision concerns the matter of size. If it has been decided to use an

---

[1] Microscopic coloured 'paintings' have, however, been made by the assembly of the brilliantly-coloured scales from butterflies' wings [1].

objective requiring strict adherence to a fixed reduction factor (p. 121) the transparency must clearly be made to the size indicated. For example, objectives covering a 1 in (25 mm) square field and working with reduction factors of 10 and 25 require transparencies 10 in (25 cm) and 25 in (63·5 cm) square respectively. In the absence of this restriction, three factors have to be considered. If transparencies are made too small, it becomes difficult to produce images with the perfection needed to avoid difficulties in the final reduction stage.

Fig. 47 *Battery of Objectives for producing Several Images simultaneously*
From Fabres' *Traité Encyclopédique de Photographie*, Paris, 1890, 4, p. 76.

Large transparencies are difficult to illuminate with the required brightness and uniformity, and by necessitating use of a longer bench complicate avoidance of vibration troubles. In the author's experience, transparencies having heights between 1 in (25 mm) and 4 in (100 mm) are a convenient compromise for the final reduction stage when microscope objectives are employed.

Large transparencies were, however, used by French manufacturers for the mass-production of microphotographs. Their equipment employed a battery of objectives to project a large number of similar images side by side on a single plate (Fig. 47). It has been stated that as many as fifty objectives were used together in this way [2]. The number of images which can simultaneously be produced by this method is limited by the angular field covered by the objectives, since those images formed by the outermost objectives must lie off the axis. This difficulty was combated by using a large negative, so that

G

an exceptionally long working distance was required to give the necessary degree of reduction, and the images formed by the outermost objectives lay relatively closer to the axis (Fig. 48). For the same reason, a relatively large transparency is needed by the I.B.M. fly-eye lens, whereby hundreds of images for semi-conductor devices are made by a single exposure (see p. 336).

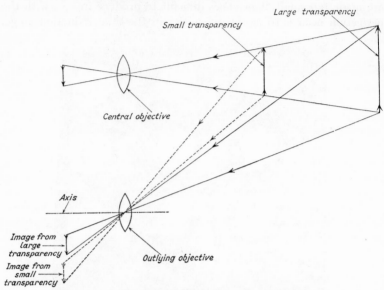

Fig. 48 *Use of Large Transparency with Battery of Objectives*
Greater working distance decreases displacement of images off axis.

The type of image chosen for reproduction and its photographic 'quality' both influence the subsequent reduction to microscopic dimensions. The production of microphotographs is a task in which the greatest obstacles occur in the final stage, and it is thus only reasonable to start with an original well-suited to the microphotographic process used. Three main matters have to be considered:

    (i) whether the original image should be a 'negative' or a 'positive',

   (ii) the contrast should be adjusted to suit both the subject matter and the characteristics of the extreme-resolution emulsion,

  (iii) the fine detail should, so far as possible, avoid features known to make reproduction difficult.

'NEGATIVE' OR 'POSITIVE' ORIGINALS AND IMAGES

Photographic line images may conveniently be classified as 'positive' when they predominantly show dark lines on a clear background, and 'negative' when they show clear lines on a white background. Whether the final microphotographic images are required to be positive or negative in this sense is one factor controlling the desired property of the transparency. In Chapters 2 and 3 we noted that extreme-resolution emulsions can be made to give tones which get darker in the same order as the tones of the original (direct-positive reproduction), or are tonally reversed and give negative reproduction. If direct-positive reproduction is used, the transparency must clearly have the same tonal direction as the final image. Conversely, the tones of the transparency must be reversed with respect to the final image if negative reproduction is used. The simplest decision is merely to select the tonal direction of the transparency on the basis of the reproduction most readily given by the available emulsion. Better results can, however, be obtained by choosing the emulsion and transparency *together* to give the best possible final result (p. 205). Factors to be considered are lens flare (p. 105), the adverse influence of some types of reversal process on image sharpness, and overriding requirements which may make direct-positive reproduction imperative (p. 91).

THE CONTRAST OR DENSITY RANGE OF THE ORIGINAL

The contrast or density range of the original transparency should be adjusted to suit the characteristics of the extreme-resolution emulsion, in the same way as ordinary photographic negatives should be made to suit the properties of the medium on which they are to be printed. We must, however, first decide whether the subject-matter is to be a 'continuous-tone' or 'line' picture.

Photographs of solid objects usually show a continuous range of tones between the extremes of light and shade present in the picture, and uniform light or dark areas in the original are depicted as patches of even density. They are more difficult to reproduce on a really small scale, since the granular structure of a transparent continuous-tone image is more readily seen than that of an opaque line image composed of developed grains of the same size. Thus for the same emulsion, lesser reduction factors are permissible for continuous-tone than for line images.

If continuous-tone images have to be made, it is desirable to remember that most of the difficulties are concentrated into the final reduction stage. It is therefore generally sensible to adjust the density-range of the continuous-tone transparency to suit the emulsion used for making the final images, rather than to modify the processing of the microphotographic emulsion to suit an existing transparency. For this purpose suitable emulsion and development conditions are chosen, and so long as the transparency is made large enough there will be no difficulty in ensuring a very sharp image. This choice means that a transparency of small density-range should be made if it is intended to make continuous-tone images on a high-contrast extreme-resolution emulsion. For this requirement it is easier to work the other way round, using a transparency of normal density-range to produce images on an extreme-resolution emulsion of lower contrast.

With line images,[1] the density range of the transparency must at least be sufficient to ensure that the lines can be recorded with an adequate density by an exposure which just fails to print through the background. A high-contrast negative must therefore be used with the softer-working emulsions such as wet-collodion or collodion print-out. The high contrast, and consequent small exposure latitude of most commercial extreme-resolution emulsions, necessitates a transparency of a special type, in which all the lines have the same density. Now the visual appearance of high-contrast line negatives is notoriously deceptive, since the great contrast between the background and the lines can camouflage the fact that the density of the lines varies from point to point. The most certain way to ensure uniform density in the lines is to make them absolutely transparent, so that the density is, in fact, zero. The transparency should be made by copying an indian-ink drawing, printed page or specially prepared art work (pp. 237–240) on a high-contrast 'process' material or on one of the modern 'lith-type' emulsions, which give a very sharp image if processed in their special developer. These emulsions should be exposed so that they give a background density not greater than 1·5 or 2 on recommended development, and this density should be quite adequate for use with the extreme-resolution emulsion. A useful test to apply to such line negatives is to view them when dry through the back, while pressing the emulsion surface firmly against a white card. Since the light reflected from the card has to pass through the emulsion twice before entering the eye, the effect of any density in the lines is doubled, and differences are correspondingly easier to see. Transparencies which do not satisfy this test may still be made usable by 'cutting' and intensifying (Appendix I).

Another most effective method for making transparencies with completely clear lines is to use one of the modern thin-layer developer-

---

[1] The production of special 'drawings' for industrial processes such as making graticules or microelectronic masks is also discussed on pp. 273 and 333.

incorporated wash-off films (such as the 'Kodagraph' Wash-Off films). These are tanned image-wise by development in an activator solution, and the unblackened areas are washed off in hot water.

THE FINE DETAIL OF THE ORIGINAL

Just as line images are simpler to reproduce than continuous-tone pictures, so certain types of line image are easier to reproduce than others. Images showing great variations in the proportions of black to white in different areas, for instance, are difficult to reproduce. As we shall see in the next Chapter, large exposed areas require substantially less exposure than smaller areas, and this combined with

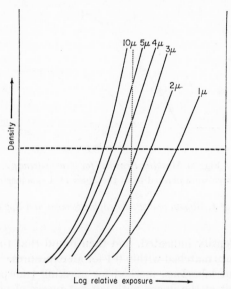

Fig. 49 *D-log E curves for slit images*

All slits were given the same exposures, but densities decreased as width was reduced.

Courtesy J. Altman and 'Photographic Science and Engineering'.

the limited exposure latitude of high-contrast emulsions can hinder the making of a satisfactory image.

When the value of the reduced images merits such a precaution the final result can be improved by masking the transparency, so that the wider lines are caused to transmit a lower light intensity to compensate for their greater printing effectiveness. In principle, this is achieved by placing layers of suitable optical density over the wider lines in the transparency.

For this purpose, Altman [3] determined the densities required in the mask from a series of exposures made while reducing a test image consisting of a series of slit images of varying width. The densities of the reduced images of the slits were plotted against log exposure, and Fig. 49 shows the family of curves so obtained. The horizontal log E shift between the curves indicates the density by which the image of each width of slit should be masked, and these values are plotted in Fig. 50. To test the effectiveness of this method, he masked 15 μ

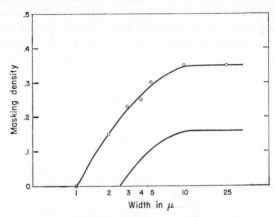

Fig. 50 *Masking Densities for Transparency*

The values shown were derived from the horizontal spacings of the curves in Fig. 49.

Courtesy of J. Altman and 'Photographic Science and Engineering'.

lines by the density indicated, and then found that the densities of 15 and 2·5μ lines matched within 0·1 for all exposures.

A direct, but laborious, method for masking transparencies is to cover each unit of the image with cut-out pieces of neutral-density filter of the appropriate density value. Hance [4] employed the simpler method of applying a dyed stencil formed from a photosensitive resist to the back or front of the transparency. The photosensitive layer was exposed selectively through the wider lines of the transparency, so that an integral mask remained when the resist was developed. If the pattern to be copied required two levels of masking, both wide and very wide lines could be masked by photoresist, and the very wide lines then masked more heavily with a neutral density filter.

An alternative is to build composite images at the final reduction stage by exposing the emulsion separately to carefully registered transparencies showing respectively only the fine and only the wide lines. This technique has been employed for making microelectronic masks, and the photorepeaters allow satisfactory registration of the two images to be obtained in the image plane.

In producing microscopic images of such originals as printed texts, the exposure of one part of an image may be increased by scattered light or flare coming from immediately adjacent areas of the image. This tendency leads to 'clogging' of the detail where several lines run together, or to variations in the 'average blackness' of words in a page of print, so that long words or words with the letters placed closer together reproduce darker than their neighbours. When specimen images are required, this trouble can be at least partially corrected by mounting the transparency with an 'unsharp mask' made from it [5]. For this purpose it may prove necessary at first to make several masks with different degrees of unsharpness and contrast, and test these by actually making microphotographic images from the masked transparency.

In using a masked transparency one is implicitly recognizing the fact that, at extreme reductions, the reproduction is introducing local tonal distortions. An attempt is therefore made to introduce equal and opposite distortions into the transparency. In the same way rounding of square corners can be compensated for by suitably modifying the drawing of line images (p. 238).

FINISHING THE ORIGINAL

All retouching of the picture must, of course, be made on the transparency, but it is not generally necessary to 'spot' line images as thoroughly as with negatives intended for either contact-printing or enlarging. This is because 'pinholes' in the transparency tend to be smaller than the lines of the image, and would need an exceedingly long exposure to make them appear in the microphotograph. Only the more obvious blemishes need therefore be painted over with an opaque medium. The reader is more likely to be troubled by small refracting or light-scattering particles in the background in cases when the transparency has black lines on a clear background. These are most troublesome with condenser illumination, since they divert the light in their neighbourhood, and will tend to be recorded as transparent spots in the reduced image. Their effect can be greatly lessened by using a microscope mounting medium such as Canada Balsam to cement a cover-glass on the surface of the transparency. This is in any case an excellent practice, since it protects valuable transparencies against dust and scratches (see also p. 245). An equally effective temporary method is to use 'microscope immersion oil, and secure the cover-glass with 'bulldog' clips or adhesive tape. When a transparency with a cover-glass is illuminated with a condenser system, it may sometimes be possible to see a 'ghost' image to one side of the main lines of the image. This is produced by internal reflections in the glass, but its intensity is much lower than the main image, and it is most unlikely to show in the reduced image.

Illumination for Microphotography

Whatever method of illumination is used, it should provide a high and very uniform light intensity over the entire area of the transparency or original. The principles employed are the same as in photomicrography or photographic enlarging, but the conditions of their application are very different. One special difficulty is that the

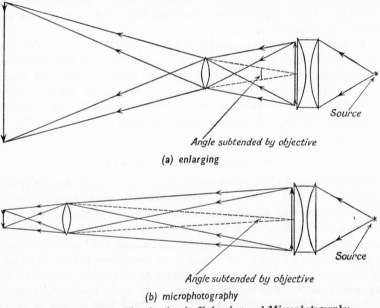

(a) enlarging

(b) microphotography

Fig. 51 *Condenser Illumination in Enlarging and Microphotography*
Because the microphotographic objective in (b) has a smaller entry pupil and is further from the condenser, it subtends a much smaller angle.

reduced aerial image given by the objective is too small to permit convenient visual examination of the uniformity of illumination in the focal plane. This has therefore to be judged by microscopic inspection of actual photographic images. The unusual dimensions of the apparatus introduce subsidiary problems. In enlargers, for instance, the distance from the objective to the condenser is usually less than twice the distance from the condenser to the illuminant. In microphotography the objective-to-condenser distance may be five or more times the condenser-to-illuminant distance, so that the objective subtends a much smaller angle at a point on the surface of the condenser (Fig. 51), causing optical problems which are discussed below.

In the remainder of this chapter we shall discuss the following three types of illuminating system:

(1) Condenser illumination for transparencies.
(2) Illumination of transparencies through a light-scattering screen.
(3) Diffuse illumination by reflected light.

CONDENSER ILLUMINATION

The principles of condenser illumination for our purpose are the same as for photographic enlarging or motion-picture projection (Fig. 52). The condenser is used to focus an enlarged image of the light source

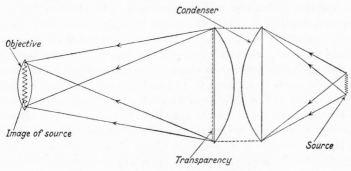

Fig. 52 *Principle of Condenser Illumination*

into the aperture of the objective. When seen from the objective, the condenser should show a uniform disc of light having the same brightness as the surface of the illuminant itself.[1] If this image just fills the opening of the objective, all the light transmitted by the transparency will be concentrated to produce a brilliant and uniformly lit reduced image, and since the objective is effectively used at its full aperture it should give its best resolution (Chapter 4).

So long as the image of the illuminant does not over-fill the objective, all the light will be concentrated into the image, whatever the degree of reduction used. The light intensity in the image will thus for one objective be almost proportional to the square of the degree of reduction. This fact makes condenser illumination ideal for the slower extreme-resolution emulsions, since very bright images are

[1] When checking this condition, do not forget that high brightnesses, particularly from mercury-vapour lamps, can be dangerous to the eyes. The condenser should therefore only be viewed through an appropriately dense filter or fogged plate.

formed at high degrees of reduction. Goldberg, for instance, even found that the light from a motor-car head-lamp bulb gave inconveniently short exposures when making very minute images on his collodion print-out emulsion [6].

A practical difficulty with condenser illumination is that the relative positions of light source, condenser and objective have to be adjusted carefully to give uniform illumination over the whole field of the image. To make this adjustment, first focus the objective, and then move the illuminant behind the condenser until an image of the illuminant is projected on the aperture of the objective. Now replace the transparency with an aperture of the same size cut in black paper. When the aerial image of this aperture is viewed with a focusing microscope, a filter should be used to reduce the brightness to a safe and convenient level. The brightness should be reduced until the aperture looks a light grey colour. This can be done by covering the aperture with a film uniformly exposed and developed to give the required density. The illuminant can then be moved until the field looks uniformly illuminated.[1] When working with high-contrast emulsions, it is particularly advisable to check this visual assessment of uniformity by making an exposure series on the illuminated aperture without a transparency. Unless the condenser and illuminant are mounted on the negative-holder (Chapter 6), this adjustment has to be repeated every time the reduction factor or focus is altered by moving the negative-holder along the bench. Even with this preferred method of mounting, the condenser focus should be re-checked, if the negative-holder is moved by more than a few per cent of its distance from the objective.

SPHERICAL ABERRATION IN CONDENSERS

Spherical aberration in condensers can be a serious problem in microphotography, since the images are usually made at high reductions with objectives having a small back aperture. This difficulty was encountered, for example, when using a double plano-convex condenser of 5 in (12·5 cm) diameter to illuminate a $2\frac{1}{2}$ in (6 cm) square negative placed at 30 in (75 cm) from a 1 in (25 mm) microscope objective. In spite of the great diameter of the condenser relative to the size of the negative, it was found impossible to secure uniform illumination over more than a 1 in (25 mm) diameter circle in the centre of the negative. On checking the equipment, the condenser was found to be correctly focused, and formed a sharp image of the filament of

---

[1] Without a filter, the re-enlarged image is often bright enough for viewing by projection on an opaque screen, so that one person can simultaneously adjust the illuminant and watch the resultant changes in uniformity.

the lamp at the back surface of the objective, but this image disappeared completely when a 2 in (5 cm) diameter circle of card was placed over the centre of the condenser. The outer zones of the condenser were transmitting plenty of light, but this was being focused at a much shorter distance, so that it was not entering the objective at all (Fig. 53). The existence of such a large aberration might appear astonishing, until it is remembered that this condenser was being used in quite abnormal conditions. The condenser-to-objective distance was more than five times the distance from

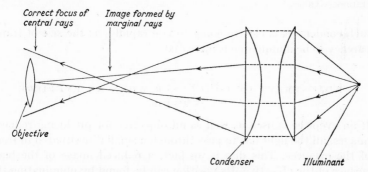

Fig. 53 *Spherical Aberration of Condenser*

The field effectively illuminated by a condenser can be seriously reduced by spherical aberration.

condenser to illuminant, whereas with normal use for this condenser the distances would have been nearly equal. The objective with which the condenser would be normally used would also have had a larger diameter, so that it would subtend a larger angle at the condenser and would be more likely to accept light from the outer zones of the condenser (Fig. 51).

With any particular objective, this difficulty will obviously become worse if higher reduction factors are used. This is another reason for making the transparency no larger than is needed to secure immaculate image quality. Uneven illumination resulting from aberration of the condenser will be less apparent if the light source is of such a size that its projected image is larger than the opening of the objective. This condition leaves a margin for errors, but necessarily means that more of the light transmitted by the transparency does not enter the objective, and is wasted for image formation.

This difficulty can be avoided by the use of more elaborately constructed condensers, such as have been described by Traill-Taylor [7] and Cox [8]. Fig. 54 shows a special three-component condenser used at the Möller graticule factory [9]. Sayce employed 'an achromatic lens of good quality' as a condenser [10]. The cost of providing

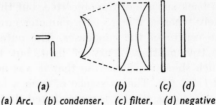

(a)   (b)   (c) (d)

(a) Arc,   (b) condenser,   (c) filter,   (d) negative

Fig. 54 *Special Condenser used for Making Graticules*

From B.I.O.S. Final Report, 1552, by permission of the Controller of H.M. Stationery Office.

such condensers is clearly going to rise rapidly, as the size of transparency to be illuminated is increased.

ADJUSTMENT OF CONDENSER WHEN AN EYEPIECE IS USED

If an eyepiece is used as well as an objective for producing reduced images, all the light has to pass through a small disc situated in front of the eyepiece. This disc is, in fact, a reduced image of the back surface of the objective. Its position can be found by illuminating the objective with the sub-stage condenser, and using a piece of paper to search the space in front of the eyepiece to find the plane in which the projected disc of light is smallest. The image of the illuminant projected by the transparency condenser then has to be focused at the position found by this test. Since an eyepiece enables a given degree of reduction to be obtained with a shorter objective-to-transparency distance, it might be expected to lessen difficulties due to aberration in the condenser, but whether any real advantage will be gained is not known.

Illumination of Transparencies with a Light-scattering Screen

GENERAL PRINCIPLES

In the preceding section we have seen how a condenser is used to concentrate a beam of light into the objective, so that the cone of rays from every point on the original is sufficiently wide to fill the back component of the objective. The objective can also be filled by placing a light-scattering screen between the light source and the original. With this system the exact position of the lamp is not particularly critical, but a much smaller proportion of the light transmitted by the transparency will enter the objective, and the brightness of the reduced aerial image will be correspondingly less. Greater latitude in adjustment is permissible with this method but certain conditions must still be satisfied.

Let us first consider the case of a 'line' transparency AA' [Fig. 55(a)] placed in front of a light-scattering screen illuminated normally by a parallel beam of light. It can easily be shown that each transparent point on the original will behave as if it were a self-luminous point with the same angular distribution of light as a point on the surface of the screen itself. Now the objective subtends an

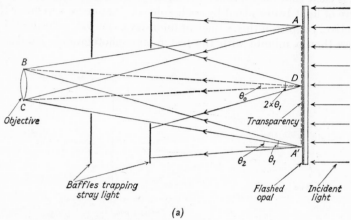

(a)

Fig. 55 *Diffuse Illumination with Light-scattering Screens*
(a) Principle of diffuse illumination.

angle $\theta_1 - \theta_2$ at the extreme ends of the transparency. and with small fields this angle will not be significantly different from the angle θ_0 subtended at the axis. The condition for even illumination is that the screen shall give a substantially constant intensity of transmitted light with angles of emergence from normal to θ_1. This means that every point on the transparency will transmit an even intensity over an angle $2 \times \theta_1$. Most of this light clearly cannot enter the image, and as much of the stray light as possible should be caught by baffles so that it cannot be reflected into the objective and contribute to 'flare'. The angular distribution of the light entering the objective will then be practically the same as with condenser illumination, and precisely the same image sharpness should be obtained.

PRACTICAL CONSIDERATIONS IN THE USE OF LIGHT-SCATTERING SCREENS

Light-scattering screens usually consist either of clear sheets of glass or plastic material with one side etched or ground, or else the whole or part of the body of the sheet is made turbid by the presence of a large number of light-scattering particles. Nutting [11] measured the angular distribution of brightness transmitted by normally illuminated light-scattering screens. He found that the surface-etched or ground screens only diffused uniformly through an angle of 5° or less, while 'opal' glasses diffuse nearly uniformly over a hemisphere. Only the latter type of screen is adequate for our purpose, and 'flashed opal' should be used since it absorbs less light than the 'pot' opal.

It is clear that only a minute fraction of the almost uniform hemisphere of light transmitted by each point on the screen will enter the objective. In spite of this, sufficient intensity to permit exposure times of less than a minute with the faster microphotographic emulsions

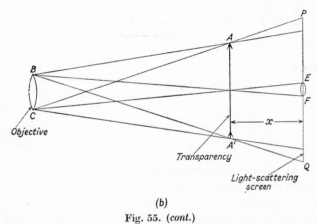

(b)

Fig. 55. (*cont.*)

(b) Diffuse illumination with the screen separated from the transparency by the distance *x*.

can readily be obtained by using a 100-watt or a No. 1 Photoflood incandescent lamp.

The area of the screen which is uniformly illuminated need only be slightly larger than the transparency when the two are in contact; but a larger area of uniformly-illuminated screen is required when it is separated from the transparency. In the latter case the uniformly-illuminated area of the screen must fill the space between lines such as AP and $A'Q$, obtained by projecting the lines CA and BA' from the edge of the objective to the most remote corners of the transparency [Fig. 55(b)]. When the screen is separated from the transparency by an appreciable distance, the image-forming light transmitted by each point of the transparency will come from a small disc of the screen, such as EF. Some separation of the screen from the transparency can be considered advantageous, since it lessens the tendency of small blemishes on the screen to result in uneven illumination of the image.

The brightness and uniformity of illumination given by the screen is controlled by the size and number of the light sources, and their distance from the screen. This means that the intensity can be adjusted to require an exposure duration convenient for hand timing by altering the distance of the illuminant from the screen: an advantage which does not occur with condenser illumination. With small sources or large distances, the intensity is inversely proportional to the square of the distance; but with 'Pearl' lamps placed at a distance of 10 in (25 cm) or less, the intensity is more nearly inversely proportional to the distance. To obtain tolerably uniform illumination, a single 'Pearl' lamp should be placed so that the distance of its envelope from the screen is at least equal to the diagonal of the transparency. Thus the distance should be 3 in (7·5 cm) for a 2 in (5 cm) square transparency. Fields larger than 6 in (15 cm) square are better illuminated by a number of lamps, since a single lamp at the distance required for uniform illumination is likely to give insufficient brightness.

Recently, compact illuminating boxes having an opal screen brightly and very uniformly illuminated by fluorescent lamps, have been marketed in U.S.A. [12] for illuminating transparencies for graphic arts and the production of images for microminiature electronic work (p. 328). Such illuminators are not cheap, but the cost of designing and building 'tailored' equipment could exceed the cost of the ready-made article built by specialists.

RELATIVE MERITS OF CONDENSER AND DIFFUSE ILLUMINATION

With diffuse illumination, the brightness of the image is almost independent of the reduction factor. This is because both the light flux collected by the objective from any point on the transparency, and the area of the reduced image are inversely proportional to the square of the distance from the objective to the transparency. In fact, as in ordinary photography, the brightness of the image at all reduction factors is controlled by the angular aperture of the objective; and the effective aperture is practically independent of the reduction factor except when objects are photographed with small reduction factors. This contrasts strongly with condenser illumination, where the image intensity increases (approximately) as the square of the reduction factor. For this reason, condenser illumination is ideally suited for use with the slower extreme-resolution emulsions. There is no doubt, however, that the adjustment of condenser illumination requires an expenditure of considerable time and care, particularly if it has to be performed repeatedly during photographic focusing tests.

DIFFUSE ILLUMINATION BY REFLECTED LIGHT

Really large transparencies have been illuminated by holding them in front of a window, outside which an inclined white screen is placed to reflect daylight through the window, but when reproducible exposures have to be given, a method using artificial light is to be preferred. The transparency may be placed over an aperture in a board

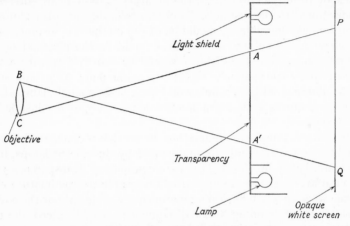

Fig. 56 *Illumination of Large Transparencies*

supporting a bank of lamps used to illuminate a white screen (Fig. 56). It is doubtful whether the image brilliance obtained by this method is any greater than that obtained by similarly illuminating an opaque drawing or a photographic print, but a transparency on a glass plate has the advantage of dimensional stability.

THE ILLUMINANT

The choice of illuminant is determined by such features as the spectral distribution, intensity, constancy and controllability of the light emitted, the size and shape of the source and the properties of any envelope protecting it. The spectral distribution of the light should permit adequate intensity to be obtained with the wavelengths required by the emulsion; and it is sometimes necessary to use a source which makes it easy to expose by monochromatic light. With extreme-resolution emulsions having the usual green sensitization (Fig. 10), for instance, a mercury-vapour lamp used with a dark-yellow filter (such as the 'Wratten' No. 8 or No. 16) causes latent-image formation to result almost entirely from the powerful 5,461 Å line. This method may gain in popularity as more workers employ non-achromatized objectives, with other aberrations specifically corrected for this wavelength (p. 111). If light filters are used to modify the quality of the light from the illuminant, they may be placed in any position between the illuminant and the transparency, so long as they do not get damaged by heat.

A variety of illuminants giving sufficient intensity are available today. Overrun incandescent lamps (in particular Photoflood lamps) are very useful for diffuse illumination, but should be handled with care since their brightness tends to fall off rather rapidly with use. With diffuse illumination the shape of the filament is relatively unimportant, but ordinary domestic incandescent lamps with clear envelopes should be avoided, because striations in the glass tend to produce dark and light bands which will affect the evenness of the image. With condenser illumination, however, the lamp should have a clear envelope, since diffusion of the light defeats the whole purpose of this method. The source itself should also be so small that its image projected by the condenser can all be accepted by the objective. Filament lamps meeting this requirement fairly well can be obtained from the range of low-voltage lamps used for motor-cars. When ultra-violet sensitive emulsions are used, mercury-vapour lamps should be considered. Any type is suitable for diffuse illumination, but a high-pressure condensed source such as the 'Mazda' (Type ME/D) is needed to obtain the full advantage of condenser illumination.

A special situation is encountered in connection with the use of extreme-resolution emulsions for making holograms for wave-front reconstruction (p. 467). In this work, the design of the systems tends to be built around the characteristics of suitable lasers. Emulsions for this purpose have been specially dye-sensitized in specific spectral regions, to record the output of particular types of laser.

On completing this section, one is tempted to wonder how the earlier microphotographers achieved their excellent results with the crude illuminants available at the time. The inconvenience caused by their illuminants was overcome with patience and ingenuity. Dancer, for instance, used a paraffin lamp and increased his rate of production by using two microphotographic cameras simultaneously, one on either side of the lamp [13]. The modern worker can be thankful that he is not reduced to such devices, but can concentrate his skill on developing further refinements or applications for his art.

REFERENCES

[1] Anon., 'Paintings in Butterfly-Wing Scales', *Ill. Lon. N.*, Christmas No. 1950, **16**. (Work of Anatole Duplan is described.)

[2] Fabre, C., *Traité Encyclopédique de Photographie*, Gauthier-Villars (Paris, 1890), **4**, p. 79.

[3] Altman, J. H., 'Photography of Fine Slits Near the Diffraction Limit', *Phot. Sci. Eng.*, **10**, 140, 1966.

[4] Hance, C. R., 'Low Density Mask Technique for High Reduction Photography', *I.B.M. Technical Report*, TR.22,262, June 1966. Also abstract in: *Phot. Sci. Eng.*, **10**, 181, 1966.

[5] Yule, J. A. C., 'Unsharp Masks', *Phot. J.*, **84**, 321, 1944.

[6] Goldberg, E., *Brit. J. Phot.*, **73**, 462, 1926 (see reference [6], Chapter 1).

[7] Traill-Taylor, J., *The Optics of Photography and Photographic Lenses*, Whittaker (London, 1892), p. 219.

[8] Cox, A., *Optics: The Technique of Definition*, Focal Press (London, 1943), p. 314.

[9] Bovey, E., B.I.O.S. report 1552, Fig. 18, p. 122 (see reference [22], Chapter 2).

[10] Sayce, L. A., 'The Measurement of Resolving Power', *Phot. J.*, **80**, 455, 1940.

[11] Nutting, P. G., 'Projection and Focusing Screens', *T. Ill. Eng. Soc. (N.Y.)*, **9**, 92, 1916.

[12] For example, Aristo Grid Lamp Products Inc. (Port Washington North, L.I., N.Y.) market a 'Trans-Luminator' FYG-54 specifically designed for use with Kodak High-Resolution Plates.

[13] Garnett, H., 'John Benjamin Dancer: A Pioneer Microscopist and Inventor', *Eng. Am. Mech.*, **1**, (new series), 430, 1927.

8 · Microphotographic Technique

In this chapter we shall consider the decisions which have to be made and the procedures to be followed in making microphotographic images. In doing this we shall assume that all necessary materials and apparatus are freely available, so that our conclusions will be determined only by the requirements of the images, and will not be restricted by questions of supply. In practice, of course, it may sometimes be necessary to compromise and obtain the best results given by available equipment.

For convenience the present chapter is divided into three sections. The first describes how the component parts are selected for making any particular image, the second deals with the phenomenon of image formation, and the last with establishing and maintaining the conditions needed to give a satisfactory image.

Selection of Components

The components which have to be collected before making any microphotograph are the sensitive material, the objective, the focusing mechanism, the original transparency and the illuminating system. Selection of these components should not be done in isolation, but all should be chosen to suit the requirements of each particular job, so that their functions interlock to give a coherent working system. It is therefore helpful to consider the different components in the following sequence:

(1) Specify the line width, line-width tolerances and field to be covered in the microphotograph, and select an *objective* likely to give the performance required. If no existing objective is capable of covering a sufficiently large field with the resolution required, three courses can be taken. When this treatment is permitted by the design of the image, it may be divided into a number of smaller units. Each of these will have to be projected through an available objective, with the plate moved precisely between successive exposures (see pp. 246–50). Alternatively lens designers may be approached about the possibility

193

of designing a special objective for the proposed task, or an original image may be generated by mechanical scribing.[1]

(2) Select a degree of reduction necessitated by the objective's design (or shown by actual tests to give the required image quality). Calculate the consequent size of original *transparency* needed, and determine whether this should be negative or positive.

(3) Select an *emulsion* to give the line width and contrast and any other image properties which may be required.

(4) Choose an *illuminating system* suitable for use with the selected emulsion, objective and size of original transparency.

(5) Choose a *focusing mechanism* having the precision required by the selected objective.

(6) Choose *processing conditions* suitable for the emulsion, the image contrast, and any special properties needed.

The factors influencing these decisions have already been discussed in preceding chapters, but the reader must always remember that each component may influence the performance of several others. This system of interactions can be visualized diagrammatically by placing the components in the centre (components are underlined in Fig. 57), and arranging the more important requirements around them (in boxes). The interactions are shown by arrows against which are placed the operating factors. This diagram is useful in that it shows that the components should never be chosen in isolation, and it can also be helpful in tracing troubles.

The way in which the components are chosen will now be illustrated by a few examples, demonstrating the different choices required by varying circumstances (Table 9).

When working out the conditions for making various types of microphotograph, the reader is recommended to tabulate his choice of components in this way. Such a table will serve as a check-list tending to prevent the overlooking of important details, and helping in the tracing of troubles when work has actually started. The notes should also assist in the progressive refinement of technique, as experience accumulates.

The Phenomena of Image Formation

While good results can be obtained by purely rule-of-thumb methods, an understanding of the process of image formation is likely to allow satisfactory results to be obtained with greater speed and certainty.

---

[1] Programmed movements of plates with exposure to electron or laser beams are also being applied for this purpose (p. 352).

This knowledge will permit the reader to visualize what has actually happened in the emulsion layer during the exposure, and this is particularly useful when the work is not going well, and puzzling results are being obtained. The source of the trouble can in favourable cases be deduced from a careful inspection of the image, thus saving hours or days of effort in trying to correct the fault empirically.

IMAGE FORMATION IN THE FOCAL PLANE OF A 'PERFECT' LENS

The image of a point source formed in the focal plane of even a 'perfect' lens is never a true point, but the light is spread out into a diffraction pattern known as the *Airy* disc (Plate 16). This means that the brightness and sharpness of very small images is less than would be anticipated from purely geometrical concepts of image

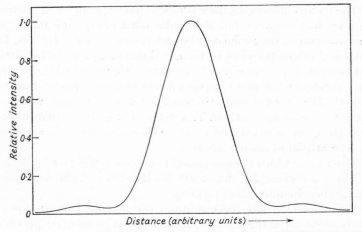

Fig. 58 *Unit Line-Profile of Light Intensity*

Intensity profile of line image calculated from overlapping of many Airy discs.

formation. *It also means that some degradation of sharpness must inevitably occur every time an image is reproduced by projection through a lens system.* Now a line can be thought of as an infinite number of points side by side, and the light distribution in its image can be computed by dividing the Airy disc into narrow bands parallel to the line, and integrating the total light flux inside each of these bands. Fig. 58 shows the resultant 'unit line-profile' plotted from figures calculated in this way by Selwyn [1].

The fact that the image of an 'infinitely fine' line possesses a finite width and unsharpness is the physical reason for the resolution limit of perfect objectives. When the centres of two parallel lines are brought so close together that their line-profiles overlap, the profile of the pair can be simply calculated by summing the point-to-point contributions of light from both images. Fig. 59 shows a number of such composite profiles for pairs of lines with their centres separated by $4\frac{1}{2}$ units of distance (curve 1), 4 units (curve 2) and $3\frac{1}{2}$ units (curve 3). These spacings, for example, might correspond to 355, 400 and 457 lines/mm respectively, or resolution increments of about 12 per cent.

Curve 1 shows that the close proximity of the two lines has resulted in extensive filling of the intensity 'valley' between them. The small

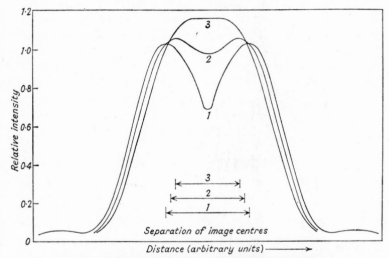

Fig. 59 *Profiles of Pairs of Lines at the Limit of Resolution*

The composite profiles for pairs of lines have been calculated by adding the light intensity derived from each. Three cases are shown for separations indicated by the arrows. Note how rapidly the density depression between the images decreases with reduced separation.

extra approach of the two lines corresponding to curve 2 results in almost complete filling of the valley, and an even closer approach with curve 3 gives a profile showing no depression at all between the two peaks. In fact, there is a critical separation of the two lines, below which there is no reduction in the light intensity between their centres, and resolution in the sense of direct recognition of the existence of two lines is then physically impossible.

In the same way that the unit line-profile can be calculated by considering the result of overlapping a large number of Airy discs in a single row, the profile of wider lines can be computed by considering the overlapping of many parallel unit line-profiles. The required calculations were made by Altman [2], who used published figures for the unit line-profile to calculate the effect of diffraction on the intensity of the images of lines of different widths. The calculations were based on the assumption that the optics were purely diffraction-limited, and that the wavelength was 5,300 Å. The computed intensity distributions were normalized, so that unity represented the illuminance given over an extended object by the lens at any aperture. Fig. 60(a) shows

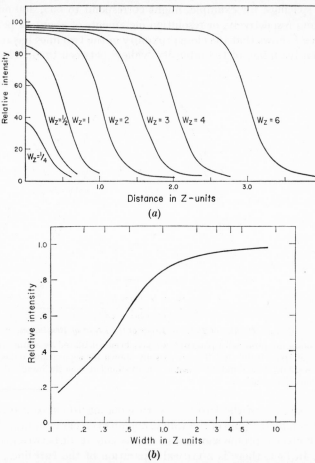

(a)

(b)

Fig. 60 *Spatial Distribution of Intensity in Aerial Images of Fine Slits*
Z-units defined as microns distance divided by F-number.
Courtesy of J. Altman and 'Photographic Science and Engineering'.

one-half of the symmetrical line profiles resulting from these calculations. In this figure, the abscissae are the distances from the line centre measured in 'Z-units'. Since Z-units equal microns divided by the F-number of the lens, they are simply converted to microns on multiplying by the F-number. Fig. 60(b) shows that the intensity at the centres of the images increases rapidly with width until the width of the line reaches about two Z-units. To an increasing extent, attempts are being made to produce images with line widths of one Z-unit or less, and the resultant changes of line profile with width have the following consequences:

(i) Since the relative intensity in the centre of an image of a line increases with its width, less exposure is needed for wider lines.

(ii) The width of the image of a line is not independent of the exposure, but the image will widen as the exposure is increased.

(iii) The narrower the line, the more rapid will be the relative increase of width with increasing exposure.

These effects are observed with 'negative' transparencies consisting of a black background containing narrow transparent lines. The circumstances are reversed when the transparency contains a uniform illuminated field interrupted by small opaque areas. In fact, the three consequences are changed so that the light intensity in a line decreases with width, the images become narrower with increasing exposure, and the relative rate of narrowing is greatest for the finest lines.

IMAGE FORMATION BY LENSES WITH APPRECIABLE ABERRATION

With other than 'perfect' lenses the diffraction pattern of the Airy disc is modified by spherical or other aberrations. These result in further widening of the patch of light from the image of a point source, with consequent widening of the unit line-profile. Sometimes the image of a point may consist of a bright annular ring, or may show a sharp, bright central spot surrounded by a less intense and 'soft' disc of light. In the latter case the image can usually be improved by stopping the objective down. So long as the objective is correctly centred, the axial image of a point source will still have a circular symmetry, and once the unit line-profile has been measured, the same method of computing the profiles of lines of practical width can be applied. However, because the unit line-profiles are widened by aberrations, the rate of broadening of a line of given width with exposure will be increased, and the increase of brightness with line width will be extended to greater line widths.

IMAGE FORMATION IN AN EMULSION

The phenomena described in the preceding sections are all concerned solely with the aerial image. It is now necessary to consider what happens when an image is projected on (or into) an extreme-resolution emulsion. The first thing to note is that the effective thickness of most industrially coated emulsions is greater than the depth of focus of medium-power microscope objectives. In particular it is unusual to coat silver-halide–gelatin emulsions uniformly on plates to give a dry layer appreciably less than 5μ (0·0002 in) thick. With objectives of N.A. larger than 0·3 (or F-numbers smaller than 1·7) this means that the emulsion thickness is no longer negligible, so that

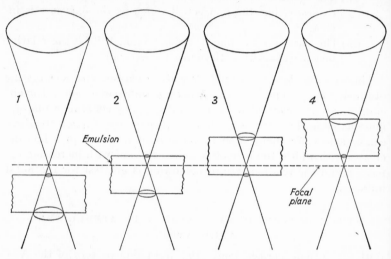

Fig. 61 *Optical Sectioning in Microphotography*

With a point source, the intensity in any plane is inversely proportional to the cross section of the cone in that plane. Cases 2 and 3 result respectively in images near the surface and near the bottom of the emulsion, and give higher densities than cases 1 and 4.

the path of the rays on each side of the focal plane must also be considered. Image formation must therefore be studied as a process which occurs in three dimensions, rather than just in a plane.

Consider the image of a point source as being produced by a cone of light from the objective which converges to a point,[1] and then diverges to make a second cone of the same angle with its apex touching the apex of the first cone (Fig. 61). Now the total light flux passing through any plane at right angles to the axis of the lens must be the same, so that the average intensity in any plane must be inversely proportional to the cross-sectional area of each cone where it

---

[1] This is a purely geometrical picture of image formation which neglects the wave theory of light, but the consequences of the physical reality of the cones is illustrated by Fig. 65, (p. 216). In any case the qualitative validity of our conclusions is not lessened by this simplification.

is cut by the plane. The intensity is thus highest in the focal plane where the apexes meet, and falls off rapidly on each side. The counterpart of this phenomenon can be readily observed in microscopy with dark-ground illumination, where the rapid falling off in the brightness of small objects on each side of the plane of focus is known as 'optical sectioning'.

We can now examine the result of projecting the image of a point source into a relatively thick and optically clear dry-plate emulsion. In cases 1 and 4 (Fig. 61) the cones only occur in the emulsions at positions where their areas are large, and the intensity is therefore relatively low. In cases 2 and 3 the apexes of the cones are formed inside the emulsion. If the contrast of the emulsion is high, and no more than the minimum necessary exposure is given, appreciable blackening will only be produced for a very short distance above or below the apexes. In fact, an image may be formed by 'optical sectioning' at any level in materials such as Kodak M-R emulsion, and photographic focusing tests can give quite sharp images definitely confined to the lower part of the layer (Plates 17 and 65).

These changes in the intensity of the image of a point source on each side of the focal plane mean that the density of a small image will depend on the focus as well as on the exposure time and on the intensity of the illuminant. The magnitude of the intensity decrease in out-of-focus planes is proportional to the increase of the area illuminated, and the proportional rate of increase in the area of each element of an image depends on its size and shape. A rough estimate of the increase in the illuminated area can be made by considering all images as consisting of large numbers of points, with the cones corresponding to adjacent points overlapping during image formation. With an infinitely fine line, which can be regarded as a single row of points, it can be shown that the increase in the illuminated area in any out-of-focus plane will be proportional to the diameter of the cone, and not (as in the case of a point) to its cross-sectional area. The reduction of density on each side of the focal plane will hence be less rapid than in the case of a point.

With real lines of finite width, the situation can be appreciated by considering how close to the edge of the line a point can approach, without losing light outside the geometrical edge of the image. Fig. 62(a) represents the image produced by an objective of N.A. 0·4, $3·5\mu$ below the emulsion surface by projection from a 'negative' transparency. The points U and B in the emulsion surface show the limits of the zone of maximum overlapping of the cones. Points in the emulsion to the *right* of B cannot lose light outside the *left* edge of the image. Similarly the line BCE defines a zone to the *right* of which points at any level in the emulsion cannot lose light outside the *left* edge, and points to the *left* of UXY cannot lose light outside the *right* edge. Within the parallelogram bounded by MCNX light is lost outside neither edge, and the highest possible light flux is obtained. The greater the geometrical width of the line being imaged (i.e. the distance CX), the greater will be the proportion of the emulsion thickness accommodated within such a parallelogram. Thus the effective exposure of wide lines is increased not only by the higher intensity in the aerial image (as a result of overlapping Airey discs), but also by the greater proportion of the emulsion depth receiving the highest possible light flux.

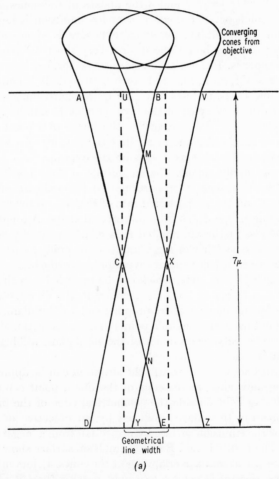

(a)

Fig. 62 *Formation of 1-micron Line in 7-micron Thick Emulsion*

Overlapping of cones from objective of N.A. 0·4 (a) with 'negative' and (b) with 'positive' transparency.

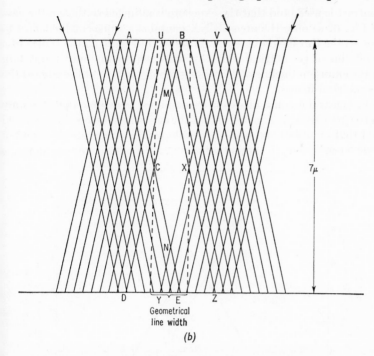

Geometrical
line width

(b)

When the original transparency being reduced consists of fine dark lines on a clear background (a 'positive' image), the argument has to be reversed. The illuminated background is then considered as an area in which an infinite number of cones from points in the background overlap, and the image of the fine line results from the *subtraction* of a relatively small number of cones. The cones ABC and CDE now correspond to the extreme right edge of the left-hand element of the background (Fig. 62(b)). By reversing the argument, it can be shown that the parallelogram MCNX now defines the zone into which no light is spilt from either the left or right elements of the background. Directly above and below this parallelogram are the triangular zones UMB and YNE, into which are spilt light from both elements of the background with resultant loss of contrast. The sharpness of the edge of the background is also eroded by areas such as ACMU, which lose light spilt into the geometrical image of the line. The production of a satisfactory image in a relatively thick emulsion and in these circumstances seems hardly possible.

The practical consequences of all this can also be visualized by using Fig. 62 to determine what proportion of the emulsion depth is used for image formation at different distances from the line centre. Let us assume that an emulsion of low absorption coefficient and high

contrast is used, and that the exposure is adjusted so that in the case
of Fig. 62(a) only the area MCNX contains a sufficient light flux to
exceed the threshold exposure. As shown in Figure 63 the centre of a
black line of geometrical width 1μ will then occupy only about $4\cdot3\mu$
of the emulsion thickness, decreasing rapidly to zero at the edge of the
geometrical image.

For clear lines on a black background, let us assume that it is only
in the area MCNX (Fig. 62(b)) that the exposure is below the threshold
and that emulsion grains fail to develop.[1] The image profile for a $1\text{-}\mu$
wide 'clear' line then shows that about $2\cdot7$ μ of the emulsion depth is

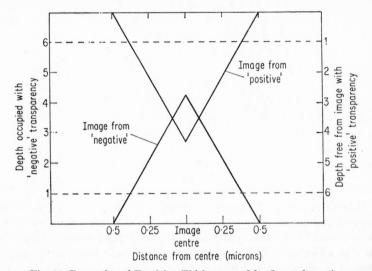

Fig. 63 *Proportion of Emulsion Thickness used for Image formation*

Figure derived from Fig. 62 as described in the text. Comparable results for
$1\text{-}\mu$ thick emulsion are indicated by horizontal dotted lines.

still occupied in the centre of the line. From Fig. 63 it is clear that
the images would be much improved by drastically reducing the
effective emulsion thickness. The horizontal dotted line drawn at a
depth of 1 μ shows that approximately $0\cdot75\mu$ of a $1\text{-}\mu$ wide black line
could then occupy the entire emulsion thickness, and that $0\cdot75$ μ of a
$1\text{-}\mu$ wide clear line in a $1\text{-}\mu$ thick emulsion should be completely clear.

In practice, the phenomena accompanying image formation are not
so straightforward as has been indicated by this idealized picture.
Thus any aberration in the objective will tend to blunt the cones of
light, so that these become connected by a region whose width is in
creased, but whose thickness changes little for some distance on each

[1] For simplification of the argument, it is assumed that the same proportion of
grains develop in all zones *outside* MCNX.

ide of the geometrical focal plane (see Plate 17). In effect, an increase
n the depth of focus is obtained at the expense of some loss of resolu-
ion. The phenomena of image formation will also become less clear-cut
f the emulsion scatters light, and conditions are further changed by
ight absorption in the emulsion. These complications only modify the
details of the process, but do not prevent effects of this type from in-
luencing the production of microphotographs.

When reproducing transparencies with a range of line widths, we
hus see that the differences in the effective exposures received by
arrow and wide lines can be influenced by:

> Diffraction,
> Optical Sectioning,
> Lens Aberration,
> Light Absorption and Scatter in the emulsion.

In this complex situation, Altman's example of using calibrating
est exposures to determine the levels of masking required in transparencies [2] (see p. 180) is to be recommended.

INFLUENCE OF THE SENSITOMETRIC PROPERTIES OF THE EMULSION

The present discussion has, so far, mainly been concerned with the
distribution of light in the *optical* image. The resultant distribution of
density in the *photographic* image, is also influenced by the characteristic curve of the emulsion used. Thus quite different conditions are
obtained when the same final image is produced by a process giving
either a 'direct-positive' or a 'negative' rendering. In the preceding
section, we have seen that the image profile in an emulsion of significant thickness is less favourable if a 'positive' transparency consisting of fine black lines on a clear background is used. Since most of the
transparency transmits light, flare will in these conditions also have
its maximum tendency to decrease image contrast and sharpness.
Thus it is better to select a negative process for producing fine black
lines on a clear background and a direct-positive process for producing
fine clear lines on a dark background, because a 'negative' transparency consisting of clear lines on a dark background will be needed
in both cases. The contrast of the emulsion also strongly influences
the result. Fig. 12 (p. 34) shows how a high contrast effectively increases sharpness by producing a steep density profile from a relatively
flat intensity profile.

Establishing a Satisfactory Image

There is one dominant requirement which all the devices of microphotographic technique must attempt to satisfy: it is that the reduced copy of the original should show the least possible change in the relative thicknesses of the lines.

Ideally the thickness of the lines should equal their thickness in the original divided by the reduction factor, but this is a degree of perfection which can only be approached when making images of a size well within the capabilities of the emulsion and objective. When using an original consisting of an opaque plate with small transparent areas, the width of the lines in the reduced image normally increases with increasing exposure. This indicates that the correct exposure is the least which gives adequate density in the finest lines. If the image also contains wider lines, they will be thickened by the increased exposure needed for the fine lines. Methods for counteracting this difficulty are discussed on p. 180.

In practice the correct exposure cannot be determined until the objective is correctly focused, since with 'negative' transparencies the light intensity in fine lines decreases rapidly when the objective is put out of focus. One must, however, also determine approximately the correct exposure in order to execute a sensitive photographic-focusing test. Too heavy an exposure will cause even a sharply focused image to appear unsharp, and thus blunt the discrimination of the test. The establishing of a satisfactory image has therefore to proceed by a series of successive approximations in which an exposure test is made at an approximate focus, followed by a focusing test at the best exposure indicated by the first test. These tests clearly cannot be executed satisfactorily without adequate control of exposure and development, because uncontrolled changes of density level will result in random and confusing changes of image quality.

EXPOSURE CONTROL

Before considering methods of exposure control in detail, it should be noted that the effective speed of developing-out emulsions is markedly affected by development conditions, and this is particularly true for such fine-grain materials as the concentrated Lippmann emulsions (p. 70). Careful exposure control is thus useless if random variations of development time or temperature are permitted, or if the developer is allowed to become stale in the dish. It should also be realized that all photographic materials may show small differences of speed from batch to batch. The exposure tolerance in microphotography is often likely to be smaller than such batch-to-batch speed variations, and a fresh exposure test for the production of any particular image should therefore be made with each batch of plates.

The factors which can be used to control the exposure are:

(i) the illuminant and the optical system with which it is used,

(ii) any light filter used to modify the spectral quality or intensity of the light,

(iii) the distance from the illuminant to the original (when diffuse illumination is used),

(iv) the current passing through the lamp,

(v) the exposure time.

In extreme-resolution photography, the lens aperture should generally not be changed for adjusting exposure, in view of the effects on resolution and focus (Chapter 4).

The usual practice in exposure control is to use the first four factors to obtain a convenient intensity of illumination, and then vary either the lamp current or the exposure time. With diffuse illumination, large changes of intensity can conveniently be made by varying the distance from the lamp to the diffusing screen. Once a convenient intensity level has been determined, the distance should be kept constant, since any accidental change will necessitate another exposure test. The maintenance of the same lamp distance requires particular care when the focusing tests are made by moving the transparency to and fro on the optical bench, rather than by moving the objective relative to the emulsion. In the former case the lamp should preferably be mounted on the base of the negative-holder, so that its distance from the original is not changed when the negative-holder is moved (Chapter 6).

Variation of the current or voltage of an incandescent-tungsten lamp is a useful means for making small adjustments of exposure, and is particularly convenient when a mechanical shutter is used to give a fixed exposure time. The most certain method is to use an ammeter in series with the lamp, since inaccurate readings due to poor contact in the lamp-holder are avoided. Whether the current is controlled by an ammeter or a voltmeter, the instrument used need not be particularly accurate, but *should* give a large deflection of the needle while the lamp is burning. This should make it possible to reproduce the current or voltage within ± 1 per cent, which will give adequately consistent exposure conditions. Control of the lamp current can also be used to guard against changes in mains voltage, or to maintain a constant light emission as measured by a photocell. For commercial-production work, use of a constant voltage supply is strongly advised. Such precautions are particularly desirable when using a high-contrast material such as a concentrated Lippmann emulsion.

H

Selection of an appropriate exposure time is a simple method of adjusting the exposure to the desired level. When making continuous-tone pictures, or using a low-contrast emulsion, a sufficiently correct exposure can usually be found by a test in which the exposures are successively doubled. This procedure is not generally sufficiently sensitive for high-contrast emulsions, and the following method is recommended.

First adjust the intensity of the illumination so that an exposure time of at least 10 seconds will be needed. When the exposure is given by hand,[1] this is the shortest time which is likely to permit the consistency needed by high-contrast emulsions. Make a widely spaced series of exposures such as 1, 3, 10, 30 and 100 seconds, and develop the test plate. If this first test indicates an exposure between 10 and 30 seconds, make a second test with a more closely spaced series such as 10, 14, 20 and 28 seconds, or 10, 12, 14, 17, 20, 24 and 28 seconds (see Appendix III). If the first test indicates an exposure outside these convenient limits, it is advisable to adjust the intensity of illumination.

DETERMINATION OF THE BEST COMBINATION OF EXPOSURE AND FOCUS

The best combination of exposure and focus can only be ensured by a series of interlocking photographic-exposure and focusing tests made with equipment permitting the conditions to be strictly controlled. Such a procedure permits the effect of any change to be assessed in terms of its influence on the final result, and this must provide the most certain route to a satisfactory image. When a few images of only moderate fineness are required, visual focusing can be used, and it is then only necessary to make one test to determine the exposure time. Visual focusing to the required accuracy is, however, a highly skilled task, and may give disappointingly variable results. This criticism does not apply to Goldberg's split-beam technique (Fig. 28, p. 133), but this method is only really satisfactory for very slow emulsions and for the making of fairly small numbers of images.

The operation of an interlocking exposure and focusing test at first seems most laborious, but it has been found that rapid inspection methods (see below) used with the following system rarely fails to give satisfactory results within two hours: a fraction of the time which can be wasted by empirical muddling.

(1) Focus the objective visually, by using a magnifier focused on

---

[1] Commercially available process-timers, with a total scale deflection of a few seconds, allow similarly finely graded series of exposure times to be made with much briefer exposures.

the plane of the negative-holder to observe an enlarged image projected from a test plate in the image plane (Chapter 5). The focus should now be sufficiently correct to permit the production of a really informative exposure test.

(2) Make a rough exposure test, with large increments of exposure-time or lamp-current between each exposure of the series. On development this plate should be used to judge the focus as well as to determine the approximate exposure needed.

(3) At this juncture at least three courses of action are possible:

    (i) If any of the images of the first exposure test are *really* sharp and located just below the emulsion surface, it may only be necessary to make a further exposure test with the time or lamp current changed by smaller increments.

    (ii) If the images in the first test are only fairly sharp, it may be thought advisable to make a further test to determine the optimum exposure for stage 4.

    (iii) If the images are obviously unsharp estimate the exposure likely to be needed in stage 4. Remember that more critical focusing will increase the density of fine lines in negative-working emulsions, as well as increasing line sharpness.

(4) Unless the sharpness of the images given by the exposures tests is irreproachable, make a series of exposures with the focus changed by suitably small increments. This may be done directly by a micrometer movement adjusting the objective-emulsion distance (p. 154), or indirectly by altering the distance of the negative-holder without adjusting the camera (p. 136). With the indirect method, it is useful to remember that the negative-holder and the focal plane move in the same direction. Thus moving the negative-holder away from the camera brings the focal plane closer to the objective.

If all goes well, stage 4 should give an image of such quality that no further tests are deemed necessary. Really critical work or the need for a large number of images may, however, justify the making of further confirmatory tests.

(5) The first confirmatory test will be another exposure test at the optimum focus indicated by stage 4.

(6) The second will then take the form of another focusing test at the exposure indicated by stage 5. Tests 4 and 6 should show not only whether the image is sharp, but also at which level in the emulsion it is formed.

PERMUTATED EXPOSURE AND FOCUSING TESTS

An alternative procedure is to combine operations 3(ii) and 4, by permutating the adjustment of exposure and focus settings. For example, exposure times such as 12, 14, 17, 20 and 24 seconds might be given for each of five appropriately spaced focus settings. Inspection of such a compound test would then give a most useful appreciation of the interaction of these two factors. For convenient operation, this method requires rapid and reliable means for changing the focus and for moving a single plate so that many images can be made on it. It has been employed particularly with 'photo-repeaters' used for making microelectronic masks (p. 337), with the focus changed by setting for a series of pressure indications on the pneumatic gauge (p. 149). With such equipment, the permutated test can be made with an ideal arrangement of the images. For example, horizontal rows would indicate results of increasing exposure, and vertical columns the effect of progressive changes of focus.

INSPECTION OF RESULTS

Effective and rapid execution of such interlocking exposure and focusing tests depends on ability to use a microscope, on convenient methods of preparing test images for inspection, and on the ability to *see* and interpret significant symptoms.

It is first necessary to be sufficiently familiar with the adjustment of a microscope to ensure that the images are viewed by 'critical' illumination, so that the image seen is a clear representation of the microphotograph. Instructions for adjusting a microscope are given in any textbook on microscopy. The objective and eyepiece used for viewing the image should be chosen so that the area of the unit image[1] fills most of the visible field. Use of lower magnifications than this will make sufficiently critical observation difficult, but higher magnifications are sometimes desirable. An oil-immersion objective is useful for checking the depth of the image in the emulsion layer, but is not normally needed for checking the sharpness of any but the very smallest images.

Images can at first by viewed in the wet state, with only a 1-minute wash following fixation. Excess water should be shaken off the plate, the back should be dried to prevent damage to the viewing microscope, and a cover-glass is preferably laid on the emulsion to prevent condensation of water on the objective. Because of the greater thickness of the wet and freshly processed emulsion layer, images observed in

---

[1] In the case of large images produced by multiple exposures, only one unit of the image should be viewed at a time.

this state often appear less sharp and dense than they will after the emulsion has dried. Reliable judgement of results is therefore hindered, and inspection of wet images is only recommended for a preliminary check, or for rough tests.

In most cases it is preferable to dry the test plates before viewing. Since the images need not be very permanent for this purpose, all the processing operations subsequent to development can be shortened. Extreme-Resolution plates need only be fixed for 1 minute, washed for 1 minute with a stream of water falling directly on the emulsion from a tap, and dried with an electric hair-dryer (or in the hot air rising from an electric fire or gas ring) after rinsing in two parts of industrial spirit and one part of water. Wet-collodion plates can be dried even more rapidly, as the water content of the layer is so low during processing.

The convenient assessment of focusing-test or exposure-test series depends greatly on the ease with which successive images can be found. Delays caused by searching for the images on the microscope are frustrating, and tend to blunt appreciation of subtle differences between successive images. With plates which have been dried, each image of test series should be encircled with a bold ink line. It is also helpful to mark the exposure or focus setting for every image of a series, so that the conditions used for making each can be positively identified while the plate is actually on the stage of the microscope. Inspection is also facilitated by making the images in a straight row parallel to one edge of the plate. When this edge is located against a mechanical stage (or against a suitably placed horizontal bar clamped to the stage of the viewing microscope), successive images can be found rapidly by moving the plate horizontally. The author has found this procedure particularly helpful when viewing images less than half a millimetre (0·02 in) high, and for inspecting resolution-test images.

INTERPRETATION OF RESULTS

However perfect may be the apparatus and emulsion used, the quality of the final result will still largely depend on the technician's skill.[1] An important constituent of this skill is the ability to perceive small differences in the appearance of each of a series of images, so that a

[1] The skill lies in setting up the conditions for optimum image quality. Once these conditions have been established and with properly designed equipment and working methods, conscientious operators should then be able to continue making satisfactory images.

reliable estimate can be made of the best conditions for the exposure. This ability can be analysed into three parts, namely:

> Visual microscopy,
> Visual memory,
> Interpretation.

A full appreciation of the significance of focusing or exposure tests depends on the inter-comparison of each of a series of images. Inter-comparison depends on the ability to retain a mental picture of the appearance of one or more images viewed previously, so that the quality of the image inspected at any instant can be related to others in the series. Comparisons of this type are fairly easy to make when a series of photographs is laid out on a table, but become more difficult when the adjustment of a microscope introduces a delay between the viewing of successive images. The very act of finding the next image tends to blur the mental impression. The acquisition of a visual memory is another faculty which only grows with practice, but it can be assisted by making notes about the appearance of each image. One should not attempt to visualize the appearance of the whole of the image, but rather concentrate attention on that part whose reproduction is likely to prove most critical.

The interpretation of the results depends on knowledge and experience. Just as with the tuning of a car or fault-finding in a radio set, experience shows:

> where to look,
> what to look for,
> how to interpret what is seen.

TROUBLE-SHOOTING BY INTERPRETATION OF EXPOSURE AND FOCUSING TESTS

Whenever satisfactory results are not being obtained, an obvious step is to make series of exposure or focusing tests to check the conditions used. The process of interpretation will then be the same as if the images concerned were being made for the first time. In either case, the following points can be watched.

(1) The finest lines in any image are the most sensitive to change of conditions.

(2) Another sensitive indication of the quality of reproduction is the degree of rounding observed at the intersections of lines.

(3) Interaction between exposure and focus should be constantly kept in mind. Inadequate density can just as well be due to incorrect focus, as to insufficient exposure.

(4) Exposure tests should give the impression of a steady and progressive increase of image strength with increased exposure.

(5) Irregularity in an exposure test may be due to inadequate exposure control, *or* irreproducibility of focus setting or vibration.

(6) A focusing test should show a smooth and progressive improvement up to the region of maximum sharpness, followed by a smooth and progressive deterioration.

(7) If a focusing test shows lack of regularity, attempts to reset the focus to a desired position after inspection of the test are likely to prove unsuccessful. After scrutinizing the images for possible signs of the consequences of vibration or poor exposure control, malfunctioning of the focusing system should be considered. Failure of the emulsion surface to seat down precisely on all the contact surfaces, after moving the plate sideways is a likely source of trouble. Alternatively, backlash in the focusing mechanism may be affecting the results.

(8) Focusing tests when making very fine images on extreme-resolution emulsion should be inspected not only for sharpness, but for the position of the images within the depth of the emulsion layer. An oil-immersion objective is then best used for inspection.

(9) Additional information can be obtained from photographic focusing tests by studying the appearance of partly out-of-focus images, or of images covering a field too large for the objective. If the objective produces the usual saucer-shaped field, the centre of the image will be the first part to become sharp as the image plane is brought down from above the emulsion; i.e. by moving the objective towards the emulsion or the negative-holder towards the camera. The area of the sharp zone should then increase as the focusing movement is continued. On passing beyond the optimum position, the centre of the image should start to become unsharp first. If the corners and the centre of the image cannot be sharply focused at the same focus position, use of a field-flattening eyepiece or reduction of aperture or employment of a longer focal length objective are indicated.

(10) Unsymmetrical distribution of unsharp areas around the centre of the image may result from failure to centre the transparency on the axis of the objective, or inadequate squareness of the transparency and emulsion planes.

(11) Inability to record fine and heavy lines satisfactorily with the same exposure may be at least partly corrected by masking the transparency (p. 180).

(12) Total inability to obtain a satisfactory image after all possibilities of malfunction have been checked, is likely to mean
that the performance demanded is beyond the capability of
the chosen objective. If use of a larger aperture objective fails
to improve the results, and vibration is absent, the emulsion
could be at fault.

Maintaining a Satisfactory Image

When conditions giving a satisfactory image have been established,
the process must be operated so that consistently good results are
obtained. The main difficulties in maintaining a satisfactory image
are usually caused by the fact that the microphotographer is likely
to be working close to the limits of performance of the emulsion and
objective. To work close to these limits is an excellent exercise for
developing technique, but does not favour the consistent production
of satisfactory images. It is better to use conditions which permit
slight variations of focus, or exposure, or development to occur
without spoiling the image.

Working tolerances can, in fact, be obtained in two ways. The first
is to work well within the limits of performance of the emulsion and
objective. The resolution of the system should, if possible, be capable
of reproducing lines considerably finer than any shown by the required images. The whole of the image should also be comfortably
contained within the central (and therefore near enough) flat field of
the objective. A working tolerance gained from the depth of focus of
the objective may otherwise be lost if the focus has to be adjusted so
that the centre of the image is at the back and the edges of the image
are at the front of the zone giving satisfactory sharpness (Fig. 64). It
is interesting to note that particular mention of the importance of
such working tolerances is made in the report on the Möller graticule
factory; and no little of the success of their production was ascribed
to such precautions [3].

The second way of obtaining working tolerance is concerned with
the correct placing of the conditions within the permissible range. To do
this, the exposure and focusing tests should be performed so that they
show not only the best conditions, but also the permissible range on
each side of the optimum giving tolerable image quality. In some cases
it is then sufficient to choose working conditions in the middle of the
range. In others, however, it may happen that the deterioration on
one side of the optimum may be more rapid than on the other. While
increasing exposure, for example, may thicken the lines, some slight
thickening of the finest lines by over-exposure may be preferable to
their complete disappearance by an equivalent degree of under-

exposure.[1] Similarly the loss of resolution resulting from placing an image slightly too deep in the emulsion layer will be much less than if the focal plane is placed in front of the emulsion. In the former case

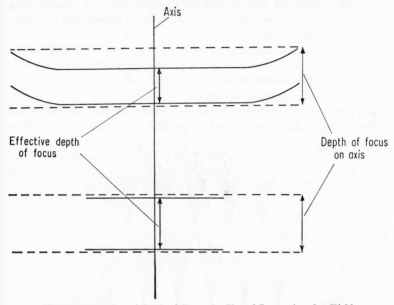

Fig. 64 *Reduction of depth of Focus by Use of Large Angular Field*

a correctly focused image is formed in a lower layer of the emulsion, while in the latter only an out-of-focus image is formed at all. It follows that estimations of the permissible range are best made directly from the images in series of test exposures.

ANOMALOUS IMAGE FORMATION

The extreme resolution of microphotographic emulsions means that they can record the fine structure of an image: a property which may sometimes lead to quite surprising results. Under conditions which might merely give an unresolved blur on emulsions with lower resolution and higher speed, a microphotographic emulsion can sometimes show an image which is more like a caricature than a straightforward reproduction of the original. Anomalous images are worth studying for insight of the process of image formation, since they constitute defects whose explanation often suggests a remedy.

[1] This gives some tolerance to decay of lamp brilliance during long exposure runs.

SPURIOUS RESOLUTION IN PROJECTION PRINTING

In the visual and photographic testing of the resolution of lenses, it has been recognized that multiple-line resolution-test images may sometimes appear to be resolved in out-of-focus planes, when coarser images are not resolved. This spurious-resolution effect has been explained by the overlapping of blurred images of several lines [4]. When reproducing images formed by microscope objectives it is sometimes possible to observe both spurious and real resolution within the thickness of a single emulsion layer.

During experiments on 'optical sectioning' (p. 200) an achromat objective of N.A. 0·4 was used to project a grating image with a

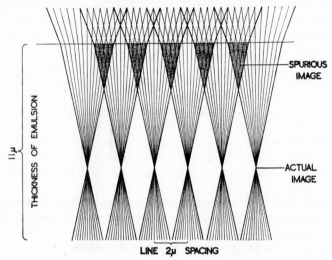

Fig. 65 *Formation of Spurious Image*

frequency of 500 lines/mm (12,500 lines/in) into a relatively thick (11 μ) coating of Maximum-Resolution emulsion. With some exposures of a photographic-focusing test, it was noticed that there seemed to be two images at different levels in the emulsion layer [5]. Transverse sections of the processed layer revealed a sharp image of dense narrow lines confined to the lower half of the emulsion layer, accompanied by poorly resolved wedge-shaped bands in the emulsion surface (Plate 17). The possible cause of this phenomenon was examined by making a scale drawing of the cones of rays forming images with their centres 2 μ apart. The angle of the cones (in air) corresponded to the objective's N.A. of 0·4, and it was assumed that, after refraction at the surface of an emulsion of refractive index 1·5, they came to a focus 7 μ below the emulsion surface. The result gave a pattern, in which the overlapping of the cones near the emulsion surface corresponded reasonably well to the spurious images with respect to position, size and shape. This geometrical construction showed that the dark bands should lie *between* the lines of the real image: a situation demonstrated by Fig. 65, and also noted by previous investigators [6]. Obviously this recording of a spurious image can only have a harmful effect on the sharpness of the main image. It constitutes another powerful argument for using emulsion layers in such a way that image formation only occurs in a very thin layer.

FINE STRUCTURE IN CONTACT PRINTING

A 4 mm achromatic Beck objective was used to make a series of negative resolution-test images on Maximum-Resolution plate. The performance of this contact resolution-test chart was periodically checked by printing on M-R plates, and at first all groups were satisfactorily resolved. After use for some time, however, it was noticed that satisfactory results could no longer be obtained. Control tests showed that some images were reproduced as groups of three instead of two lines (Plate 18). It was then seen that the emulsion surface of the test chart had been scratched, and had crumpled heaps of gelatin piled up at the ends of many of the scratches as in Plate 19. These must have prevented effective contact, in spite of high pressures applied by the printing frame.

It was clear that some agency had caused light to be deflected outside the edges of the geometrical images and into the space between each pair of lines. Now high-contrast line images on silver-halide–gelatin emulsions usually show a relief effect at the emulsion surface. Cross sections of images on M-R plates showed that the layer thickness was greater in the dark parts (Plate 20). Thus the emulsion surface in a narrow transparent line bounded by dark areas must be concave, and refraction will cause the light to diverge as by a negative cylindrical lens. Printing with xylene (refractive index about 1·5) as an immersion fluid between the test chart and emulsion surfaces markedly improved sharpness, presumably by eliminating refraction at the surface of the test chart.

A related phenomenon was encountered during experiments on the production of small graticules by contact printing. For these tests, negatives were made on M-R plates by projection with a $\frac{2}{3}$ in (16 mm) Watson achromatic objective. The field covered by such an objective is small, so that the negatives consisted of black circles of diameter about 1·5 mm ($\frac{1}{16}$ in), in the centres of which were the images with 28 μ scale divisions and lines 3 μ wide (Plate 21). Since light spreading in from the remainder of the unblackened plate was likely to spoil contact prints; a photographic 'opaque' medium was painted around the negatives.[1] This proved to be a blunder, since the dried-down layer of opaque medium was found to be from 10–30 μ (0·0004–0·0012 in) thick. Not surprisingly, only unsharp prints were obtained, but the extraordinary banded and spiky appearance of some of the prints could hardly have been anticipated. A cellulose-acetate cast

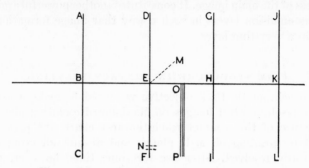

Fig. 66 *Modes of Interference shown in Plate* 21(e)

from the surface of the negative image showed a strong relief. It was found that the size of the pattern was enlarged by deliberately increasing the spacing; and by then exposing with monochromatic light, the pattern was markedly sharpened and caused to show clearly defined multiple fringes. With the original conditions, use of xylene as an immersion fluid again greatly improved the sharpness (Plate 21). These circumstances indicated that refraction at the lenticular surface of the negative was a major factor, and the details of the pattern could be satisfactorily interpreted as a complex interference phenomenon (Fig. 66).

Although the results in this section were obtained in experiments using conditions hardly likely to be employed for industrial processes, the author has been told that analogous phenomena have been observed by graticule manufacturers in workshop conditions.

TECHNIQUE OF CONTACT PRINTING

When any process is operated near the limits of its technical potentialities, even apparently simple procedures merit careful thought. The preceding section demonstrates that this is even true for the straightforward process of contact printing.

A contact-printing procedure for microphotography is likely to have to satisfy several conditions. Obviously it should reproduce the original image as accurately as possible: a requirement which is

[1] See p. 249, for a description of other methods for blackening the background.

particularly necessary when large numbers of images are made by a succession of printing stages. The printing operation should also minimize the risk of damage to the surface of the negative, and should not cause distortion of the image.

Preservation of sharpness depends firstly on securing close contact between the surfaces of the negative and printing emulsion and on using a narrow-angle beam of light so that little light is directed outside the geometrical edge of the image. For critical work, the normal type of printing frame cannot apply sufficient pressure to ensure overall contact between two plate surfaces. It is therefore necessary to use a vacuum printing-frame, such as those used for photomechanical work, or a stoutly built pressure frame capable of apply-

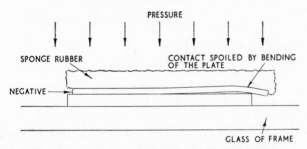

Fig. 67 *Contact Spoilt by Bending of Sensitized Plate*

The bending can occur when the sensitized plate is larger than the plate bearing the master image.

ing considerable pressure (say at least 10 lb/in^2 or 700 grams/cm^2) to a stiff sponge-rubber sheet behind the light-sensitive plate. The vacuum frames are particularly effective, for they not only distribute the pressure very evenly, but remove the risk of contact being spoiled by air trapped between the emulsion and negative surfaces.

When prints are made on a rigid support, such as glass or metal, pressure should not be applied to any part of the sensitized plate overhanging the edge of the negative (Fig. 67). There will otherwise be a serious risk of breaking the plate, or of bending it so that the emulsion surface just inside the edge of the negative is forced out of contact. This difficulty is avoided by never using a plate larger than the negative, and by placing the plate so that its edge never overlaps the negative.

The effect of using a light source subtending an appreciable angle at a point on the negative surface is indicated in Fig. 68. From purely geometrical considerations, it can be seen that there should be a penumbra region at the edge of an image, and in this region the light intensity changes gradually over an appreciable distance, with resultant formation of an unsharp edge. The possible magnitude of this effect can be seen from a numerical example. For example, the light from a No. 1 'pearl' Photoflood comes from an illuminated area approximating to a 36 mm (1½ in) diameter disc. With rather poor 'contact' corresponding to a separation of 12μ (0·0005 in), this illuminated disc at a distance of 46 cm (18 in) would produce a penumbra 1μ (0·00004 in) wide. Such calculations suggest that pinpoint sources or the use of light collimated by a lens are only likely to be needed for the most critical work, or when there are special reasons for avoiding close contact between the negative and emulsion surfaces.

Close contact may be hindered by dirt, by scratches on the negative,

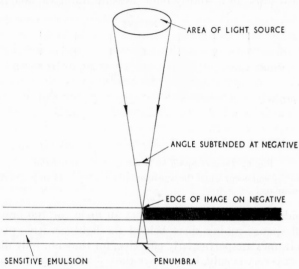

Fig. 68 *Penumbra in Contact Printing*

or by bowing or lack of flatness of the glass. Dirt on either the negative or the sensitive-plate surface will both tend to hold the two surfaces apart, and damage the negative surface when the plates are pressed together. For these reasons, cleanliness precautions are particularly important for contact printing. The extent of the damage caused to the negative surface also depends on how the surfaces are brought together and subsequently separated. If lateral sliding is allowed to occur, accumulation of debris by scratching can rapidly and progressively produce serious damage from very small dirt particles. It is therefore desirable to locate the emulsion-coated plate with respect to the negative before even the feeblest contact is made between the two surfaces. Unexposed plates can, for instance, be located on kinematically designed jigs, so that they can be lowered vertically on the negative surface. Much attention to details of this type has been embodied in contact-printing equipment designed for the electronics industry [7]. Safe removal of exposed plates from the negative surface, can be a problem, since the two surfaces may tend to become 'wrung' together when pressure is applied. To deal with this type of problem, Holthaus [8] coated the negatives with a thin layer of Carnauba wax or with a 3M product called EC2253 applied to the negative on a whirler. When the layer of EC2253 became dirty, it was removed with solvent and a fresh layer was applied.

The effects of lack of flatness of either the negative or the plate being printed depends on their thickness and size. The glass used for small photographic plates (around 1·5 mm (0·06 in) thick or less) is sufficiently elastic to offer a reasonable chance that a vacuum or pressure frame will be able to force the two surfaces together, and hence secure sufficiently good contact over a large proportion of the plate area. Since the lack of flatness will tend to be randomly distributed over the plate surfaces, the separation to be eliminated by pressure is likely to increase with the area to be brought into contact. Thus the smaller the plates on which prints are made, the better will be the chance of securing uniformly good contact (but see [14]).

When uniform contact is obtained as a result of bending, the dimensional accuracy is likely to be decreased by distortion of either the negative or the plate to be printed. For this reason, manufacturers of the most precise graticule images are making both negatives and prints on 'optical flats'. Optically worked glass is quite expensive, and usually the graticule manufacturers supply their own glass.

Refraction at the lenticular surface of the negative tends to decrease sharpness and alter line/space ratios: effects which are particularly objectionable for production schedules involving contact printing through more than one generation (p. 253). As shown in Plate 21, the effects of refraction can be eliminated by using an immersion liquid of appropriate refractive index between the two plate surfaces. Studies on use of immersion fluids with motion-picture film, show that they are also most effective in eliminating image defects caused by scratches in the negative surface [9]. Xylene has been used with Maximum-Resolution plates [5], and Delwiche, Clifford and Weller give a detailed discussion of other factors to be considered when immersion printing long lengths of film [10]. Use of an immersion fluid also reduces image defects arising from contamination of the surfaces of either the negative or the plate to be printed. This is because a large proportion of dirt particles are transparent or only absorb light feebly. Such dirt particles disturb the incident light beam mainly by refracting light themselves, or by producing local distortions of the gelatin surface of the negative or the plate to be printed, if they are present when the gelatin dries. In all such cases disturbance of the beam can be largely eliminated by an immersion fluid.

The more difficult problem of choice of immersion fluid when printing on layers of Photosensitive Resist has been discussed by Martinson [11]. The fluid should attack neither the hydrophilic gelatin of the master mask nor the hydrophobic layer of the unexposed resist. With some resists, moreover, lack of absorption by the fluid in the violet or near ultra-violet is clearly desirable. In the discussion following this paper, Martinson considered that a perfect immersion fluid had not yet been found. Later, Martinson [12] discussed the influence of the viscosity of the immersion fluid. With a microscope immersion oil, a vacuum of 5 mm of mercury had to be held for 30 minutes to ensure adequate contact, and separation of the negative from the plate being printed was difficult. Lower viscosity oils with lower boiling points could only be used when contact was secured by pressure, because bubbles were formed during evacuation. The pamphlet describing the 'Kodak' Photosensitive Metal-Clad Plate mentions XOL-40 varnish oil (Sherwin Williams Co.) or TG2320 (Swift and Co.) as suitable for immersion printing [13].

REFERENCES

[1] Selwyn, E. W. H., 'The Limit of Visual Resolution', *Proc. Phys. Soc.*, **55**, 286, 1943.

[2] Altman, J. H., *Phot. Sci. Eng.*, **10**, 140, 1966 (see reference [3], Chapter 7).

[3] Bovey, E., B.I.O.S. report 1552, pp. 46 and 100 (see reference [22], Chapter 2).

[4] Hamblin, J. R. and Winser, T. H., 'On the Resolution of Gratings by the Astigmatic Eye', *T. Opt. Soc.*, **29**, 28, 1927.

[5] Stevens, G. W. W., 'Some Optical Complications of Graticule Production', *Phot. J.*, **87B**, 34, 1947.

[6] (a) Washer, F. E., 'Resolving Power and Distortion of Typical Airplane-Camera Lenses', *J. Res. Nat. Bur. Stand.*, **22**, 729, 1939.
(b) Selwyn, E. W. H., 'The Photographic and Visual Resolving Power of Lenses', *Phot. J.*, **88B**, 6, 1948.
(c) Hotchkiss, R. N., Washer, F. E. and Rosberry, F. W., 'Spurious Resolution of Photographic Lens', *J. Opt. Soc. Am.*, **41**, 600, 1951.

[7] See, for example 'Model 682 Mask Alignment System', Leaflet of Kulicke and Soffa Manufacturing Co., Fort Washington, Pennsylvania. Also U.S. Patent 3,192,844.

[8] Holthaus, D. J., 'The basic ABC's of Photo Mask Making', in *Second Kodak Seminar on Microminiaturization*, Eastman Kodak Co. (Rochester, N.Y., 1967). Pamphlet No. P-89.

[9] Printing Motion-Picture Films Immersed in a Liquid'.
(a) Stott, J. G., Cummins, G. E. and Breton, H. E., 'Part I. Contact Printing', *J. Soc. Mot. Pic. Tel. Eng.*, **66**, 607, 1957.

(b) Turner, J. R., Grant, D. E. and Breton, H. E., 'Printing Motion-Picture Films Immersed in a Liquid. Part II. Optical Printing', *ibid.*, 612, 1957.

[10] Delwich, D. E., Clifford, J. D. and Weller, W. R., 'Printing Motion-Picture Films Immersed in a Liquid. Part III, Evaluation of Liquids', *J. Soc. Mot. Pic. Tel. Eng.*, 67, 678, 1958.

[11] Martinson, L. E., 'Microresist Technology', in *Kodak Seminar on Microminiaturization*, Eastman Kodak Co. (Rochester, N.Y., 1966), Pamphlet No. P-77.

[12] Martinson, L. E., 'The technology of Microimage Resists', in *Second Kodak Seminar on Microminiaturization*, Eastman Kodak Co. (Rochester, N.Y., 1967), Pamphlet No. P-89.

[13] Eastman Kodak Co., *Kodak Photosensitive Metal-Clad Plates* (Rochester, N.Y., 1967), Pamphlet No. P-128.

[14] Carlson, C. O., Scherr, B. F. and Rondas, R. V., *Contact Printer*, U.S. Patent 3,316,825 (assigned to National Cash Register Co.). This deals with contact printing from assemblies of thousands of high-reduction ratio document images. Both the general problem of securing ultimate contact over a substantial area, and its solution by use of a convex backing plate and a matching concave glass-supporting frame are described.

9 · Graticules (Reticles)

The optical parts of measuring instruments have often to be provided with fine reference marks to assist in determining the size, position, shape or distance of the object under observation; and these have come to be known as graticules (reticles in the United States of America). These names have been used to describe a variety of objects of very different size such as stage micrometers, eyepiece micrometers, scales for the eyepieces of military instruments, thread-profile gauges and non-parallax scales, so that a precise definition of their scope is hardly possible. The images of many graticules are relatively large, but even these frequently contain lines of such a quality that only inspection at a considerable magnification will give the full precision which the scale can offer.

The study of the design of graticules and their methods of use and production is a substantial and technologically important subject, which has so far received only scant attention in books dealing with optical instruments. It is, in fact, a subject so wide that the material in this chapter could be expanded to fill a volume by itself; the present treatment should therefore only be regarded as an introduction.

History

In 1639, Gascoigne constructed an eyepiece micrometer, which contained adjustable pointers whose adjacent edges formed a slit. In this and the following century, 'slits' and cross-wires were fabricated by stretching threads of silk, silver or spider's web and by diamond ruling on glass [1]. The art of making fine rulings had already reached an advanced stage before photographic methods were introduced. Thus, in the 1851 Exhibition in the Crystal Palace in London, M. Nobert of Prussia showed groups of ruled lines used for assessing the resolution of microscope objectives. A glass slide contained ten groups of lines of fineness ranging from 11,265 up to 49,910 lines per inch (approximately 450 to 2,000 lines/mm).

Within a few years of perfecting his process for making microphotographs, Dancer showed its potentialities for producing optical graticules. In 1857, Sir David Brewster described Dancer's results, and discussed the advantage of the photographic process in circumventing

224

limitations of mechanical production methods. Interest in Great Britain subsequently waned, and the microphotographic method was applied by German and Austrian instrument makers. By 1915, the Allies' stock of German manufactured optical munitions (such as gun sights) was smashed, and microphotographic production of graticules (practically forgotten in Great Britain) had to be resurrected by a 'crash' programme. This proved a turning point in British activity. J. Rheinberg was at the forefront of this work, and his firm (now Graticules Ltd) is still active.

It has been suggested that the British failure to exploit inventions (such as photographic graticules and synthetic dyestuffs) was caused by the past reluctance of industrialists to support any scientific endeavour which was not an immediately paying proposition [2]. The advantage derived from Great Britain's initial lead in the Industrial Revolution may have blinded them to the need for continuous technical improvement, in a period when other countries were extensively applying the results of research. A determination to avoid repetition of these past mistakes was one of the motives for the foundation of the Department of Scientific and Industrial Research, by an Order in Council on July 28th, 1915. One of the units formed by the D.S.I.R. was the British Scientific Instrument Research Association. At the request of member firms, Dr E. Bovey started on investigation into production methods in 1928. The methods developed were widely adopted by British Instrument makers, and were greatly expanded in volume during the Second World War [3]. In this period additional investigations and production were undertaken at the London School of Photo-Engraving, and in the Laboratories of the Eastman Kodak Co., and Kodak Ltd. American instrument makers now joined in this work [4], and have been particularly active in the generation of large photographic scales on dividing engines.

In 1919, Rheinberg discussed possible future trends in the use of graticules [2]. He suggested that production of suitable graticules would permit optical-instrument designers to improve existing instruments or develop completely new types. A quarter of a century later, substitution of 4 in (10 cm) diameter glass divided circles instead of 15 in (38 cm) metal scales enabled theodolites to be made with greatly reduced size and weight, but with no loss of accuracy. The glass circles were read by optical micrometers, and new optical systems permitted graduation at opposite ends of a circle diameter and from both vertical and horizontal circles to be read from a single eyepiece. The use of photographically fabricated scales also facilitated the introduction of new types of instrument. In the next chapter, it will be seen that scales adapted for automatic reading permit high-accuracy observations to be made at rates up to *hundreds per second.*

Instruments with such capabilities, which are conferred by electronic techniques used with photographic scales, are integral parts of important applications of computers.

Technical Problems of Graticule Production

Two main groups of technical problems can be discerned in the application of extreme-resolution photography to scientific instruments. Many graticules are an essential and integral part of the observation system of their instrument, and can remain in the field of view for many hours. They can thus play a decisive part in determining the accuracy obtainable from the instrument, and the comfort or fatigue experienced by the operator. The study of the influence of graticule design on working efficiency and accuracy of observations is clearly a part of ergonomics (study of man in relation to his working environment).

The production of graticules presents many technical problems, and the intrinsic difficulties have sometimes in the past been increased by the way in which the work was executed.

A potential user has been known to commission a draughtsman completely inexperienced in this work to produce a design. The user has then approached the production unit in the expectation that the graticules will be produced in a short time, in spite of insoluble (and unnecessary) production problems introduced by the inexperienced user and draughtsman. Efficient production of graticules clearly calls for co-operation between the draughtsman, the production technician and the instrument designer. They should attempt to find a compromise which achieves the ultimately required result with the minimum cost.

FACTORS AFFECTING THE DESIGN OF GRATICULES

It is convenient to group the factors which have to be considered in designing a graticule according to our two types of technical problems.

GROUP 1 FACTORS CONCERNED WITH THE VISUAL PERFORMANCE OF THE GRATICULE
  (1) Nature of the pattern.
  (2) Line width.
  (3) Visual appearance and illumination of the scale.
  (4) Dimensional accuracy.
  (5) Degree of cleanliness required in the background.

Designs of scale suitable for machine reading are described in the next chapter.

GROUP 2 FACTORS INFLUENCING THE PRODUCTION AND LIFE OF THE GRATICULE
  (6) Nature and specification of support.
  (7) Nature of material forming the pattern.
  (8) Resistance of the scale to adverse handling.
  (9) Special physical properties of the image.
  (10) Influence of design on price and production.
  (11) Suitability of photographic methods.

(1) *Nature of the Pattern.* Graticules are used for estimations of distance, or position, or shape, or size, or numbers, and analysis of the proposed observations into their essential component operations will usually indicate the general form the pattern should take. Optimum results are, however, only likely to be obtained if one also considers the way in which the eyes and brain function while making the observations. Useful guidance on such problems can be obtained from ergonomic experiments in which the influence of line width or scale design on accuracy of reading have been studied.

Rheinberg [2] has pointed out that several details in the design of a graticule may influence its efficiency and the ease with which it can be used. The nature of the pattern should be designed with a view to:

  (i) the ease with which the eye can find and concentrate on essential details;
  (ii) the avoidance of distracting details;
  (iii) the ease with which any feature in the object plane can be seen, inspected and identified, even when part of the pattern is superimposed on it.

He emphasized the importance of simplicity in the design and suggested that the ease with which extra matter can be inserted in photographic graticules may act as a temptation to load the pattern unnecessarily.

A number of suggestions have been made for obtaining the greatest accuracy when making coincidence observations. Thus, Martin discussed the arrangement of cross-wires for measuring microscopes [5]. When the cross-wires have to be set on a diffuse line, such as the line of a spectrum taken on a high-speed plate, arrangement (a) (Fig. 69) is bad, as the line is obscured; (b) is better but not good; and (c) is very good. With arrangement (c), the separation needs to be adjusted to the line width, so that the slightest movement will permit extra light to show on one side. For very fine lines, such as on a scale,

(b) is very good. Martin notes that the making of such readings depends essentially on the photometric estimation of small changes in the amount of light on each side of the index mark. A sense of symmetry is probably also important. Lambertz examined the arrangement of a scale and index mark designed to give the greatest precision when the index mark was made to coincide with any line of the scale [6]. In such scales the unit marks and the index marks are sometimes drawn in the shape of an acute isosceles triangle, and the apex of the index mark is placed opposite the apex of any desired mark on the scale. This arrangement only gives poor accuracy unless the two apexes are exactly touching, a condition not very easy to satisfy. The accuracy

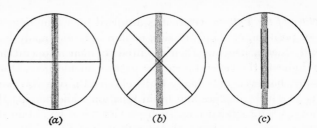

(a)   (b)   (c)

Fig. 69 *Setting of Cross-Wires*
Courtesy of Messrs Blackie and Son, Ltd, and Professor L. C. Martin.

is less critically dependent on the precise adjustment of the index mark to the scale when the apexes of the triangles are truncated.

The design of instrument scales or dials for obtaining numerical readings rapidly and accurately has recently received considerable attention. This question is very important for aircraft instruments, when several dozen dials may be displayed on a single panel, but the lessons learnt are certainly applicable to graticule design. Murrell has summarized much of the published work on this subject, and gives the following findings [7].

(i) Bad numbering of dials often leads to inaccuracy. Scales are spoiled when the main markers are numbered in fifteens or twenty-fives. Experiments show that scales numbered in units (or decimal multiple units), i.e. 1, 2, 3, 4, or 10, 20, 30, 40 . . . are best. Numbering in multiples of twos and fives is acceptable, but threes, fours, sixes and eights are all bad. Under the same conditions, 80 per cent of the readings made with a scale numbered in eights were inaccurate, compared with only 20 per cent for a scale numbered in units.

(ii) The accuracy and speed of reading increases with the size of the scale, until the graduation-interval subtends 10 minutes of arc at the eye. No further improvement was obtained by increasing the size beyond this critical point. Ten minutes corresponds to an interval of 0·03 in (0·75 mm) viewed with the unaided eye at a distance of 10 inches (25 cm). For scales viewed with an optical instrument, this interval should be divided by the magnification.

(iii) The accuracy is not improved by increasing the number of graduations beyond the point where the desired sensitivity is obtained by interpolating to divide one scale division into fifths. Visual division into fifths is definitely more accurate than division into tenths.

Murrell suggested the following rules for guidance in designing divided scales.

(a) Use the simplest scale possible, with the number of divisions just sufficient for the scale to be read with the accuracy required.

(b) Intervals should be numbered in ones, twos or fives (or a decimal multiple of these), using the lowest possible number of figures, to avoid overcrowding.

(c) The number of subdivisions should be a minimum, and never more than five between numbered divisions.

(d) The graduation interval should, whenever possible, be interpolated into five parts.

Specifications for the relationship of the thickness and length of the dividing lines to the graduation interval were given, as were suggestions for the size and shape of the figures.

Murrell also stated that unnecessary details such as maker's name, type and purpose of each scale, etc., should not show on the dial itself, and that the best dials are those with the clearest and fewest markings consistent with the observations desired. He concluded:

'Dials designed with this in mind will do full justice to the quality of the instrument and will lighten the task of the user, when he has been convinced that he is getting value for his money in a dial not crowded with graduations.'

Further guidance on dial design was given by Shackel [8], who advised that all dials should read clockwise. Lower-case letters and figures were more legible, and all instruments should be oriented so that desired readings were in the same position—upright, for example. Such factors should be discussed by all interested parties, before work on the graticule drawing is commenced.

(2) *Line Width.* The width of the lines of a graticule is a critically important property, and must be related to the capabilities of the eye.

Rheinberg [2] stated that a 0·001 in (25 μ) line, viewed at 10 n (25 cm) and subtending 20 seconds of arc, is too narrow for comfortable observation. About twice this width is the lower tolerable limit. When scales are viewed with a ×5 or ×8 ocular, a line thickness of 0·0005 in (12 μ) is sufficient. He also stated that the thickness required depends on the circumstances in which the graticule will be viewed. An opaque line seen against a white background looks narrower than it really is, whereas a transparent line seen against a white background looks markedly narrower than an opaque line of the same width. Transparent lines do not need to be excessively fine, since objects seen through them can be centred with great accuracy.

Rheinberg' opinions about the lower tolerable limit of line width are supported by experiments done later by J. Guild, who measured the errors (or insensitivity) obtained when observers had to set a cross-wire graticule on a fine line [9]. As the thickness of the line was decreased, so that it subtended less than 40 seconds at the eye, the insensitivity of the measurements increased rapidly. With increasing line width, the sensitivity remained substantially constant when the wire subtended between 60 and 120 seconds, and then gradually decreased with further increase of thickness. The fall of sensitivity with widths below 40 seconds was explained in the following way. The eye does not actually see the wire, but perceives the two bright areas on each side which are separated by the image of the wire. When the wire is too narrow the light diffracted from these areas into the geometrical image of the wire overlaps from each side, with resultant loss of image contrast and increased visual discomfort. In fact, the edges of the images of the bright areas on each side are no longer properly resolved. Guild also showed that the inaccuracy of setting of the position of the rather wider lines corresponded to an angle of only 2 seconds, or about one twenty-fifth of the resolution of the eye!

The orientation of the image of fine lines also appears to influence the certainty of recognition. Ogilvie and Taylor found that horizontal and vertical wires only needed to subtend half a second of arc for 50 per cent recognition, whereas one second was required for oblique lines [10].

From this discussion it can be seen that the accurate setting of an eyepiece scale on the aerial image of another object is an exacting task. Such visual readings are also strongly dependent on day-to-day personal performance. Instrument designers have devised a number of methods for delegating this operation to an impersonal photocell. The aim was to gain improved accuracy and speed of measurement, particularly when large numbers of readings produced fatigue. Twenty years development of such instrumental methods have been reviewed by Bradsell and Bottomly [11].

The designer must also remember that the limitations of production processes also set a lower limit to the achievable line width. It may happen that the user will demand lines of such fineness that it would be necessary to use an objective which could cover only part of the field. A decrease of field size or an increased line width may then be considered. In this connection, it should be remembered that a larger field can often be reproduced more satisfactorily if the lines at the edge of the field are arranged radially with respect to the axis of the objective (Chapter 4). Difficulties in production can also be caused when the design includes lines of different thickness (p. 180), and it may prove helpful to break the heavy lines into dots. Another complication is that all lines tend to become thickened by optical projection and by most photographic-reproduction processes, and the proportional increase is greater with the fine lines. Rheinberg actually published figures indicating the percentage increase obtained when producing lines of different width, and suggested that the line width in the drawings should be adjusted to compensate for this [2]. Such correction factors will differ with the properties of the objective and photographic process used, and the reader should therefore use a factor determined from his own observations.

A most stringent method of line-width control was employed by Hariharan [12] for the production of accurate resolution-test images (but see pp. 257–60). At the final stage, he reduced the images with a series of increasing exposures. For each group of lines in the image he determined the exposure needed to give the correct line width, by plotting the line width against exposure.

(3) *Visual appearance and Illumination of the Scale.* Photographic graticules were first made with opaque black lines on a clear background, but the appearance of the scale can be modified to suit viewing requirements. Transparent grey or coloured lines can be used when no part of the observed target should be obscured. The use of coloured lines permits the visual contrast to be changed by use of colour filters. Contrast control might also be achieved by making the image from a polarizing material of the type used in 'Polaroid Vectographs', and rotating a polarizing screen in the light path. It has been found that eye-strain in using graticules was materially lessened by viewing the graticule through a green filter [13]. The extra discrimination derived from the use of coloured lines when measuring such targets as monochrome photographs could also reduce eye-strain.

Many graticules are simply illuminated by transmitted light coming from the observed field, but auxiliary methods are used when the field is dim. In such cases graticules are usually made with lines in white pigment or mirror ('silver-line' graticules) or the pattern is etched in the glass. Glass-etched lines can be made to appear self-luminous by light scattered from a beam projected sideways into the edge of the glass bearing the image, so that no direct light enters the eyes. Graticules for use at night can also be made with a phosphorescent material, or with a fluorescent material illuminated by ultra-violet.

When instruments incorporate a scale, whose position has to be compared with a fiducial mark, it is no longer necessary to submit the user to the physical restraint involved in observation through an eyepiece. Transparent scales can be illuminated so that an enlarged image of part of the scale is projected on a light-scattering screen bearing the fiducial marks. This method is increasingly used in such instruments as analytical and commercial balances, and in circular dividing heads. It not only reduces fatigue, but eliminates the risk of parallax errors when unskilled observers are superimposing the image of an eye-piece graticule on the scale.

(4) *Dimensional Accuracy of the Scale.* The requirements for dimensional accuracy in graticules vary greatly according to their type and purpose. Thus in 'sighting' graticules and cross-wires used for aligning instruments, the main requirement is that the line width be kept within certain limits, and errors in size of the order of a few per cent would hardly be noticeable. Stage micrometers and other types of measuring or eyepiece scales for use with a microscope should have smaller errors, and it would seem reasonable to expect the overall length of such images to be within 0·1 per cent of the stated value. Distortion in the objective used for producing the images may cause the individual graduations to vary slightly, but this is usually of little consequence when stage micrometers are used to make visual estimates of size. In any case distortion is likely to be present in the objective and eyepiece of the viewing microscope, and great accuracy cannot be expected when the image of a divided scale is superimposed on a natural object with rounded edges, and which may not all be in focus at the same time. A precision of 1 per cent can be considered quite good for such measurements.

The highest possible accuracy is required for divided circles and similar large scales used in theodolites and measuring instruments. Thus with a 4 in diameter (10 cm) divided circle, 0·00004 in (1 μ) at the circumference is equivalent to 4 seconds of arc, and an accuracy of 1 second of arc has been claimed for instruments using such scales.

The dimensional accuracy of photographic graticules is determined by the accuracy and stability of the original drawing, by the absence of distortion in the objectives used at all stages, by the alignment of the apparatus and correct centring of the image on the axis of the objective, and by the dimensional stability of the emulsion layer in which the image is formed. The dimensional stability is likely to be best when the emulsion has adequate adhesion to, and is kept permanently on the support on which it is exposed. Excessive swelling during processing should be avoided. Additional precautions which may be adopted with gelatin emulsions are to form the image so that no part is less than 0·4 in (1 cm) from the edge of the plate, and to condition the emulsion before exposure to relieve stresses in factory-dried emulsions (p. 83).

Dimensional stability of the emulsion is particularly important when the final graticules are made by contact printing, since mass-production methods may involve the making of a succession of 'master' negatives and positives, and without suitable precautions errors can creep in at every generation.

(5) *Cleanliness in the Background.* There is a tradition, probably originating from the days when graticules were made mainly by ruling on glass, that graticule images should be absolutely flawless. Although such an immaculate standard can be admired as a praiseworthy goal, it can greatly increase the cost of the industrial-scale production of graticules. It is therefore not impertinent to enquire what effect flaws can have on the use of a graticule. Flaws may take the form of breaks in the lines of the image itself, which may have a distracting effect and, if unsymmetrically positioned on the line, can actually cause an error when setting cross-wires on the line. With graticule images small enough to be formed by a single exposure, the avoidance of line breaks is largely a matter of inspection and acceptance of a moderate rejection rate due to this cause. Line breaks can, however, cause great difficulty in the making of large images, or of images built up from many individual exposures (see below).

The background generally occupies a large proportion of the area of most graticules, and greater difficulties are caused by dirt in this site. Contamination usually consists of transparent particles with a refractive index different from the mounting cement. Their appearance depends greatly on the conditions used for illuminating the graticule. If the graticule can be illuminated with a relatively wide cone of rays, such as on the stage of a microscope, the visual contrast of the refracting particles will be low and they may not be too noticeable. The same particles illuminated by the narrow cone of light entering the eyepiece of an optical instrument may appear quite black, and interfere seriously with such operations as particle counting.

The rejection rate resulting from dirt depends both on the size of the graticule and the magnification at which it is viewed. With stage micrometers one dirt particle on the scale can ruin the image because it is viewed at high magnifications, but the area of the images is so small that there is a good chance that no dirt will be found in the image area. Higher rejection rates are likely to occur with larger scales viewed at a moderate magnification. These difficulties have stimulated work on processes giving a stencil image with the background devoid of colloid, and thus unable to hold any dirt particles.

It seems probable that the difficulty of reconciling the conflicting requirements of cleanliness in the images and low production costs could often be eased by closer co-operation between the makers and users of graticules. In cases where minor blemishes will not interfere with the use of the graticule, users might be persuaded to accept a less immaculate scale at a fraction of the cost of a perfect image.

With some of the largest and most elaborate scales, and particularly with types developed for automation systems, inability to achieve an adequate standard of cleanliness can cause entire projects to be postponed (p. 281).

(6) *Nature and Specification of the Support.* In some cases, graticules have been simply made by producing images on photographic plates, cutting out the area containing the image, protecting the emulsion with a temporary lacquer layer and edge-grinding the glass so that the image is correctly positioned. The glass support may, however, exert a critical influence on the optical or mechanical performance of the instrument in which it is used. It may have to conform to exacting specifications with respect to thickness, size, stiffness, absence of strain or bubbles, flatness and parallelism of the two surfaces. Images are also sometimes required on a curved or optically worked surface. Often the blanks are prepared and rigorously inspected for dimensions and optical properties before coating with photographic 'emulsion'. In such cases the graticule manufacturer should consider how the blanks are to be coated. He may find it convenient to send the blanks to a photographic manufacturer for coating with a silver-halide emulsion. Alternatively, he may use a sensitive material permitting him to apply it to his own blanks. This latter procedure tends to reduce delays and eliminates losses or breakages in transport. It also permits convenient re-coating of blanks with rejected images. For this purpose, Kodak Ltd supply a 'Pre-Stripping M.R.' plate (p. 43), from which liquid emulsion can be rapidly produced.

When graticules are made on prepared blanks, the sensitized blank must be carefully positioned during exposure, to ensure that the image is correctly placed. Special jigs, for instance, have been used to ensure that the centres of the scale and the blank coincided within a small tolerance.

(7) *Nature of the Material forming the Pattern.* The image of a graticule may take the form of a pigment suspended in a colloid layer, or a colloid-stencil image bearing a pigment, or a metal image on the surface of, or sintered in, glass, or a metal image in the body of the glass or a pattern etched in the surface or right through the support. These forms produced by different processes are described in later sections of this Chapter. We should, for the moment, only note that choice of the process is an important decision, since it can influence not only the resolution, but also the background cleanliness, the amount of retouching needed, the robustness of the image and the production cost.

(8) *Resistance to Adverse Handling.* Most graticules, and particularly those used for civil-engineering or military field-survey instruments, are likely to be exposed to rough handling. They may be subjected to mechanical shock, arctic or tropical conditions, rapid changes of temperature or pressure, or to high humidities which can permit fungi to grow even on the glass itself, and exposed to salt water, dust and sand. Moreover, a graticule will be of little use if the surfaces cannot be polished at intervals to remove dirt and smears. In many cases, satisfactory resistance can be obtained by covering the graticule with a cemented cover-glass, with the image left embedded in the original colloid layer in which it was produced. This type of graticule should be able to show the full intrinsic sharpness of which the emulsion is capable. The substitution of polymerizable resins of suitable refractive index for Canada balsam should make the use of a cover-glass more acceptable than it has been hitherto. Graticules in which the image consists of a stencil on the surface of the glass tend to be damaged when wiping and the resistance may be improved by 'burning-in'. Heat treatments can be used either to insolubilize the colloid stencil or to burn away the colloid and 'sinter' the pigment on to the surface of the glass [14].

The most resistant scales of all, however, are undoubtedly those in which the image is actually incorporated in, or etched into, glass. Graticules in which a photomechanical process gave an image etched into the glass were widely used in the Second World War. Towards the end of this period, metal 'graticules' were also used and these had the pattern etched right through the base but still showed very sharp edges.

(9) *Special Physical Properties.* The graticule manufacturer should be prepared to meet the demand that the graticule pattern should do more than just look satisfactory when viewed through an eyepiece or by projection. It must obviously conform to any special requirements imposed by particular types of illumination and viewing system. Some photocells used for automatic reading or for automatic setting on the line-centre have a spectral sensitivity extending into the infra-red, and the pattern therefore has to show adequate density in this region. Use of graticule-production techniques has also been extended to applications in which quite diverse properties are required. Resolution-test images have been physically intensified with mercury to confer opacity to X-rays, or have been 'toned' with radio-active salts for testing the resolution of emulsions designed for auto-radiography (Chapter 13). The ability of high-resolution photo-mechanical procedures to produce 'images' with useful mechanical or electrical properties has led to important industrial applications discussed in Chapter 11.

(10) *Influence of Design on Price and Production.* Consideration of the factors in design already discussed will have indicated the general form of a graticule, but some of the decisions may have to be modified to permit economic production. The methods used in production should be related to the number and rate of output likely to be needed. Some production methods will lend themselves better to periodic revision of the design, such as may be necessary with graticules used in military instruments. Rheinberg [2] pointed out that quite trivial matters may influence the cost of the graticule. Thus, the substitution of a 0·4 in (10 mm) disc for a 0·6 in (15 mm) disc may increase the cost by 5 per cent. A substantial increase in cost may also result if the lines are required to go right up to the edge of the disc. While photographic methods make it almost as easy to produce a complicated instead of a simple pattern, the cost of 'spotting' and retouching the latter may be much higher.

A specification which imposes close working tolerances for the production of graticules can be a major factor in increasing cost. It is so easy for a draughtsman to specify that line widths should be within 1 or 2 per cent of a nominal value, but unless this is necessary for functional reasons it wastefully increases inspection costs and rejection rate. The rejection rate resulting from the demand for blemish-free images can also cause the cost of finished graticules to mount alarmingly. Where they can be satisfactorily applied, moiré-fringe scales have the advantage of functioning satisfactorily even when the visual appearance is far from clean (p. 296).

LIMITATIONS OF PHOTOGRAPHIC METHODS

Although photographic methods for making graticules are undeniably effective and versatile, it would be absurd to overlook their limitations. The first is concerned with the limited useful area covered by high-resolution lenses. For instance, a $\frac{1}{6}$ in (4 mm) microscope objective will only give 1,000 lines/mm over a circle of diameter about 0·004 in (0·1 mm), whereas mechanical ruling can produce the same close packing of lines over many square inches. Such grating patterns can also be produced over substantial areas by placing a photographic plate in the 'focal plane' of an interferometer [15], but this method cannot give a numbered scale.

When large graticules are required with very fine lines, mechanical dividing and photographic techniques have been combined. Mechanical ruling has been used to generate master images, which are subsequently reproduced by contact printing. A more convenient and versatile method is to replace the ruling mechanism with an optical projection unit. With a photographic plate mounted on the table of a dividing engine, many successive images can be projected side-by-side on the plate, which is accurately re-positioned before each exposure (p. 246).

Photographic methods could also be less economic if the images are only to have a simple pattern readily made by a pantograph or dividing engine. This could be particularly true if only a few images were required. An advantage of direct mechanical ruling on the final support is that the process essentially only has a single stage, and thus saves the retouching and inspection at several stages usually needed in the production of photographic graticules.

Production Methods

The production of most graticules can generally be considered as occurring in three stages. Firstly, there has to be made a pattern or drawing, from which the images are made by photographic reduction. This is followed by the purely photographic stages, leading to the formation of an image of the final size required. When the physical form of the graticules requires them, photomechanical procedures are then used to complete the production process. All graticules have to pass through the first two stages, but only some go on to the photomechanical stage.

Drawings and Master Negatives

THE 'DRAWING' OR 'PATTERN'

It was at one time considered that the drawing for a graticule need only represent an exact enlargement of the finally desired result, with no allowance being made for any errors which might occur in the subsequent stages. This frequently occurred when graticule production was commissioned by customers without previous experience.

To cope with the difficulties so caused, Smethurst preferred to make a token charge for producing a drawing from a 'blue-print' submitted by the customer [16]. This enabled him to check whether the image had been laterally reversed (sometimes the blue-print showed no obvious indication of this), and whether dimensions had been converted correctly from the metric units probably employed by the designer. A conversion factor of 25 millimetres to the inch (25 microns to the 'thou' or 'mil') was commonly used instead of the factor 25·4,

Fig. 70 *Compensation for Image Thickening at Line Intersection*

In preparing master drawings in the Möller graticule factory, the width of the lines is reduced at intersections to compensate for thickening during photographic reproduction.

From B.I.O.S. Final Report,1552,by permission of the Controller of H.M.Stationery Office.

which is accurate to one part in a million. The resultant error could be outside the tolerance for size set by the instrument designer.

A more useful and modern approach is to regard the drawing as only the first stage of a closely integrated production process. With this concept, later stages can be materially assisted by introducing corrections for the errors of reproduction likely to occur in the final stages. For example, in the Möller graticule factory, it was found that the appearance of figures such as 4 and 8 suffered from thickening of lines at intersections [17]. This defect of photographic reproduction by a lens system was counteracted by a sharp local reduction in the line thickness of the drawing (Fig. 70). It has also been suggested that outside corners could be sharpened by serifs, and the sizes and tapers required for different lens apertures have been plotted against the overall reduction ratio [18].

Another possible measure is to calibrate the changes of line width occurring when lines of different thickness are reproduced, and introduce appropriate corrections in the drawing. Distortion in the lens may also be allowed for. This could be done, by placing an accurate grid, such as a moiré-fringe grating from an N.P.L. original, in the focal plane of the final reduction camera. By illuminating the grid with transmitted light, an enlargement should be made on a photographic plate placed in the position normally to be occupied by the master negative. The enlarged image should, in turn, be further enlarged through the first reduction camera, on a plate or other distortion-free sensitive material located on the copy-board. Measurement of the resultant distortion of the grid should indicate the corrections to be incorporated in the drawing. For this method to be effective, it should be used only with the lenses actually to be used for making both the master negative and the finally reduced images. Furthermore, neither the setting of the cameras nor their positions relative to the copyboard or master negative should be changed once the calibrating exposures have been made.

Before starting drawing, it is necessary to decide whether the artwork should be 'positive' or 'negative'. This decision may be based purely on the final image and the proposed number and nature of photographic stages. Alternatively, the chosen drafting method may indicate a particular form, for instance scribing on plates coated with a thin opaque layer lends itself more easily to the production of a 'negative' image. If necessary, an extra contact-printing operation (usually at the intermediate negative stage) can then be used to produce the master image. A crucial decision is the scale of the drawing, which depends largely on the precision required. Often, production of a specified line width constitutes an exacting requirement even at the drawing stage. For pen-and-ink drawings, it has been suggested that $\frac{1}{4}$ in (6 mm) line width is needed to ensure ± 5 per cent line-width tolerance [18]. This sets a lower limit to the scale of the drawing. For example, if the final graticule requires 0·001 in (25 μ) lines to ± 5 per cent, a pen-and-ink drawing should be made at 250 times the scale of the final images, with lines $\frac{1}{4}$ in wide.

The original drawing or artwork really constitutes a pattern made solely for the purpose of providing an image of the desired configuration after photographic reduction. The basic skills required are those of the draughtsman, and it is worth noting that the requirements of drawings for graticules, for profile-projector images, for printed and micro-miniature circuits and for the fabrication of small metal parts, have much in common. Many techniques can be employed, including pen and ink (Indian or plastic-type) on paper or polyester drafting materials. Flexible supports such as paper or polyester have been laminated to glass or metal to prevent changes of dimensions with

I

variations of relative humidity. Achievement of a required line width is assisted by use of mechanically slit adhesive drafting tapes, with which 'drawings' are made by simply sticking suitable lengths in the required place on the support. With these, it would be sensible to adjust the scale of the drawing to suit an available tape width. Artwork can also be produced by using special tools to cut or scribe an actinically opaque layer firmly adhering to glass, or a strippable layer on stabilized 'Mylar' support. This method has been preferred by some producers for its ability to produce accuracy and fine lines on a smaller original than could be produced by drawing.

In some graticules, really fine limits are only specified for the central part of the image. Smethurst suggested that this central part may accordingly be drawn on a still larger scale, and reduced to provide a photographic print which can be pasted on the drawing of the rest of the graticule [16]. With the aid of a magnifier, he stated that images can be aligned within 0·001 in (25 μ), corresponding to a very small error after reduction. Shadows at the joins can be concealed with gummed paper and 'Process' white, and minor blemishes such as compass pricks removed by retouching the negative. Since the only function of the drawing was to be photographed, its visual appearance was quite unimportant. Draughtsmen new to this work have been known to make a poor job for lack of understanding of this point. They should be instructed to concentrate on essential details rather than on 'prettiness'.

A meticulous technique for the production of original drawings was employed at Möller's graticule factory [17]. The drawings were made on a white baryta-coated paper fixed with gum arabic to a rigid glass, metal or wood support to minimize distortion or the changes of scale which paper drawings show as the humidity varies. The drawings were made on special linear or circular dividing-tables, in which a bow pen slid in a holder supported from an overhead girder. One operator moved the pen, and another moved the holder by the required amount between the lines. Attention was given to several details influencing the appearance of the final image. Thus, the lines were drawn rather longer than desired, so that the ends could be made square by ruling over them at right-angles with white paint. The figures were drawn separately and were stored as prints on bromide paper which bore registration marks so that the correct orientation could readily be found. Drawings of improved accuracy can also be made with an apparatus developed by Lee at the National Physical Laboratory [19], or by a 'co-ordinatograph' on which a skilled draughtsman can achieve a precision of 0·004 in (0·1 mm) [20]. There are, nevertheless, cases in which drawings of reasonable size could never give the required accuracy, and other methods (described later) have to be used.

MASTER NEGATIVES MADE FROM DRAWINGS

Graticules are generally made either by optical reduction from a master image of size intermediate between the drawing and the graticule, or by contact printing from a negative of the same size as the final image. Negatives for contact printing are also frequently made by a two-stage reduction process, and may contain many identical images, produced by printing successive exposures on different areas of one plate ('step-and-repeat').

Whatever form the master image takes, care is needed during optical reduction to prevent distortion, to maintain the over-all dimensions within the required limits and to avoid blemishes. Exact parallelism of the image plane, the lens-mounting board and the copy-board is essential, and can be checked by the use of mirrors (p. 167).

Before making the intermediate negative, it is necessary to decide whether the size of the final image should be adjusted to the desired value at the first or second reduction stage. Either method is feasible, but it is better to use a fixed-focus apparatus for the final reduction stage, and calibrate its reduction factor once and for all. The final size of the image is then adjusted by accurate sizing of the intermediate negative. This method is, in any case, required when employing one of the modern objectives specially computed for use at one specific reduction ratio.

Because of the small size of some graticules, checking their dimensions to the specified accuracy can be quite a difficult matter. The final graticule itself can be measured with a travelling microscope or interferometer, or the enlarged projected image can be measured. In the latter case, the enlargement and distortion given by the projection apparatus would itself have to be carefully checked. It has been suggested that techniques of image sizing used for photomechanical work or cartography can also be used for graticule work [21], but these methods may be limited by the small useful field often obtained in graticule work. Anyone faced by this problem should seek advice from institutions such as the National Physical Laboratory or the U.S. Bureau of Standards. For many years such institutions have paid much attention to this question, and in suitable cases can issue certificates of the dimensions of individually numbered graticules.

In the production of intermediate and master negatives, the most critical requirement is likely to prove the preservation of the specified line width or line/space ratio. Choice of a suitable emulsion is of crucial importance, and an extreme-resolution material should obviously be used for negatives to be used for a final contact-printing operation. With intermediate negatives, however, the requirements are not so stringent. For example, in a negative ten times larger than the final image, lines eventually to be 0·0002 in (5 μ) wide will be approximately ten times wider. Such a line width (0·002 in or 50 μ) can be reproduced reasonably satisfactorily on a 'Process-type' or 'Lith-type' emulsion. Because of the higher speed of these materials, drawings will not need to be illuminated with the very high intensities required for copying directly on extreme-resolution plates.

In spite of the substantial light scatter and image spread by Lith-type emulsions, they can reproduce some images as sharply (or more sharply) than extreme-resolution emulsions. To ensure proper use of Lith-type emulsions, it is useful to understand that this paradox arises from special phenomena only occurring during their development in special developers. With a properly designed emulsion-developer system, the development process is autocatalytic. At first, development is very slow and produces only an image of very low density. Once a critical stage has been reached, accumulated development products initiate rapid local development to a high density. Thus development can be simultaneously proceeding at different rates from place to place on a single plate. The most heavily exposed areas reach the autocatalytic stage first, and lesser exposed areas are triggered off successively in order of decreasing exposure. During the autocatalytic stage development is exceedingly rapid, and this, combined with the duration of the time delays between the triggering of differently exposed areas, produces higher contrast than can be achieved by most other emulsion-developer combinations. Gamma values of 10–15 are often quoted.

The high gamma values by themselves give a high density gradient at the edge of even a very unsharp image, and this gradient is further steepened by complicated chemical edge effects. As a result, development at the edge of an unsharp optical image such as a half-tone dot acquires the nature of a 'go-no-go' process. The consequent density gradient (and subjective sharpness) approaches the steepness only obtained by cutting and intensifying images on the older types of high-contrast 'Process' emulsion.

So potent are these chemical effects, that they enable the Lith-type emulsions to produce line images with a sharp edge even when the aerial image is quite unsharp. In many applications the results are beneficial and pleasing, but control of the process is complicated by the fact that optimum results are only secured by rapidly stopping the process when development is far from complete, and when the effective emulsion speed is increasing at its maximum rate. For this reason, photomechanical workers often develop Lith-type emulsions in a transparent dish over a safelight. Progressive growth of density, line width or dot size are followed with a hand lens, and development is stopped when the desired appearance is obtained.[1]

The practical consequences of this development process for graticule production (and other extreme-resolution tasks) were demonstrated by reducing a simple negative with parallel lines of different

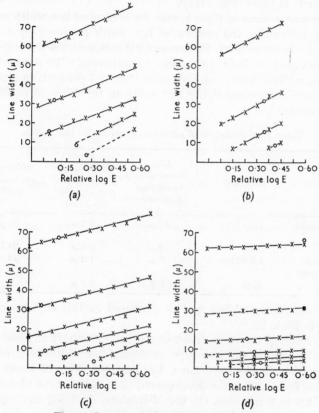

Fig. 71 *Increase of Line Width with Exposure*

(a) Lith-type plate and (b) M-R plate exposed with F/17 objective; (c) Lith-type plate and (d) M-R plate exposed with microscope objective. In this and Fig. 72, circles show geometrical line width, and broken line indicates inadequate density.

Courtesy of 'Journal of Photographic Science'.

width [22]. Series of exposures increasing by 20 per cent (one-quarter of a 'stop') were made, and the widths of the lines were measured and plotted against log exposure. With a photographic objective used at an aperture of F/17, the lines on a Lith-type plate increased in width

[1] In photomechanical shops, this method of handling is being replaced by machine processing.

by about 11 μ on doubling the exposure [Fig. 71(a)]. In these conditions, use of an M-R plate gave no improvement, and doubling the exposure increased line width by 12 μ. On repeating the experiment with a 16 mm microscope objective (N.A. 0·28), the rate of line-broadening was halved with the Lith-type plate, and was reduced to 1·5 μ on M-R plate [Fig. 71(d)].

The consequences of these results for control of line width can be seen by estimating the increase of line width produced by a small change of exposure level. For example, if it is assumed that effective exposures may be liable to random variations of ± 10 per cent and that line widths should not vary more than ± 5 per cent, an estimate of the minimum controllable line width in the different conditions can be made.

Table 10. Calculation of minimum controllable line widths

Objective	Emulsion	Line broadening for doubled exposure	Line broadening for ± 10 per cent exposure variation	Minimum controllable width
Photographic F/17	Lith-type	11 μ	2·2 μ	22 μ
,, ,,	M-R	12 μ	2·4 μ	24 μ
Microscope N.A. 0·28	Lith-type	6 μ	1·2 μ	12 μ
,, ,,	M-R	1·5 μ	0·3 μ	3 μ

The differences of line quality produced in this experiment are shown in Plate 22.

As a result of the successive triggering of differently exposed areas in development of the Lith-type emulsions, line widths also increase rapidly with development time. For example, Fig. 72 shows 10 μ widening for doubling the development time of Lith-type plates from 1 min 40s to 3 min 20s. On the M-R plate, doubling development from 2 to 4 min only increased the line width about 1 μ.

The conclusion to be drawn from these results is that failure to produce a sharper image on an extreme-resolution emulsion is a consequence of inadequacies in the projection system. Lens aberrations, inadequate aperture, poor focus or vibration are all possible causes.

The basic techniques used for preserving the correct relative line width in master negatives are similar to those used for securing the best possible line quality in other high-resolution images (Chapter 8). Apart from the precautions already prescribed, the copy-board should be evenly illuminated and the plates should be given no greater exposure than the minimum required to produce an adequate working density in the background. If heavier exposures are used to obtain a completely opaque background, it may result in no further increase in the contrast of the final images, but can introduce image spread.

If the intermediate negative consists of narrow transparent lines on a clear background, pinholes can easily be blocked out, but refracting particles in the background of a negative with large clear areas can present a more difficult problem. The extent to which they

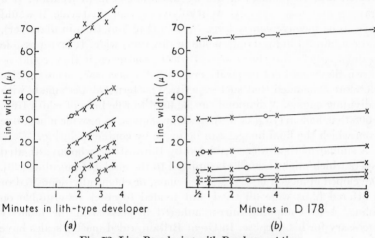

Fig. 72 *Line Broadening with Development time*
(a) Lith-type plate, (b) M-R plate.
Courtesy of 'Journal of Photographic Science'.

show will be enhanced by printing with highly collimated light, and is reduced by increasing the diffuseness of the illuminating light. As already noted on p. 221, their effect in contact printing is greatly lessened by use of an immersion fluid. For projection printing, the same type of improvement can be obtained by mounting a cover-glass on the surface of the negative with a medium such as Canada balsam. Microscope cover-glasses are not required, and ordinary sheet glass of quality adequate for photographic plates can be used. As a result of the time and care expended on them, master negatives can constitute a substantial asset. Preserving with a cover-glass, or stabilizing the silver image by converting it to silver iodide, or making at least two masters to guard against loss or breakage are all sensible precautions.

MASTER NEGATIVES PRODUCED ON A DIVIDING-ENGINE

The method of producing master negatives by optical reduction from a drawing is no longer practicable when graticules are required with a length of several inches and with the position of each line accurate to a micron or so. Geiser [4] has graphically illustrated the dilemma by considering the production of a 4 in (10 cm) diameter circle divided into 10 minutes of arc by lines 0·0003 in (8 μ) wide. If a drawing were made to only twenty-five times the final scale, it would have to be inconveniently large (over 8 ft (2·5 metres) in diameter), and contain 2,160 lines only 0·008 in (0·2 mm) wide. It is impossible to draw satisfactory lines of this width, and even if they could be drawn they could not be positioned with the necessary accuracy. He therefore concluded that such repetitive patterns are best made with a dividing-engine. A diamond can be used to rule lines of width from 0·003 to 0·0002 in (75 μ to 5 μ) on silvered glass, to provide a negative from which the final images can be made by contact printing.

A similar method was considered by Burmistrov, who investigated layers which might usefully be applied to the glass before ruling [23]. Developed emulsion layers, smoked glass, or chemically deposited or sputtered films were all tried, but tended to crack or crumble on ruling. A lead-sulphide mirror adhered to glass with the tenacity necessary for his purpose. In Great Britain, ruled master scales have also been made by ruling of waxy or bitumen layers on glass, followed by etching of the glass, and filling of the etched lines with black pigment [1].

An interesting technique for speeding the production of large masters on a dividing engine, is to mount an extreme-resolution plate on the moving table, and traverse it underneath a projection head [4]. The projection head is really a compact microphotographic bench, since in one rigid unit it comprises illuminant, master negative and (usually) a microscope objective. At each position of the moving table, an element of the final scale was projected, and the plate was then moved very precisely before the next exposure. In fact the projected image takes the place of the engraving tool, with the advantage that whole groups of lines or figures can be imprinted at once. Lines of greatly varying width and numerals can likewise be produced, and if desired, the negative can be changed before each exposure. Unlike an engraving tool, a light beam can never become blunt, nor can it leave debris on the surface of the plate.

To achieve the line quality required for this work, it is usual to employ a 1 in or $\frac{2}{3}$ in (25 or 16 mm) microscope objective capable of producing satisfactory lines a few microns wide, but covering only about $\frac{1}{25}$ in (1 mm) diameter of emulsion surface at each exposure. The potentialities of the method can be visualized in terms of Geiser's example quoted above. The circumference of a 4 in circle is $12\frac{1}{2}$ in (32 cm), so that each degree of arc would fill a space of 0·034 in (0·85 mm). The performance of the objective should allow units of scale of 6, or 30 or even 120 spaces with satisfactory quality to be produced within this space at each exposure. The composite scales would then give direct division to 10 minutes, 2 minutes or 30 seconds of arc respectively.

The building of such accurate and complex images by multiple exposures is clearly a major undertaking, and merits greater precautions for each unit exposure than are used for single images. Obviously, the plate must be mounted so that the distance of any part of the emulsion surface from the objective does not vary by more than a very small amount. For this purpose neither the flatness nor the rigidity of ordinary photographic-quality glass is likely to prove satisfactory, and concentrated Lippmann emulsions have been coated on $\frac{1}{4}$ in (6 mm) plate glass or on optical flats. A method of ensuring uniform focus irrespective of the flatness of the glass, is to employ a pneumatic gauge to provide a continuous indication of the objective-to-emulsion distance (p. 149). This can be used as a monitor for purely manual focusing, or can be used to actuate an alarm or a servo-operated focusing mechanism. For the complete scales to have a satisfactory appearance, not only must each individual image by itself be satisfactory, but they must be so exactly matched that no sign of their multiple-exposure origin is visible. Means for satisfying this stringent requirement are discussed later (p. 255).

The multiple-exposure procedures appear, so far, to have been used mainly for the generation of linear or circular scales along a narrow track (Fig. 73). In the production of binary-coded scales (Chapter 10), the scope of this method is extended to produce two-dimensional patterns, by laying down many narrow tracks of image side by side. These methods, however, would be a clumsy way of producing continuous isolated straight lines, and would be particularly difficult to apply to the production of curved lines.

Interesting possibilities of circumventing these limitations are suggested by Cooper and Stewart working at the United Kingdom Atomic Energy Research Establishment. To produce long narrow 'slits', M-R plates were held by a spring against a distance piece fitted with low friction contact surfaces [24]. A motor-driven mechanical stage was then used to move the plate for several inches in front of the objective, while it produced a reduced image of an illuminated aperture on the emulsion surface. To generate a long line of uniform width, the rate of drive and lamp brightness had to be carefully controlled, and the emulsion–objective distance had to be kept constant to close tolerances.

The flexibility of such a procedure could clearly be extended by

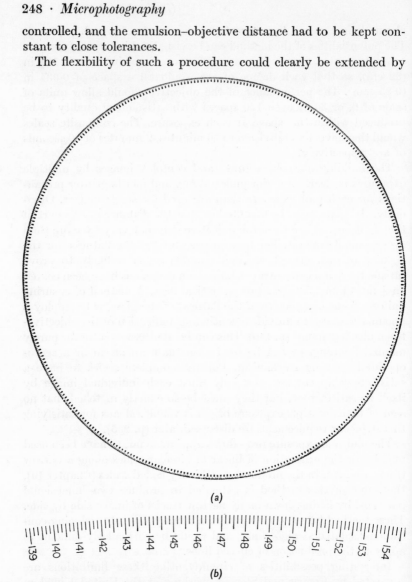

(a)

(b)

Fig. 73 *2½-in Circle Produced by Microprojection on Dividing Engine*
(b) shows × 17 enlargement of a section of the circle.
Courtesy of Optical Measuring Tools Ltd.

techniques already used for other purposes. By systems of the type used for computer control of machine tools (p. 298), it should be possible to use the projected light spot to 'draw' lines of any desired curvature and to produce large two-dimensional patterns. The computer programme would have to indicate not only the momentary changes of x and y co-ordinates needed to give required curvatures, but also the instantaneous rates at which x and y should be changed to maintain a constant rate of movement of the light spot. Alternatively, the illuminant brightness might be modulated to compensate for momentary changes in the rate of movement. Feasibility studies of such systems have been made for the production of microelectronic masks (p. 355).

For what purposes such techniques might be applied is an interesting speculation. In principle they could be applied to the production of reduced engineering drawings on a scale not achievable by direct photographic reproduction, because of the limited field of high aperture objectives. A 24 inch wide (61 cm) drawing with lines 0·02 in (0·5 mm) wide might be reduced 200 diameters to give a copy 0·12 in (3 mm) wide with 0·0001 in (2·5 μ) lines. The cost of producing a computer programme for this purpose would obviously be quite high. The techniques might, however, be applied to the production of simpler patterns, such as graticules showing screw-thread-form profiles or the orbits of artificial satellites. The methods could also be applied to the generation of elaborate geometrical patterns, such as a true spiral grating.

When large scales are built up by making numerous exposures on one plate, it is often useful to arrange the process so as to obtain a 'negative' image, in which most of the area of the plate is black, and only the lines of the scale are transparent. Such a result is required when the final images are to be printed directly from the first master negative, in order to avoid the risk of spoiling image quality or dimensional accuracy by multiple-stage contact copying.

On direct development, ordinary extreme-resolution emulsions give a 'negative', so that the desired tones would have to be obtained by projecting a 'positive' transparency. The field covered by each element of the exposure is, however, likely to be so small that the blackened area containing the images will be confined to a narrow strip or circle on the plate, the remainder of which remains unblackened. Backgrounds have been 'spotted' with opaque medium under the microscope, but the dry thickness of the medium can spoil contact when printing (p. 218). The desired result can, however, be obtained in other ways. One method is to expose the plate to a positive transparency, and then develop, treat with an acid-stop bath (Appendix I), and wash and dry without fixing. The area of the plate containing the images is then carefully painted with a waterproof lacquer (such as 'Peridak' staging paint), and the unblackened areas are completely developed by immersing in a developer by artificial light. So long as the lacquer does not extend beyond the edges of the developed images, this procedure causes the background to blacken completely. In the meantime the transparent lines have been protected by the lacquer, and the process is completed by removing the staging paint with the recommended solvents, followed by fixing, washing and drying in the usual way.

A more direct method for achieving the same result is to expose to a 'negative' transparency, so that the lines first develop black. The plate is then reversal-processed by bleaching and re-developing to give a negative image (Appendix I). The author has seen satisfactory master negatives with line widths just over 0·0001 in (3 μ) made on M-R plates by this method.

SENSITIZATION OF PLATES FOR GRATICULE PRODUCTION

How glass destined for graticule production should be coated depends on many factors, including the size and shape of the glass, the number of units and delivery date required, the ease of transport from the photographic manufacturer and the nature of the 'emulsion' to be used. Other factors are discussed on p. 252. It is convenient firstly to consider the extreme-resolution silver-halide emulsion, since the necessity for applying a relatively thick layer (dry thicknesses of 0·0002 in (5 μ) or more are common) requires special methods of handling to minimize meniscus effects at the edge of the plates. Many users either make graticules by cutting plates of the required size from commercially coated plates, or arrange for their own blanks to be coated commercially.

If only small quantities are required, quite simple methods may be used. When the extreme edge of the blank is not important, satis-factory coatings can be made by applying the required volume of emulsion to the levelled blank previously warmed to about 40° C. (104° F.) If the emulsion is rapidly made to wet the entire plate surface by spreading with a glass rod, delay of setting by warming of the glass permits gravity to level out the coating. Rust avoided the meniscus difficulty by placing six circular blanks in accurately machined apertures in a metal plate having the same thickness as the glass [25]. The whole assembly was coated as a single unit, and after drying, the coated blanks were cut from their matrix by pressing against a cutting plate with sharp-edged holes slightly larger than the blanks.

An effective method for applying a reasonably uniform emulsion layer right up to the edge of the blank is the procedure employed for applying stripped autoradiographic emulsions to radioactive speci-mens [26]. Blanks can be coated by immersing in a water bath, float-ing a stripped emulsion layer on the water surface, and lifting the floated emulsion layer so that it is draped against the surface of the blank (Fig. 74). This method has the advantage of being readily applicable to concave or convex surfaces, but two conditions need to be met for its satisfactory operation. Firstly the method certainly

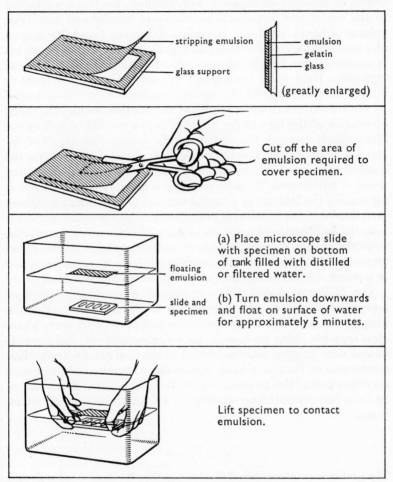

Fig. 74 *Autoradiographic Coating Procedure*
From Kodak Ltd. Data Sheet SC-10.

adds to the difficulty of dirt control. A static water surface is a natural collecting site for air-borne dust and for grease and bubbles. Such contaminants are very likely to be trapped between the emulsion and the plate surface. The method also requires the provision of dry-strippable extreme-resolution emulsion layers of suitable thickness.

With all coating methods, the blanks should be coated with a sub-stratum to ensure adhesion during processing [27].

Sensitive layers such as the photosensitive resists, which only re-quire a final layer thickness around one micron (0·00004 in) can be coated by 'whirling' or 'dipping'. For 'whirling', the blank is attached to the centre of a horizontal turn-table or spindle and a suitable volume of liquid 'emulsion' is applied. When the turn-table is spun at a controlled speed[1] excess liquid is flung off. The film of liquid left is usually so thin, that it will not drain even when the blank is stood vertically. With some 'emulsions', the solvent mostly evaporates during the spinning. With this method, coating thickness is controlled by the concentration and viscosity of the solution, and by the speed of rotation of the turn-table. 'Dipping' is the method of pulling the blank slowly through the surface of the solution, as described by Davis and Pope [28]. The layer thickness obtained depends on the concentration, surface tension and viscosity of the solution and the speed of withdrawal. Dipping probably represents the best method for coating the internal or external surfaces of cylinders. Cleanliness (and freedom from bubbles) of both the liquid and the plate surface is essential for obtaining a uniform coating with either of these methods, since the coating quality depends on unrestricted flow of the liquid film across the surface. Quite minute dirt particles can cause formation of a streak a tenth of an inch (a few millimetres) or more long.

The Möller Graticule Factory applied a completely different approach to the production of graticules on prepared blanks. Multiple images were made by the wet-collodion process on temporary plate-glass supports. After processing, the collodion was cut, and the unit images were stripped and transferred to the final blanks. Bovey [29] commented on the risk of image distortion or alteration of dimensions occurring during this process, but the fact remains that it was stated to have been operated successfully on a commercial scale for many years.

EXPOSURE

The graticule producer has to decide whether the final images should be made by contact or projection printing, and the decision is in-fluenced by the photographic speed of the emulsion to be used. Since each image with projection printing has to be made by a separate exposing operation, this method is better adapted to the faster emulsions, in order to achieve a conveniently brief exposure. With

[1] In Great Britain, the usual practice is to whirl at speeds up to 200–300 r.p.m., but in the United States of America, operators use more viscous solutions with rapid acceleration to much higher whirling speeds (see p. 315).

really small images made with a microscope objective, however, condenser illumination can be used to concentrate so much light into the image that exposures of a second or two can be used even with a print-out or bichromated-colloid emulsion (p. 184).

Projection printing has the advantage that only one master negative is needed, and this is not subjected to the wear inevitable in contact printing. Moreover, the master negative is usually substantially larger than the final images and is correspondingly easier to spot or retouch. Changes in the design of the image will cause only a slight interruption of production with projection printing, whereas they can cause complete dislocation with contact-printing methods. Projection printing implies not only that the images have to be made individually, but that a separate camera has to be used for each type of graticule being produced at any one time. The proportion of the cost of each graticule represented by the exposing operation is therefore likely to be higher than with contact printing, but this may only be a serious consideration when very large numbers of each type of graticule are required. Apart from the limits imposed by the speed of the emulsion used, the finest line which can be produced by projection printing is a function of the field which has to be covered (Chapter 4).

Contact-printing methods can always be used, however slow the emulsion, and they lend themselves to the rapid production of large numbers of images from step-and-repeat negatives containing dozens or hundreds of images. Since the final negatives can only be used a few dozens of times because of damage caused during printing, it is usual to arrange a production schedule employing one or more generations of intermediate positives or negatives. This ensures that long production runs can be made with frequent replacement of the final negatives, without using the early-generation masters more than very few times. So long as flat enough glass is used, contact printing assists in maintaining a high standard of dimensional uniformity in the images and in permitting practically identical images to be made in separate factories. Contact printing is the only practicable method for duplicating large images with fine lines, from master negatives made on a dividing engine.

Although contact printing appears a simple operation, attention to detail is required to produce the best possible results (p. 218). Even then, practical experience shows that the quality of really fine lines tends to be inferior to that achieved by projection printing with a microscope objective. Perhaps this is because a reduced image produced by projection printing is always a 'first generation image', whereas a contact print can never be earlier than a second generation image. It is clearly difficult to specify a line width below which contact printing should not be used, but when practicable, projection printing makes it easier to achieve satisfactory quality on line widths of 0·0002 in (5 μ) or less.

EXPOSING EMULSIONS ON A CURVED SURFACE

A number of interesting problems arise when the graticule image is needed on a curved surface. With spherical surfaces it has been the practice to produce a negative on a surface with a curvature complementary to that required in the final image. Thus a negative on a concave surface would be used for printing images on to a convex lens. The negative must, of course, be made by projection and it may

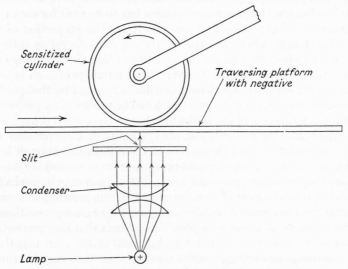

Fig. 75 *Printing Scale around Circumference of a Cylinder*
Principle of equipment developed by the Royal Naval Scientific Service.
Courtesy of 'British Journal of Photography', and E. W. Jackson

sometimes be possible to obtain the necessary depth of focus by stopping down. If the work proved sufficiently important, however, it would be better to use an objective specially designed to give a concave spherical field. Schmidt optical systems might be useful for this purpose. Another difficulty is the distortion introduced by the use of curved surfaces for receiving the image, and the Wadsworth Watch Company have patented the use of a correcting lens to compensate for distortion even if the objective has a sufficiently great depth of focus [30]. Graticule images have also been printed directly from a flat negative on to a cylindrical surface. After sensitization of its outer surface, the cylinder was exposed by placing it opposite a narrow illuminated slit, and then smoothly pushing the negative between the slit and the cylinder so that it caused the cylinder to roll without any slip [31] (Fig. 75). The slit was of such a width that only the area of the cylinder very close to the negative was exposed and hence the straight scale was, in effect, wrapped round the cylinder.

EXPOSURE CONTROL

Of the defects which may result in rejection of graticule images, incorrect exposure should not be tolerated, since the possible causes can be effectively controlled. As discussed on p. 207, a stabilized power supply can be employed, with the illuminant used in conditions in which its brightness only changes imperceptibly during hundreds or thousands of exposures. The exposure duration should be consistent, preferably within $\pm 2\frac{1}{2}$ per cent.

When exposure schedules on one plate take many hours to complete, latent-image decay of extreme-resolution emulsions has to be allowed for. In one test, for example, Kodak High-Resolution plates gave densities of 2·1, 1·5, 1·4, and 1·25 when developed immediately after exposure, and after delays of 5, 10 and 15 hours respectively [18]. Similar losses are shown by M-R plates. Since loss of density can be counteracted by increasing exposure and cannot be easily seen in line images, it should itself not matter greatly, but it is usually accompanied by a reduction in line width. This can be particularly noticeable when producing circular scales or gratings on a dividing engine. At the completion of the exposure cycle, the last unit image is projected right next to the first, which may have been exposed many hours previously, and decrease of line width is then particularly objectionable.

The results of latent-image decay can be combated in various ways. The exposure can be increased to give the desired density when development is delayed for several times the duration of the exposure cycle. All the images will then have decayed by nearly the same amount, and the differences should no longer be seen. Alternatively the lamp current can be decreased gradually during an exposure-run, to compensate for decay of the first formed images. Since reduction of line width is usually the most obvious and objectionable result of decay, the source of this phenomenon may usefully be attacked. Change of line width with change of exposure (or change of effective emulsion speed resulting from decay) is a consequence of the intensity profile of fine images having less than ideal steepness. Anything that can be done to improve the optics and produce a steeper intensity profile, will lessen this consequence of latent-image decay.

Another obvious measure is to shorten the entire exposure schedule by moving the dividing-engine table faster, or by using a brighter source and a shorter unit exposure. It is clear that exposures can be greatly speeded up by such means. An extreme example was demonstrated at a National Physical Laboratory Open Day [32]. The table on which the plate was mounted was moved continuously, and the slit, whose reduced image was projected on the emulsion surface, was illuminated by an electronic flash tube giving an exposure duration of about a microsecond.[1] A cam was used to trigger the lamp each time the continuously moving table reached a desired position, but photoelectric signals can be used for the same purpose (p. 277). With this method, the error due to movement of the table during the exposure can be negligible, even if the entire exposure cycle is reduced to a few minutes. For example, if the flash duration is 3 microseconds and the table is rotated at an angular speed of 1 degree per second, the movement during the exposure will be about one-hundredth of a second of arc, and the complete circle could be exposed in 6 minutes. The complexity and cost of the apparatus obviously has to be increased to secure such results, but such equipment also has an improved output.

PROCESSING

Processing methods used for making graticules are similar to those described in Chapter 3, but factors such as the high cost of exposing multiple-unit masters and exacting demands for image cleanliness (see p. 80) or high dimensional accuracy, are likely to justify stringent applications of the appropriate precautions. When making multiple-unit masters or producing long runs of identical images, special attention should be given to controlling development so as to obtain reproducible density and line widths from accurately metered exposures. The activity of the developing solution, and the time and temperature of development should be carefully controlled. Although agitation of the solution cannot strongly influence development of the finest black lines (p. 74), a positive means of mechanical agitation may assist general reproducibility.

To stint the developer for graticule production is false economy, and two working methods seem suitable. The main hazard is likely to be the decay of activity when developer is spread in a thin layer in a dish. A solution depth at least equivalent to 100 cc in a half-plate dish (about $\frac{1}{6}$ in or 4 mm depth), and use of a fresh volume of thermostatted solution poured out just before the development of each dishful of graticules will assist the production of consistent images. The alternative is to use the developer in a tank 2 inches (5 cm) or more deep. Aerial oxidation of even caustic developers such as Kodak D.8 or

---

[1] Some Photo-Repeaters for production of microelectronic masks employ a continuously moving plate with exposures to electronic flash (p. 339).

D.178 is then less likely to produce a perceptible change within a working day, and the useful working life (for sporadic use) may be found to extend to several days if a 'floating lid' is used to minimize oxidation. Each time a fresh volume of developer is compounded, it is a good plan to make a batch large enough for several days' (or even several weeks') work, and bottle in volumes sufficient for one day's use or for a tank-full. A test may then be made to confirm that no change of development or exposure time is required when a new batch first comes into use.

The problem of handling a large number of individual units of plate or coated blanks can be solved by using racks to hold the plates, so that all the images processed at the same time can be transferred as a single unit from one solution to the next. Contamination of the emulsion during processing can be lessened by making the racks so that the plates are held vertical or upside down. Racks also lessen the risk of chipping the edges of glass blanks: an important point when blanks made to an exacting specification have to be used repeatedly because of a high rejection rate for the final images. 'Perspex' or rigid 'Polythene' are excellent materials for constructing racks, since they are easy to work, will not chip glass and have a satisfactory resistance to ordinary photographic solutions.

RESOLUTION TEST CHARTS

In concluding these sections dealing with the photographic stages of graticule production, special problems arising in the production of resolution-test charts merit attention. Resolution-test charts are still widely used for qualitative or quantitative observations of the performance of optical or physical imaging systems (see p. 39). The charts generally consist of groups of lines of different widths, and the results of a test are assessed by deciding the smallest group in which the lines can either just be distinguished or show the desired sharpness (see Plates 58 and 62). Other test charts concerned with assessment of legibility have been made with pseudo-alphanumeric characters, and the task is then to decide in which direction these characters are oriented.[1] The groups of lines (or characters) are made so that the decrease of size from one group to the next has a constant ratio for all groups of the chart. This ratio is often made as small as 10 per cent, and to maintain a smooth progression, each group should be sized within 1 per cent or better. It is also important that all groups should be reproduced with the spaces between the lines substantially equal to their widths.

A method used for production of test charts is to make a drawing

---

[1] According to their size, these are called 'mire' or 'micro-mire'.

of one group, from which are made intermediate reductions at appropriately graded reduction ratios. The scale of the intermediate reductions is adjusted so that even the smallest group occupies a piece of film or paper of manageable size, and so that subsequent reduction of the complete test chart is required. The initially reduced images are then assembled in an array which will ultimately present all the images within an adequately small proportion of the field of the lenses used for copying or testing. Considerable ingenuity may be necessary to meet this requirement while achieving a lay-out aiding ready identification of each group right up to the limit of resolution. For these purposes, the charts are often arranged spirally, with image sizes decreasing progressively towards the centre and identifying numbers can be added at the assembly stage.

The production of this mechanically assembled test-chart master image is a relatively straight-forward (if tedious) task, but the subsequent photographic reduction of the entire chart requires special care. Unless required for one specific and restricted purpose, resolution test charts necessarily have to be made with a large overall range of line widths. They therefore deliberately incorporate a feature which is best avoided for microphotographic reproduction (see p. 179). The problem is aggravated by the fact that the lines must not only be sharp, but that line/space equality is also demanded for all groups in the chart. Ideally, these requirements should be met by arranging that reproduction of the smallest group does not approach the working limit of the emulsion or lens used. The demands of the situation often make this impossible with ordinary photographic materials. Consider, for example, the testing of a 'Process Apochromat' objective with resolution approaching 250 lines/mm, at reduction ratios designed not to exceed 5. The line spacing and width of the smallest group would then have to be equal to or smaller than 10 μ (0·0004 in), corresponding to 50 lines/mm. To ensure the desired performance requires use of an extreme-resolution emulsion with microphotographic techniques for focusing the objective and ensuring register.

Images much finer than this can be demanded for testing microphotographic or projection objectives, or for different types of contact-resolution test (see pp. 450–57). Many or all the groups may then have to be imaged within a millimetre field, and minimum line widths of very few microns necessitate use of microscope objectives for making the test images. The problem of preserving line/space equality for all image sizes then becomes quite acute.

There is no complete solution to this problem, but three lines of attack are open to us.

(i) One cause of difficulty arises from the depth of focus of high-aperture microscope objectives being less than the thickness of commercially coated emulsions. (The consequences of this were discussed on p. 200.) This can be counteracted by using a 'whirler' or dip-coating to apply an emulsion layer only about 1 μ (0·00004 in) thick. If insufficient density is obtained, cautious application of a physical intensifier may be used. An alternative is to restrict light penetration into the emulsion by heavily dyeing the gelatin. Dyes suitable for this purpose were investigated by Kowaliski [33]. Examples of the results obtainable are shown in Plate 61.

(ii) Even when method (i) is applied, the need for greater exposures to produce adequate density in the finest groups will still be found. In principle, this can be offset by masking the larger test-chart groups with neutral densities of progressively greater value. The necessary labour might be justified for the commercial production of long runs of test-chart images.

(iii) A supplementary method is to make intermediate negatives, in which the tendency of the wider lines to broaden is compensated by reducing the width of the transparent areas. Line/space equality of the wide lines should then be achieved with the degree of over-exposure required for satisfactory imaging of the fine lines. With parallel-line test-charts, this could be accomplished by using a 'drawing' consisting of matte-black louvres silhouetted against an illuminated background. Tilting of the louvres would alter the line/space ratio. The correction achievable by this method would be limited by customers' tolerance of rounding of the ends of the test-chart lines.

The methods described above are suitable mainly for the production of high-contrast or master test-chart images, in which the actual density is unimportant so long as the 'lines' are completely clear. Test charts of lower density range have to be made with a specific background density, and contact-copying assists the production of the same density for all line widths. Another property sometimes demanded is that the test chart should be spectrally neutral. Possible solutions are to use modified developers with extreme-resolution emulsions (p. 71), or to print on a photoresist layer applied on a uniform thin film previously made with the required density and neutrality. The pattern would then be etched through the stencil formed in the photoresist layer.

Increasing interest in the reproduction of images with sinusoidal rather than square-wave intensity profiles has generated a demand for test-chart images embodying this property. In a review article on such test charts, Lamberts described their production from variable-width images (Fig. 76) in which the width varies sinusoidally with distance [34]. By reducing the variable-width images with an +8-dioptre cylindrical lens in front of the photographic image, the images were 'smeared' vertically to give a sinusoidal transmittance. The projected sinusoidal patterns were recorded on a fine-grain (but not

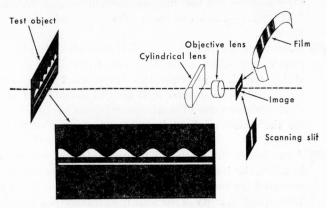

Fig. 76 *Production of Sinusoidal Test Patterns*
Courtesy of R. L. Lamberts and 'Journal of Optical Society of America'.

extreme-resolution) emulsion, chosen to give a good range of densities with unit gamma when printed on Kodak Special Fine-Grain Aerial-Duplicating Film, Type SO-278. This procedure gave positive prints reasonably free from tonal distortion, and with sinusoidal transmittance. The modulation characteristic of the smallest group (42 lines/mm) was 50 per cent, but all the other groups were adjusted to 65 per cent by following the image-wise exposures with carefully controlled uniform ('flash') exposures. The sinusoidal images were finally assembled in a convenient array, together with a series of neutral-density patches for measuring large-area contrast.

Photomechanical Stage

MODIFICATION OF THE ORIGINAL IMAGE

The variety of properties which have been required of different graticules have led to the application of many production methods. These include photographic processes, photomechanical processes employing stencils and etching and vacuum evaporation, which unit processes have been often used in complex hybrid procedures. The methods may involve modification of the original photographic image, or all traces of the material of the initial image may finally be removed. A convenient way of visualizing the scope of these methods is to consider the transformations that can be applied to the original image.

The image produced by the initial exposure and development may be

  (i) used directly, possibly with a toning process to modify its stability or optical properties;

 (ii) a suitably blackened stencil image;

(iii) a stencil resist used with etching of the support or an underlayer, or to mask the application of fresh material to the support;

(iv) formed adsorbed to or actually within the surface layers of a glass blank.

These transformations have also been combined in complex procedures, when the desired result required such an elaboration.

(i) DIRECT USE OF SILVER IMAGE

When the conditions for viewing are relatively tolerant of small particles in the colloid, or when cleanliness precautions succeed in securing an acceptable proportion of passable images, the direct use of developed silver images on an extreme-resolution emulsion gives graticules of fine line-quality. Almost invariably the processed image is covered with an optical cement and cover-glass. Not only must the cement have the mechanical properties required for bonding lenses, but it must itself be exceptionally free from dirt [1]. Direct silver images in this form were used for many eyepiece graticules during the Second World War. They are still used for a variety of eyepiece graticules, and for the projected scales in analytical balances. Direct silver images are also used commercially for stage micrometers, with divisions down to 0·1 mm (0·004 in) divided in 50 parts. In the Möller factory, images made by the wet-collodion process on a temporary support were stripped, and transferred to a prepared blank and protected by a cover-glass.

(ii) DIRECT USE OF STENCIL IMAGES

When coated sufficiently thinly, bichromated glue (and the majority of photoresists) are capable of giving washed-off images with fine lines as narrow as one micron (0·00004 in). These virtually invisible images in the glue have been blackened by loading the colloid with colloidal silver and physically developing,[1] or by alternately bathing the stencil

---

[1] Details of a glue–silver process used in the Kodak Research Laboratories were described in a booklet supplied on request [35].

in solutions of a lead salt and sodium sulphide. The resultant images can be produced with a very clear background, and can be made resistant by baking or may be protected with a cover-glass. Resistant stencil images have been made by a photo-ceramic process, and Rheinberg stated that Messrs Adam Hilger Ltd produced beautiful results by this process during the period 1915–18 [2]. Resistant graticules have also been made from commercially coated silver-halide–gelatin emulsions, by using the 'etch-bleach' process to make a positive stencil and heating to 300° C to darken and insolubilize the gelatin [36]. Because of the relatively thick layer, only somewhat coarse images can be made by this method.

(iii) STENCIL IMAGES USED AS RESISTS

Once a washed-off stencil image has been produced by an essentially photographic method, it can be used to control the distribution of material etched from the support or from an underlayer. It can also be used as a mask to control the application of fresh material to the support. In these processes the stencil image is usually destroyed after it has served its purpose. The processes used are generically related to the production of blocks for printed illustration, and many of the skills applied have been derived from this source. Since the stencils are required to have somewhat different properties, it is useful to distinguish between processes involving etching and those using application of fresh material.

(a) *Stencils as Resists against Etching.* A dominant theme in the history of graticule production, has been the urge to produce resistant images on glass, so that they can be safely cleaned. Since the reagent used to etch glass (hydrofluoric acid) is most corrosive, the material of the stencil had to be carefully chosen to give adequate resistance with the thin layers required to ensure high resolution. For many years, adequate results were only obtained by firstly coating glass with a resistant inert layer such as silver or 'Bakelite'. A chemically weaker primary stencil made from such materials as bichromated gelatin or bichromated gum-acacia was then used to control the etching of the underlayer, to produce a much tougher secondary stencil. With such processes, much care and skill was employed to minimize undercutting and line-spread during the etching of the under-layer. These double-layer processes are being replaced by the use of photosensitive resists (p. 52), in which organic chemists have endeavoured to combine the properties of photosensitivity and extreme chemical resistance in a single material.

In spite of their inconvenience, it must be conceded that double-layer processes have certain advantages. The secondary resist is generally not photosensitive and is formed from a layer which can be applied to the support by methods not applicable to a photosensitive 'emulsion'. Silver or lead-sulphide layers are produced by mirror-plating solutions, and silver, aluminium, chromium and other metals are applied by methods such as vacuum evaporation. When a silicon support is used (see p. 345), the secondary resist layer is applied by controlled tarnishing at a high temperature. By such methods layers can be made with a great variety of optical and chemical properties, and these properties can be checked *before* coating with the emulsion. It has been claimed that some of these processes give results which are exceptionally free from pinholes. Substantial savings could thereby be achieved with respect to inspection, retouching or spotting and a reduced rejection rate. Such double-layer processes are, of course, also appropriately used when the etched secondary stencil in some material such as lead sulphide or chromium constitutes the finally desired result (see p. 343).

(b) *Stencils as deposition masks.* Stencil images have also been used to protect the support against the deposition of fresh material. Perhaps the most elegant method of this type is the application of metal vacuum-evaporation and sputtering by the B.S.I.R.A. in Great Britain [37], and in the United States of America by R. D. Geiser of Messrs W. and L. E. Gurley [4]. In this process the metal deposit covers the entire surface of the blank but is only deposited in contact with the glass through the gaps in the stencil. The background can therefore be cleaned by dissolving the stencil away so that it brings with it the metal it has received. This method has the attraction that it can be used for the application of metals such as aluminium or platinum or rhodium, which it would be difficult to apply by other methods. It can also be used for application of non-metallic materials such as magnesium fluoride, and Guellich has proposed making the light-retarding discs used in phase-contrast microscopy in this way [38]. Bovey noted that the photosensitive material used for this type of process must be chosen so that the stencil both withstands the high vacuum, and yet permits ready removal after being heated by the evaporation process [1]. The washing-off process used to form the primary stencil must also leave the support so clean that the deposited material can adhere firmly. Almost invisible residual scums can have a disastrous effect on adhesion.

(iv) 'FILMLESS' PROCESSES

A variety of processes for making resistant images on glass without a colloid medium has been described. More than forty years ago Rheinberg made and sold 'filmless' graticules [2], and his successors now market an analogous product under the Trade Mark 'Maxta' [39].

Three methods of achieving the same sort of result have been published. Burmistrov [40] formed images as a result of adsorption of silver compounds to glass, and Möller made very resistant graticules from their silver images in wet collodion. The silver image was converted to platinum by chemical toning, and the graticules were heated to a temperature just below the softening point of glass. This caused the combustion of both the collodion and albumen in which the images were embedded, and the platinum was effectively sintered into the surface of the blank. There was a tendency for the blanks to distort during this fixing process [41].

Hall and Haynes [42] devised an interesting process for producing images within the surface layers of the glass itself, rather than right on the surface. An image in metal (usually silver or copper) was first formed on the glass by any of the methods outlined above. The image-bearing glass was then heated to 250° C or above, and a potential (usually between 40 and 100 volts) was applied by flat electrodes pressed against a loose graphite film on each side of the glass. It appears that under the influence of the applied potential, thermally ejected electrons from the metal film were drawn off to the positive electrode on the image side, and the positive metal ions so formed were drawn towards the negative electrode on the other side. After treatments usually lasting from 15 seconds up to 20 minutes, the metal on the glass surface was found to have been bleached, but the presence of the metal ions in the surface layers of the glass could be recognized by the fluorescence or the increase of refractive index they produced. The image was then finally darkened by heating to 400° C in a reducing atmosphere (usually hydrogen) to reduce the metal ions back to the metal.

By these methods it was shown that extremely resistant graticules could be made with the images mainly confined to the top micron or two of the glass. Because the metal ions diffuse between the atoms of the silica network, these images have been called 'Interstitial Patterns'. Sharp lines down to a width of a few microns were produced, and the processes could be modified to give opaque lines, or transparent lines in a variety of attractive colours. When viewed at high magnifications, the lines usually showed a slight coloured halo, which precluded their use for the finest images such as stage micrometers. From samples I have seen, I would judge this halo to be negligible for eyepiece graticules. The ability to produce resistant lines in a variety of colours seems a feature of considerable merit. Similar processes were developed by the Corning Glass Co., who called their process 'Photo-Staining' [43].

It seems that the 'Diadur' process might also be described as 'filmless'. Graticules made by this method were stated to be climatically, chemically and mechanically resistant, in spite of being in a layer less than 0·1 μ (4 millionths of an inch) thick [44].

ORGANIZATION OF GRATICULE PRODUCTION

The commercial-scale production of graticules introduces its own organizational problems. A major preoccupation will necessarily be the working out of handling procedures and layout of work-rooms and equipment to keep dust to a minimum. Methods of dust control should be adapted to the requirement of the final product, but will be influenced by the processes and procedures employed. Some of the methods for minimizing dirt in images are discussed in pp. 76–82. In recent years the requirements for dust control have been keenly appreciated in connection with manufacture of electronic devices and precision gyroscopes. When the expense of 'clean rooms' seems to be merited, the literature of these subjects can usefully be consulted [45]. Other precautions are to minimize movement by arranging for each type of operation to be done in separate rooms connected by service hatches, and to use non-fluffy protective clothing. It has been noted that the dust problem can be aggravated by disturbing deposits which are relatively harmless in their settled condition. Trouble can increase seriously immediately after rooms have been cleaned, or when camera bellows are moved [46].

Another problem is the selection and training of operators to perform exceptionally exacting repetitive work. Inspection and spotting of graticules, for instance, is not particularly difficult, but imposes such strains that only a small proportion of candidates for this work are likely to prove suitable. Such difficulties can be eased by provision of suitable equipment. Binocular microscopes, for instance, are less trying to use than monocular instruments, and working comfort is further improved by using projection viewers whenever practicable for inspecting images. Spotting or repair of damaged images can be facilitated by use of a micromanipulator. Whatever facilities are provided, the degree of success will still be conditioned by workshop morale. Corporate pride in the results achieved is a valuable stimulus for the maintenance of the attention to detail required to achieve top quality continuously.

The most detailed account yet published of the industrial production of graticules is the B.I.O.S. report on the Möller graticule factory. In addition to descriptions of the processes worked, it includes comments on such subjects as workshop layout, testing and selection of lenses and training of operators. Readers proposing to undertake graticule work are advised to consult this document.

DIVERSIFICATION BY GRATICULE MANUFACTURERS

The power and versatility of the unit processes employed for graticule manufacture have stimulated wide-ranging diversifications. These can conveniently be considered in two groups.

The first group stems from the use of extreme-resolution emulsions on a dividing engine, so that large but very fine scales can be produced by hundreds or thousands of successive exposures. Geiser extended this method by exposing many parallel tracks to produce binary-coded discs [4]. Other multiple-exposure methods are used to produce gratings for moiré-fringe instruments. These components are primarily intended for self-reading instruments, and their production and applications in automation and computer technology are described in the next chapter.

The second group (reviewed in Chapter 11) can be traced to the demand for increasingly robust graticules to be employed in military optical instruments. When only simple designs were required, graticules were made by forming resist layers on both sides of a thin sheet of copper, and printing so that the stencils on each side were in register. The metal was etched right through its thickness, and the silhouette of the pattern so formed then constituted the graticule image (see Chapter 11). Such graticules were the forerunners of the variety of delicate metal components made by the powerful techniques now known as photo-etching and photoforming. It is applied to the fabrication of such parts as foils for electric shavers, vanes for ciné camera shutters, precision springs for instruments, and a variety of elements with the conducting or magnetic properties needed by electrical or electronic manufacturers. Manufacturers of electronic semi-conductor devices also use thin metal foils with precisely etched apertures, as the masks through which a variety of substances are evaporated to produce transistors and micro-miniature electronic circuits. Photosensitive resin stencils applied directly to a semi-conducting substrate are also widely used for this purpose, particularly when the finest tolerances are demanded.

Another chemical method for producing delicate structures is to deposit metal electrolytically through a photographically formed stencil adhering to the support. This procedure was applied to the fabrication of strain gauges, and under suitable conditions, very fine patterns formed in this way can be stripped from their substrate, to give completely self-supporting structures such as electron-microscope specimen grids and precision sieves. As has happened so frequently before, the diversifications show signs of eclipsing the importance of the manufacture from which they originally stemmed.

REFERENCES

[1] Bovey, E., 'Graticules and Fine Scales: their Production and Application in Modern Measuring Systems', *J. Sci. Inst.*, **39**, 405, 1962.

[2] Rheinberg, J., 'Graticules', *T. Opt. Soc.*, **20**, 1, 1919. Much the same material, with further additions, is included in a later article by the same author: *Glazebrooks' Dictionary of Applied Physics*, Macmillan (London), **4**, 120, 1923.

[3] See reference [1]. Also pages 195–6 of *Microtophotography*, 1st Edition, Chapman and Hall, (London, 1957).

[4] Geiser, R. D., 'Reticle Production: Photographic, Mechanical and High Vacuum Techniques', *Inst. Maker*, **16**, July–August, 1948.

[5] Martin, L. C., *Optical Measuring Instruments*, Blackie and Son (Glasgow, 1924), p. 26.

[6] Lambertz, A., 'Skalen und Zeigeranordnung zur Erhöhung der Ablesengenauigkeit', *Z. Inst. K.*, **62**, 163, 1942.

[7] Murrell, K. F. H., 'The Visual Presentation of Instrument Data', *T. Soc. Inst. Tech.*, **4**, 1, 1952.

[8] Shackel, B., 'Human Engineering and Electronics', *Brit. Communications and Electronics*, **4**, 350, 1957.

[9] Guild, J., 'The Insensitivity and Personal Equation Errors of Optical Settings', *T. Opt. Soc.*, **31**, 1, 1929.

[10] Ogilvie, J. C. and Taylor, M. M., 'Effect of Orientation on the Visibility of Fine Wires', *J. Opt. Soc. Am.*, **48**, 628, 1958.

[11] Bradsell, R. H. and Bottomly, S. C., 'Development of the Photoelectric Microscope', *Instrument Practice*, **19**, 1010, 1965.

[12] Hariharan, P., 'The Production of Precision Resolving Power Test Reticles', *Phot. Sci Eng.*, **2**, 77, 1958.

[13] Nebe, W., 'Ist eine Herabsetzung der Ermüdung bei genauen Kreisteilungablesungen an geodätischen Instrument durch Zwischenschaltung von Farbfiltern möglich?', *Z. Vermw*, **63**, 337, 1935.

[14] Bovey, E., B.I.O.S. report 1552, p. 44 (see reference [22], Chapter 2).

[15] Burch, J. M., 'Photographic Production of Scales for Moiré Fringe Applications', in International Commission for Optics, Colloquium, Brussels, 1958. *Optics in Metrology*, Pergamon Press (London, 1960), p. 361.

[16] Smethurst, P. C., 'Graticules', *Phot. J.*, **84**, 147, 1944.

[17] Bovey, E., as reference [14], p. 44.

[18] Eastman Kodak Co., *Techniques of Microphotography*, Industrial Data Book P-52 (Rochester, New York, 1963), p. 9.

[19] (a) Lee, W., 'Making Large Precision Drawings', *Machinist*, 24th August, 1946.
(b) Nickols, L. W., 'Prepared Metal Sheets for Large Precision Drawings', *Machinist*, 31st August, 1946.

[20] Novotny, J., 'Preparation of Drawings, Layout-Artwork-Details', in Schlaback, T. D. and Rider, D. K. (ed.). *Printed and Integrated Circuits*, McGraw-Hill (New York, 1963), p. 76.

[21] Smith, F. H., 'Accuracy in Printed Reproduction', *Proc. 1st Conf. Assoc. Print. Tech.* (London, 1957), p. 5. (May be filed as Vol. 1, *Printing Technology*.)

[22] Stevens, G. W. W., (*a*) 'Reproduction of Aerial Images of Different Sharpness on "Lith-type" and Extreme-Resolution Emulsions', *J. Phot. Sci.*, **14**, 153, 1966.
(b) 'Control of Line Width in Photographic Masks', *Trans. Inst. Metal Finishing*, **44**, 123, 1966.

[23] Burmistrov, F. L., *Tech. Phys. U.S.S.R.*, **5**, 43, 1938 (see reference [29], Chapter 2).

[24] Cooper, K. D. and J. C. J. Stewart, 'The Production of Narrow Slit Images by a Scanning Procedure', *J. Phot. Sci.*, **11**, 326, 1963.

[25] Rust, E., 'The Photomechanical Production of Graticules', *Microtecnic*, **6**, 242, 1952.

[26] (a) Pelc, S. R., 'Autoradiographic Technique', *Nature*, **160**, 749, 1947.
(b) Berriman, R. W., Herz, R. H., and Stevens, G. W. W., 'A New Photographic Material—A High-Resolution Emulsion for Autoradiography', *Brit. J. Radiol.*, **23**, 472, 1950.

[27] Kodak Ltd, Data Sheet, SC-10, *Autoradiography*.

[28] Davis, R. and Pope, C. I., *National Bureau of Standards*, Circular 565, August 1955 (see reference [35], Chapter 2).

[29] Bovey, E., B.I.O.S. report 1552, p. 8 (see reference [22], Chapter 2).

[30] Wadsworth Watch Co., British Patent 183,859.

[31] (a) Jackson, E. W., 'Cylindrical Scales', *Brit. J. Phot.*, **96**, 427, 1949.
(b) Société et Précision de Levallois, 'Appareil destiné à la Reproduction Photographique d'Échelles sur Cylindres Métalliques', *Rev. Opt.*, **22**, 101, 1943.
(c) Smith, F. H., 'The Production of Graticules', *Phot. J.*, **88B**, 18, 1948.

[32] (a) Light Division of National Physical Laboratory, 'Production of Precision Scales on Glass', *Handbook 37th Exh. Sci. Inst. Phys. Soc.* (London, 1953), p. 255.
(b) Anon, 'Applications for Replica Gratings', *Times, Rev. Ind.*, **7**, 37, November, 1953.

[33] Kowaliski, P., *Versuche zur Verbesserung des Auflösungsvermögens Photographischer Schichten* Effiingerhof (Brugg, 1944).

[34] Lamberts, R. L., 'Measurement of Sine-Wave Response of a Photographic Emulsion', *J. Opt. Soc. Am.*, **49**, 425, 1959.

[35] *Photographic Reticle Productions by the Glue-Silver Process*, Eastman Kodak Co. (Rochester, N.Y., 1958).

[36] Coppin, F. W. and Gresham, D. C., British Patent 549,463.

[37] *See* Bovey, E., reference [1]. Also, Stevens, G. W. W., *Microphotography*, 1st Edition, Chapman and Hall, (London, 1957), p. 196.

[38] Guellich, G., United States Patent, 2,399,799.

[39] Anon., 'Abrasion-proof Graticule', *The New Scientist*, 21st August, 1958, p. 660.

[40] Burmistrov, F. L., *Phot. J.*, **76**, 452, 1936 (see reference [5], Chapter 2).

[41] Bovey, E. As reference [14], p. 27.

[42] Hall, A. J. C. and Hayes, J. G., 'Interstitial Graticules', *Australian J. Appl. Sci.*, **9**, 207, 1958.

[43] (a) Stookey, S. D., U.S. Patent 2,732,298.
(b) Ross, H. G. and F. W. Schuler, U.S. Patent 2,904,432.

(c) Stookey, S. D., U.S. Patent 2,911,749.

(d) Corning Glass Works, German Patent 965,266.

See also, Kosar, J., *Light-Sensitive Systems*, John Wiley (New York, 1965), p. 25.

[44] *Reticles, (Graticules) and Weighing Charts*, Dr. J. Heidenhain, Traurreut über Traunstein, W. Germany.

[45] See Chapter 3, pp. 80–2 and reference [12].

[46] Bovey, E., As reference [14], p. 36.

[47] Biberman, L.M., *Reticles in Electro-Optical Devices*, Pergamon Press (Oxford, 1966). This book describes graticules as functional components in systems, and extends the word 'reticle' to include 'patterns used to modulate or demodulate beams or images, to impart information into or extract it from a beam or to generate specific functions linking mechanical responses to basic properties of a controlled beam or image'.

10 · Applications to Automation and Metrology

Introduction

In our modern civilization, children from an early age are conditioned to interpret dialled instruments. Many toddlers learn to tell the time even before they can read. Now a clock is an instrument in which the passage of time relative to a certain point is depicted by the movement of a hand in front of the face. In fact the distance moved is *analogous* to the time elapsed, and the clock can therefore be called an *analogue* instrument. In just the same way the position of the speedometer needle is analogous to the speed of the parent's car, and the weighing machine needle depicts the child's increase in weight. At school he may meet other analogue instruments such as thermometers, a barometer and simple electrical instruments; and in the workshop the young man may have to read fuel and pressure gauges and other diverse dialled instruments used to extend the range of his observations.

Now consider the operation of using these instruments. It amounts to the application of definite prescribed rules, whereby a reading is converted into actual numbers, or digits. Only then can the reading be expressed in words, be conveniently thought about, or recorded or communicated. In many circumstances all the reader requires to do is to give an instrument a quick glance, to provide a momentary mental check. In this case nothing else is needed, and the instruments and reading methods we are all familiar with are quite adequate. In other cases human readings made by the traditional method are not ideal. In moments of stress, for instance, mistaken readings have sometimes produced tragic results: for instance when an aircraft altimeter was misread by 10,000 ft. The traditional method is also none too satisfactory when very large numbers of readings are required, so that mistaken transcription becomes increasingly likely. Moreover, it has become increasingly realized that activities such as the recording of dial readings do not utilize man's critical discernment. In doing this work a man only employs relatively lower mental faculties, and the job in fact can be suitably delegated to machines. In appropriate cases a large increase in efficiency may occur and the

1. Early microphotograph produced by J. B. Dancer

Ninety-year-old microphotograph, sold at price of one shilling. Inset, size of original image.
From the Kodak Museum, Harrow.

(a)

(b)

2. Microphotograph of cheques

(a) 16 mm film containing row of negatives reduced 18-fold,

(b) comparison of original cheque (top) with enlargement (bottom) from film shows all significant details are reproduced.

Courtesy of Recordak Division, Kodak Ltd.

(a)

Patented Apr. 14, 1953

2,635,048

UNITED STATES PATENT OFFICE

2,635,048

PHOTOGRAPHIC TRANSFER PRODUCT
AND PROCESS

Edwin H. Land, Cambridge, Mass., assignor to
Polaroid Corporation, Cambridge, Mass., a corporation of Delaware

Application July 6, 1948, Serial No. 37,252

18 Claims. (Cl. 95—8)

This invention relates to photographic processes involving the development of photosensitive
silver halide emulsions, and to products useful in
the performance of said processes.

It has been proposed to carry out the processing of a photosensitive element comprising a
silver halide emulsion layer by distributing a
predetermined quantity of processing liquid uniformly over the area of the photosensitive element to be processed in a position to permeate
the photosensitive layer. This distribution of the
processing liquid may be obtained by doctoring,

photosensitive emulsion is employed to produce
the imagewise distribution of some component
which tends to form a positive image in another
layer of material associated with the emulsion,
the tendency for continued development in the
unexposed regions of the negative will render
more critical the control of the time of formation
of the positive image. More serious than this,
however, in the latter case is that the developing
agent which permeates the associated layer will,
because of the oxidizable condition of the developing agent, tend upon exposure to air to form

(b)

3. 'Microcard' used for the re-publication of scholarly information

(a) The 5×3 in ($12 \cdot 5 \times 7 \cdot 5$ cm) card shows easily legible bibliographical details, and reduced images of 46 pages. This card contains the complete text of ten United States patent specifications.

(b) Photomicrograph ($\times 12$) of part of one of the images.

Original by courtesy of the Microcard Foundation.

4. Loading plate in film camera

M-R plate placed against registration guides. Because of transparency of emulsion, plate is mostly detected by reflection and by tape used to position it until camera was closed.

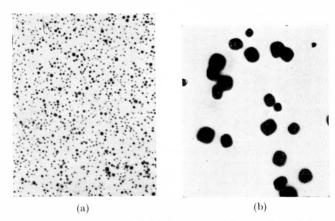

(a)   (b)

5. Grains of concentrated-Lippmann and document-copying emulsion

(a) Electron-micrograph ($\times 10,000$) of undeveloped Maximum-Resolution emulsion.

(b) Grains of document copying emulsion at same magnification.

Courtesy of Miss J. Tabor, Kodak Research Laboratories, Harrow.

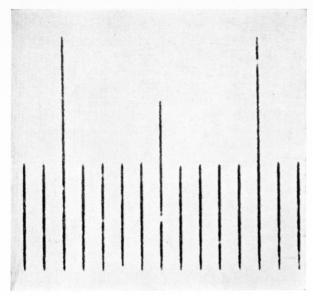

(a)

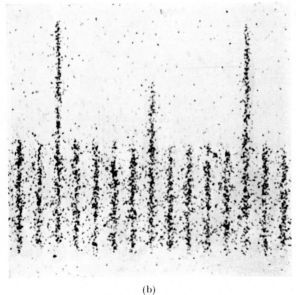

(b)

6. Sharpness given by concentrated-Lippmann and document-copying emulsions

(a) Image on Maximum Resolution plate ($\times 540$). The only sign of graininess is a slight roughening of the edges of the lines.

(b) Similar image on document-copying emulsion. Note how turbidity has spread the lines and reduced the contrast.

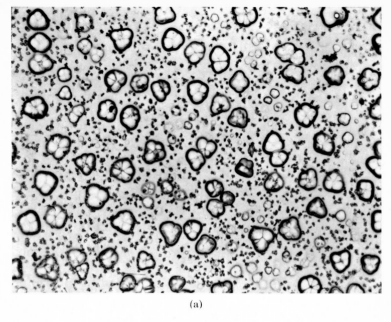

(a)

(b)

7. Crystals in unwashed emulsion

(a) Potassium nitrate crystals ($\times 96$) formed in unwashed emulsion coated on plates.

(b) Coarse and fine distortions of image, corresponding to large and small crystals.

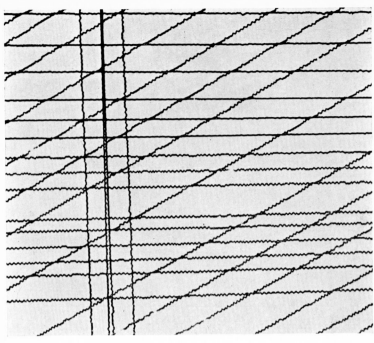

8. Distortion of fine lines of stencil image

Photomicrograph ($\times 23$) of image made by developing Maximum-Resolution plate to a negative, and washing-out the background with etch-bleach solution. Removal of the physical support of the gelatin background permitted the straight lines to distort into waves. Note how the thicker lines (at the top) have practically resisted this tendency.

9. 'Tadpole' image on M-R Plate

ιotomicrograph ($\times 150$) of image produced by microprojection of slit with segments n successively doubled exposure intensities. Since the exposure needed for adequate ity was (in this example) less than that producing appreciable spread, the emulsion suitable for extreme-resolution work.

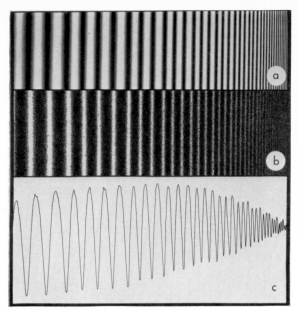

10. Influence of line frequency on image contrast

(a) Sinusoidal test chart image with progressively increasing line frequencies.

(b) Photomicrograph of image produced by optical reduction of test chart on emulsion layer.

(c) Microdensitometer trace of (b) showing contrast decreasing with line frequency.

Courtesy of Eastman Kodak Co.

11. Result of excessive physical intensification

The grains of this image on M-R emulsion ($\times 540$) have been enlarged by intensification to the developed grain size of a document-copying emulsion, but the improvement of resolution due to the low turbidity of the undeveloped layer is not all lost [compare Plate 6(b)].

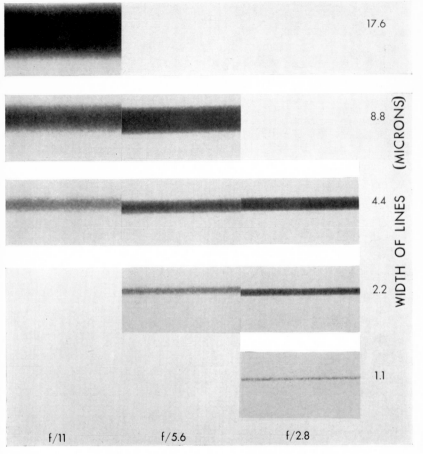

WIDTH OF LINES (MICRONS)

17.6

8.8

4.4

2.2

1.1

f/11 f/5.6 f/2.8

12. Dependence of line quality on width and lens aperture

Photomicrographs ($\times 2{,}500$) of images of different width reproduced at range of lens apertures. The diagonal lines connect images which should have similar modulation transfer function, and similar density and relative line quality was observed.

Courtesy of H. J. Fromm and Journal of Photographic Science.

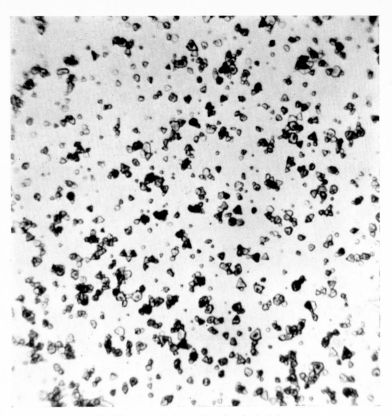

13. Single-grain-layer focusing test plate

Photomicrograph ($\times 750$). Note how the field curvature of the objective is shown by decrease in sharpness at the edge of the useful field.

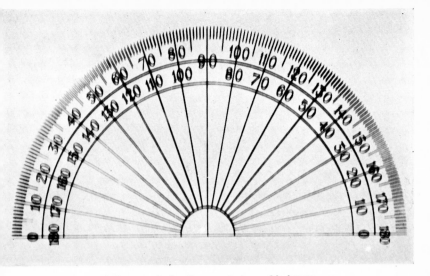

14. Influence of vibration on photographic image

No loss of sharpness occurs along the 90° radius parallel to the vibration, and maximum unsharpness is produced at right angles to this direction. Note how the simple harmonic motion has tended to split the image into two lines, and coincidence of intensity maxima displaced by one line interval produces spurious sharpness of the scale at 0° on the left.

(a)

(b)

15. 'Telephotographs' made with microscope objective

(a) Photomicrograph (×36) of image on Kodak M-R plate, made with 2-inch Watson 'Holos' objective.

(b) Further enlargement (×130) of spire, which was $1\frac{1}{2}$ miles away.

16. Representation of 'ideal' Airy disc

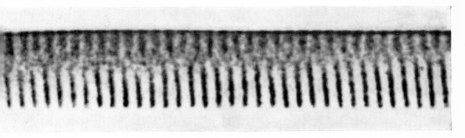

17. Emulsion bearing image in its lower half

Transverse section ($\times 1,800$) of dry emulsion layer showing sharp image in lower half and various resolution in upper layers. Note how the lines of the spurious image are staggered with pect to those of the genuine image.

Photomicrograph by courtesy of J. A. Carter, Kodak Research Laboratories, Harrow.

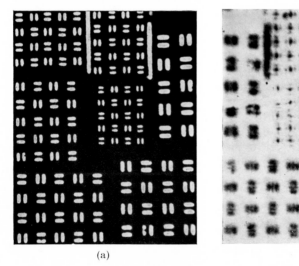

(a)   (b)

18. Spurious resolution in contact-printing

(a) Test chart image ($\times 460$). The groups shown correspond to resolution figures of 400, 360, 330, 295, 270, 245 and 220 lines/mm.

(b) Contact print on Maximum-Resolution plate made after test-chart surface had been scratched in use. Some groups are reproduced by *three* lines instead of two.

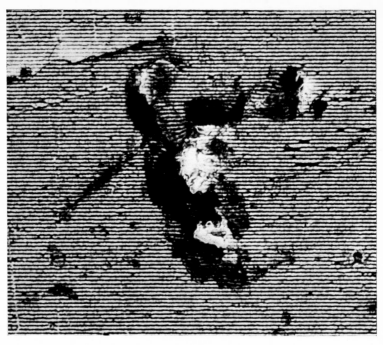

19. Scratched surface of diffraction-grating copy used as contact test chart

Photomicrograph ($\times 580$) of image on Maximum-Resolution plate. The way in which the emulsion has piled up in the scratch can be seen from the distortion of the lines of the grating.

20. Lenticular surface of processed image

Section of dry Maximum-Resolution emulsion containing a graticule image ($\times 950$). Note how the thickness is increased in the blackened parts.

Photomicrograph by courtesy of Miss J. Tabor, Kodak Research Laboratories, Harrow.

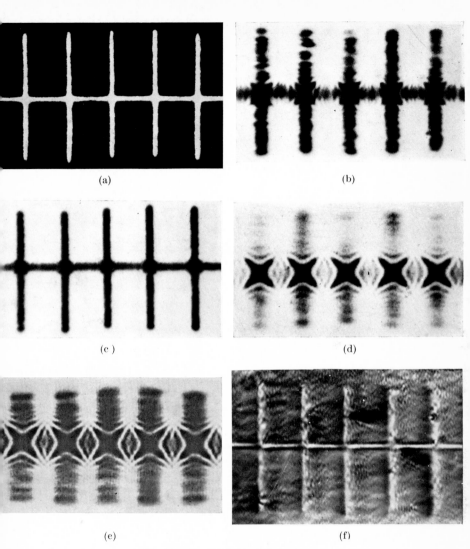

21. Image contorted by interference

(a) Negative graticule image ($\times 460$).
(b) Contact print on Maximum-Resolution plate from negative spotted with opaque medium.
(c) Print with space between negative and emulsion filled with xylene.
(d) Print by parallel light and air space increased to 70 μ (about 0·003 in).
(e) As (d), but print made by monochromatic light. Note complex interference fringes.
(f) Photomicrograph of cast from negative surface.

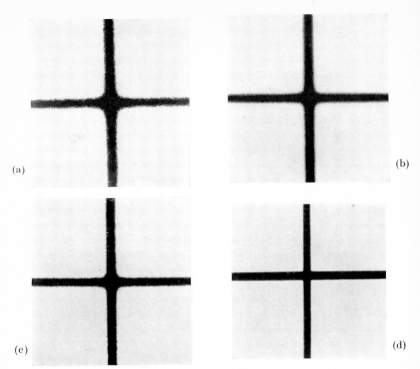

22. Line quality obtained with different lens-emulsion combinations (×360)

(a) Lith-type plate and (b) M-R with F/17 lens; (c) Lith-type plate and (d) M-R with microscope objective.

Courtesy, Journal of Photographic Science

23. Hilger-Watts 'Universal' mechanical digitizer

(a) Base plate bearing tracks for each contacting ball, (b) contacting ball-bearings each positioned to detect one track, (c) etched commutator disc.

Courtesy Hilger-Watts Ltd.

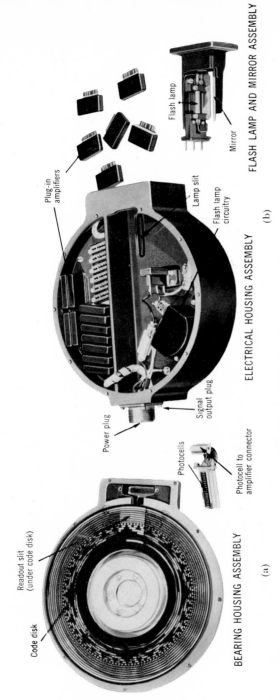

Plug-in amplifiers

Lamp slit

Flash lamp circuitry

ELECTRICAL HOUSING ASSEMBLY

Power plug

Signal output plug

Photocells

Photocell to amplifier connector

Readout slit (under code disk)

Code disk

BEARING HOUSING ASSEMBLY

(a)

Flash lamp

Mirror

FLASH LAMP AND MIRROR ASSEMBLY

(b)

24. Baldwin 16-Digit shaft-angle encoder

Note (a) 8 in (20 cm) optical digitizer disc and bank of photocells, (b) flash lamp and electronic assemblies. Each amplifier employs a 3-stage circuit with silicon transistors (see Chapter 11).

Courtesy of Baldwin Piano Co.

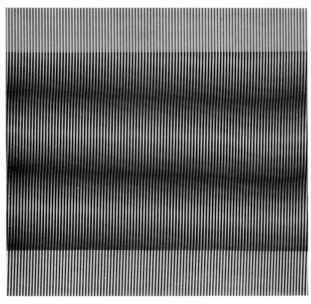

25. Moiré fringes

The fringes were formed by superimposing a grating with black lines (lower half) on a similar grating with grey lines at an angle of 5°.

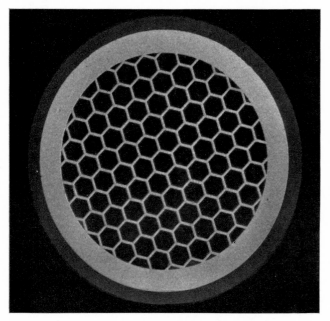

26. Electron-microscope grid made by photo-forming.

Photomicrograph ($\times 25$) of grid used to support specimens in electron microscope. The grids are made by electrodeposition of copper on nickel through a photoresist stencil, followed by stripping of resultant image.

Courtesy of P. C. Smethurst.

27. Cross-section of micromesh sieve ($\times$100)

The very thin electroformed mesh was stretched over a thicker and coarser grid, and the two were bonded by electrolytic deposition.

Courtesy of H. W. Daeschner of Shell Development Co. and American Society for Testing Materials.

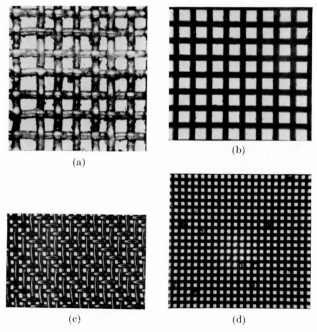

28. Photoformed and woven micromesh sieves ($\times$55)

    (a) U.S. standard woven-wire, 74 μ nominal.
    (b) Photoformed sieve, 75 μ.
    (c) German precision woven-wire, 15μ.
    (d) Photoformed, 20 μ.

Courtesy of H. W. Daeschnor of Shell Development Co. and American Society for Testing Materials.

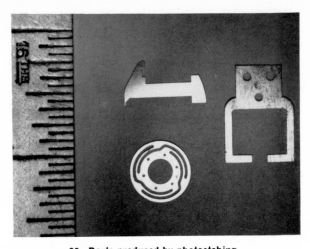

29. Parts produced by photoetching

Samples provided by Microponent Development Ltd

30. Continuous sensitization of steel strip

This cleaning and sensitizing unit operates the preliminary stages in the production of aperture masks for colour television tubes. After scrubbing, washing and degreasing, the strip is sensitized on both sides and is here emerging ready for exposure.
Courtesy of Buckbee Mears Co.

(a) Bank of double-sided vacuum-printing frames and xenon arc light sources.

(b) Detail of one side of double frame. The circle is the array of fine dots on the master negative.

31. Exposure of sensitized steel strip from both sides
Courtesy of Buckbee Mears Co.

32. Development and etching of exposed strip

The exposed strip is entering the developing unit, after which the resist stencils are baked and etched. (A later machine of cleaner design has now been constructed.)

Courtesy of Buckbee Mears Co.

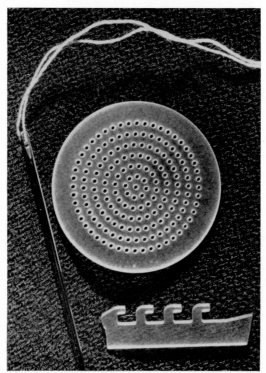

33. Thick glass components produced by 'Fotoform' method

Plates for holding thermocouple tips and relay pusher-bar compared with needle and thread. Note squareness of etched edges in 0·055 in (1·4 mm) thick glass.

Courtesy Corning Glass Company.

34. Borrowdale overhead camera

Equipment of this type is used for making precision intermediate transparencies.
Courtesy R. W. Borrowdale Co.

35. Borrowdale 'V-block'

System for reproducible camera setting within 0·0001-in.
Courtesy of R. W. Borrowdale Co.

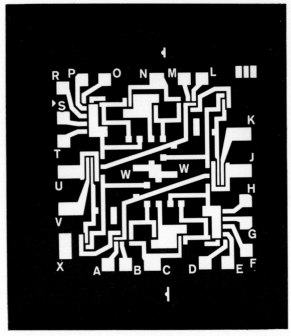

(a)

(b)

**36. Intermediate transparency and multiple-image mask
for production of integrated circuits**

Courtesy of R. Freestone and Ferranti Ltd.

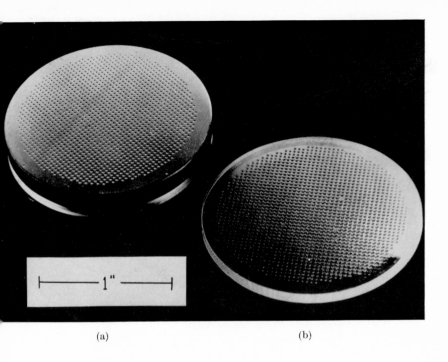

(a)   (b)

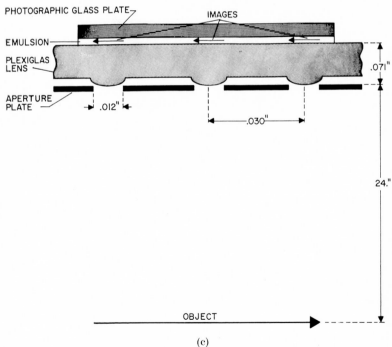

(c)

37. Multiple Stanhope (fly's-eye) lens

(*a*) Master indented copper disc.
(*b*) Moulded Plexiglass lens.
(*c*) Schematic drawing of principle and representative dimensions.

Courtesy of I.B.M.

38. Harry Diamond Laboratories multiple-image camera

Left to right: focusing microscope, plate mounted on toolmaker's micrometer stage, microphotographic microscope. Note pin-locating holes on micrometer drums.

Courtesy of T. C. Hellmers Jr. and J. R. Nall, and U.S. Army, Army Materiel Command. Harry Diamond Laboratories.

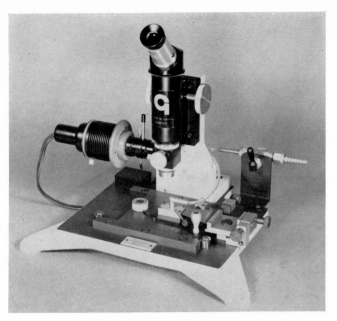

39. Master-reticle alignment device (Type 992A)

Reduced transparencies are aligned by micrometer, and cemented in kinematically designed frames to ensure registration of each image.

Courtesy of David W. Mann Co. and Geophysics Corporation of America.

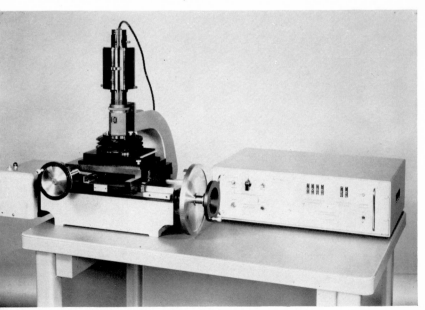

40. David W. Mann photorepeater, Type 1080

Left, the photorepeater with mechanically driven cross-slides and flash lamp; *right,* control unit for setting exposures per row, spacing and flash intensity.

Courtesy of David W. Mann Co. and Geophysics Corporation of America.

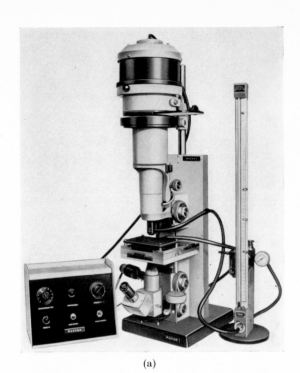

(a)

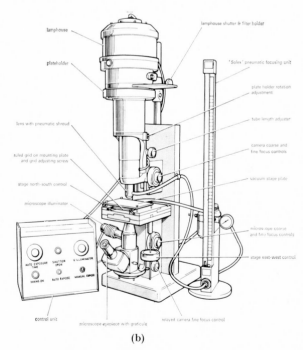

lamphouse

lamphouse shutter & filter holder

plateholder

'Solex' pneumatic focusing unit

plate holder rotation adjustment

tube length adjuster

lens with pneumatic shroud

camera coarse and fine focus controls

ruled grid on mounting plate and grid adjusting screw

vacuum stage plate

stage north-south control

microscope illuminator

AUTO EXPOSURE TIME   SHUTTER OPEN   V. ILLUMINATOR

MAINS ON   AUTO EXPOSE   MANUAL EXPOSE

microscope coarse and fine focus controls

stage east-west control

control unit

microscope eyepiece with graticule

relayed camera fine focus control

(b)

41. Watson step-and-repeat camera Mark III

Courtesy of W. Watson and Sons Ltd.

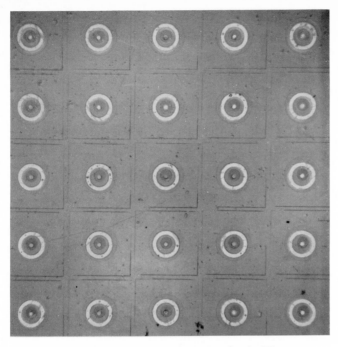

42. Silicon planar transistors on wafer (×45)

*Courtesy of J. C. Hellmers Jr., J. R. Nall of U.S. Army Materiel
Command, Harry Diamond Laboratories and
Semiconductor Products.*

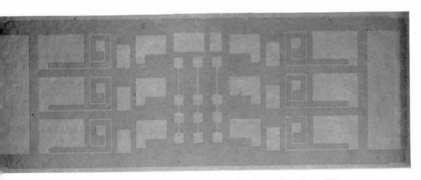

43. First *n*-type diffusion for semiconductor network (×23)

Forty separate areas (some inter-connected) were formed.
Courtesy of P. Shaw and Texas Instruments Incorporated.

44. Wafer bearing forty semiconductor networks
Diameter approximately 1 in (2·5 cm) (×3).
Courtesy of P. Shaw and Texas Instruments Incorporated.

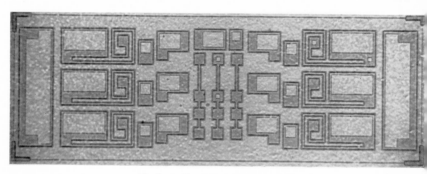

45. Second *p*-type diffusion (×23)
At least twenty-nine extra areas, precisely registered with respect to the first diffusion
have been formed.
Courtesy of P. Shaw and Texas Instruments Incorporated.

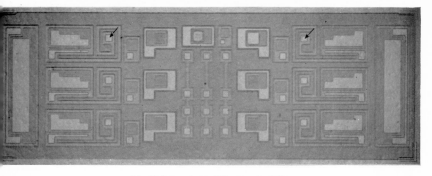

46. Third *n*-type diffusion (×23)

At least forty-eight further areas precisely registered with respect to the first two diffusions were formed.

Courtesy of P. Shaw and Texas Instruments Incorporated.

47. Circuit mounted in package and connected to leads (×17)

The connections were made with 0·001 in (25 *μ*) gold wire, and a lid was finally soldered
on in an inert atmosphere.

Courtesy of P. Shaw and Texas Instruments Incorporated.

(a)

**48. Scale divided into fractions of
a micron**
Image produced by a scanning
electron beam on a collodion film.
*Courtesy of G. Möllenstedt and
R. Speidel*

(b)

49. Image borne by a Dagron pellicle

(a) Reproduction (actual size) of pellicle made by Dagron in 1871.

(b) Photomicrograph ($\times 40$) at intersection of pages. In addition to a readily legible image, print shows edges of sheets and partial covering of official stamp, proving that many printed sheets were copied with a single exposure.

From Photographic Museum, Kodak Ltd, Harrow.

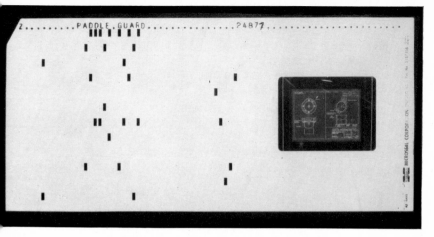

50. Microfilm mounted on aperture in punched card
Note holes punched for automatic sorting.

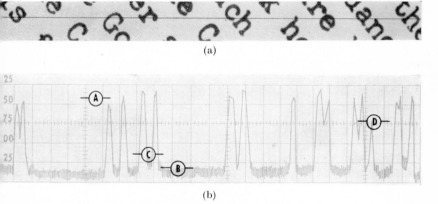

(a)

(b)

51. Trace produced by rapid scanning microdensitometer
(a) Print from image of microfilm projected on scanner.
(b) Corresponding microdensitometer scan. A, average line density; B, background
density; C, lower background density between closely spaced lines; D, high indication of
line density when scan aperture "nicked" the letter n.

Courtesy of B. Jamieson and National Microfilm Association.

RL | London Library Catalog By C. T. Hagberg Wright and C. J. Purnell
LR | A Rowman and Littlefield Library Resource Microform · Rowman and Littlefield, Inc., New York, N.Y. 10011

BIB/CA1

35.92
1226 pp.

NCR

TRADEMARK REG. U.S. PAT. OFF.

(a)

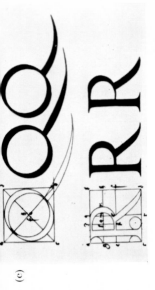

(c)

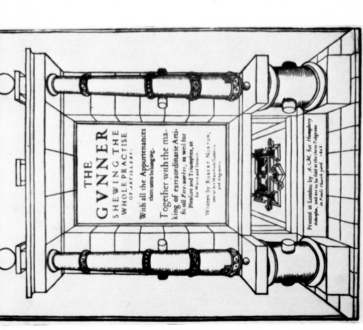

(b)

(d)

& la marine de S., 18
Sulaimán, *the merchant, see*
[by S. &c.], tr., 1733.
Sulaimán, *pasha* [†Sèvè:
Pasha], *see* VINGTRINIER
égyptiennes, ou hist. des
Sulaimán III [SOLYMAN],
Travels into Persis &c.
III, 1686.

52. National Cash Register transparency

(a) Image (natural size) bearing 91 columns and 31 rows of images (2,821 pages) at 1:30 : 1 reduction ratio.
(b) Photomicrograph of book title page (×60) from left of top row.
(c) Detail from right of top row (×50).
(d) Typical catalogue entry (×300): approx 2½ times size of original text.

*Courtesy of National Cash Register Co. and Rowman and Littlefield Inc. Photomicrographs by F. Judd,
Kodak Research Laboratories, Harrow.*

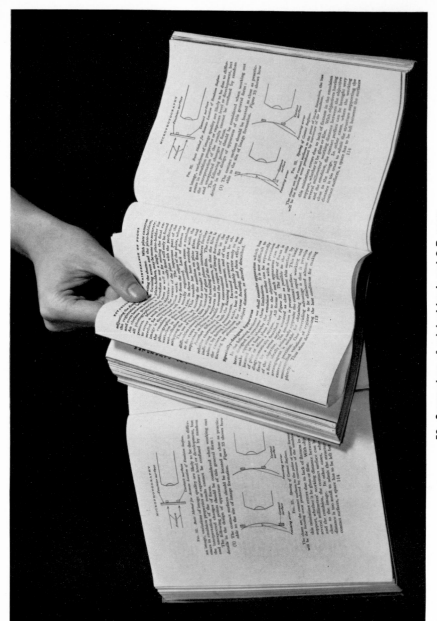

53. Comparison of original book and O.P. copy

Note right/left transposition of pages and double ply of each page.

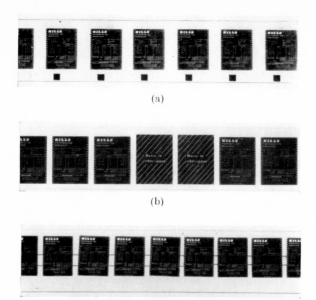

(a)

(b)

(c)

54. Methods of indexing microfilms

(a) Image-control marks in margins.

(b) Result from microfilmed target-flash cards.

(c) 'Datamatic' code marks between frames, which can be seen even during rapid winding of film.

Courtesy of Recordak Division, Kodak Ltd.

55. Miracode film

In this system, any number of columns of coded information can be recorded between frames.

Courtesy of Recordak Division, Kodak Ltd.

56. Recordak MICROSTRIP system

Each of the three Access Files shown accepts 100 holders (see inset), each carrying ten lengths of film. When the holder is inserted in reader, one mechanism selects the desired strip, and movements of the Index Selector rapidly locates the desired

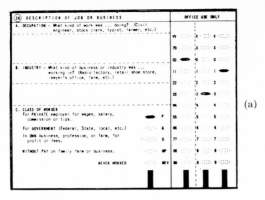

(a)

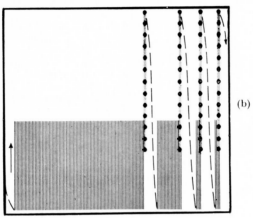

(b)

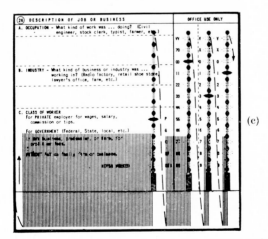

(c)

57. Flying-spot scanning of census documents in FOSDIC system

(a) Portion of image of document to be read, with index bars for locating columns.

(b) Scanning pattern with vertical excursions produced by recognition of index marks. Black dots indicate where beam stops to allow read-out on tape.

(c) Scanning Pattern superimposed on documents.

Courtesy Director, National Bureau of Standards.

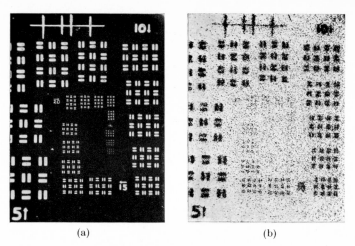

(a)   (b)

58. Resolution testing by contact printing

(a) Test-chart image on Maximum-Resolution plate ($\times 40$). The finest image corresponds to 200 lines/mm.

(b) Contact print on high-speed negative emulsion, clearly showing loss of resolution due to turbidity and graininess.

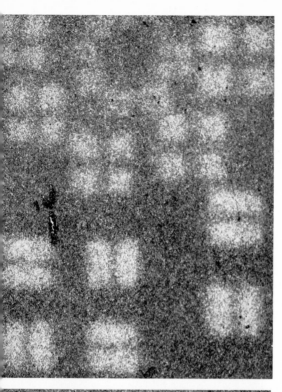

(a) Photomicrograph ($\times 50$) of contact print on high-speed X-ray film exposed with intensifying screens to 55 K.v. X-rays.

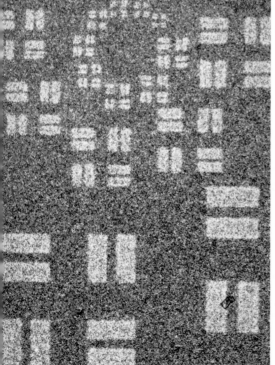

(b) Image similarly produced but with direct exposure to X-rays.

59. Contact-resolution comparison of screen and direct radiography

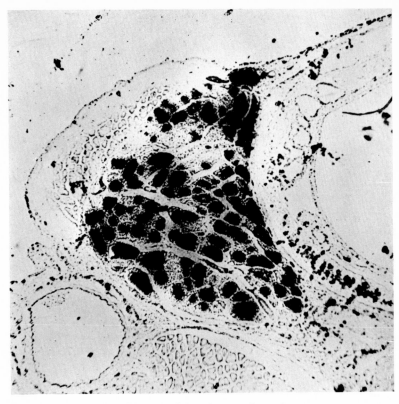

60. Tissue section and autoradiograph

Section ($\times 35$) from thyroid of rat injected with I^{131}. The outline of the unstained tissue only shows faintly, and certain restricted areas (mainly in the centre of the print), contained much radioactivity resulting in heavy blackening of the emulsion mounted on the section.

Courtesy of S. R. Pelc.

61. Section of element of test image

Transverse section ($\times 380$) of emulsion with images confined to the surface.
*Photomicrograph by courtesy of Miss J. Tabor, Kodak Research
Laboratories, Harrow.*

(a)   (b)

62. Radioactive test chart, and autoradiograph from it

(a) Photomicrograph ($\times 280$) of central portion of reduced test chart.
(b) Autoradiograph on Kodak AR.10 Autoradiographic stripping emulsion.
Group 25 (corresponding to 215 lines/mm) is still clearly resolved.

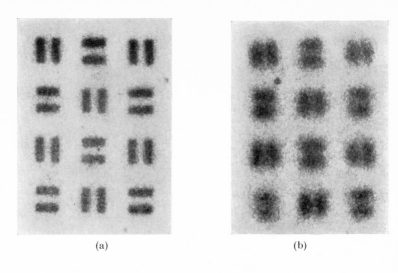

(a)   (b)

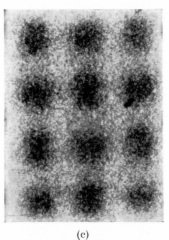

(c)

63. Effect of separation on sharpness of autoradiograph

Photomicrograph ($\times 250$) of image corresponding to 56 lines/mm.
(a) with perfect contact; (b) with 3 μ separation between emulsion and
test chart; (c) with 10 μ separation.

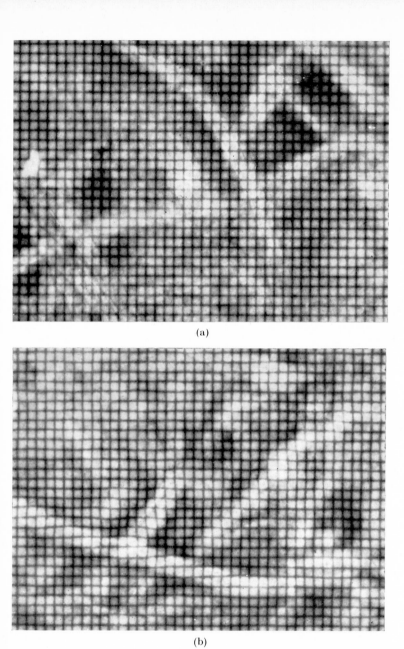

(a)

(b)

64. Image shifts produced by glazing of prints

(a) Photomicrograph ($\times 200$) of grid image on paper sensitized with heavily dyed Maximum-Resolution emulsion.

(b) Distortion in grid produced by glazing. Note how the largest shifts follow strong paper fibres.

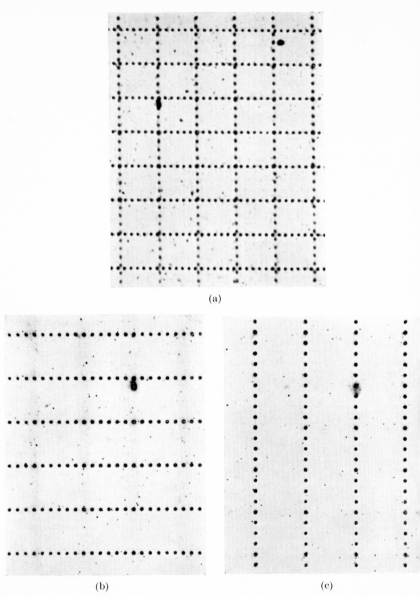

(a)

(b)

(c)

65. Separate images in the upper and lower layers of the same emulsion

The images were produced by giving two exposures at different focus settings, with negative turned through a right angle for the second exposure.

(a) Photomicrograph ($\times 950$) with objective stopped down to show both images.

(b) Horizontal lines and blemish in emulsion surface ($\times 1,200$).

(c) Vertical lines in emulsion depth, lying just underneath blemish ($\times 1,200$).

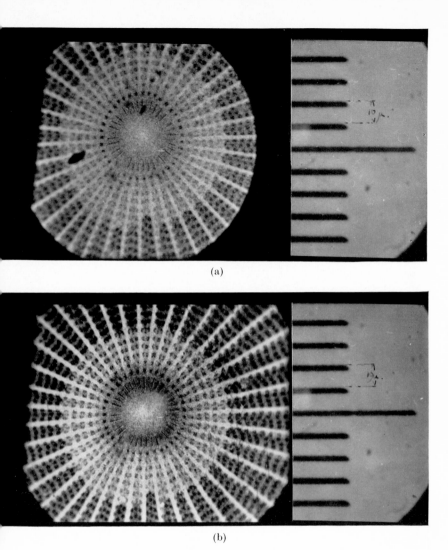

(a)

(b)

66. Effect of emulsion thickness on microradiograph

(a) Image ($\times$ 700) from diatom produced on 6 μ thick emulsion.
(b) Image on 1 μ emulsion.
Courtesy of Professor W. Ehrenberg and M. White and British Journal of Radiology.

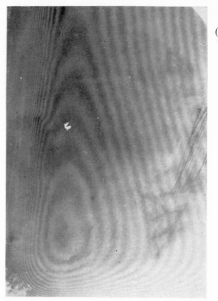

(a) Hologram.

(b) Reconstruction.

67. Hologram and reconstruction of a portrait
Courtesy of E. N. Leith, J. Upatnieks, and Journal of the Optical Society of Americ

overall results are then well worth while. Machines for dial reading can also work at fantastic speeds, and when linked with computers enable many otherwise almost overwhelming tasks to be performed. In important groups of these dial-reading machines, photographic techniques for manufacturing the scales have proved of decisive importance. As we shall see in this chapter, the bringing together of microphotographic scales and electronic equipment have provided important contributions to automation systems.

Binary-coded Scales

Mathematicians and engineers interested in developing instruments suitable for automatic reading have first to consider what physical principles had to be used to read the scales. The choice was fairly obvious, and it was decided that the scales should be read by arranging for them to generate electrical impulses. Electrical instruments can be made to detect the magnitude as well as the presence of an impulse, but if they are only required to detect the presence, there is less chance of trouble and less chance of error. It was therefore decided that the scales should only be required to indicate the presence or absence of a signal.

Now any whole number can be analysed into *binary digits* by successively subtracting decreasing powers of two.

Table 11. Analysis of the number 499 into powers of two

Powers of two	Value of digit	Present or absent	Remainder	Code
8	256	Present	243	
7	128	Present	115	
6	64	Present	51	
5	32	Present	19	
4	16	Present	3	
3	8	Absent	3	
2	4	Absent	3	
1	2	Present	1	
0	1	Present	0	

As a result of this operation, any number can be depicted by a code in which the presence of each digit may be indicated by a white area and the absence by a black.[1] If we lay the code diagrams for a series of successive numbers side by side, they then constitute a *binary-coded*

---

[1] Whether this convention is used or the reverse, in which the presence of the signal is indicated by black, seems to be determined by the requirements of the interpreting system.

K

scale (Fig. 77). It will be seen that such a scale consists of a series of parallel tracks along its entire length, and each track shows, in each position along the scale, the presence or absence of its own power of two. In actual practice, a simple scale such as is indicated here is subject to the possibility of serious ambiguity from small errors in

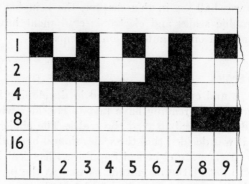

Fig. 77 *Simple Binary-coded Scale*

Presence of *black* in each horizontal row indicates *presence* of indicated power of two.

mounting or in the adjustment of the reading equipment. Mathematicians have devised variations of this simple code which minimize these difficulties [1]. Codes have also been used in which each digit of a decimal scale is depicted by four tracks of a binary code, or which correspond to non-linear functions. The design of codes for this type of equipment is a specialized subject outside the scope of this book.

GENERATION OF BINARY-CODED SCALES

From processes described in the literature, it is clear that many methods can be used for generating these scales. Selection of a suitable method has to be made on the grounds of the accuracy required, the number of scales needed, the cost, equipment and techniques available. Scales can be linear as already seen in Fig. 77, where the tracks for each digit run parallel to each other. The scale can also be wrapped around a circle, and then the tracks form concentric circles. Some methods are unsuitable for the production of linear scales. Four methods will be described to demonstrate the main principles involved.

(1) PRODUCTION OF DRAWING OF COMPLETE SCALE FOLLOWED BY PHOTOGRAPHIC REDUCTION

The production of a binary-coded scale can be treated just like the production of any graticule image. A large drawing may be produced, followed by straightforward reduction to the required size, but the usefulness of this method is restricted mainly to circular scales. The image distortion of lenses with properly centered components is along the radii from the axis, and with circular scales small radial distortions

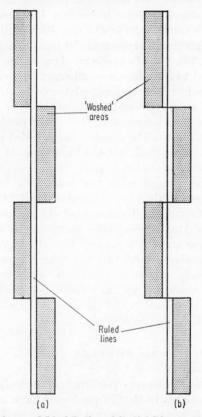

Fig. 78 *Direct and Ideal Ruling of Radial Line for Binary Code*

(a) direct ruling produces radial displacement between *left* of top and *right* of next unit, (b), ideal ruling avoids this.

are unimportant. With linear scales the same distortions could cause appreciable loss of accuracy.

The production of a master drawing of a binary-coded scale cannot be any easy task. The reader can easily convince himself of this by ruling a small section of a coded pattern on graph paper, and filling in the appropriate rectangles with a brush. It is apparent that the technique required will be notably different from that used in making master drawings for graticules. In conventional graticule drawings, the centre of the line represents the 'correct' position, so that the precision of the scale is not necessarily decreased by fluctuations of line width. With binary-coded patterns, however, it is the *edges* of the elements of the image which cause the signals to be switched off. The exact position of the edges depends on the width of the ruled lines used to define each element of the image. To secure high accuracy thus demands a specialized drafting technique. Furthermore, the same radial line on some tracks represents a transition on the left side of an image, and in other tracks represents the transition at the right side of the image (Fig. 78). Use of a single ruled radial line across all tracks is therefore bound to introduce a small error. The very narrow cuts which can be produced on scribing plates or in strippable opaque layers on 'Mylar' support should minimize this type of error.

These considerations suggest that the task of producing the drawing in itself sets a limit to the sub-division of coded pattern that can be produced by this method, but the limitations of available objectives also have to be considered. In designing circular coded scales, engineers have been much concerned with possible errors in their reading equipment. It therefore seemed natural for them to place their finest sub-divisions in the outermost circle, where there is more space and in optical terms fewer lines per millimetre would be needed to obtain the same angular precision. Unfortunately the outermost circle will be reproduced farthest away from the axis, and the lens performance is likely to be correspondingly worse. On these grounds, it is obviously inadvisable to have the finest sub-divisions in this position and the more tracks and the finer is the sub-division of the circle the worse does the problem get.

(2) THE PRODUCTION OF COMPLEX CODED PATTERNS ON
A DIVIDING ENGINE

The problem facing engineers requiring more finely divided coded patterns was analogous to that of producing large finely divided instrument scales. It was fortunate that workable methods had already been developed for this purpose. The procedure used was to mount a photographic plate on the table of a dividing engine, so that it could be traversed underneath an objective through which was projected an element of the image every time the table was stopped (p. 246).

To produce binary-coded patterns, Geiser described the making of a master drawing with a row of thirteen wedge-shaped windows [2]. These were reduced, and the master negative projected on the plate so that the image of each window formed 1/8,192 of thirteen concentric annular rings. Separate electrically operated shutters were installed in front of each window, and a bank of relays determined the combination of shutters which was opened and closed for each consecutive position of the table of the dividing engine. This procedure was used to generate the pattern shown in Fig. 79, in which 180° of the innermost ring is opaque, and each successive ring has twice as many light and dark areas until the last has 8,192 (2^{13}). This method

Fig. 79 *Binary-coded Scale produced on Dividing Engine*
Composite image generated by multiple exposure to projected image of sector slit divided into 13 segments in front of computer-controlled shutters. Exposure of master negative took more than 20 hours.
Courtesy of R. D. Geiser, Messrs. W. and L. E. Gurley, Troy, New York, U.S.A.

is flexible, since it can equally well be used for producing linear scales and for generating patterns representing geometric and other non-linear functions. It has been stated that the complete scale may be exposed several times over, so as to average out errors and produce a pattern of improved accuracy [1(a)].

(3) USE OF 35 MM FILM FOR GENERATING BINARY-CODED PATTERNS
Elliott, Robbins and Evans divided the problem of generating discs into two parts [3]. They firstly exposed 35 mm film in a special camera,

pointed at a bank of lamps behind rectangles of opal glass. The lamps were illuminated in suitable combinations according to each fourteen-digit binary code required. For this purpose, a simple electronic calculator was run in synchronism with the automatic camera. In this way they produced a length of 35 mm film containing a fourteen-digit binary code represented as rows of clear or opaque marks across the width of the film. These marks are really analogous to the signals

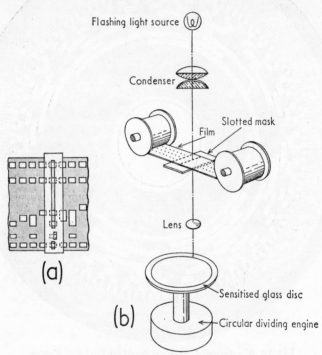

Fig. 80 *Generation of Disc from coded 35 mm Film*
(a) Underside of film showing slotted mask.
(b) Diagram of projection system.
Courtesy of Elliott Automation Ltd and Institution of Electrical Engineers.

passing to the relays of the Gurley apparatus. The marks needed only to be accurate in so far as their edges were parallel to and a fixed distance from the edge of the film, and this defined along the radius the space ultimately occupied by each of the tracks of the pattern. The width of each component mark was substantially wider than the final angular width required. As shown in Fig. 80, each 'frame' of this film was brought in front of a slotted mask. It was the reduced image of this mask which defined the accurate angular position of each unit of the final image. By this method no great precision was demanded of the operations of exposing and subsequently moving the 35 mm film.

The apparatus for generating the scales was operated by rotating the table of the dividing engine smoothly and continuously. A mechanically generated signal indicated the movement of the table through each angular step, and caused the light source to flash and expose the digit for the next number in all tracks simultaneously, after which the film was automatically advanced for the next digit. Dymott also employed 35 mm film for generating binary-coded scales, but spliced the film to form a continuous loop [5]. Thus information for the finer divided tracks was repeated with each passage of the loop, while supplementary means were used to expose the coarser tracks.

Tindale [4] used the same type of method but employed photo-electrically generated signals. Around the outside edge of the dividing table there was fixed an annular glass ring on which was marked fine lines at 2 degree intervals. These were moved in front of a graticule containing 144 fine slits. As the lines passed in front of each slit, a photocell actuated the exposing and film-advancing mechanism. This method also is suitable for producing linear scales, and it is clear that a 'library' of coded 35-mm films can be accumulated, so that any required image can be made at short notice. It was suggested that the method could be applied to producing a disc with separate scales depicting angles, their sines and their cosines.

(4) GENERATION OF MULTIPLE-TRACK DISC BY PHOTO-ELECTRIC IMPULSES FROM SINGLE-TRACK PATTERN

An interesting method for generating binary-coded patterns was described by E. N. Jones (Baldwin Piano Co.) and B. Lippel and K. N. Doering of the U.S. Signal Corp. Engineering Laboratory [6]. A vertical shaft was supported by an 'air bearing' to give frictionless and very steady rotation. On the lower part of this shaft was mounted a glass reference plate, having a circular photographic transparency of 16 in diameter with 65,536 uniformly spaced radial marks (Fig. 81). This reference disc was illuminated by a projector, and a microscope objective was used to project sixty divisions of the scale on a graticule with a matched stationary pattern. The light transmitted by the graticule then fell on a photocell, and as the disc rotated, inter-action of the projected and stationary patterns produced a sinusoidal fluctuation of light intensity. The electronic circuit then transformed the resultant signals into square waves which triggered frequency dividers, enabling the frequency to be divided by any required power of two, according to which track was being exposed. Since the signals were a result of the coincidence of sixty divisions of the reference pattern, the effect of dust and defects was negligible, and some averaging of residual errors occurred.

As shown in Fig. 81, the top of the shaft bore a turn-table on which an Eastman Kodak High-Resolution plate was mounted. A separate optical system employed a 16 mm achromatic microscope objective to project a reduced image of a Westrex Motion Picture Sound Recording Light Valve. Now if the square waves generated by this rotation of the reference ring were fed directly to the light valve, the movement of the photographic plate relative to the projected image would have given unit images with unsharp edges. To prevent this,

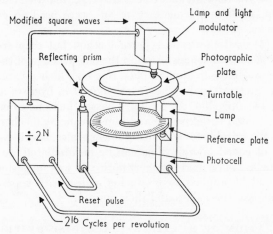

Fig. 81 *Generation of Disc by signals from Circular Grating*
Courtesy of E. M. Jones, B. Lippel, K. M. Doering and Proceedings of National Electronics Conference.

the wave-form was further modified so that when the light valve opened or closed, the movement of the projected image of the edges of the ribbons in the light valve followed the rotation of the plate. Hence the edges of the unit images were sharp and distinct. The projection system producing the image of the light valve could be moved very accurately along a radius, so that the images were formed on successive concentric circles representing the different tracks of the scale. As the projector was brought into position for each track, the frequency was adjusted according to the number of divisions required for the next track. An obvious difficulty of this method is to ensure that the images on the separate tracks are accurately in phase with each other. This requirement was controlled by a short re-setting pulse which was generated optically by a reflecting prism on the turntable as the shaft rotated, and initiated the start of the exposure

of each track. By this means all the tracks were produced with a satisfactorily precise phase correlation.

The typical rate of rotation used for this work was three revolutions
per minute, and with the High-Resolution emulsion, eight revolutions
of the shaft were needed to secure adequate density. This means, of
course, that any errors in the functioning of the equipment tended to
be averaged.

These figures show that less than 3 minutes would be required for
the exposure of a single track even if it depicted more than 60,000
separate image elements. Thus it is not surprising that the rapidity
of this method was considered to be one of its most important features,
and it was stated that a complete 16-track pattern could be made in
2 hours. This relatively rapid operation made it practicable to produce
several discs and only use the best as the master. It is even reasonable
to use an original disc in an instrument rather than make contact
copies.

TESTING OF DISCS

In the same paper there was described a rapid and elegant method
for testing the accuracy of discs. The disc was placed on a kinematic
mount, and was spun at up to 15 r.p.m. The outer track and another

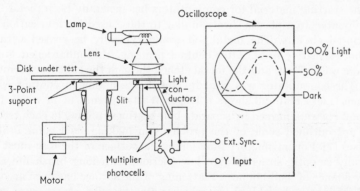

Fig. 82 *Comparison of the Phase Relationship of Different Tracks by Oscilloscope
Courtesy of E. M. Jones, B. Lippel, K. M. Doering and Proceedings of National
Electronics Conference.*

track were scanned by separate photocells, and the signals so generated fed to an oscilloscope, where the phase relationships of the
transmissions of the two tracks was displayed (Fig. 82). A single
transmission element out of place could be easily detected and the
consequence of pinholes and black specks were readily seen.

METHODS OF READ-OUT FROM BINARY-CODED SCALES

To obtain the read-out from binary-coded scales it is necessary to bring them close to some sensitive device which will generate electrical signals as the scale moves in front of it. Ward mentioned the use of magnetic devices for this purpose [7], but most frequently, direct electrical contact or photo-electric sensing seem to have been used. Thus the reader is likely to find that binary-coded scales are mainly used in one of two forms. The first is in the so-called 'commutator' or mechanical 'digitizer'. In this the scale is made from the master negative by a printed-circuit technique, and the read-out is obtained by direct electrical contact through minute brushes. Optical digitizers use a transparent scale, which is usually in the form of a print from the master negative made by any suitable graticule process (see Chapter 9). The read-out from this type of instrument is by photo-electric means. The contact-printing process used for making the final scales clearly has to be adjusted to the requirements of the read-out method. For instance, if used for an optical digitizer, the scale must show adequate density for the region in which the photo-cells are sensitive.

COMMUTATORS

The starting material for commutators has generally been metal foil laminated to a plastic sheet, similar to those used for fabrication of printed circuits. The metal foil would typically be coated with a photo-sensitive resin. After contact printing, the unhardened areas were washed out, and the metal etched through the stencil so formed.

The commutator was read by 'brushes' running in contact with each track. Plate 23 shows a Hilger Watts instrument in which the contacts were formed by separate ball-bearings running in each track. Ward outlined some of the problems in making such commutator discs [7]. For satisfactory functioning the surface of the disc must be really smooth, so as to give low friction, with long brush life and avoidance of 'ball-bounce'. Flattening of the surface has been accomplished by 'planishing', in which process sufficient pressure was applied to press the raised metal pattern into the under-lying plastic. Another method was to fill the gaps with resin, and machine until the whole surface was satisfactorily flat. For satisfactory accuracy, undercutting during etching had to be controlled, and could be compensated by shifting the position of the edges slightly when making the master pattern. It has been stated that the smallest effective contact area for the brushes is a circle of diameter 0·005 in (0·125 mm), and that the narrowest usable segments are therefore about 0·02 in (0·5 mm) wide.

OPTICAL DIGITIZERS

In the paper already quoted [3], Elliott, Robbins and Evans, employed a 'flying spot' technique, in which the 'flying spot' on a cathode-ray tube was imaged by an objective so that it followed a radial path on the surface of the disc. Light transmitted at any instant was sensed by a photo-multiplier tube. This method was devised to give rapid and frequent readings, but the optical requirements of the system demanded that the image of each track should be confined to a radial length of only 0·003 in (0·075 mm). Since the tangential width of the finest image was only just over 0·001 in (0·025 mm) there was a serious risk that a proportion of the small images would be obscured by dirt. As a result, the cost and difficulty of making satisfactory discs was so high, that although the basic design of the equipment was proved on trials, little further work was done. In fact, the use of photographically produced transparent scales for high-resolution digitizers at one time seemed impracticable.

A few years later the situation was transformed by the development of very small semi-conductor photocells. These were so compact, and the area needed to detect a signal so small, that it was now possible to use a separate photocell for every track [1(d)], [8]. It then became practicable to increase the radial width of each track. The consequent increase in the area of the unit images greatly reduced the frequency of erroneous signals from emulsion blemishes. Usually the disc was illuminated on one side, and the light transmitted by the pattern fell on a narrow slit in front of the photocells (Plate 24). An alternative to the use of small photocells was to place the end of a transparent rod close behind each slit, and use light guides to conduct light from each track to a photo-multiplier [9].

MERITS OF MECHANICAL COMMUTATORS AND OPTICAL-DIGITIZERS

The mechanical commutator is much the simpler device, since it can conduct sufficient current to actuate such devices as relays without need for an amplifier. Moreover it is literally a switching device, since there will be a relatively sharp 'make' or 'break' when the ball enters or leaves a conducting segment. By contrast, optical digitizers generally have to be used with an amplifier, and when employed with a flashing tube for a rapid read-out, the amount of light may be so small that a separate amplifier is needed for each track (see Plate 24). To minimize the effect of blemishes, the masking slits should be nearly as wide as the width of the narrowest image. Hence a sinusoidal signal is generated, and an external amplitude discriminator would be needed to give the required abrupt starting and stopping of the signals.

The assembly of brushes in mechanical commutators has been stated to be difficult to adjust and maintain [7]. The adjustment is likely to deteriorate as a result of friction, vibration or accelerating forces. The digitizer also offers a frictional resistance to the shaft on which it rotates, and wear occurs whether the scale is being read or not. More severe wear occurs through sparking if readings are taken while the disc is rotating, and Hilger Watts Ltd recommend that readings be taken only when the digitizer is stationary. For read-out in motion, they suggest that a valve-buffer stage should be introduced between the digitizer and the decoder [8].

With optical digitizers, the slits are analogous to the brushes, and can be made very robust and of constant width. They can also be rigidly fixed so that they cannot move once their position has been adjusted. There is no frictional wear on the scale or the sensing device during the running of the instrument. The read-out mechanism also exerts no friction, so that the disc can more accurately follow the smallest forces applied to the shaft. Even from this short and super-ficial treatment, it is obvious that a wise choice of digitizer requires a detailed knowledge of the attributes of the instruments and a care-ful analysis of the special requirements of different types of job.

APPLICATIONS OF HIGH-RESOLUTION BINARY-CODED SCALES

Binary-coded scales have already been used in a variety of ways, and it was decided to collect some examples into groups, and consider what benefits are derived from the scales in each group.

AVOIDANCE OF MISTAKES, INCREASING SPEED AND LESSENING FATIGUE

Many measurements in science and industry are made by photograph-ing an original 'event', and subsequently measuring the photographic record so produced. Consider, for instance, a scientist's actions when measuring wavelengths from the position of lines on a spectrographic plate. Having adjusted the position of the plate on the table of a travelling microscope, the lead-screw would be carefully advanced until the eyepiece graticule was accurately centred on the first line to be measured. The position would then be read to the nearest micron by viewing first the coarse (millimetre) scale, and then the divided drum and vernier. The resultant five-figure number (for example 25·436 mm) would then be transcribed by hand, and this process would be repeated for every one of the dozens or hundreds of lines to be measured. When each setting of the graticule on a line had been made, the eyes had to be removed from the microscope, and refocused for reading the scales and subsequently for writing down the figures. This process of reading the scales and recording the results often takes longer and causes more fatigue than the actual setting of the instrument. Mistakes can creep in during reading the scales, writing down the results, or on subsequently copying the figures for calculation.

This tiresome type of operation can be delegated to binary-coded digitizers. Having set the microscope on any desired line image, it is only necessary to press a button, and the digitizer automatically generates signals corresponding to the position of the scale. When these signals are fed into appropriate de-coding devices the results can be recorded by an automatic typewriter, or on magnetic or perforated tape. Binary-coded results are also in a very convenient form for feeding directly into a digital computer.

This principle of the automatic recording of manually made settings has been used in several other ways. For example:

(1) A digitized measuring microscope has been used at the Royal Observatory for measuring the position of scale images relative to fiducial marks, from photographs on 35 mm film made at six positions around the declination circle of a telescope [10].

(2) Digitized scales have been used on film-readers employed for measuring target co-ordinates and orientation within the frames of film from kinetheodilite observations of meteorological balloons or aircraft and rocket tests [11].

(3) In some types of photogrammetric instrument, pairs of prints from adjacent frames of aero-survey film are viewed to measure the apparent displacements which indicate height above sea level. The separate x and y co-ordinates for the left and right-hand prints have been recorded from digitized scales [12].

TRANSMISSION OF INFORMATION

The electrical impulses generated by binary-coded instruments are in a form particularly suitable for unambiguous transmission by land-line or radio link. For instance, aircraft have been equipped with binary-coded altimeters. The altitudes of incoming aircraft can hence be instantaneously transmitted to airport control towers [13]. This type of measurement at a distance has been called 'telemetry'. Furthermore, it can also be arranged that readings indicated by a binary-coded instrument can be compared with readings provided by an incoming signal. Servo mechanisms can be provided to respond to the difference, until the shaft reaches a desired position [3]. This remote control of shaft position has sometimes been called 'telerotation'. Both these facilities are obviously applicable to satellites or other vehicles for exploration of hazardous or remote locations. For example, Griffin illustrated a paper with reproductions of binary-coded discs used respectively for Hound-Dog and Polaris missiles, for navigation and fire-control systems in Convair fighters and in the American space programme [1(c)].

RECORDING INSTRUMENTS AT PERIODIC INTERVALS

Complicated industrial plant such as in oil refineries requires the periodic checking and recording of numerous dials. In this field of data-logging, binary-coded instruments are finding considerable use [14]. They permit records to be collected from a large number of points and here again the information can be fed to a digital computer, so that the data can be reduced to its desired form very soon after it was generated. Scales attached to the slides of machine tools also permit the continuous observation of the position of the workpiece as machining proceeds [15].

RAPID DATA COLLECTION

With the continuing development of aircraft, space-vehicles and weapons, the demand has grown for increasingly elaborate testing techniques. During tests, the events to be studied may either be very rapid in themselves, or (and) the power consumption of testing installations is so large that much information needs to be collected in the shortest possible time. Rapid collection of data is even more necessary with one-shot trials such as ballistic or rocket tests.

With flashing light sources used with optical digitizers it is possible to read a disc divided into 8,192 segments up to one hundred times *per second*, and the instantaneous precise position of shafts can be measured even when they are rotating at several hundred revolutions per minute [1(d)]. The range of quantities which can be measured is virtually only limited by the scope of the instruments used to measure the status of the test. Velocities, pressures, currents, voltages, fuel-flows and many other quantities are equally readily measured. In such tests an enormous quantity of data is given off and recorded, and the whole system is ultimately linked to a computer for working out the results. Such operations include wind-tunnel tests of jet engines and air-frames [9], [16], and rocket and space-vehicle firings [17]. It has also been proposed that information from radar warning installations should be handled by similar means so that the defence of an entire population can depend on the satisfactory operation of digitized instruments [18].

In short, binary-coded scales are of immense value for automatic data collection. This is obviously an important precursor to automatic data processing and data utilization. It is pointless to argue at precisely what stage the operations made possible by these scales can be described as automation. What *is* significant is the fact that binary-coded scales and mechanisms associated with them are at the core of many a number of important developments. The facility which high-resolution photographic techniques have provided for the generation of the scales has been vital in making these systems available.

Photographic Techniques in Grating Production

The development and applications of binary-coded scales has been paralleled and rivalled by a completely different system. In this, the scale takes the form of a *grating* divided uniformly into many equally spaced lines and spaces, of frequencies between a hundred and several thousand lines per inch. In use, light transmitted or reflected from the scale grating is viewed through a short length of similar grating, which is mounted on a moving part of the equipment, and constitutes a 'cursor' [19]. With a simple optical system the interaction of the two sets of rulings produces a pattern of fringes which is easily detected by a photocell. The intensity fluctuation in the fringes is nearly sinusoidal, and one cycle corresponds to a relative movement of exactly one grating spacing.

To appreciate what happens, consider the superimposition of two line screens, not quite parallel to each other. These will show a pattern of *moiré fringes* as indicated by Plate 25. If the two screens are examined under a magnifier it will be seen that the dark zones correspond to positions where the lines of one screen coincide with the spaces of the other, and the light zones are where the spaces coincide and hence let light through. Further inspection of the Plate reveals that movement of the top (less dense) grating to the right would cause the dark zone to move upwards. From the inclination of the lines of the grating, it is clear that a small relative movement of the two screens will produce a large movement of the fringes. With finer gratings, the optical phenomena are more complicated than this, and take the form of the interference of two diffraction patterns. Nevertheless, as shown by Guild [19], strong fringes which are easily detected by a photocell are formed by a correctly adjusted optical system, and again one cycle of fringes exactly equals one grating spacing.

With electronic counting of the fringes, these scales provide rapid and sensitive systems for detecting small relative movements. In the following sections we shall consider how microphotographic techniques are contributing to the manufacture of the gratings, how their indications are read, and how the complete systems are used.

PRODUCTION OF LARGE DIFFRACTION GRATINGS

Much thought has been devoted to the possibility of using photographic methods for the generation of diffraction gratings, and an extensive discussion of early work on the subject was given by Gundlach and Rzymkowski [20]. The present applications, however, mainly evolved from work at the National Physical Laboratory on the production of gratings by a mechanical technique. A precision lathe was used to cut a very fine helical thread, with up to 5,000 lines to the inch (200 lines/mm), on one end of a lapped metal rod. The first thread so cut showed marked periodic errors. A more precise thread was then produced by using the first thread to drive an engraving tool cutting a second thread on the other end of the rod. The nut used to drive the engraving tool consisted of three pieces of cork clamped around the first thread (Merton 'nut'), and as a result of the resilience of the cork, the nut adopted a position averaging out the position of the many turns with which it engaged, with a resultant cancelling out of many of the periodic errors [21]. Such threaded rods constituted the master gratings from which copies were cast in a polymerizing plastic. From the plastic copies, there were then made copies in hardened gelatin on optical flats [22].

It was found only convenient to make single gratings up to 10 in (25 cm) long by this method, but longer gratings were made by placing a number of the gelatin replicas end-to-end. For this purpose their rulings had to be exactly in phase with each other and precisely parellel. By this ingenious technique, grating scales 30 in (76 cm) or more long were made, but the assembly of a number of units end-to-end with the required precision proved a difficult and expensive operation for industrial production. There was also an unsightly gap at the joins.

Alternative means were therefore sought for duplicating long gratings made by mechanical means. For this purpose Burch devised a travelling 'printing frame' [23]. The master grating was lightly held by clamps and spacers against a long Kodak M-R plate, and the sandwich so formed was traversed on a moving carriage past a $\frac{1}{2}$ in (12 mm) wide collimated beam from a high-pressure mercury-vapour lamp. Exposures were made with the mercury 5461 Å line, and as the carriage moved at about 2 in (5 cm) per minute, each area of the emulsion received an exposure of 15 seconds.

In this equipment the master would either be a transparent replica with wedge-shaped rulings, or else a photographic absorbing grating made from it. Burch discussed the importance of the spacing between the master and the photographic emulsion, which has to be adjusted to give Fresnel diffraction with good intensity modulation in the plane of the emulsion.

With the transparent grating he showed that

$$S = \frac{(N - \frac{1}{2})W^2}{\lambda}.$$

Where W is the grating ruling interval, λ is the wavelength, N is a positive integer and S is the required spacing. For a 1,000 lines/in (40 lines/mm) grating he used a spacing of 0·023 in (580 μ). Four phased-up sections of replica were used to produce a grating 36 in (90 cm) long. Now copies made by this method necessarily showed the joins between the individual sections, but since the join is only a small proportion of the area finally scanned by the cursor grating, it is of little consequence.

When a master on M-R emulsion was used, refraction by the surface corrugations of the processed emulsion (p. 218) tended to influence the result. In fact, the grating then had some of the characteristics of a phase-retarding grating in addition to those of an absorption-grating, and because of this, Burch recommended that the precise spacing should be ascertained by trial exposures. In fact when copying a 1,000-line per inch photographic grating, he found that an increased spacing of 0·042 in (just over 1 mm) was needed. With the fine grain and high contrast of M-R emulsion, adequately defined line patterns were obtained and exactly similar second-generation copies could be made by the same procedure.

CALIBRATION OF GRATINGS AND CORRECTION FOR ERRORS
WHILE CONTACT PRINTING

An important feature of Burch's printing method was the possibility of correcting for known progressive errors. Master gratings were calibrated either by repeated comparison with another grating, or directly against a known line standard. From such a calibration, there would be derived a table of correction factors to be applied at different parts of the scale when making the contact copies. Because of the small but finite separation of the copying emulsion from the master, relatively large changes in the angle of incidence of the exposing beam produced very small lateral displacements of the image transmitted by the master grating. The corrections were achieved by pivoting the entire optical bench about a point x vertically below where the light hit the sandwich (Fig. 83). The required movements were controlled manually and were observed by an optical lever via a mirror mounted on the optical bench. By these means scales correct to within 5 micro-inches (about ⅛ of a micron), could be made.

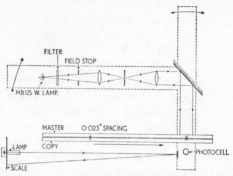

Fig. 83 *Travelling Printing-frame for simultaneously calibrating and copying Long Metrological Gratings*

Crown Copyright. Courtesy of J. M. Burch and Director, National Physical Laboratory.

GENERATION OF SELF-CORRECTING GRATINGS BY A 'BREEDING' PROCESS

We have already seen that the movement of one grating over another of similar spacing can, by means of a simple optical system, be made to give a sinusoidal signal. Burch proposed to use this phenomenon for the 'breeding' of gratings of accuracy superior to that of the original gratings used to generate the sinusoidal signals [24]. This idea was illustrated by a proposed apparatus for making master radial gratings. An imperfect radial grating was accurately centred on a vertical spindle and was steadily rotated past a similar stationary grating also centred with respect to the axis of the spindle. The errors of the gratings could be appreciable so long as they did not exceed one-quarter of a ruling width. As the spindle rotated, light from an axially placed lamp was collected by a Fresnel lens and deflected by an annular prism to illuminate the gratings around the complete circle, from whence it was collected and passed to an axially placed photocell. By this means the photocell received information produced by the complete circles of the gratings, and the resultant sinusoidal signals averaged the errors over the entire circle.

On the same spindle there was also mounted an unexposed photo-graphic plate, which could be exposed by light from a source modula-ted by the sinusoidal signal falling on a small piece of stationary grating of the required frequency very close to the emulsion surface.

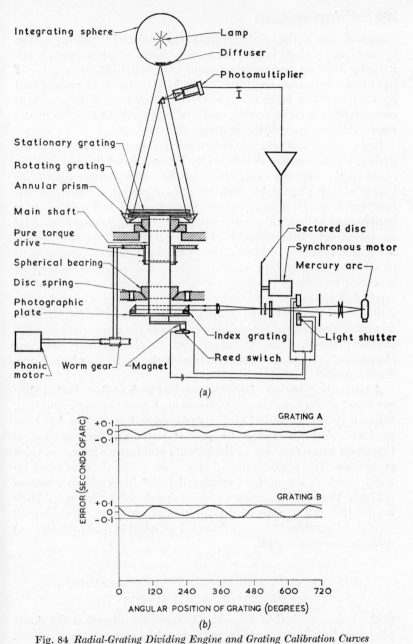

Fig. 84 *Radial-Grating Dividing Engine and Grating Calibration Curves*

(a) Functional diagram showing how sinusoidal signal from interaction of rotating and stationary gratings modulates exposure of photographic plate rotating on same shaft.

(b) Calibration curves for two gratings showing errors within ± 0·1 second of arc.
Crown Copyright. Courtesy of Director of National Physical Laboratory, A. H. McIlraith and A. B. Penfold and Institute of Physics.

Thus each line in the master grating was produced by averaging the effect of many short exposures, with consequent smoothing of any irregular function, and ready provision of enough light for exposure of an extreme-resolution emulsion. The light source was to be modulated by triggering the firing of an electronic flash tube or by a synchronously driven chopper disc, and it was possible to increase or decrease the frequency of the gratings.

Reduction of this principle to practice has been effected in a radial grating dividing engine developed by McIlraith and Penfold [25]. To assist in the uniform illumination of the entire circle required for effective averaging, light from an axially placed diffuser over an aperture in an integrating sphere was caused to fall on the outer periphery of a 'Perspex' annular prism [Fig. 84(a)]. After reflection by the prism, light from around the entire circle passed upwards through the pair of gratings, and was directed to a photomultiplier by a small axially placed prism. The resultant amplified sinusoidal output signal was used to drive a synchronous motor bearing a sectored disc interrupting light from a steady source. For one-quarter of each revolution of the disc, light was allowed to fall on diametrically placed 4° sectors of a radially oriented index grating of the same spacing as the control gratings. Thus the exposure of the photographic plate was electronically coupled to the rotation of the shaft, on which it was itself mounted.

A fascinating feature of dividing engines such as these is that they can breed new generations by a process analogous to genetic selection. When a pair of improved gratings of a second generation has been produced, they can replace the original gratings in the control positions, and hence function as the parents of a further improved third generation. The performance of this system was demonstrated by tests, in which the authors employed moiré-fringe observations to calibrate two third-generation gratings produced in this way. Their results [Fig. 84(b)] showed a peak-to-peak error not exceeding 0·2 seconds of arc: the distance subtended by 0·074 in (just under 2 mm) at a distance of one mile.

GENERATION OF GRATINGS BY PHOTOGRAPHY OF INTERFERENCE FRINGES

Still another method of considerable scientific interest is the direct photography of systems of fringes produced by an interferometer [23]. Collimated light from a mercury lamp was divided by a dividing plate (bismuth-oxide coating) (Fig. 85). The light transmitted and reflected by the mirror was then passed along paths of equal length, and the two beams were brought back to a plane, where interference occurred.

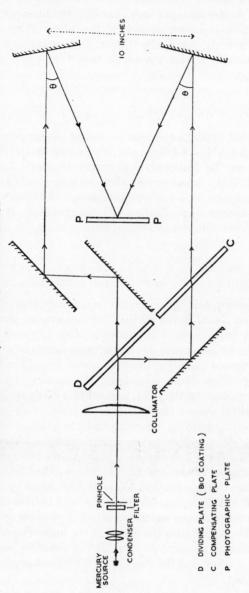

INTERFEROMETER FOR PRODUCTION OF PHOTOGRAPHIC TRANSMISSION GRATINGS

3 INCH APERTURE: DISPERSION BETWEEN 12,000 AND 60,000 LINES PER INCH

MERCURY SOURCE

CONDENSER

FILTER

PINHOLE

COLLIMATOR

D   DIVIDING PLATE (BIO COATING)

C   COMPENSATING PLATE

P   PHOTOGRAPHIC PLATE

FRINGE SPACING = $\dfrac{\lambda}{2 \sin \theta}$ ADJUSTMENT BY ENANTIOCYCLIC WHITE LIGHT FRINGES

10 INCHES

Fig. 85 Interferometer for Production of Photographic Transmission Gratings
Crown Copyright. Courtesy of J. M. Burch and Director, National Physical Laboratory.

By altering the obliquity of the beams, the spacings could be adjusted from 11,000 to 60,000 lines per inch (440 to 2,400 lines per mm). An extreme-resolution emulsion placed in the plane P recorded the images and effectively 'froze' the fringes. In this equipment it was found that Kodak M-R plates resolved 60,000 lines per inch (more than 2,000/mm).

GENERATION OF GRATINGS BY DIVIDING ENGINES

Burch stated that gratings ruled on a circular dividing engine have been made both by Messrs Hilger and Watts and by Dr Timms and his co-workers at the National Engineering Research Laboratory, East Kilbride [24]. In the same way that the projection of successive elements of an image on a plate mounted on a dividing engine has proved advantageous for production of large graticules, it is evident that the same procedure can be applied to the production of gratings.

THE PHYSICAL FORM OF GRATING IMAGES PRODUCED BY PHOTOGRAPHIC EMULSIONS

Photographic absorption gratings are necessarily wasteful of the light incident on them. Burch stated that two similar photographic sinusoidal copy gratings used in a moiré system adjusted to receive first order light at minimum deviation gave accurately sinusoidal moiré fringes of good visibility, but only about 1/6 of the brightness produced by gratings which modulated the incident beam by retardation of the phase of the light, instead of by absorption [23(b)]. Photographic silver images can be converted from an absorbing form to a phase-retarding form by bleaching them to a light-stable colourless image of high refractive index. Indeed, early workers with the Lippman colour process bleached their images with mercuric chloride for just this purpose. It would seem that success must depend on the absence of scatter by the colourless compound produced by the bleaching reaction. This will depend on the size of the individual particles forming the bleached image, which as a result of physical development may prove to be coarser than the grains of the undeveloped emulsion (p. 72). To minimize physical development it would be advisable to use a heavier exposure and the shortest development required to give sufficient contrast.

The method for producing phase-retarding images described by Burch was to make 'Marco' resin replicas from the corrugated surface of the processed gelatin emulsion. Not only were these replicas pure phase-gratings, but several could be pulled from each photographic copy. The physico-chemical origins of these corrugations in the surface of the processed emulsion are interesting. Undoubtedly, there must be an increase of layer thickness due to the mass of the developed silver in high density areas, but additional differences of thickness can often be attributed to the behaviour of the gelatin. Perrin noted that most developers produce tanning reaction products, which lead to image-wise hardening of the gelatin [26]. As a result, high density areas of a developed emulsion may be less swollen at the end of processing, and will dry more quickly than the more swollen low density areas. In these circumstances, the high density areas shrink on drying, and tend to pull the still moist and flexible low density areas with them. Perrin noted that these shifts of the gelatin have been called the *gelatin effect*.

If small areas of high density indeed behave in this way, it seems likely that the local mass of gelatin per unit area will be increased, with a consequent increase of thickness in just those areas which were thinnest (least swollen) at the end of processing. The reality of these phenomena is increasingly being demonstrated by published experiments. For example, Lau, Kind and Roose showed that the height of the relief image in conventional photographic plates was proportional to image density, but that the differences in thickness were greatly decreased if drying was modified by passing processed images through an alcohol bath [27]. Altman extended this type of experiment to microphotographic images on Eastman Kodak High-Resolution Plates, and showed that the amplitude of the relief image was increased fourfold by use of a tanning developer [28]. In another note, he showed that pure relief images of 3 μ height were obtained by exposing narrow lines on Kodak Spectroscopic Plates, Type 649-F to give a density of 4, and bleaching the developed silver in a tanning bleach before fixation and washing [29]. The control developed and fixed normally only showed a relief height of 1 μ. A noteworthy feature of this experiment is that the developed silver was quantitatively removed by the bleaching and fixation, and could therefore have contributed nothing to the thickness of the layer.

Even when the contractions, which seem to be responsible for these relief images, are marked, they need not necessarily decrease the accuracy of a scale or grating, since the contractions should normally be symmetrical about the centre of each line, and should not alter its effective position.

AUTOMATIC READING OF GRATINGS

We have already seen that a relative movement of the cursor and scale gratings causes one fringe to cross the field for the relative motion of one line interval. Consider now how the photo-electric detection of fringes forms the basis of automatic reading methods. The essence of the method is that the counting of fringes demonstrates movement relative to the original starting position. Thus the reading systems must be capable of not only detecting the passage of the fringes but also their direction of movement. The count must be increased for forward movements, and fringes moving in the other direction must cause subtraction of figures from the count. In the Ferranti system this has been achieved by placing four photo-transistors behind a short fixed length of grating, and spacing them by quarter wavelengths of the moiré fringe pattern [30]. The signal-output from the transistors was of a sinusoidal form and was modified to a square wave-form from which two discrete pulses were derived for each abrupt change in wave amplitude. These signal pulses were the basic units of linear measurement, and the amplitude was not important, so long as the pulse was detectable.

It is not essential to use fringes as such, and Messrs Paton Hawksley consider a pair of gratings with parallel rulings as constituting a multiple shutter [31]. In this case the direction of motion was detected by fitting four units of cursor grating out of phase by quarter wavelengths.

Usable moiré fringes can be formed by gratings so fine that their accuracy is beyond the limits of most of the existing mechanical components with which they might be used. Thus both manufacture of the gratings and of their read-out system would demand exceptionally accurate (and expensive) construction and control. For industrial use, the opposite trend is desirable. To simplify the use and manufacture of grating devices, ingenious methods are being developed to obtain interpolated readings by optical or electronic means [32].

An interesting example of optical sub-division is provided by a method for use with 'Autograt' scales [33]. A coarse 10-line-per-inch grating was fitted with a double cursor, with the two parts separated by half a wavelength (Fig. 86). Position 1 shows the left half of the cursor acting as a complete shutter, cutting off all light, whereas the right half is in a position transmitting as much light as possible. The light from each part of the cursor was collected by opposed photo-voltaic cells and lack of balance caused a current to flow. In position 1 the current from the photocells showed the maximum lack of balance, and the largest possible current was passed. Consider what happens on moving the cursor to the right, so that the left half starts to open and the right half starts to close. At position 2 this movement has been continued until the areas exposed by the two halves of the cursor are equal. The output from the photocells are then exactly balanced and the micro-ammeter shows no current. It will be seen that a very small displacement on either side of this position will rapidly upset the balance.

With this simple system, stability was a few parts per thousand of a grating spacing over a period of several hours. Such schemes for

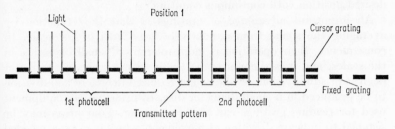

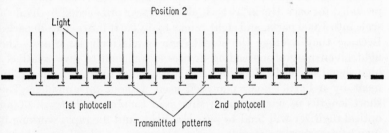

Fig. 86 *Method for setting Coarse Grating accurately to Fixed Positions*

This method was developed for use with 'Autograt' scales. Position 1 shows maximum imbalance, but moving the cursor a quarter wavelength to the right produce s balanced signals.

obtaining fine sub-division from coarse scales are currently a matter for much inventive effort. We need only notice here that they are likely to modify the specifications demanded from photographically produced gratings.

COMPARISON OF USE OF BINARY-CODED SCALES AND GRATINGS

At this juncture it is convenient to consider the relative merits of coded optical scales and grating systems. From the user's point of view, coded discs are analogous to numbered scales with each division separately numbered. So long as the sensing equipment functions properly at the instant of reading, there is no doubt as to the position of the scale. By contrast, gratings are 'incremental' patterns, in which all the divisions and from which all the signals are indistinguishable. Hence from the start of the operation of the instrument, *all* signals must be counted and accumulated by a suitable device. It is, therefore, essential that the apparatus should be continuously connected to a numerical 'store'. If there is any momentary interruption of operation, or counts are lost or added by any malfunction (see p. 340), the position of the scale is no longer known until the instrument is returned to zero, and the scale is again moved to the desired position with continuous counting.

An important advantage of gratings is that they function by averaging the signal from a relatively large area of the scale. In consequence, their operation is more tolerant of small blemishes in the scales, and it is therefore practicable to use scales with greater degrees of sub-division, or allowing a required degree of sub-division to be produced in a small diameter disc. In principle, the equipment used for reading gratings can also be simpler. Four areas may be scanned to indicate direction of movement, whereas in binary-coded instruments a separate detector with its associated circuit has to be provided for each track. At least eleven tracks are needed to divide a scale into 1,000 parts, and eight tracks to divide it into even 100 parts. Because they average the signal from a relatively large area, the light given by grating-reading devices is sufficient to give relatively high signal strengths. In some cases it is enough to actuate the equipment by a barrier-layer photocell used without an amplifier. The short lengths of narrow-width slits used to scan each track of an optical digitizer will tend to pass less light, and for rapid working it may be necessary to provide a separate amplifier and pulse-amplitude discriminator for each track [1(a)].

In the forms so far discussed, binary-coded scales are read by detecting the rapid transition from black to white, and interpolation is effected by providing additional tracks. McIlraith has, however, shown that a single binary-coded track can be treated as a narrow-width grating, to give a sinusoidal output amenable to interpolation by methods used with gratings [34].

In deciding whether to use binary-coded or grating instruments, factors such as cost, weight, inertia of moving parts, robustness, reliability and servicing requirements will all have to be considered. Engineers faced with such a decision have to weigh one characteristic against another.

APPLICATIONS OF GRATINGS

It is clear that gratings with moiré-fringe read-out and appropriate circuitry will fulfil many of the tasks that binary-coded instruments can do. In this section, therefore, it seemed desirable to consider applications in which the grating system seems to have the advantage.

Because of their tolerance of blemishes and the relative simplicity of securing adequate signal strength from very fine rulings, gratings are appropriate when high resolution or very compact instruments are required. For instance, in their inclinometer, Messrs Hilger and Watts use radial gratings with 4,300 lines on a disc with a diameter of only ¾ in (1·9 cm) [35]. This instrument is used for indicating the attitude of models in wind-tunnel tests. The moving parts are gravity operated, and the small weight and low inertia of the disc are important.

Grating systems are being used for the sensitive detection of small movements, for instance in the measurement of vibration [36]. Gratings are also being applied to the measurement of velocity or acceleration by using circuits which are sensitive to the frequency at which fringes are passing the datum point [37].

At the National Physical Laboratory, it was realized that a particular virtue of gratings was their potentiality for giving very accurate measurements [38], [23]. For example, a measuring microscope fitted with gratings will give automatic read-out with at least as good accuracy as an instrument depending solely on a lead screw. The screw then becomes merely a device for moving the microscope, and the precision derives entirely from the grating, which will not wear even with extended use. With measuring microscopes fitted with coded discs it should be noticed that the disc merely indicates the angular position of the lead-screw shaft, and accuracy still depends ultimately on the lead-screw.

For some applications the continuous and precise observation of position offered by grating methods is particularly advantageous. For instance, the National Physical Laboratory fitted a standard lathe with a 1,000-lines-per-inch grating to measure the displacement of the saddle, and a 100-division cursor grating to follow rotation of the head stock. Because of gear and lead-screw errors in cutting a thread, the errors were plus or minus 0·0004 in (plus or minus 10 μ). By using the fringes to operate a closed-loop servo system, the errors were reduced to 0·00001 in (plus or minus 0·25 μ) [39].

Another instance, where the continuous accumulation of counts and information is applied, is in the computer control of machine tools. The potential of this type of device is well illustrated by the Ferranti system of automatic machine-tool control [40].

Consider the operation of machining a complex metal component from the solid, in accordance with directions indicated by a machine drawing. In the Ferranti system this involved the following stages.

(1) From the draughtsman's drawing the Production Planning Engineer defined the required shape of the work-piece in terms of geometrical information describing every separate surface of the part. These definitions were entered on a programme sheet,

in the order for which the planner required the part to be machined to shape. In addition he had to insert information about such factors as the cutter diameter, the feed-rate and the cutter speed in conjunction with the application of coolant. Whereas the engineer would in any case already supply a great deal of this information, for automatic control the programme had to be so complete that every machine-tool function was precisely defined. Nothing could be left for adjustment on the shop floor, and everything had to be entered on the programme sheet.

(2) A typist transcribed the information from the programme sheet on a power-operated teletypewriter. The operation of the keyboard both recorded information as holes punched in paper tape, and produced a typed record from which the accuracy of transcription could be checked.

(3) The data from the punched tape was then fed to a digital computer. The information on the programme sheet and the derived tape only constituted 'raw' design data. There was an irreducible minimum of calculation needed to convert this into a form suitable for machine-tool control. The calculations can be done by hand computer, but Ferranti's decided to use a digital computer, and the complete results of the calculations were recorded on magnetic tape. The computer produced a tape at eight times the speed it would be used in the machine tool, so that even if each tape were only used once, one computer could keep eight machine tools busy. A rapid method for checking such tapes by using the instructions to produce a 'drawing' which can be recorded on microfilm is described on p. 439.

(4) The magnetic tape was inserted in the machine-tool-control console, and the work-piece was clamped on the table of the machine tool. The table was moved to the datum-zero position with respect to the X, Y and Z slides, which were fitted with gratings and the reading heads already described. As the magnetic tape passed the tape-reading head on the machine-tool-control console, it issued commands as a series of pulses, controlling the servo moving the table in the X, Y or Z directions. When the table moved on its slides, pulses from the gratings were emitted for every 0·0002 in (5 μ) of movement. The driving power supplied to the servo motor in either direction, was controlled by the difference between the number of pulses given from the tape and the number of pulses generated by movements of the gratings. The machine could be automatically stopped if this difference in the number of pulses exceeded a pre-set value. In fact the magnetic tape provided all the in-

formation normally supplied by a skilled machinist, who translates the information in the draughtsman's engineering drawing into commands, to which the machine tool can respond, by turning hand-wheels. These commands control feed-rates and cutter-speed, and setting levers that determine the level of other associated machine functions. Furthermore, there is no need to stop the machine and clean the workpiece in order to measure it, and hence follow the progress of the work. Thus the time spent by the machine in actually cutting metal is greatly increased by eliminating 'thinking' time.

Systems such as this are having very far-reaching consequences for mechanical production technique. They have already revealed inadequacies about such matters as our information concerning optimum cutter speeds, the yield of workpieces under loads, and the inadequate precision and performance of gear trains previously considered satisfactory for machine tools. Essentially the same control methods have also been applied to a very large machine for milling aircraft spars, which has a table 24 × 7 ft [39]. Another machine automatically controls the flame cutting of steel plates, using the same type of measuring procedure [39].

'CIRCULAR' GRATINGS

The principle of using a high-resolution photographic emulsion to generate systems of equally spaced lines has also been applied to the making of gratings consisting of many concentric circles. The method of making and using these is so different from the gratings already considered that it seemed convenient to consider them separately.

It has been found that a system of equally spaced concentric circular lines has optical properties useful for metrology. Dyson showed that great precision in manufacture was required to achieve the theoretical performance of such a circular grating [41]. Thus even with a relatively coarse grating, having only 155 lines per inch of radius, all the lines had to be concentric to within 0·0001–0·00004 in ($2\frac{1}{2}$–1 μ) according to the method of use. The pattern must also only depart from true circles by one-quarter of a line separation. Fortunately it was a simple matter to test the accuracy of such gratings. If the original grating has been made on a photographic plate, it can be reproduced without distortion by photographic printing. If the print after processing was replaced exactly in the position the plate occupied during the printing exposure, the combined effect of the two gratings should appear as a uniform grey tint. If one grating was then rotated by 180°, distortions in the pattern would show as fringes. When the centres of the gratings were offset by a very small amount, they gave moiré patterns which provided a sensitive indication of the quality of the grating. It was established that offsetting of the centres of a 400-lines-per-inch grating could be detected with a shift of about 0·00004 in (1 μ).

PRODUCTION OF MASTER IMAGES FOR CIRCULAR GRATINGS

Dyson first attempted to produce master circular gratings by the photographic reduction of lathe-cut masters. The method proved a

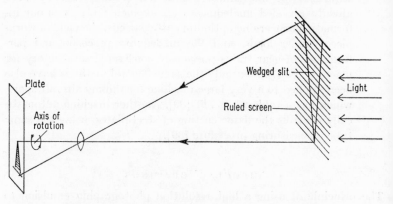

Fig. 87 *Dyson's Method for generating Circular Gratings*

complete failure, since the tests described above showed the presence of relatively large distortions, due to image distortions in the best copying lens available. Adequate results were finally obtained by a mechano-photographic method. A section of photo-engravers line screen (100 lines per inch) was placed in contact with an illuminated wedge-shaped aperture of narrow angle (Fig. 87). Thus only a short length of each line of the screen was visible through the aperture. A reduced image of the aperture was projected on a Kodak M-R Plate, which was mounted on an accurately ground spindle, running in a suitable bearing. The position of the illuminated aperture was adjusted so that the apex of the wedge was projected on the emulsion just at the axis of rotation. On rotating the plate uniformly, the image of each line of the screen described its own concentric circle. Since the width of the wedge and the tangential velocity were proportional to the radius, the effective exposure was independent of the radius. If the plate was properly squared, there could be no error of concentricity, and any departure from true circular form was also independent of the radius. Distortion by the lens could introduce a small irregularity of spacing of the lines, but fortunately this was unimportant. By this method, gratings were made fulfilling the necessary requirements. The light intensity was adjusted to require an exposure of 10 minutes, during which time the plate rotated 100 times. As a result of the high contrast of M-R emulsion, good line quality was achieved, and excellent contact prints were secured.

For the gratings finally used in instruments, various photomechanical processes were used to obtain images giving greater brightness in the diffraction patterns. In some cases images were made on bichromated gelatin or Kodak Photo Resist, and the glass was etched; and in others the pattern was produced on a mirror coating applied to the glass or on a phase-retarding layer of silicon monoxide [42].

METHODS OF USE

Circular gratings have properties similar to zone plates, in that diffraction and interference phenomena cause them to behave as image-forming systems. Dyson described how these gratings illuminated by transmitted or reflected light from a point source formed an image with a central bright spot, surrounded by concentric circular fringes of decreasing brightness [41]. The same pattern was observed at all distances at which sufficient light was available for observation. Thus the central bright spot constituted a narrow axial shaft of light, on which a graticule observed with an eyepiece could be centered. Moreover, the concentric pattern of fringes around the spot constituted a reference grid. This was most helpful in locating the centre, since it showed in which direction the eyepiece had to be moved to coincide with the centre.

Dyson demonstrated the surprising accuracy possible with such a simple device. With an aperture of $1\frac{1}{2}$ in (3·7 cm), and a relatively coarse image of 155 lines per inch (6 lines per mm), the cross-wires at a distance of 20 ft (6 m) could be set on the central spot with an uncertainty not greater than 0·0001 in (2·5 μ), corresponding to 0·08 seconds of arc. With a 2 in (5 cm) aperture grating and 400 lines/in (16 per mm), the setting sensitivity was more than twice as great.

Instruments embodying such circular gratings were developed in the laboratories of Amalgamated Electrical Industries, and have been manufactured under licence by Messrs Cooke, Troughton and Simms with the trade mark 'Rodolite' (rod of light). In one form, a transmission grating was mounted over a shallow pool of mercury, and constituted an optical analogue of a plumb-line of quite exceptional sensitivity. Applications of the 'Rodolite' have been described by

Dyson and Tillen [43]. It was shown that errors in a gear-hobbing machine could be analysed in great detail. The same principles could be equally well applied to machine-tools (such as lathes and pinion hobbers) with horizontal guideways.

USE OF SUPERIMPOSED GRATING PATTERNS FOR RECORDING OF DIGITAL DATA

In addition to their application to scales for automatic reading of instruments, binary-coded patterns are also employed for the coding of document contents for information storage and retrieval systems such as 'Filmorex' and 'Miracode' (p. 426 et seq.). In these systems, a line of the code pattern is commonly made to correspond to a numerical code describing subject matter or key-word descriptors. Because

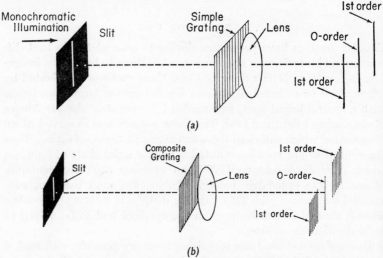

(a)

(b)

Fig. 88 *Detection of Grating Patterns*

(a) Simple grating detected by first-order diffraction image of slit.

(b) Each grating pattern superimposed in composite grating produces its own first-order image.

Courtesy of R. L. Lamberts, G. C. Higgins and 'Photographic Science and Engineering'.

of the optical potentialities of extreme-resolution emulsions, enormous storage capacities (up to 1,000,000 bits/mm^2: or 600,000,000/in^2) have seemed possible. In practice, nothing like this performance has been realized because of false signals from dirt and scratches (see also p. 281), and because of the mechanical difficulty of locating the film so that all the coded bits registered with the appropriate slits over the photocells.

Lamberts and Higgins [44] have examined the use of superimposed grating patterns to circumvent these difficulties. A single 'bit' of information[1] was recorded as a small area of regular grating, and the presence of this bit was detected by the method shown in Fig. 88. When monochromatic light passing through a slit fell on the grating, the central (zero-order) image projected by the lens was flanked by two first-order lines produced by diffraction. The *position* of these first-order lines was determined by the wavelength, the geometry of the apparatus and by the line-frequency of the grating pattern, and photoelectric devices in the appropriate position were used to detect

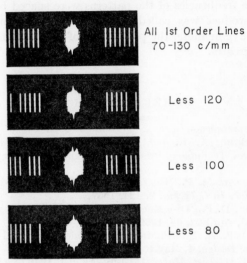

All 1st Order Lines
70-130 c/mm

Less 120

Less 100

Less 80

Fig. 89 *Detection of Superimposed Grating Patterns*
Multiple first-order diffraction images from composite gratings with superimposed patterns of (a) all frequencies 70, 80, 90, 100, 120 and 130 cycles/mm, (b) 120 omitted, (c) 100 omitted, (d) 80 omitted.
Courtesy of R. L. Lamberts, G. C. Higgins and 'Photographic Science and Engineering'.

the presence of the 'bit'. As with moiré-fringe gratings, ambiguous readings due to dirt were less frequent because the system responded to the average condition of a substantial area of film. For the same reason, the problem of locating the film was eased. In addition, the diffracted lines did not move when the grating pattern moved.

A single bit recorded by this method clearly requires a larger emulsion area than a conventional binary-coded bit, but the unit areas of emulsion were used to record the superimposed images of several grating patterns of different frequency. The optical system then produced parallel first-order lines positioned at distances from

[1] In computer technology, binary digit is abbreviated to 'bit'.

L

the zero-order proportional to the frequency of each unit grating pattern (Fig. 89). Because of the possible formation of second-order lines, all the frequencies had to be contained within a single octave. In practice, seven or eight superimposed patterns with an arithmetic series of frequencies appeared to be the limit that could be detected with adequate reliability.

The limit of resolution of this system was shown to be approached when the product of the effective length of the grating (at right-angle to the lines) and of the spatial-frequency increments of the patterns was unity. This would occur, for example, when the length was 0·1 mm, and the frequencies of the patterns were spaced by 10 cycles/ mm. This product was called the redundancy factor, and as it approached five or more, the probability of false readings from dirt diminished greatly.

REFERENCES

[1] See for example:—
(a) Susskind, A. K. (ed.), *Notes on Analog-Digital Conversion Techniques*, Technology Press of M.I.T. and John Wiley (New York, 1957).
(b) Atkinson, M. P., 'Digital Codes in Data Processing Systems', *Trans. Soc. Inst. Techn.*, **9**, 124, 1957.
(c) Griffin, D. P., 'Disc Encoder Design Avoids Ambiguities', *Electronics* **33**, April 22, 63, 1960.
(d) Mitchell, A. L., 'Photoelectric Analog-to-Digital Converters', *Electronic Design*, **4**, May 1, 20, 1956.

[2] Geiser, R. D., *Inst. Maker*, **16**, July–August, 1948 (see reference [4], Chapter 9).

[3] Elliott, W. S., Robbins, R. C. and Evans, D. S., 'Remote Position Control and Indication by Digital Means', *Proc. Inst. Elect. Eng.*, **103B**, Supplement No. 3, 437, 1956.

[4] Tindale, J., British Patent 703,161.

[5] Dymott, E. R., 'Making Precision Coded Scales', *Trans. Soc. Inst. Techn.*, **17**, 114, 1965.

[6] Jones, E. M., Lippel, B. and Doering, K. M., 'Manufacture of Disks for Optical Shaft Digitizers', *Proceedings 11th National Electronics Conference, Chicago*, October, 1955, p. 1.

[7] Ward, J. E., 'Coding and Decoding Techniques for Translational and Angular Motion', Chapter 6 in: Susskind, A. K. (Ed.), *Notes on Analog-Digital Conversion Techniques*, see reference [1(a)].

[8] Hilger and Watts Ltd, 'Digitizers', Trade leaflet CT 109/3.

[9] Airey, L., 'A Digital Instrumentation System for use in the Testing of Jet Engines', *Trans. Soc. Inst. Techn.*, **11**, 163, 1959.

[10] Tucker, R. H. and Evans, D. S., 'A Digitized Measuring Machine for determining Stellar Declinations', *Hilger Journal*, **5**, 26, 1958.

[11] Admiralty Research Laboratory, Teddington, 'Film Assessor', *Hand-*

book of Scientific Instruments and Apparatus, Physical Society (London, 1959), p. 95.

[12] Hilger and Watts Ltd, 'The Watts Stereocomparator, Mark 1', Trade leaflet CS 119.

[13] Anon., 'Optically Coded Altimeter Reports Aircraft Height', *Electronics*, **35**(8), 8, 23 February, 1962.

[14] (a) Lawes, C. A., 'Data-reduction Equipment as an Aid to Plant Control and Analysis', *Fed. European Petroleum Manufacturers Equipment, Liege Study Day. Petroleum Equipment*, May 1956, p. 290.
(b) Churchill, J. L. W., 'Some Data-logging Equipment for Process Plant', *Trans. Soc. Inst. Techn.* **10**, 145, 1958.

[15] Hilger and Watts Ltd, 'Remote Indication of Position by Direct Reading System', Trade leaflet, June 1956.

[16] Tiffany, A., 'Wind Tunnel Instrumentation', *Electronic Engineering*, **29**, 514, 1957.

[17] Schendel, A. H., 'Optical Tracking Instrumentation', *J. Soc. Mot. Pict. Tel. Eng.*, **67**, 237, 242, 1958.

[18] Susskind, A. K. and Ward, J. E., in Chapter 1 of reference [1a] discuss SAGE system for Air Defence.

[19] Guild, J., *Diffraction Gratings as Measuring Scales*, Oxford University Press (London, 1960). (This is a key reference for further study of the subject.)

[20] Gundlach, K. and Rzymkowski, J., 'Die Herstellung Optischer Gitter auf Photographischem Wege', *Z. Wiss. Phot.*, **45**, 8, 1950. (This article gives information on both historical and emulsion aspects of the photographic production of diffraction gratings.)

[21] Merton, Sir Thomas, 'On the Reproduction and Ruling of Diffraction Gratings', *Proc. Roy Soc.*, **201A**, 187, 1950.

[22] (a) Dew, G. D. and Sayce, L. A., 'On the Production of Diffraction Gratings. I. The Copying of Plane Gratings', *Proc. Roy. Soc.*, **207A**, 278, 1951.
(b) Hall, R. G. N. and Sayce, L. A., 'II. The Generation of Helical Rulings and the Preparation of Plane Gratings therefrom', *Proc. Roy. Soc.*, **215A**, 525, 1952.

[23] (a) Burch, J. M., 'Photographic Production of Gratings for Measurement', *Research*, **13**, 2, 1960.
(b) Burch, J. M., 'Photographic Production of Scales for Moiré Fringe Applications', in *Optics in Metrology*, Pergamon Press, (London, 1960), p. 361.

[24] Burch, J. M., 'The Possibilities of Moiré Fringe Interferometry', *Symposium on Interferometry, at National Physical Laboratory, June 1959*, Paper 3–3.

[25] McIlraith, A. H. and Penfold, A. B., 'A Radial Grating Dividing Engine of High Accuracy', *J. Sci. Inst.*, **44**, 903, 1967.

[26] Perrin, F. H., 'The Structure of the Developed Image', in Mees, C. E. K. and James, T. H., *The Theory of the Photographic Process*, The Macmillan Co. (New York, 3rd Edition, 1966), p. 523.

[27] Lau, E., Kind, E. G. and Roose, G., 'Die Schwärzungsplastik als Mittel zur Photographischen Photometrie', *Optik*, **15**, 162, 1958.

[28] Altman, J. H., 'Microdensitometry of High Resolution Plates by Measurement of the Relief Image', *Phot. Sci. Eng.*, **10**, 156, 1966.

[29] Altman, J. H., 'Pure Relief Images on Type 649-F Plates', *Applied Optics*, **5**, 1689, 1966.

[30] Williamson, D. T. N., 'Automatic Control of Machine Tools', in *Conference on Technology of Engineering Manufacture*, Institute of Mechanical Engineers (London, 1958), paper 41.

[31] Paton Hawksley Electronics Ltd, Trade Literature, Rockhill Laboratories, Keynsham, Bristol.

[32] (a) Guild, J. As reference [19]. Methods of interpolation are discussed in Chapter 5, and in Appendix II 'Recent Developments'.
(b) Barber, D. L. A. and Atkinson, M. P., 'Method of Measuring Displacement using Optical Grating', *J. Sci. Inst.*, **36**, 501, 1959.

[33] (a) Davies, B. J., Robbins, R. C., Wallis, C. and Wilde, R. W., 'A High-Resolution Measuring System using Coarse Optical Gratings', *Proc. Inst. Elec. Eng.*, **107B**, 624, 1960.
(b) Brake, D. G., British Patent 1,002,954.
(c) McIlraith, A. H. and Scott, A. D. L., 'A Dynamic Moiré Fringe Interpolator', *J. Sci. Instruments*, **43**, 585, 1966.

[34] McIlraith, A. H., Private Communication.

[35] (a) King, R. J. and Gates, J. W., 'Sensitive Method for Measurement of Small Rotations', *J. Sci. Inst.*, **36**, 507, 1959.
(b) Lewis, A. and Young, I. R., 'Use of Radial Gratings in a Small Inclinometer', *J. Sci. Inst.*, **36**, 153, 1959.

[36] Aitchison, T. W., Bruce, J. W. and Winning, D. S., 'Vibration Amplitude Meter using Moiré-fringe Technique', *J. Sci. Inst.*, **36**, 400, 1959.

[37] Hodgson, G., 'Use of Moiré-fringe Techniques for the Measurement of Velocity', *National Engineering Laboratory, Plasticity Report, 172*, December, 1959.

[38] Sayce, L. A., 'The Preparation and Industrial Applications of Diffraction Gratings', *Trans. Soc. Inst. Techn.*, **9**, 139, 1957.

[39] Blake, D. V. and Sayce, L. A., 'Machine-Tool Monitor using Diffraction Gratings', *Trans. Soc. Inst. Techn.* **10**, 190, 1958.

[40] Farmer, P. J., 'Digital Control and Programming', *Aircraft Production*, **18**, 256, 1956.

[41] Dyson, J., 'Circular and Spiral Diffraction Gratings', *Proc. Roy. Soc.*, **248A**, 93, 1958.

[42] Ennos, A. E., 'Preparation of Phase Diffraction Gratings by Vacuum Evaporation', *J. Opt. Soc. Am.*, **50**, 14, 1960.

[43] (a) Dyson, J. and Tillen, R. J., 'The Rodolite: A New Method for Machine Tool Testing, and Some Applications', *Int. J. Mach. Tool. Des. Res.*, **2**, 201, 1962.
(b) Tillen, R. J., 'Engineering Application of the Rodolite', *Production Engineer*, **42**, 462, 1963.

[44] Lamberts, R. L. and Higgins, G. C., 'Digital Data Recording on Film by using Superposed Grating Patterns. I. General Theory and Procedure', *Phot. Sci. Eng.*, **10**, 209, 1966
Lamberts, R. L., 'Digital Data Recording on Film by using Superposed Grating Patterns. II. Analysis of the System', *ibid.*, 213.
Blackmer, L. L., Van Kerkhove, A. P. and Baldwin, R., 'Digital Data Recording on Film by using Superposed Grating Patterns. III. Recording and Retrieval Technology', *ibid*, 263.

SUPPLEMENTARY REFERENCES

BINARY-CODED SCALES

Much information can be obtained from Trade Leaflets, for example from firms such as Baldwin Piano Company, Elliott-Giannini, W. and L. E. Gurley Company, Hilger and Watts Ltd.

Proceedings of Data Conversion Conference, Military College of Science, July 1950.

Tustin, A. (Ed.), *Automatic and Manual Control*, Academic Press (New York, 1951).

Richards, R. K., *Digital Computer Components and Circuits*, van Nostrand (New York, 1957). Chapter 11 deals with analogue-digital converters and gives many early references.

Evans, D. S., 'The Digitizer—A High-Accuracy Scale for Automatic Data Processing', *British Communications and Electronics*, June, 1957.

Tiffany, A., 'A Simple Shaft Digitizer and Store', *Electronic Engineering*, **29**, 568, 1957.

MOIRÉ FRINGES (GENERAL READING)

Tollenaar, D., 'Moiré Interference Phenomena in Halftone Printing', *Research Institute T.N.O. for Printing and Allied Industries* (Amsterdam, 1957).

Oster, G. and Nishijama, Y., 'Moiré Patterns', *Scientific American*, **208**, 54, 1963.

Brewer, R. C., 'Recent Developments in the Numerical Control of Machine Tools', *The Engineers Digest*, **22**, 89, August, 1961. This article shows how optical gratings and other devices are used in machine-tool control.

Oster, G., 'Moiré Optics: A Bibliography', *J. Opt. Soc. Am.*, **55**, 1329, 1965.

11 · Microphotographic Production Tools

Technical developments in the last three decades have demanded drastic reductions in the size and weight of many types of mechanical and electronic equipment. In some cases, such as in aircraft guidance and space research, weight reduction by itself was a dominant requirement. In others, particularly with computer-linked systems, space and power and heat dissipation requirements of early models were seen as disadvantages, and the working speeds were limited by the times taken for electrical signals to traverse the relatively long connections. Ancillary advantages from size reduction also came from the materials and techniques developed for the purpose. For instance, some types of semi-conductor circuits were found to give improved reliability, and reduction in the area of components fabricated by vacuum evaporation meant that more units could be made in each cycle of operations.

Now to reduce the size of an equipment without loss of functional usefulness normally implies that the miniaturized forms have to be made so that the dimensions are controlled with about the same percentage tolerances as are permissible in the full-size article. This means that the absolute tolerances have to be decreased, and the fineness of the articles therefore necessarily has to be improved. For these developments, mechanical production methods have been refined, and skills derived from such arts as the watch-maker's have been applied. Beyond a certain stage, however, mechanical machining tends to become complicated by vibration and backlash and by distortion of the work-piece. Dimensions needed to be reduced to the point where the width of an element of an article was comparable with the width of the edge zone distorted by stamping with press tools. In such situations, photomechanical techniques for shaping materials offered an attractive solution. Not only did they permit the achievement of high precision, but two-dimensional shapes of almost any complexity could be produced with little extra cost.

During the initial evolution of these methods, very little information was published, but technical journals and books [1] and commercial pamphlets are giving increasing attention to this subject.

This chapter is intended as an introduction, and aims to provide a framework for wider reading.

EARLY PRODUCTION OF METAL GRIDS AND DIAPHRAGMS

Some of the first published examples of these applications of photo-mechanical methods concerned the production of accurately perforated metal diaphragms. These were used as a particularly robust form of graticule in a range-finding gun-sight employed to combat the German V-1 flying bomb in 1944. For this application, it was found that rolled copper sheet at least 0·012 in (0·3 mm) thick had to be used

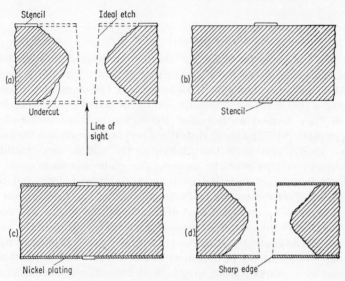

Fig. 90 *Correction of Under-Cutting*

(a) *Deep etch through negative stencils.* Serious under-cutting results from failure of stencil to protect side-walls, (b) *Application of positive stencil,* (c) *Electrolytic formation of negative stencils in nickel,* (d) *Deep etch through stencils.* Although under-cutting still occurs, edges are now sharply defined by nickel stencil.

to give the required stiffness. A 'Bakelite' stencil was formed on each side of the metal by exposing the plate coated with bichromated gum acacia between a pair of registered negatives so that the resist corresponded to the 'lines' which were to be etched away. When the graticules were used, the eye would only see a silhouette, and this needed to be defined by only one side of the metal. One of the negatives was therefore made with somewhat wider lines to give greater tolerance for the registration of the images. In spite of this, the undercutting occurring during etching produced errors greater than the design tolerances, and a better method of control was required. An elegant solution to the problem was found by Gresham [2], who argued that some undercutting did not matter for this application, so long as the correct line width was preserved at the very surface of the metal. Stencil images were therefore formed corresponding to the lines of the image, and the background on both sides of the metal was electro-plated with a 0·0005 in (12 μ) layer of nickel. On removal of the 'Bakelite' stencil, the nickel layer now served two functions. It not only acted as a resist during electrolytic etching of the copper, but also (by virtue of its own resistance to the etching) preserved the exact width of the lines at the surface of the metal in spite of considerable under-cutting (Fig. 90).[1]

PHOTOFORMING

Another technique (used for the fabrication of electron-microscope specimen grids) deposited copper electrolytically through a stencil. In this process (now called *photoforming*) Gresham and Loening printed a step-and-repeat negative on bichromated gum acacia, from which they formed a 'Bakelite' stencil on polished nickel-plated copper plate [3]. For a short time the nickel layer was made the anode in an electrolytic bath to 'passivate' the surface and facilitate subsequent stripping of the images. The plate was then made the cathode in a copper-plating bath, and metal was deposited to a thickness of 0·0002–0·0004 in (5–10 μ), so that the thickness of the metal layer never exceeded that of the stencil. As soon as the metal became thicker than the stencil, rapid sideways spreading of the image occurred. The central part of the pattern so formed (Plate 26) had a diameter of about 0·1 in (2·5 mm), divided into 0·005 in (0·12 mm) squares by lines 0·001–0·002 in (25–50 μ) wide. The limited thickness of plating gave rather fragile structures, and this central part was therefore covered with a bitumen varnish, and a further 0·003 in (75 μ) thickness of copper was plated to form an annular ring strong enough for convenient handling. Finally the stencil was dissolved away, and the grids were stripped to give entirely self-supporting objects. Basically the same method is still used, and very large numbers have been made. Grids made by this method have also been used in radio equipment.

An interesting description of the production and application of precision micromesh sieves made by a similar procedure has been published by Daeschner, Seibert and Peters [4]. The sieves were produced by the Buckbee Mears Company, by first using a ruling engine to produce etched and filled masters on glass with the required

[1] The use of a similar method for making microelectronic masks was described by Strauss [33].

number of lines (500 lines per inch or less). The negative was printed on photosensitive resin on a nickel-plated copper plate, and nickel was electroplated to a thickness of 3 μ (just over 0·0001 in). The fragile 'micromesh' was stripped, and stretched tightly over a relatively coarse grid pattern with 14 lines per inch etched in sheet copper 0·015 in (0·4 mm) thick. Nickel was then again deposited electrolytically, and this stage both bonded the two networks together (Plate 27) and widened the micromesh 'wires' until the apertures had the required dimensions. The widening of the lines during this process was monitored by measuring the integrated optical density of the sieve.

By this method, sieves were made by the Buckbee Mears Company with an accuracy superior to that obtained with woven wires (Plate 28). Thus woven-wire sieves of nominal aperture size 75 μ and 45 μ showed mean standard deviations of 12 μ and 5 μ respectively, whereas the photomechanically produced sieves showed deviations of only 1·4 μ and 1·3 μ. The micromesh sieves proved advantageous for determining the particle-size distribution of the finely powdered catalysts used in the fluidized bed method for the catalytic cracking of heavy oils. It has also been claimed that interference filters for the far infra-red, with unparalleled peak transmittance and off-band rejection, can be made from micromesh sieves.[1]

CHEMICAL MILLING AND PHOTOETCHING

In the last twenty years, it has been realized that the process of applying a stencil resist to metal and removing unwanted metal by chemical action has widespread usefulness. These processes can be broadly described by the term 'chemical milling'. In one form, metals were deeply etched (removing structurally unwanted metal) to reduce the weight of structural members of aircraft and rockets. The results were analogous to those obtained by mechanical milling, and the low resolution resulting from this deep chemical milling or '*photomilling*' excludes the subject from this book. Intrinsically the same process has also been used with much shallower etching to produce parts with micrometric precision. It has been suggested that the term *photoetching* be reserved for this application [5]: a convention adopted in the remainder of this chapter.

Photoetching is now widely used for making accurately controlled shapes from thin metal strip. Although apertures cannot usually be made with widths less than the thickness of the metal, the process has been applied to the production of shapes with a size or tolerance demanding microphotographic techniques.

[1] Rawcliffe, R. D. and Randall, C. M., 'Metal Mesh Interference Filters for the Far Infra-red', *Applied Optics*, 6, 1353, 1967.

MASKS FOR PHOTOETCHING

The initial stage in photoetching is the production of a large drawing, from which reduced photographic copies are made. In principle, the same methods are used for the production of all precision 'drawings', whether these be used for graticule production, or for photoetching or for electronics manufacture (see pp. 237–40). For photoetching, a major problem is the control of the width of narrow etched apertures, and the normal procedure is to adjust line widths in the drawing to compensate for undercutting which occurs during etching (see also p. 316). The negatives resulting from this photographic stage have been likened to the tools employed in other processes of metal fabrication, and are often called 'masks'. They are often required in pairs, so that the work-piece can be printed on each side with identical images in register. In fact, the requirement is that the pair of images should exactly fit, when the two masks are placed face to face. With symmetrical patterns, identical images can be used so long as the pattern is accurate enough, and these should preferably contain registration marks to assist exact positioning. With asymmetric patterns, exact mirror images are needed, and can be made by contact printing the first image on an extreme-resolution plate, followed by reversal processing.[1]

Special requirements of masks for transistor production are discussed later.

PREPARATION OF THE SURFACE

Trouble-free operation of photoetching processes demands careful preparation of the metal (or substrate) surface, to promote uniform etching and satisfactory adhesion of the stencil. According to the nature of the substrate, vapour degreasing, treatment with organic solvents, abrasion with dry or wet abrasives, and bathing in acid or alkaline solutions may be employed [1(e)], [6]. The last trace of abrasive should be removed from the surface, and the final drying is often effected by baking to remove the last traces of water or absorbed gases.

With some materials, simple cleaning of the surface is not enough, and the results are much improved by formation of 'conversion coatings'. Typical examples are metal phosphate or chromate coatings such as are used to promote rust-proofing or corrosion resistance.

---

[1] When one image of a mirror-image pair needs line widths slightly 'oversize', the adjustment can usually be made by controlled over-exposure when contact printing.

STENCILS FORMED FROM PHOTORESISTS

When Gresham and Loening were doing their early work, no single composition combined photosensitivity with the high chemical inertness required to provide adequate resistance to corrosive etchants in the thin layers needed for high resolution. They therefore produced their stencils by coating bichromated colloid on an inert resist layer, but the need for this indirect process has now been avoided by synthetic organic compounds incorporating most of the required properties (pp. 50–3).

Photoresists now on the market consist of solutions which can be applied to the support by spraying, dipping or whirling. When the layer is dry, it can usually be stored for months in the dark. Compositions are available giving stencils in which the exposed areas are

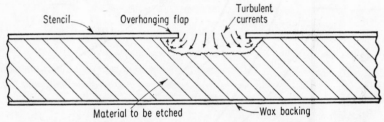

Fig. 91 *Risk of turbulence due to agitation of etchant raising edge of stencil*

retained (negative working) or selectively washed-out (positive working) on developing the layer after exposure.

Not only must the stencil formed from a photoresist have excellent resistance to the etchant, but it must also adhere firmly to the substrate, so that sideways penetration under the resist is not possible. This requirement is particularly stringent when etching to a considerable depth with a vigorously agitated fluid. The risk of the turbulent fluid lifting the overhanging flap at the edge of the stencil is obviously very real (Fig. 91). When Barditch added a fluoro-carbon non-ionic surface-active agent (3M L 1060) to KPR coated on silicon or silicon monoxide, the resist withstood etching fifty times longer because of improved adherence [7]. The same author also found that thorough drying of solvent from the photoresist layer before use was important for the etching of fine lines and delicate designs. He employed infrared and electric-field drying.

Because of the economic importance of stencils formed from photoresists, their manipulation and performance is being studied in great detail. Some results of this work were described in papers read at a Kodak Seminar on Microminiaturization. For example, filtration of all liquids and resists down to particle sizes of 1 μ or less, and monitoring filtration performance by a Silting Index Apparatus (Millipore Filter Corporation) were precautions applied before coating [8]. Moisture was said to be one of the primary causes of poor adhesion on silicon, and coating wafers[1] as soon as possible after removal from the furnace, or storing under a dilute solution of resist was recommended [9]. In addition, moisture could be averted by preparing

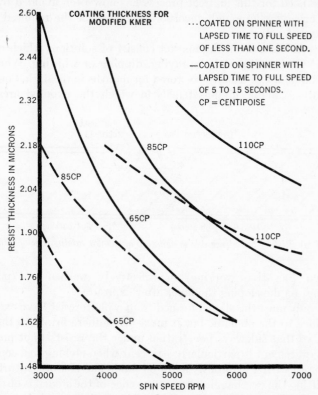

Fig. 92 *Dependence of Photoresist Thickness on Viscosity and Spinner Speed Courtesy of C. J. Taylor and Kodak Seminar on Microminiaturization.*

resist mixtures and loading applicators in dry nitrogen in a 'dry box', so that the resist mixtures never came into contact with the atmosphere until actual application to the wafers [10]. The same author described prewetting the wafers to improve adhesion, by spinning on a dilute solution of resist before the main application.

Coating by whirling (spinning) has been developed far beyond

[1] *Wafer* or *slice* describes thin slices of silicon used for microelectronics, which may be subdivided into *chips* or *dice* (p. 344 *et seq*).

normal photomechanical practice. For example, spinners are being brought to rotational speeds of 3,000 to 7,000 r.p.m. exceedingly rapidly (Fig. 92) [11]. Refined equipment for this stage is now marketed, and incorporates such features as driving shafts continuously rotating at the required speed combined with magnetic clutches to bring the spinner heads to full speed in one second or less. The wafers or substrates are held in vacuum chucks, and the bowls surrounding the spinners are continuously exhausted by a down draught which removes both fumes and cobwebs of resist which might spoil the coatings [12]. Damon [13] made a detailed study of the connection between whirler performance and the properties of resist coatings, and found that coating thickness for a given resist could be adequately predicted by the formula:

$$T = \frac{kP^2}{S}$$

where T is the coating thickness,

P is the percentage solids content of resist solution,

S is the whirler speed,

k is the whirler constant.

The constant 'k' was different for each whirler, and seemed to depend on acceleration characteristics. The same paper includes high-speed photographs of films of resist during the actual spinning operation, and the results were related to the profile of the resist thickness across the area of the substrate.

The connection between the observable properties of resist layers and etching performance was examined in various ways. Accurate and detailed delineation of variations in film thickness was achieved by Variable Angle Monochromatic Fringe Observation [14]. In assessing the performance of resist layers, it was noted that resolution improved with decreased thickness (p. 23) but the probability of etching through pinholes increased. Various etchants were used to test resists, and make pinholes readily visible when the resist was removed [15]. A test closely linked to ultimate usage was to take a pair of identical wafers on which silicon dioxide layers had been grown (p. 345), and coat one with photoresist, expose uniformly, develop and etch as if an image had been present. After removing the resist, an aluminium layer was evaporated on the 'etched' wafer and on the control, so that the silicon dioxide layers formed the dielectric of a capacitor. The ability of the silicon dioxide layers to support applied voltages was studied, and a satisfactory resist allowed the etching to produce no increase in current leakage [16].

Papers in this Seminar also contained comparisons of different resists, methods of development and removal of stencils and resistance

to different etchants. The final paper contained a review of the evolution of the Kodak resists, and an account of their physical properties [17].

Experiments on the production of blocks for printed illustrations by
etching metal through a stencil formed from a bichromated colloid
were described more than a century ago. For many years the resultant
processes have been the mainstay of book and newspaper illustration,
and in the printing trade much attention has been given to the control
of metal etching. The basic problem is that a stencil can only protect
the *surface* of the metal. As soon as the etchant penetrates to a significant depth, it exposes completely unprotected sidewalls. Minimizing
the resultant undercutting has been a dominant theme in studies of
the process.

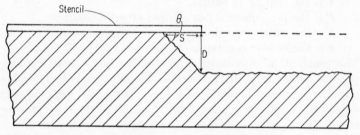

Fig. 93 *Concept of Etch Factor*
The ratio of Depth (D) to Spread (S) equals the tangent of θ.

It has become customary to evaluate the performance of an etching
process by dividing the *depth* of etch by the amount of sideways
etching or *spread*. The ratio $\dfrac{\text{D(epth)}}{\text{S(pread)}}$ (Fig. 93) is called the etch
factor, and is the tangent of the angle between the side-wall and the
plane of the metal. To limit the effect of undercutting, craftsmen have
experimented with the composition of the etching medium and its
temperature and mode of application. The work-piece may be simply
immersed in a stirred bath, or may be etched by vapour or spray, or
by making it the anode in an electroplating bath. It has been stated
that the etch factor can be increased by a spray impinging normally.
Maximum agitation then occurs at the bottom of the etch-pits, and
undercutting may be lessened by the overhanging flap of stencil reducing turbulence. It has also been stated that etch factors are with
some metals influenced by differences of etching rate in layers near
the surface. The differences are probably the result of 'work harden-

ing' during rolling of the sheet. While improved precision can be obtained by attention to details of this sort, none of these factors would be expected to achieve a radical cure.

In the printing industry, undercutting has been minimized by two means. In one process, the partly etched work-piece was washed and dried, and a resinous powder (Dragon's Blood) was wiped across the surface so that it collected against the side-walls. When fused by warming the work-piece, the resin formed a protective layer against the next stage of etching. Further etching, of course, undercut the fused deposit, so that etching had again to be interrupted, and the

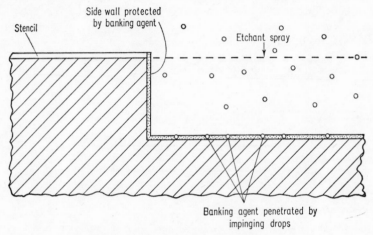

Fig. 94 *Principle of 'Powderless' Etching*

whole procedure of washing, drying and applying Dragon's Blood repeated.

These tedious manipulations have been superseded by a process known as 'Powderless Etching'. Conventional etching fluids were modified by addition of so called 'banking' agents, which caused any exposed metal surfaces to be covered by a thin, fragile layer of protective agent [1(d)]. In one form introduced by the Dow Chemical Company for the etching of zinc and magnesium, diethyl-benzene which can act as a resist was emulsified in the bath, to which a surface-active agent (dioctyl sodium sulphosuccinate) was also added [18]. The surface-active agent adsorbed on all free metal surfaces, and the 'resist' molecules adsorbed on the 'fatty tails' of the surface-active agent. A process developed at Photo Engravers Research Inc. for etching of copper employed a complex derivative of thiourea as an additive [19]. Wherever the etching bath attacked the metal, cuprous ions were formed, and these immediately reacted with the additive

to form a tenacious gelatinous precipitate. With either form of the
process, etching was effected by spraying the etching solution normally against the metal surface. The velocity of impingement was
adjusted so that the force dissipated on the normal surfaces (i.e. at
the bottom of the etched pits) was just sufficient to break through
the protective layer, and etching proceeded. On side-walls, the force

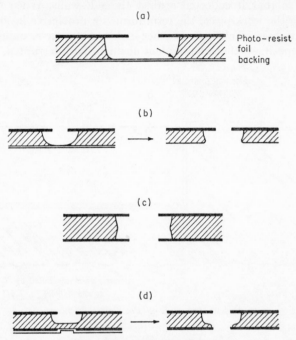

Fig. 95 *Minimizing of Undercutting*

(a) Etching from one side with back covered with wax, (b) as (a), but etch interrupted, wax removed and final dilute etch applied, (c) etching from both sides
through matched stencils, (d) as (c) but with second stencil covered with wax until
last stage of Etching.

*Courtesy of R. Peacock and Director of British Scientific Instrument Research
Association.*

was insufficient to penetrate the 'banking' agent, and little if any
etching occurred (Fig. 94). Not only was the process quicker, but
better control of the etching of fine dot patterns was achieved. Processes of this type have been perfected for use with magnesium and
zinc and copper alloys, and resulted in greatly increased etch factors.
In principle, they seem capable of extension to the etching of other
materials.

When the slope of the side-wall is unimportant, for example with
work-pieces used to screen layers from light or from vacuum-diffusion

beams, the consequences of undercutting can be circumvented by other means. Peacock has described the results obtained by etching differentially with stencils on one side or on both sides of the metal [20]. Etching right through the metal from one side, and with the back protected by wax, produced a ragged edge where the etched walls intersected the back surface obliquely (Fig. 95). By interrupting etching as soon as the metal was penetrated, removing the wax and giving a further etch in a dilute solution, clean edges were obtained. With stencils on both sides, the pattern of undercutting normally obtained was improved by covering the stencil with wax on one side, and first etching from the other side until two-thirds of the thickness was penetrated. Continuation of etching from both sides after removal of the wax completed the penetration before much undercutting of the second side could occur.

If vertical side-walls are required for mechanical components, the slope can be steepened by continuation of etching, but only at the expense of further widening of the apertures and rounding of the corners of the pattern.

ADVANTAGES OF PHOTOETCHING

It is instructive to enquire how the advantages of photoetching are related to the intrinsic nature of the process. Firstly there is the speed and exactness with which the pattern indicated by a drawing can be converted to the final metallic shape. With mechanical methods, the information in the drawing has to be transferred to the work-piece virtually point by point, and the opportunities for making mistakes are correspondingly great. The cost of the work, therefore, increases rapidly with the complexity of the pattern. With photoetching, the 'tool' is the reduced photographic transparency, and all the information in the pattern (however elaborate) is automatically transferred to the work-piece in one operation. This advantage resembles that obtained by photocopying of documents as compared with manual copying. When the units to be photoetched are small (say less than 6 in (15 cm) square), many units can be made at one time by using a step-and-repeat transparency. If the metal has to be etched through stencils from both sides, every unit pattern has to be accurately registered with its mate.

Once a drawing of the required accuracy has been made, the entire process of producing a reduced transparency, printing on the sensitized metal, developing the stencil and etching the metal can be completed in a few hours. This rapidity is especially attractive for engineers concerned with the design of equipment and the production of prototypes. For the same reason, the design of photoetched components can be modified relatively cheaply and easily.

The above named advantages are inherent in the photographic nature of the production process, while others accrue from the nature of the etching process. In etching, the shape of the work-piece is changed virtually by the removal of atoms one by one, and the material a few atomic distances below the surface at any moment is not affected at all. Thus the tendency of mechanical shaping methods to distort the work-piece or modify the crystalline structure by the transfer of mechanical or thermal shock is avoided. Etching cannot bend even the thinnest foil, neither can it burr the edges nor change the magnetic state of metals. Since the crystalline structure is not altered, metals can be annealed or tempered before etching. This avoidance of the side effects of mechanical methods means that it is now feasible to produce parts with a delicacy and refinement not previously possible. An indication of how these methods have been applied is given in the next section. Further development of applications is likely to occur, as the potentialities of photoetching become more widely known.

APPLICATIONS OF PHOTOETCHING

To appreciate these applications, it is firstly convenient to review the range of materials which have already been worked commercially. These include:

> aluminium, magnesium, zinc, iron, steel, stainless steel, copper, nickel, chromium and alloys of these metals.

Other materials are:

> molybdenum, titanium, silver, gold, germanium, silicon, silicon dioxide, glass and ceramics.

In fact the range is determined by the availability of etchants which will attack the substrate without penetrating available stencils. The operations involved include:

> Production of parts from flat sheet,
> Partial etching to give relief patterns, such as are required by tools and dies,
> Surface etching to provide useful or decorative patterns, production of name-plates, pure decoration and even jewellery.

Many of the articles made by photoetching are relatively large, but the use of emulsions, lenses and resist layers giving accurate line-width control endows these photoetching methods with a valuable precision. Examples of parts produced are illustrated in Plate 29 and described below.

Table 12. Parts produced by photoetching

Material	Thickness	Description	Tolerance	Reference in Plate 29
Hymu metal (annealed)	0·003 in (75 μ)	Pole piece for recording head	0·001 in (25 μ)	1
Stainless steel	0·003 in (75 μ)	Spring	0·001 in (25 μ)	2
Beryllium Copper	0·005 in (125 μ)	Spacer Yoke	0·005 in (125 μ)	3

Precision photoetching has also been applied when many units requiring high accuracy over a large area were required. An example is the production of aperture masks for use in colour-television tubes by the Buckbee Mears Company [21]. Their raw material was 800-pound rolls of 24 in (61 cm) wide cold-rolled steel strip 0·006 in (0·15 mm) thick. In a continuous machine this was scrubbed, washed and degreased in at least five stages; sensitized on both sides with photoresist, dried and rolled interleaved with paper to prevent scratching of the resist (Plate 30).

In the next machine (Plate 31) the sensitized strip was unrolled and passed into vacuum printing frames in which it was exposed behind a pattern of dots corresponding to the holes to be etched. The exposing operation was a critical stage, since 400,000 dots on centres 0·027 in (0·68 mm) apart had to be printed from the two sides so that the images registered with each other to 0·0001 in (2·5 μ) over the 20 in (51 cm) diameter of the image. The vacuum printing frame had not only to secure this high positional performance, but it had to be able to accept a continuous strip of sensitized metal, and the entire unit had to achieve an exposing rate reasonably adjusted to the two-to-four units per minute output of the etching operation.

Techniques developed for the printing stage of this process have been described in a series of patents issued to the Buckbee Mears Co. To produce patterns of dots with sizes diminished controllably from 0·0119 in (302 μ) at the centre to 0·0106 in (269 μ) 8 in from the centre of the image, a master image with uniform dots was printed slightly out of contact on another photographic plate. By use of a sector wheel, the printing exposure was increased progressively from the periphery of the pattern to the centre, to produce the required gradation by controlled image spread [22]. The effects of abrasion of the expensive master images by the metal web were minimized by producing the working masters on an emulsion coating on matted glass [23].

The masters were held in pairs of frames hinged from the top and the apparatus was equipped with devices for accurately adjusting the register of the mated images to be printed on each side of the metal [24]. A particularly interesting patent described the hydraulic and electrical controls employed to ensure rapid and satisfactory functioning of the contact printing operation, [25] and embodies many refinements. For example, after the frames had been evacuated and the resist layers exposed, compressed air was applied to the frames to produce a uniformly smooth but positive opening rather than a sudden jerk. A preferred form of the invention employed three double frames, with their centres separated by slightly more than two

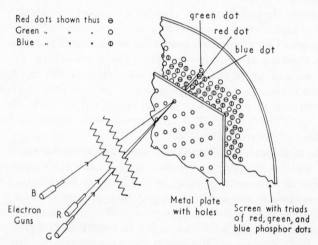

Fig. 96 *Principle of Synthesis of Colours in R.C.A. Compatible System of Colour Television*

The aperture mask is an essential component ensuring that each phosphor dot only receives electron beam from appropriate gun.

From *The Reproduction of Colour. Courtesy of R. W. G. Hunt and Fountain Press*

image diameters, and with the spaces between the frames shielded from light. After each operation simultaneously exposing three images the metal web was advanced by three image diameters, so that a new set of images was printed in the previously screened areas.

After exposure, the strip passed to an automated developing and etching unit 80 ft (26 m) long. This developed the image in the photosensitive resist, conditioned the stencil for etching, and etched the metal from both sides in precisely controlled conditions. The etched strip was washed (Plate 32) and dried, and the average size of holes in every aperture mask was checked with an integrating densitometer. The achievement of a high rate of output with such fine work over a large area is both a remarkable achievement and a fine example of the potentialities of photoetching.

In use, the photoetched masks were positioned inside the cathode-ray tube at a short distance from a phosphor layer provided with groups of three dots, in which each emits a primary colour. Electrons from three electron guns traversed the aperture mask, which ensured that only electrons from the appropriate gun could activate the phosphor dots of each primary colour (Fig. 96). In fact these aperture masks are an essential component of the R.C.A. compatible system of colour television, in which the signals can also be received by monochrome receivers.

PROCESSES PERMITTING OPTICAL CONTROL OF SIDE WALLS

The scope of photo-fabrication techniques has been further extended by the invention of photosensitive systems which allow a light beam to penetrate to a great depth in the layer, and modify its solubility throughout the entire thickness.

PHOTOSENSITIVE GLASS

One example is the photosensitive glass produced by the Corning Glass Company. As described on p. 53, the speed of etching one form of glass ('Fotoform') can be greatly increased by heat treatment after exposure to ultra-violet [26]. Clearly, such a material has most interesting potentialities. Since the original glass is optically clear, exposure behind a mask to a parallel beam of ultra-violet can produce a three-dimensional latent image whose effective depth is only limited by absorption in the layer. If the beam is truly parallel, little spread will occur, and a parallel-sided rod of glass will be exposed behind each aperture in the mask. The rods will lie at an angle to the surface determined by the angle of incidence of the parallel beam. In the simplest case the beam would be normal, but for special purposes it can be inclined at an angle. Thus the mask controls the shape of the exposed area in the surface of the glass, and the exposing technique can be used to modify the shape of the holes in lower layers.

When the exposed and heat-treated glass was etched in stirred aqueous hydrofluoric acid, the exposed areas were found to etch at fifteen times the etching rate of unexposed areas. Thus the downwards etching of an exposed rod was far more rapid than the etching of the unexposed surface, or of the unexposed side-walls reached by the etchant as the process proceeded. This was found to result in holes with a taper of four degrees. As with etching of metals, the results could be modified by etching from both sides or from one side only.

Etching from both sides produced a profile with two truncated cones, and gave the minimum overall increase of hole diameter. Etching one side with the back protected by wax produced single cones. Because the etched pattern was controlled by the bulk properties of the exposed glass rather than by a surface stencil, completion of etching at the bottom of the pits was effected with very little erosion of the side walls at the lower surface. This produced truncated cones whose smallest diameters corresponded closely to the diameters of the openings in the mask.

It is clear that such a process must be capable of giving smaller and more closely spaced apertures than could be obtained by etching to the same depth through a surface stencil. The performance achievable is indicated by a table of tolerances and spacings published by the Corning Glass Company (Table 13).

The significance of this table can be seen by considering a specific case. With etching from one side and glass of nominal thickness 0·055 in (1·4 mm) for instance, a minimum clearance of 0·007 in (178 μ) is suggested. This means that the unetched fillet of glass between the holes will be 0·007 in wide at the wax surface which is etched last. With the side walls having a slope of 1 : 15, the fillet should be reduced in width at the first etched surface by 0·055/15 in (0·0036 in or 90 μ) on each side. Thus the side-walls will just about meet at the first-etched surface. The same basis of calculation has been used for the minimum clearance with thicker glass, and etching of holes with diameters appreciably less than *one-tenth* of the thickness of the glass was not recommended.[1] The minimum recommended spacing of 0·013 in (330 μ) corresponds to a screen with 76 holes per linear inch or more than 5,000 per square inch. With etching from both sides, the spacing allows more than 100 lines/inch for 0·055 in glass. In fact glass of approximately the same thickness as normal photographic half-plates could be etched right through with as many holes as the dots of a fairly fine half-tone screen.

The process has been operated by the Corning Glass Co. to produce insulating components to customers' requirements. These have included spacers for electronic valves, components for digital converters and thermocouple holders (Plate 33). By further heat treatment after etching, some forms of the glass can be made opaque, or can have their internal molecular structure modified to give properties resembling a ceramic rather than a glass.

Another interesting application of the potentialities of photosensitive glass is the fabrication of intricate and precise channels for liquid or gas flow to perform logic, control and computational

---

[1] This should be contrasted with the widely held opinion that photoetched holes in metal should not be made with a diameter less than the thickness of the sheet.

Table 18. Suggested tolerances and spacings for 'Fotoform' photosensitive glass

	One side etch						Two side etch					
Nominal thick. before etch (t), in	0·055	0·080	0·125	0·150	0·180	0·250	0·055	0·080	0·125	0·150	0·180	0·250
Min Clearance ($S-D$), in	0·007	0·010	0·015	0·019	0·022	0·031	0·003	0·005	0·008	0·009	0·011	0·016
Hole dia (D), in	Spacing (S), in						Spacing (S), in					
0·006	0·013						0·009					
0·010	0·017	0·020					0·013	0·015				
0·015	0·022	0·025	0·030	0·034			0·018	0·020	0·023	0·024		
0·020	0·027	0·030	0·035	0·039	0·042		0·023	0·025	0·028	0·029	0·031	
0·025	0·032	0·035	0·040	0·044	0·047	0·056	0·028	0·030	0·033	0·034	0·036	0·041
0·050	0·057	0·060	0·065	0·069	0·072	0·081	0·053	0·055	0·058	0·059	0·061	0·066
0·100	0·107	0·110	0·115	0·119	0·122	0·131	0·103	0·105	0·108	0·109	0·111	0·116
0·250	0·257	0·260	0·265	0·269	0·272	0·281	0·253	0·255	0·258	0·259	0·261	0·266
0·500	0·507	0·510	0·515	0·519	0·522	0·531	0·503	0·505	0·508	0·509	0·511	0·566

Hole tolerances, in
Up to ¼ dia. ± 0·001
¼ to 1 dia. ± 0·002
Over 1 dia. ± 0·005

Centre-to-centre tolerances, in
0 to 1 ± 0·001
1 to 4 ± 0·003
4 to 7 ± 0·005

Edge tolerances, in
0 to 1 ± 0·002
1 to 4 ± 0·005
Over 4 ± 0·010

functions. The photosensitive glasses permit accurate chemical milling of the channels, with the required depth of etching and precise curve profiles. For this purpose, the Corning Glass Co. has made devices by etching a flat sheet to the desired depth from one side, converting to the ceramic form, and completing the passages by sealing to a flat surface of another layer. In a sample I have seen, four layers were sealed to give a complex structure in which interacting fluid flows were controlled in three planes at the sealed interfaces. As with other articles produced from these materials, all processing was done by the Corning Glass Co., which offered for sale standard units providing the functions of components such as flip-flops, OR–NOR gates, AND gates, proportional amplifiers and fluid resistors [27]. The Company also undertook to integrate a number of devices into functional circuits.

Such components are used in 'fluidic' devices, which can achieve many of the unit functions of electronic circuit components, but with response times measured in milliseconds rather than nano-seconds [28]. When the high speed of electronic devices is not required (as frequently seems to be the case in systems for industrial control), it has been suggested that fluidic devices can compete for simplicity, cheapness and the ability to operate in very hostile environments such as high temperatures and intense radiation levels. Whether fluidic devices will displace any electronic circuits is a question outside the scope of this book. For our purpose, however, we can note how precise photofabrication once again depends on the optical properties of extreme-resolution photosensitive materials. The optical control of etch factor demands a layer which is non-scattering and has a glass-smooth surface. These are the conditions which allow the sharp edges of the image in the master negative to be preserved in planes well below the surface.

PHOTOSENSITIVE NYLON

In Chapter 2, it was shown that photosensitive nylon can be polymerized image-wise by exposure to parallel ultra-violet, and that on washing-out the unexposed areas, thick stencils with exceptionally square and clean side-walls can be obtained. An early suggested use was to give accurate control of side-spread in the photoforming of thick metal deposits by electrolytic deposition [29]. This type of material was first developed for the 'Dicryl' Plastic Printing Plate by the Dupont Co., which now also markets sheets of 'Templex' photopolymer. This is normally supplied in thicknesses from 1 mm to 0·2 mm (0·04 to 0·008 in) bonded to carbon steel, aluminium or 'Cronar' polyester film [30]. With this material, users can make fluidic devices of their own design. Once the channels have been etched, they are sealed by laminating 0·175 mm (0·007 in) 'Cronar' film to the surface of the processed 'Templex' Sheet.

APPLICATION OF MICROPHOTOGRAPHIC TECHNIQUES TO THE ELECTRONICS INDUSTRY

This chapter has so far dealt mainly with photomechanical production of mechanical components, but applications to the electronics industry have been of at least equal importance. In the last quarter of a century, important developments have stemmed from the fusion of two trends. For a variety of reasons, demands for a reduction in the size and weight of electronic equipment have become increasingly insistent. One example was the development of a complete radar transmitter and receiver for the radio proximity fuse housed in the nose-cap of an artillery shell. During the same period, techniques for

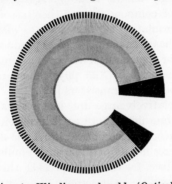

Fig. 97 *Potentiometer Winding produced by 'Optical Meandering'*
Courtesy of G. V. Planer.

the production of printed 'circuits'[1] were developed primarily to reduce the cost of assembly and wiring of complex circuits [1(a)]. One highly successful technique used thin copper foil laminated to a plastic board. The required design was etched in the copper through a stencil in a photoresist layer. Thus an essentially photographic technique was being used for the production of circuits, and was capable of providing a useful degree of *miniaturization*. The resolution obtainable was, however, limited by the fact that printed circuits were made from copper layers 0·001 in (25 μ) or more thick. With some circuit functions, layers 0·00004 in (1 μ) or less thick still provided sufficient conductivity, and etching or deposition of metals or metal-oxide

---

[1] As K. J. Dean has pointed out, printed circuit is a misnomer, since the predominant rôle of the patterns is to generate inter-connections (i.e. wiring) rather than functional elements.

films through photomechanical stencils provide resolution comparable to that obtained in graticule manufacture. For such purposes, the master transparencies could be produced by two-stage reduction from a large drawing, or as with large scales (p. 246) could be made by successive projection of elements of the image on an extreme-resolution plate mounted on a dividing engine and moved very precisely between exposures. The latter process, which has been called 'optical meandering' [31], has been used for making long lengths of 'wire' for such components as coils, resistances and potentiometers (Fig. 97).

MICROELECTRONICS

In addition to the use of photomechanical methods for the production of small individual components, series of operations, controlling the deposition of different images in conductors or insulating dielectric materials sequentially on the same substrate, have been used for making a variety of components and their associated inter-connections on a single insulating support such as glass or ceramic. This 'thin-film' concept has been mainly used to produce 'passive' functions such as resistance or capacitance, and components supplying 'active' functions are introduced by the physical connection of attached semi-conductor diodes and transistors [32].

Because of the relatively large unit-image sizes and modest resolutions required for thin-film structures, it has been suggested that film materials such as Kodak Kodalith Ortho Type 3 film on Estar base can give adequate results [33]. While such emulsions have considerable image spread (see, for example, p. 244), this property has been used to adjust line widths over a range of several thousandths of an inch (25 μ or more) without affecting the spatial relationships of different parts of the image and thereby to adjust the values of resistors. Several authors have described the making of accurate masks for thin-film work by photo-forming a nickel stencil on sheet copper and then etching through the copper [33], [34] (see p. 309).

Since thin-film circuits use discrete and separately made transistors, optimum performance is considered to be more readily obtained, and the performance of different structures providing other circuit functions may be effectively optimized [35]. In relation to the potentialities of microphotographic processes, the images produced for thin-film work are neither particularly small nor fine, and *for this reason alone* are of less microphotographic interest, and will therefore not be discussed further in the remainder of this chapter. It should, however, be noted that thin-film methods may be used to provide the interconnections for large assemblies of the complex integrated circuits discussed later [36], and see p. 352.

MASKS FOR FABRICATION OF SEMICONDUCTOR DEVICES

Photomechanical processes applied to the production of diodes, transistors or complete circuits on wafers of silicon or germanium have required finer optical performance, and for this reason are of greater interest to us. The processes employ series of photomechanically produced stencils to control the image-wise treatments of the semiconductor material.

According to the manufacturing operations involved different types of stencil or *mask* have been used.[1]

(1) Firmly adherent stencils in molecular contact with the surface were required when the agent was applied to the work-piece by a non-directional method.

    (a) The traditional non-directional method was by etching of metallic or oxide layers on the surface of the substrate, using solutions which would readily spread sideways through the smallest gap between the stencil and the work-piece.

    (b) The electrical properties of silicon have been modified by heating in the vapour of a doping material. Wherever the surface was not protected, the doping atoms entered the silicon lattice and diffused to a depth controlled by the temperature and the duration of the operation. For this type of process, techniques were developed for producing adherent stencils resisting the very high temperature in the doping furnace (p. 345).

(2) Many materials can be applied to substrate surfaces by evaporation or sputtering in a high vacuum, with pressures so low that mean free paths exceed the distance from the source to the substrate. Highly directional depositions can then be achieved by use of small sources at relatively great distances, or by using an electrostatic potential to accelerate charged particles in the desired direction. In this type of process the deposited patterns were essentially shadows, and deposition could be controlled by self-supporting and re-usable masks placed over the substrate. These masks were commonly made by photo-etching of metal foils or by electrolytic deposition of metal through photoresist stencils (p. 310). Frequently two or more such masks were used. A thin foil mask might be used to define the pattern, and was held in contact with the substrate by a

---

[1] For a detailed discussion of the properties required in masks, readers should consult P. D. Payne's article 'Technology of Transistor Mask Fabrication' [37].

thicker contact mask with larger registered apertures (Fig. 98). In other cases, a third spacer mask (also with larger registered

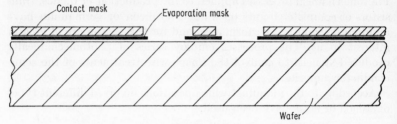

Fig. 98 *Control of Deposition by Evaporation Mask*

apertures) separated the defining mask from the substrate, and successive evaporation of two materials from different directions laid down adjacent stripes of each material (see p. 349 and Fig. 99).

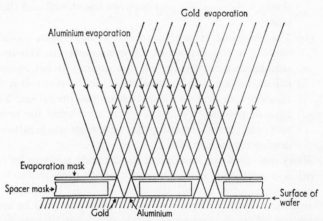

Fig. 99 *Production of Parallel Images of Different Metals through Composite Mask.*
Courtesy of 'Journal of Photographic Science'.

Usually the required electrical properties could only be obtained by a succession of evaporation, diffusion or etching operations applied to the work-piece. Each operation required its own mask to define the unit of the pattern being produced, and photoresist or metal-foil stencils were used in accordance with the demands of each stage of the operation. Not only did each mask in a set have to define the outline of the unit pattern, but it also had to determine the position of each unit with respect to the complete structure. The tolerances demanded for positioning of successive masks are often comparable to those for the line width of the finest lines in the image.

Now only a very small mass of semi-conductor material is required to give the electronic function of a diode or transistor, and components were made from thin slices or 'wafers' of germanium or silicon about 0·008 in (200 μ) thick. The small size and power consumption of these components greatly favoured miniaturization, and their small weight of a milligram or so (about one-sixtieth of a grain) was desirable because of the cost of the wafer material. The production of wafers with the desired extreme purity and critically adjusted crystalline state involves expensive processes. Since each component needed to occupy only a few square millimetres (or a fraction of a square millimetre—say squares of sides 0·1 to 0·02 in), multiple-image masks containing dozens or hundreds of images were produced by step-and-repeat (p. 337). Thus inter-locking sets of masks were required with very many images, and with strict tolerances imposed for the registration maintained for every single component image.

By using these methods, the electronics industry has adopted microphotography as a major production technique, and the results of this *microelectronic* work are described in a great mass of technical literature.[1] The majority of contributions are, however, concerned with such topics as:

    (i) circuit design,
    (ii) purification and properties of raw materials,
    (iii) vacuum evaporation to give thin films of
    (iv) desired properties,
    (v) cost, reliability and servicing,
    (vi) performance evaluation,
    (vii) power requirements and heat dissipation,
    (viii) environmental protection, and
    (ix) application to specific projects.

Thus although these processes have been built around photographic techniques, these are naturally of secondary interest to electronics engineers *so long as all is going well*. Discussion of the photographic methods also appears to have been retarded by military and commercial secrecy. Photographic technicians delving into this literature may be baffled by incorrect use of the word *'photolithographic'* to describe production methods involving the use of photoresists. Photolithography is the art of printing by using a photosensitive layer to generate patterns of ink-accepting and ink-repellent areas on the surface of a stone plate or specially prepared sheets of metal or paper (see p. 413). In fact, true photolithographic printing *has* been used for producing

---

[1] For a period, the word *microminiaturization* was used to describe this work but now appears to be used less frequently.

resist layers on relatively large printed-circuit boards [1(a)], but this method is quite rare in microelectronics.

The treatment of this topic in the remainder of the chapter is from the directly opposite point of view. Our attention will be concentrated primarily on the photographic stages, and electronic topics will be outlined merely to suggest why the processes have been developed in specific directions.

SPECIAL PHOTOGRAPHIC PROBLEMS OF MICROELECTRONICS MANUFACTURE

As microphotography was applied to electronics, it was found that a number of factors were unusually important. Microelectronics manufacturers are especially concerned with cleanliness and dust control, not only because of the required dimensions of the unit components, but because high packing densities to make maximum use of the available surface *and* multi-stage processes greatly increased the statistical probability of trouble. The problem of dirt control is common to all industrial microphotographic procedures, and is discussed on p. 76 et seq. But for microelectronics it is necessary not only to produce effectively defect-free photographic images, but also to make from them defect-free masks and stencils and to perform defect-free diffusions through the stencils. Filtration procedures are therefore important before coating photoresists in 1 μ thick layers, in developing and etching, and in cleaning the carrier gases bearing the dopant vapours to the silicon surface.

Other problems of special interest are line-width control, registration and the ensuring of optimum image quality over relatively very large fields.

LINE-WIDTH CONTROL

The importance of line-width control can be appreciated by considering the production of a resistor with a value of resistance specified to within a few per cent for use in a tuned circuit. To achieve both the resolution and the resistance values required, thin films of conducting material have been deposited on insulating substrates to form layers usually well under 1 μ (0·00004 in) thick. The intrinsic resistance of such a layer (or *resistance per square*) can be controlled reasonably well by deposition of a given thickness, but is subject to variations depending on age and crystalline structure. The value for the final device is then determined by the intrinsic resistance of the layer, the length of 'wire' produced by photofabrication and the line width. Even if the properties of the layers were completely uniform, a ± 4 per cent tolerance on a 0·001 in (25 μ) wire means a width control to

$\pm 0 \cdot 00004$ in (1 μ), although this line width corresponds to only 20 lines/mm! To hold this tolerance for large numbers of 'images' through both the microphotographic and the photomechanical stages demands the production of microphotographic images with steeper edge-density gradients than are required even for graticules. A line width of 25 μ is already considered large by many electronics designers, and devices are being made commercially with line widths of $0 \cdot 0002$ in (5 μ) or less. Such dimensions with real control of line width can only be achieved by a resolution beyond the limits theoretically obtainable with lenses because of the finite wavelength of light (p. 105). Four per cent of 5 μ is 2,000 Å: two-and-a-half times smaller than the wavelength of blue-green light.

Thus electronics manufacturers are increasingly concerned with making images right up to the diffraction limit of lens performance, and in addition the resolution-limiting factors of every material and operation are being analysed in detail. For example, Schuetze and Hennings [38] found that with extreme precautions lines down to $0 \cdot 8$ μ wide could be obtained by contact printing. They considered the working limit of High-Resolution plates to be 1 μ line width, whereas metal-on-glass masks could be made with $0 \cdot 4$ μ lines. By direct optical reduction of images with violet light on a $0 \cdot 3$ μ thick layer of positive-working photoresist, they produced tantalum resistors with lines $0 \cdot 4$ μ wide.

In principle, some further improvement of resolution by a factor of perhaps 30 per cent might be anticipated by exposure to far ultra-violet with quartz objectives. More radical solutions of this problem are discussed at the end of this chapter.

REGISTRATION

Some circuit functions demand the laying down of two or more materials, each being applied in a precisely defined pattern accurately spaced with regard to the others. In addition it has been found useful to generate 'components' with different functions and the required inter-connections on a single substrate by a succession of stages involving depositions or selective removal. For such processes several inter-related masks are required, and the final electrical properties depend not only on the shape deposited through each mask, but also on the correct positioning and avoidance of encroachment of the different depositions (see Plates 43 to 46). Success therefore depends on satisfactory registration of the different masks. The 'drawings' for this work are now normally made on a co-ordinatograph (p. 240), to ensure that each image is correctly positioned with respect to an identical set of registration marks on every drawing [39].

To maintain registration in a series of masks through the primary and secondary reduction stages, it is advisable to use very rigid copying equipment with arrangements for accurate location of all the component parts. If the cameras are only to be used at a fixed reduction ratio, the copyboard, lens panel and plate-holder can be constructed as cross members built into a rigid rectangular framework. The framework may be mounted so that it is able to rock without distortion, to minimize the effects of vibration. Three-pin locating jigs or registration pins can be used to locate both the drawings and the unexposed plates. By this means, all images can be reproducibly placed with respect to one corner and one edge of the plate (Fig. 100).

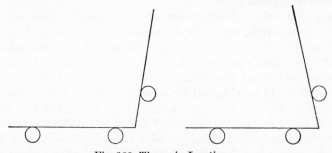

Fig. 100 *Three-pin Location*
Reproducible placement is secured, even when plate corner is not square.

Fixed-focus equipment is simple but inflexible, and its use means that all work must be sized by calibrating the reduction cameras, and then making the drawings with the appropriate dimensions. For more flexible working, variable reduction is needed, and ensuring the necessary accuracy with convenient working requires considerable precautions. Special cameras developed by the R. W. Borrowdale Company demonstrate the sort of refinements that have been introduced. Copyboard and camera were all borne by machine-ground load rails designed to give a minimum of sag and torque [40]. The movable components were aligned under load with an alignment telescope, and were checked with an autocollimator to ensure parallelism. The equipment was built either with a flat-bed or with overhead rails (Plate 34), and was mounted on ball bearings cushioned on rubber to avoid the effects of vibration. Rapid and reproducible setting up was effected by a patented system, in which 'V' plungers were located in 'V' blocks (Plate 35), to give settings reproducible to $\pm$ 0·0001 in ($2\frac{1}{2}$ μ). Copyboard, lenses and photographic plates were all located by three-point jigs, and a step-and-repeat movement was constructed from ground and polished cast-jig-plate material. When the masks had finally been produced, they were located during the photofabrication process by the same edges and corners located during photographic reduction.

FIELD SIZE AND MULTIPLE-MASK PRODUCTION

For economic production and quality control, the masks must cover an adequate area. Any production process would become prohibitively expensive if the unit area which could be processed at any one time was restricted to the one millimetre ($\frac{1}{25}$ in) field of a 16 mm microscope objective. This must be particularly true of vacuum-evaporation processes, in which the vacuum has to be broken at each stage for the insertion of the work-piece. The control of each evaporation stage to give electrical properties within the designed tolerances must be a critical operation, and the rejection rate tends to rise geometrically with the number of operations. Masks are therefore made with an area of a square inch or more filled with step-and-repeat images. For the fabrication of semiconductor diodes and transistors, this means that several hundred constituent images may be produced in a single mask (Plate 36). When such multiple masks are used to produce a great many devices simultaneously, the cost *per image* of applying and controlling the evaporation process is automatically reduced. In addition, one processing cycle gives a large number of units, and the results of any idiosyncrasies in an individual processing cycle will tend to be shown by all the units. Thus this method gives substantial batches of devices with closely matched electrical properties: an aim much desired by electronics manufacturers.

The methods used for producing multiple masks have been devised to comply with two stringent requirements. Image sharpness and dimensional precision of a high order has to be achieved over an unusually large field. In addition the registration requirements discussed in the previous section must be maintained for every single unit in a multiple mask, when production requires the use of a series of interlocking masks. Thus the two-dimensional array of images must have all the images placed with exactly the same orientation in a completely regular array, or any errors of orientation or positioning for any particular unit must be manifested by every member of a set of masks.

The precision required is indicated by a numerical example given by Payne [37] for the fabrication of a transistor. He considered an emitter mask giving 0·001 in (25 μ) wide emitters on which were to be placed 0·0006 in (15 μ) wide contacts. The clearance was thus only $\pm$ 0·0002 in ($\pm$5 μ), and the distance between images nominally 1 in apart had to be between 1·0002 in and 0·9998 in. Outside these limits, some of the contact metal would have been deposited on the edge of the emitter and would have shorted it to the base of the transistor.

M

Two basic methods have been used for the production of many identical reduced copies of the same set of drawings. One employs the multiple pinhole or 'fly's-eye' concept, and the other produces the images by step and repeat exposures.

MULTIPLE PINHOLE AND FLY'S-EYE CAMERAS

The multiple pinhole or fly's-eye method depends on the use of a large illuminated original placed at a sufficient distance to ensure that the sharpness of the outermost images of the array is within tolerance, in spite of them being formed off the axes of their corresponding lenses or pinholes (see Fig. 48, p. 176). Murray and Maurer used as their multiple 'pinhole' an 85 line/inch cross-line photomechanical screen at 55 in (1·4 m) from an illuminated aperture [41]. This was placed 0·3 in (7·5 mm) in front of Kodalith film, so that each element of the screen acted as a pinhole to produce an image reduced 185 times. Although the aerial images produced in this way would have edges with soft intensity profiles, the development properties of a Lith-type emulsion (see p. 242) produced steep density profiles. In these circumstances, special care was needed to obtain a desired line width, and the authors noted that the method was unsuitable for production of images with small pointed areas. Better resolution was obtained by the fly's-eye lens developed by Rudge, Harding and Mutter [42]. A hard polished steel ball was used to make a series of indentations in a block of copper, which was then used as a mould to produce a number of convex spherical lenses on one surface of a thermoplastic 'Plexiglas' disc (Plate 37). The passage of stray light through the spaces between the lenses was blocked by an aperture plate made from blackened steel-shim stock 0·001 in (25 μ) thick. The disc was made of such a thickness that reduced images were produced at the back surface, when the lenticular surface faced an illuminated drawing at the required distance. In fact the block was a multiple 'Stanhope' lens (p. 3), and although the lenses were not corrected for spherical aberration, their short focal length and large aperture allowed an axial resolution of 800 lines/mm to be measured. The virtue of both multiple pinholes and fly's-eye cameras is that they ensure completely repeatable spacing of every image throughout any number of masks, even if some of the lenses in the array are displaced.

MULTIPLE IMAGES PRODUCED BY STEP-AND-REPEAT

Electronics manufacturers have applied the step-and-repeat method at the intermediate or final reduction stages. For intermediate reductions, graphic-arts equipment normally used for such tasks as the printing of images of postage stamps was used to make a multi-image transparency some 10–20 in (25–50 cm) square. The problem was then how to ensure that all the component images were satisfactorily resolved when the complete block was reduced to 1 in (25 mm) square with a single lens. Cameras, such as the Burke and James 'Yale' have been developed for this purpose,[1] and employ lenses of aperture around F/6 specially selected to show minimum loss of sharpness over a relatively large angular field [43]. The demand for special lenses suitable for this sort of task motivated the financial backing for the design of monochromatic objectives used at a fixed reduction ratio (pp. 110–14). The advantage of the method (as with the multiple pinhole) is that any desired mask can be made very quickly, and damaged masks can be rapidly replaced. So long as the camera construction is sufficiently precise, images on the new masks will have a register identical to that on the original, damaged masks.

As a variant of these methods, some users employ the pinhole method to produce a multiple-image intermediate transparency, which is subsequently reduced in the same way as the multiple step-and-repeat image. Since the angular resolution given by a pinhole of appropriate size is independent of the distance from the pinhole to the plate, no optical advantage is likely from this method. The greater dimensions of the image projected on the Lith-type plate, however, probably facilitate line-width control and graininess will be less obtrusive.

When the required sharpness and line-width control just cannot be met by lenses covering a one-inch field, the step-and-repeat process has been used at the final reduction with image formation by a microscope objective. This method gives an optical performance much closer to the limit of emulsion capability, but demands exceptional mechanical precision to meet the registration required.

T. C. Hellmers Jr and J. R. Nall (of the U.S. Army Materiel Command, Harry Diamond Laboratories) appear to have published the first account of a camera and optical bench specially constructed for this purpose [44]. At the object end were mounted intermediate transparencies which had been meticulously reduced from master drawings. The transparencies were firmly held over an aperture in a metal plate mounted on a slide, so that each could in turn be centred on the axis of the objective. The slide was mounted on a circular stage for orienting to one-tenth of a degree, and the whole assembly was carried by a toolmaker's micrometer stage giving movements controlled to 0·0001 in (2·5 μ) in the X and Y co-ordinates. Thus each component image could be very precisely located with respect to a graticule in the focusing microscope. The lamp-house was originally

---

[1] The same cameras can also be used for making more elaborate unit patterns which may cover an inch-square field.

cooled by a fan, but as this caused vibration it was replaced by water cooling.

At the image end of the optical bench, were rigidly mounted two microscopes. One formed the image, and the other was used for focusing and for checking the position of each transparency at the object end. The plate-holder had a milled surface perpendicular to the axis of the objective, and the extreme-resolution plates were held against this surface by three pins and spring pressure. The plate-holder was itself mounted on a second toolmaker's micrometer stage, equipped with large drums bearing circumferential pin-locating holes corresponding to 0·001 or 0·00025 in (25 or 6 μ) movements in the X and Y co-ordinates (Plate 38). This camera was used both for making complex masks, in which different images in register were printed on different parts of one mask, or for making series of inter-registering multiple-image masks, each bearing many images of one constituent of a complex structure (Plates 36 and 44).

This direct step-and-repeat projection of truly microphotographic images is practised widely by electronics manufacturers in the United States of America and in other countries. Commercially available equipment for this purpose has been developed, and the David W. Mann Co. (a division of the Geophysics Corporation of America) for example, offer a complete system of equipment for this purpose [45].

The master drawings, which always included two register marks, were first reduced 10 or 20 times on a precision camera. To ensure register of all images in a set, all the reduced transparencies were registered on 'master reticle frames'. For this purpose, the frames were mounted kinematically on the base board of the locating apparatus (Plate 39). The transparency was held in a vacuum chuck, and was moved by a micrometer until each of the register marks coincided with a cross-hair, when the slide of this instrument was moved to two extreme positions. When correctly positioned, the transparency was held by the chuck, until cement fixing it to the reticle frame had set. The kinematic mounting of the frames allowed them to be rapidly located on the final reduction apparatus with a reproducibility of 0·0001 in (2·5 μ). It was therefore possible to build a file of patterns, from any of which production of accurately registered masks could be commenced with minimum delay.

The mounted transparencies were finally used in the Mann Photo-repeater (Type 1080). This apparatus (Plate 40) employed a motor driven spacing stage, and the position of this stage was continuously monitored by a Mann Two-Co-ordinate Precision Screw Comparator (Type 829C). The main lead screw of the comparator was connected to an optical shaft encoder, which generated an electrical pulse for each 0·0005 in (12 μ) of linear motion on the X axis. By means of pre-set counters, which determined the number of images (up to 99) per line and the size of the spaces between the images, appropriate pulses were selected to trigger a xenon electronic flash tube.

After setting the number and spacing of the exposures per line on the control unit, the operator adjusted X and Y slides to the required start positions. Up to 15 seconds was stated to be needed for each slide adjustment. A press on a button then started the travel along the X axis, and when the plate reached each appropriate position, the pulse triggered the flash tube without interrupting steady motion of the plate. Since the plate was traversed at 0·058 in (1·45 mm) per second, the exposure duration of 3×10^{-6} second corresponded to the negligible plate shift of one-fifth of a micro-inch (0·005 μ). 27 seconds was required for the plate carriage to traverse $1\frac{1}{2}$ in (38 mm) during which a line of up to 99 precisely spaced images could be recorded on the extreme-resolution plate. A further 27 seconds was required to return the carriage to the start position, after which the operator reset the X and Y slides for the next line. Thus about $1\frac{1}{2}$ minutes overall was required for each line, and about 30 minutes should be needed to produce a 20-line mask with 400 or more images. During tests, the Mann Company successfully recorded bars 0·0003 $\times$ 0·0001 in (7·5 $\times$ 2·5 μ) separated by 0·0001 in, and an overall positional repeatability of 0·00004 in (1 μ) is claimed for this equipment.

Further refinements have been incorporated in the Mann Type 1480 series of photorepeaters, including larger image fields, 1, 4 or 6 barrels, optional automatic operation and tape-controlled programmes, and positional precision to 0·00001 in (0·25 μ) [71].

If the quantity of masks required for any project does not seem to justify the capital outlay of equipment such as the Mann Photo-repeater (over \$16,000 for the photorepeater alone), multiple-image masks can be made by simpler apparatus costing much less. For example, W. Watson and Sons Ltd have developed a manually advanced step-and-repeat camera. The central feature of this equipment is a mechanical stage carrying the sensitive plate on top, and a glass plate with a semi-transparent durable metal film ruled with a grid of very fine lines underneath (Plate 41). This grid is viewed with an inverted microscope, and the stage is manually advanced to centre cross-hairs successively on each intersection of the grid lines. The newly designed mechanical stage was made so that back-lash was automatically taken up, and so that the grid could be set smoothly and rapidly to the exact position required for each exposure. Settings reproducible to $\pm$ 1 μ (0·00004 in) were stated to be readily obtained.

Because the ruled metal film is not opaque, the inverted microscope could also be used to inspect the focal plane, and hence to check focus and to align and orientate the master negatives. An interesting feature of this equipment was that it could be supplied with objectives of focal length 25 mm, 16 mm or 8 mm, each shrouded with a pneumatic gauge. The pressure developed in the gauge was indicated by a commercial manometer incorporating its own pressure stabilizer (p. 150).

It is obvious that the use of multi-image cameras with manual advancement implies the acceptance of higher labour costs to avoid the greater capital outlay of automatic equipment. A crucial question in the acceptability of the simpler equipment is therefore the speed and ease of making precise settings on the cross lines. Examination of this instrument convinced this sceptical author that 5 seconds was ample time for setting on the next intersection in a horizontal row. With practice, setting times of a second or two seemed practicable, because of the smooth and positive action of the special mechanical stage. The makers suggest that this equipment is particularly suitable for research and development, where flexibility rather than automatic output is required.

Step-and-repeat microphotographic cameras have also been developed for their own use by individual electronics manufacturers, and have employed a variety of means for securing the required precision of advancement and registration. Reliance on micrometer lead-screws alone has been decried, because of loss of accuracy from wear. Control of position by moiré-fringe gratings (p. 298) has been stated to be effective, but has required precautions to avoid false counts induced by triggering of the flash tube used for exposing. Fine-ground metal wedges have also been employed for reproducible generation of the small displacements. The Marconi–Slee Automatic Step and Repeat Camera employed stepped gauges (made from high-speed steel or tungsten carbine) to control the stepping intervals.

A photorepeater developed by the Ferranti Co. for their own use demonstrated some interesting features [46]. This comprised a battery of nine complete units (Fig. 101), each projecting greatly reduced images upwards on the underside of plates placed face-down on apertures in a large heavy table. This table was raised 7 μ (0·0003 in) into the focal plane by air bearings, and air bearings were also used to ensure very accurate horizontal and cross motions and to minimize rotation of the table. The cross motion of the table was continuously driven, and a moiré-fringe system generating impulses for every 0·0001 in (2·5 μ) movement (p. 298) actuated the control system for triggering the flash lamps. Since the same movements of the table were used to effect step-and-repeat movements on plates used to form nine separate masks of a set, any errors of movement should be practically constant for all the masks in each set with a consequent advantage in registration of the successive printings. Furthermore, the multiple unit speeded production, so that a set of 9 masks, each with many hundreds of images could be exposed in 30 minutes.

There are clear indications that further development of photo-repeaters to meet the increasingly stringent demands of design engineers will continue. For example, Maple [71] foretells the application of advanced techniques for improving the accuracy of stepping systems, and mentions the use of a photovoltaic sensing device, and an interferometric system using laser light for monitoring stepping

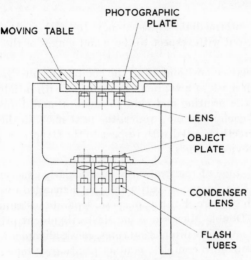

STEP & REPEAT CAMERA

Fig. 101 *Cross-section of Ferranti Multiple-Mask Camera*

By simultaneously exposing nine photographic plates, each rigidly mounted on moving table, and with image from appropriate object plate projected on it by its own projection system, registration discrepancies between different masks of a set are avoided.

Courtesy of R. Freestone and Ferranti Ltd.

intervals. Positional precision of 0·00001 in (0·25 μ) has been claimed (see also p. 339), and was considered adequate for the production of devices with line widths down to 0·00002 in (0·5 μ). Two manufacturers had developed multi-barrel photorepeaters, and high-intensity short-wavelength projection systems are being constructed for direct reduction of images on layers of photoresist with the brief unit exposure times required for the economic operation of a photorepeater.

Two other features of Maple's paper merit attention. He gave a detailed analysis of factors limiting the performance of micro-electronic masks, including the influence of humidity and temperature on the dimensional accuracy of 'cut-and-strip' plastic drafting materials. A useful Appendix provided a directory of suppliers of the many specialized instruments and products used in the manufacture of microelectronic masks.

To recapitulate what has already been written, registration in the production of complex devices on silicon wafers involves precautions at three stages:

(1) Each intermediate transparency (reticle) must be correctly orientated with respect to the x and y axes of the multi-image masks.

(2) The relative positions of all the component hundreds of images in each mask of a set must be identical within tight tolerances.

(3) After the printing and photomechanical and diffusion processing of each stage on a wafer, the next mask in the series must be correctly located with respect to the structures produced by the previous stages.

The third stage of registration is a particularly exacting task, since registration to a micron or better may be demanded over an area of a square inch or more. For this purpose, separate instruments such as the Watson Double Microscope for Mask Alignment [47] have been used. To achieve high production rates, mask alignment microscopes have been built into complete contact-printing systems, such as the Kulicke and Soffa Model 682 Mask Alignment System [48].

It has been noted that this problem of mask alignment is likely to become especially severe when devices are made with micron or submicron line widths. High numerical-aperture objectives will then be needed to observe alignment, and their depth of focus is so small that the mask and wafer surfaces can only be very few microns apart [33]. Achieving registration in these circumstances without scratching mask or wafer surfaces could be quite a problem.

Ables noted that microscopic observation of mask alignment is also difficult when masks with large opaque areas have to be registered within fine limits [49]. He eased this problem by bleaching the developed silver image with the mercuric-bromide intensifier already described (p. 86), and redeveloping in a sodium sulphite solution. The resultant images had excellent resolution, little graininess at the edge of the image and a red colour having much higher effective density for printing on photoresist than for visual observation. Thus registration through the opaque areas of the mask could be readily observed even when more than adequate density for photoresist printing was present. A further contribution to the registration of very fine images has been to reproduce two or more unit-stage patterns in the same reticle image [50]. Thus the relative positions of the several unit-stage patterns are completely fixed when producing the multiple-image mask. The different areas of the resultant composite masks are then used for the different stages of fabrication. In this method, some efficiency in usage of the wafer and mask areas is sacrificed for elimination of residual registration errors.

CHROMIUM-ON-GLASS MASKS

As already noted (p. 217), the physical handling involved in the contact printing of minute photographic images subjects the emulsion layer of the master negative to very damaging treatment. In addition to the scratches that are in any case likely to occur (Plate 19), fragments of colloid from the photoresist stencils tend to transfer to the emulsion surface, and cannot be cleaned off without damage. As a solution to this problem, several authors have described the use of masks made by photoetching thin vacuum-evaporated chromium layers on glass [9] [51]. The original masks produced on a photorepeater were then only used for the production of working masters by printing on a photosensitive resist layer on a chromium coated plate. The resultant chromium-on-glass masks showed little loss of sharpness, were more resistant to scratches and could be chemically cleaned without harm.

The commercial production of such plates already pre-sensitized has been undertaken by the Eastman Kodak Co [52]. These consisted of selected glass blanks coated successively with a chromium layer, a thin layer of photosensitive resist and a water-soluble protective colloid layer. Each plate is packed in clean conditions in its own plastic box, in which the resultant masks can be stored after the plates have been exposed and processed to produce masks. Just before use, the protective colloid layer is washed away, taking with it any debris which might have reached the surface in spite of all precautions. In the preparation of these plates, particular attention was given to the elimination of pinholes.

PRODUCTION OF SEMICONDUCTOR DEVICES FROM SILICON WAFERS

As has already been made clear, these sections do not claim to be a guide to microelectronics manufacturing processes. Nevertheless, more detailed consideration of a few specific examples seemed necessary to demonstrate how these methods have been reduced to practice. It appears that silicon is now rapidly replacing germanium as the basic substrate, and processing of silicon wafers strikingly demonstrates the ingenuity that has already been applied. With such a rapidly developing technology, however, it is possible that these processes may have been further modified by the time these pages are read.

CHEMICAL BASIS OF DIFFUSION INTO SILICON

It has been found that the electrical properties of semi-conductors are modified by very small amounts of impurity. The very purest silicon that can be produced by conventional chemical procedures was therefore further purified by the technique of 'zone refining'. From the purified material, single crystals of the required crystallographic orientation were grown by zone refining or by controlled withdrawal from a crucible. The crystals, which were rather rough rods of about 1 in (2·5 cm) diameter, were cut in slices around 0·008 (200 μ) thick by a diamond impregnated saw. The slices were then polished and lapped, and a polishing etchant was sometimes applied to give a 'work-free' surface. To obtain the required electrical properties, final epitaxial vapour deposition of a surface layer of silicon a few microns thick has been used. For example, in the production of transistors, an epitaxial layer of good electrical properties might be mounted on a substrate of advantageously low resistivity and good thermal properties. Thus the silicon wafer, which is the raw material for microelectronics manufacture, is itself the end-product of an intricate and expensive series of processes. Before any photo-fabrication processes have been applied, 1-inch diameter silicon wafers are said to cost around £1 sterling.

The fabrication of devices on silicon wafers has been devised around the chemical properties of silicon and silicon dioxide. When silicon was heated to temperatures of 800° C or above in an atmosphere containing the vapour of doping elements or compounds, dopant atoms diffused into the silicon lattice and modified its electrical properties [53]. Pentavalent atoms such as phosphorus produced a higher electron density than that of the tetravalent silicon, with a resultant increased conductivity and electron-donating tendency. The conductivity resulted from movement of the negatively charged (electron) charge carriers, and this form of silicon is called 'n-type'. The opposite chemical mechanism occurred with trivalent dopants such as boron. The dopant atoms then caused local electron deficiencies (positive holes), whose movement as positive charge carriers also increased the conductivity. From the sign of its charge carriers, this form of silicon was called 'p-type'. Junctions producing rectifying and other properties required for 'components' including diodes and transistors can be produced by alternate diffusion of p-type and n-type dopants into the same substrate.

The scope of this method was severely limited so long as the whole surface of the wafer was exposed uniformly to a diffusion process. An adherent stencil was needed to restrict the diffused material to selected parts of the surface, but the material of the stencil had to resist the high temperatures required for doping.

This problem was solved by the use of thin films of silicon dioxide formed by controlled oxidation of the silicon surface. When heated in atmospheres of oxygen or water vapour, 'tarnishing' reactions caused a silicon-dioxide film to grow, and its thickness increased in proportion to the square root of the reaction time [1(c)]. The thickness formed could be monitored by observation of interference colours. Heating for one hour to 1,200° C in atmospheres of oxygen or water vapour gave films 0·2 μ (0·000008 in) and 0·9 μ (0·000036 in) thick respectively. Silicon dioxide (silica) withstands high temperatures, and films up to 2 μ (0·00008 in) thick could be cooled and re-heated to doping temperatures without cracking due to differential expansion. Such tarnished layers were quite pinhole free, and only very thin layers were needed to form a barrier against phosphorus and boron. 0·3 μ (0·000012 in) was needed to mask against high-concentration phosphorus diffusion for one hour at 1,000° C. Stencils could be formed from these silicon-dioxide layers by etching through a photoresist stencil with a hydrofluoric acid solution which does not attack the underlying silicon. When dopants were diffused through the silicon-dioxide stencils, the depth of penetration of the dopant below the silicon surface could equal or exceed the thickness of the silicon-dioxide layer. In such cases, sideways penetration of the dopant probably limits the resolution as much as undercutting during etching of the silicon dioxide.

Another valuable feature of this method is that a further layer of silicon dioxide can be readily grown with little interference from the previous doping operation. Thus the 'windows' opened by photo-etching through the first formed stencils can be closed by growth of the desired depth of silicon dioxide, and further (usually smaller) windows can be cut by forming a second registered stencil from a second photoresist layer and etching with hydrofluoric acid again (Fig. 102). During the exposure of the second (or subsequent) photoresist layers, the mask has to be registered on the wafers so that the images are correctly positioned with respect to images produced by previous operations. According to the required structural complexity the same cycle of operations has been applied repeatedly. Flexibility in these processes was obtained by using both diffusion and vacuum evaporation processes on the same substrate. For example, inter-connections between different areas on a silicon wafer have been made by evaporating aluminium, and etching the layer through a photo-resist stencil. On areas still covered by silicon dioxide, the aluminium stripes so formed are insulated from the silicon wafer. Both evaporation and diffusion have also been applied to treatments with a single substance. For instance, gold doping of silicon has been effected

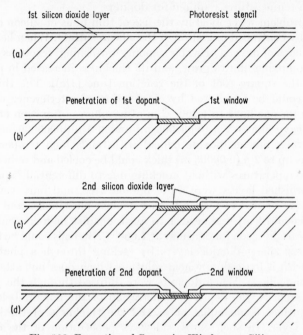

Fig. 102 *Formation of Successive Windows on Silicon*

(a) Silicon dioxide layer bearing photoresist stencil, (b) First diffusion after etching of silicon dioxide, (c) closing of first window by second oxidation process, (d) second diffusion after formation of another window by etching through second photoresist stencil.

by evaporating a gold layer first, and subsequent heating of the wafers allowed gold atoms to diffuse into the silicon crystal lattice.

These manufacturing processes may be exceedingly complex. A case has been quoted in which a semi-conductor integrated circuit required five indexed masking operations, two metal-film evaporations and nine high temperature furnace operations. In production each of these major stages are broken down into steps. For instance, each masking stage involves cleaning, coating, exposing, developing, etching and stripping off the resist. After such a breakdown, the total number of process steps was seen to be well over one hundred.

EXAMPLES OF STRUCTURES PRODUCED ON SILICON WAFERS

SILICON PLANAR TRANSISTORS

Hellmers and Nall illustrated the use of microphotographic masks for the production of germanium diodes and silicon planar transistors [44]. The latter were produced by the following steps.

(1) The wafers were coated with photoresist, on which was printed images forming a stencil with circular apertures of diameter

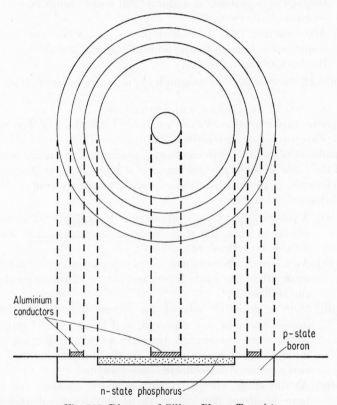

Fig. 103 *Diagram of Silicon Planar Transistor*
Courtesy of T. C. Hellmers, Jr. and U.S. Army Materiel Command. Harry Diamond Laboratories.

0·015 in (375 μ). After etching through the silicon-dioxide layer, boron was diffused to form p-state collector-base junctions of the same diameter (Fig. 103).

(2) After oxidizing to re-seal the silicon surface, another photo-resist layer was applied, and used to form circles of 0·009 in

(225 μ) diameter concentric to the first images. After etching of the silicon dioxide, phosphorus was diffused to form n-state emitters.

(3) After a further oxidation, a third photoresist layer was applied. On this was printed a composite image consisting of a circle of diameter 0·0017 in (43 μ) in the centre of the emitter, and an annular ring of external and internal diameters 0·013 and 0·011 in (325 and 275 μ) respectively on the outer zone of the collector-base junction. The silicon dioxide was again etched through this pattern, and aluminium was vacuum evaporated to form ohmic contacts.

(4) After cutting into individual pieces, contacts were thermo-compression bonded to the aluminium spot and circle, and to the back of the transistor.

Plate 42 shows a photomicrograph of the wafer before cutting.

DOUBLE-DIFFUSED MESA TRANSISTORS

For photographic readers, Payne's article 'Technology of Transistor Mask Fabrication' is particularly informative [37]. In addition to descriptions of mask requirements and production methods, he outlined the masking steps for making several types of silicon transistor. For example, n–p–n double-diffused mesa transistors were made by the following operations.

(i) A p-type dopant was diffused over the entire area of n-type silicon to form the collector-base junction, and a silicon-dioxide layer was grown.

(ii) As a result of formation of photoresist stencils, windows were cut in the oxide layer, and n-type diffusion produced the emitter.

(iii) With a selective solvent for silicon dioxide, the entire protective layer was removed, and three parallel strips of metal were evaporated through a metal-foil mask. The middle strip formed a contact on the emitter, and the outer two conducted the collector-base junction.

(iv) At this stage, all the transistors had a common collector-base junction. To isolate them and form collector-base junctions of the correct size, the entire structures were covered with resists evaporated through a foil mask. The wafers were then etched with a mixture of acetic, nitric and hydrofluoric acids right through the p-type surface layer (Fig. 104).

Thus the transistors remained on raised plateaus of p-type silicon on the n-type substrate. When this type of isolation is employed, the results are known as *mesa* transistors.

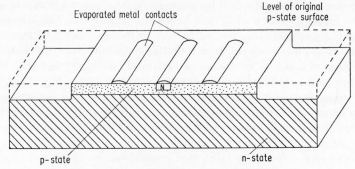

Fig. 104 *Use of Mesa Etch to isolate Transistor*

With the transistor structure protected by a resist stencil, the silicon was etched right through the *p*-state layer, giving electrically isolated islands.

After P. D. Payne and *Semiconductor Products.*

ALLOYED-DIFFUSED MESA TRANSISTORS

p–n–p alloyed-diffused mesa transistors were made by a modified procedure.

(i) *p*-type silicon was submitted to an overall *n*-type diffusion to form the collector-base junction, but no oxide film was grown.

(ii) The wafer was positioned underneath a three-mask assembly. The lowest component was a molybdenum spacer mask 0·002–0·003 in (50–75 μ) thick with etched clearance holes. In register on this was placed the defining mask made from photoformed nickel 0·001 in (25 μ) thick. The assembly was completed by a molybdenum clamping mask 0·008 in (200 μ) thick also with etched clearance holes.

The assembly was positioned in a vacuum evaporation system, and the wafer was heated. Two different metals were then evaporated from separate sources, which were placed so that side-by-side deposits of the two metals would be produced through each slot in the defining mask (Fig. 99). One of the metals diffused into the silicon lattice and acted as a dopant forming the emitter junction and contact. The other metal formed the base contact.

(iii) Isolation of the transistors was completed by a mesa etch as in the previous example.

SEMICONDUCTOR INTEGRATED CIRCUITS

So far, we have only considered the production of single components, which have to be mounted and interconnected with other components to produce circuits with useful functions. With this approach, the usefulness of size reduction by photographic techniques was realized to be limited. With unit devices beneath a certain size, the difficulty of making connections tended to raise rejection rates and increase costs. It has also been considered that mechanically made connections constituted points of weakness, and adversely affected reliability. For such reasons, electronics engineers considered the possibility of applying microphotographic methods to the production and interconnection of many separate components on a single wafer. Even if this approach was only applied to the production of units such as amplifiers or a 'gate' for digital computers giving a single function, the number of mechanically fabricated connections would be drastically reduced.

For success in this enterprise, it was desirable that all the structures needed to produce the required variety of individual circuit elements should be produced by a series of mutually compatible processes on a single wafer. In fact, the production processes evolved for silicon wafers were designed with this in mind, and the properties of the silicon-dioxide layer proved invaluable for this purpose. Many manufacturers' Research Departments have worked on this approach, and it is not the purpose of this section to give any indication of preference for one or another. One example has been chosen because the available photographs so graphically illustrated the scope of this work.

The Texas Instruments 'Solid Circuit' semiconductor networks start with a p-type silicon substrate [54]. After growth of a silicon-dioxide layer and opening of windows through a photoresist stencil, n-type diffusion was applied. From Plate 43 it can be seen that no less than forty areas (some connected by a thin stripe) were applied to a single circuit, and no less than forty complete circuits were made on a single wafer (Plate 44). After re-growing of the oxide film and opening of a further set of windows through stencils formed from a second registered mask, p-type diffusion was applied on at least twenty-nine separate areas for each circuit (Plate 45). A further cycle of operations with a third mask was used to give a final n^+–type diffusion,[1] which produced at least forty-eight doped areas on each circuit (Plate 46).

These photographs show that different structures were produced by the omission of one or other of the dopants, and by the positioning of the patches. In some areas the masks caused the final n^+–type diffusion to occur in an area by the side of or within the doped area produced by the preceding p-type diffusion. Fig. 105 demonstrates more clearly how the different circuit functions were generated by the diffusion programme controlled by the masks.

[1] The description n^+-type is applied to areas very heavily doped with pentavalent atoms to give increased conductivity.

The steps so far described produced a number of components, and their integration into a functioning circuit was effected by vacuum evaporation of a pattern of aluminium lines over the insulating silicon-dioxide layer. Contact with the underlying silicon was made through windows in the oxide layer (Fig. 105). The completed circuit networks were separated by scribing into pieces about 0·2 × 0·07 in (5 × 1·75 mm) which were mounted in a package with a low-melting-point

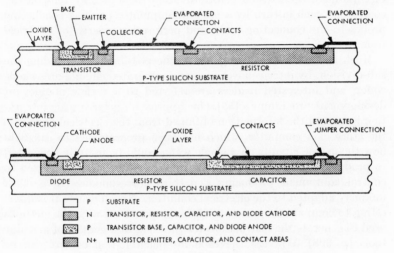

Fig. 105 *Diagrammatic Cross Section of Silicon Wafer*
Showing diffusions used to form each circuit function and method of connection.
Courtesy of P. Shaw and Texas Instrument Co.

glass. The appropriate parts of the network were connected to leads by 0·001 in (25 μ) diameter gold wires bonded by thermo-compression (Plate 47), and the final articles were completed by welding or soldering of a lid in an inert, clean and dry atmosphere.

The precision required in the masking operations can be appreciated by studying Plate 46. The structures could only have been produced by precisely sized masks most accurately registered. In particular, the concentric rectangular structures (denoted by arrows) demanded especially accurate positioning to ensure the necessary isolation of the component areas. It should be realized that this accuracy had to be maintained not only for all the structures in each single circuit, but for all the forty circuits on the wafer. Those outside the electronics industry must feel that results such as this represent a literally marvellous performance!

LARGE SCALE INTEGRATION

Much extra labour and equipment has obviously had to be deployed for the operations of dividing wafers into chips bearing individual integrated circuits, and then connecting these into larger sub-systems. These additional manipulations are also potentially unfavourable to reliability and high-frequency operation, but were employed so that only satisfactorily functioning circuits could be selected and applied. Circuits have been tested before dividing the wafer by temporarily connecting each in turn by a micro-manipulator pressing conducting probes to the connecting pads, and performing a series of electrical tests.

Much attention has been given to the possibility of avoiding the sub-division, by inter-connecting many integrated circuits on a single wafer, and interested readers are referred to a review of relevant development programmes [55]. One approach for large scale integration is to feed the information obtained from the electrical tests into the store of a computer, which has been programmed to calculate how the usable circuits on a single wafer could be usefully connected to produce a large sub-system. Instructions were then generated to control equipment producing a pattern corresponding to a mask uniquely adapted to the electrical condition of each wafer. It is interesting to compare the concepts of these operations with the methods used to generate the instructions for the computer control of machine tools (p. 298). Whereas the tape for machine-tool control can be used for repetitive production of parts, the random occurrence of defects on a wafer requires production of a new pattern for each wafer.

In the Texas Instrument 'Discretionary Wiring' system, the physical agency used for the generation of the patterns was a cathode-ray tube, on which the required pattern was drawn by the electron beam [56]. Optical reduction on film was stated to give masks with line widths and spaces down to 0·001 in (25 μ). The three-dimensional inter-connecting structures produced from these masks were, in themselves, quite complex structures involving etching of two metallized layers and two insulating layers of radio-frequency sputtered quartz. For a similar purpose, the Standard Telecommunication Laboratories have employed a system analogous to Thermal Recording by Laser (p. 58) [57]. The light from a helium-neon laser was focused to a small spot on the focal plane occupied by the work-piece held in a tape-controlled micropositioner. The tape controlled both on-off switching of the laser beam and the movements in the X and Y axes. Three methods had been examined for obtaining the required inter-connecting structures on the wafer. The energy from the laser beam was used to evaporate metal from a coated plate in contact with the slice. The evaporated metal condensed on the wafer to form lines with widths down to 0·001 in (25 μ). In a second method, the wafer was coated with a thin light-absorbing layer such as graphite, in which the pattern was cut by the laser beam. Aluminium was then deposited and lifted from the unwanted areas by chemical etching of the underlying mask. These two methods were in the development stage, and the most accessible procedure was the production of a printing mask by the beam cutting the pattern in a chromium layer on the glass. The required structures were then produced by photo-resist methods. In this work, the authors concentrated their attention on the use of this method for producing inter-connecting patterns, since the methods appeared to have little or no advantage for the production of regular patterned processing masks for semiconductor manufacture.

APPLICATION OF MICROELECTRONIC DEVICES

From what has already been written, it is obvious that immense sums must have been spent in evolving the elaborate production techniques used in microelectronics. This, by itself, is evidence of the importance of the subject, but what appears to have been the aims of the exercise? Historically, one of the first incentives seems to have been the reduction of size and weight for military devices and airborne electronic equipment which was rapidly increasing in complexity.

In relatively few years, microphotographic production methods succeeded in producing components so small that their connection to the rest of the circuit became increasingly expensive and difficult. Operators had to work with a micro-manipulator and binocular microscope, and techniques such as thermo-compression bonding had to be evolved. It was then realized that size-reduction should be regarded as a means to various ends, rather than an end in itself. From the processes first developed for weight reduction, it was seen that other advantages might accrue. The reduced weight of material in products photo-fabricated with step-and-repeat masks and automated handling offered ultimate promise of reduced cost. For example, Dean [58] stated 'it was important to put as much circuitry on a single chip as possible, since, with decreasing costs, the state has now been reached in which the cost of connection and interconnection is greater than that of producing the silicon chip'.

The semiconductor diodes and transistors were less mechanically vulnerable and more durable than thermionic valves, and their power consumption and heat dissipation were much less. In high-speed logic circuits, signal-propagation delays became a limiting factor, and miniaturization to shorten the propagation paths became a necessity.

With the growing complexity of electronic equipment, in which components were counted in their thousands rather than in dozens, achievement of improved reliability became a dominant aim (see, for example, reference [54]. A statistical probability of failure which was quite acceptable for components used in a domestic radio receiver would be quite intolerably high for computer and satellite applications. To ensure the satisfactory operation of an unmanned satellite has been said to be the equivalent of operating 60,000 television sets for a year without maintenance and without a single failure. Greater reliability was also demanded because the reduced size of circuits made repair increasingly difficult and expensive. As already noted, use of photo-fabrication methods rather than soldering for making a large proportion of inter-connections is considered a useful step to improved reliability.

According to the readiness of users to employ microelectronic devices, one can grade three broad groups of applications.

The first group comprises applications in which cost was a secondary consideration. The projects have usually been concerned with national defence and/or prestige. Obvious examples are guided missiles, weapon systems, nuclear research and space exploration. In this type of work the disadvantage of being without a particular device often seemed to outweigh a cost which frequently overran original estimates.

The next group comprises devices intended for civilian applications such as air-liner navigation, computer applications and automation systems. Cost is now a major consideration, but reliability and other advantages of microelectronic techniques seemed to justify construction costs still too high for domestic users.

The third group is concerned with domestic appliances, and in particular television and radio receivers. At first, plenty of photographically produced printed circuits (wiring) was being used, but the economic reasons for miniaturization were not so pressing. It has been suggested that microelectronic techniques will only be fully used for domestic appliances when the hoped-for cost reductions are finally achieved. Even here, however, there are special applications for which size and weight reduction are most important. Examples are pills carrying a transmitter for studying digestive disturbances, and a complete amplifier and battery for a hearing aid which weighed only one-quarter of an ounce (7 grams).

At short notice, however, future developments may make this picture completely out of date.

LIMITS OF OPTICAL METHODS FOR MASK PRODUCTION

Two major limitations of microelectronic production based on optical methods for mask production can be discerned. Firstly the size of field that can be covered with a single coherent image and with line width controlled to a micron or so is very limited. It is true that producers of graticules and binary-coded scales have produced large coherent images by effectively step-and-repeating with a dividing engine, but the method is relatively slow, expensive and inflexible. An alternative possibility is to project a small unit dot or rectangle on the emulsion surface, and generate the pattern by programmed movements of the plate. The use of this method for generating long narrow slits was described on p. 247. Feasibility studies on the production of microelectronic masks have also been published [59]. This approach has obviously much in common with procedures developed for large scale integration (p. 352).

The second limitation is that diffraction of light prevents effective control of line width when the dimensions approach the wavelength of light (p. 243). This applies both at the photographic stage of reducing the final mask image, and at the photomechanical stage of producing some sort of stencil from this. The most radical answer to this problem has been the application of electron-beam methods. By using focusing techniques of the type developed for electron microscopy or electron-microprobe analysis, electron beams of high power density and only a few hundred Ångstroms in diameter have been produced. So long as the accelerating voltage is not too high, the electrons will only have a very small range in the material they hit, and the resultant physical or chemical changes may be confined to narrow areas of the specimen surface.

In fact, a wide variety of methods have been investigated for the application of this concept of electron-beam technology to the shaping of materials. Crawford [60] distinguished between 'thermal' and 'nonthermal' processes. In thermal processes, electron beams having power densities up to 10^9 watts/cm^2 were directed on the work-piece to produce a very rapid and localized heating with resultant volatilization of material. The electron-beam milling machines developed under the direction of K. H. Steigerwald at Carl Zeiss A. G. have been used for such purposes as the fabrication of ferrite memory core elements, the dicing of semiconductor wafers, and the production of spinnerets. E. Bas used similar methods for the drilling of rubies, and produced 30 μ (0·0012 in) diameter holes right through a ruby 400 μ (0·016 in) thick. More pertinent for the production of microelectronic masks were Nixon's experiments on the machining of thin aluminium layers on glass [61].

In the non-thermal processes, the energy of the electron beam was used to initiate chemical reactions. Reactions which have been investigated were:

(i) the decomposition of organo-metallic vapours such as tetraethyl-lead or tetramethyl-tin,

(ii) catalysis of the oxidation of diamond at such a low temperature that no breakdown of the unetched parts occurred.

(iii) the decomposition and carbonizing of a cellulose nitrate layer,

(iv) polymerization of such compounds as tetraethoxy-silane adsorbed from the vapour state as a monolayer on the bombarded substrate.

With some of these reactions, images have been produced by a variety of methods. Samples have been exposed to a relatively wide beam behind a previously formed mask, which really constituted contact printing by an electron beam. Presumably, the fact that an electron beam would suffer less divergence by diffraction than a light beam, means that the outline of the mask could be more faithfully reproduced. Images have also been made by scanning methods, using electronic beam deflection or precisely controlled movements of the sample. Both scanning methods have been used successively in the forming of a pattern on a single substrate. By the scanning method, Möllenstedt and Speidel [62] produced patterns on collodion films which after shadowing showed a scale of just over a micron (0·00004 in) length divided into ten parts by lines about 0·03 μ (just over a millionth of an inch!) wide (Plate 48).

One of the most interesting developments has been Buck and Shoulder's application of the polymerization of silicon compounds to produce resists for subsequent vapour etching of vacuum deposited metal layers [63] (p. 58). In this work, the objective lens of an electron microscope was used to produce reduced images of the pattern of electrons emitted by a photocathode. The application of such processes to the production of micro-circuitry for cryatrons has been discussed by Wells [64], and it seems that controllable production of lines of width 0·3 μ or 0·1 μ (0·000012 to 0·000004 in) can be achieved.

There is no doubt that these electron-beam techniques are inherently capable of producing information-packing densities much higher than can be achieved with light optics. It has even been suggested that they should be used for document copying. Because such very high densities can be achieved, there is a temptation to suggest that the entire group of light-optical methods will become obsolete. Many considerations point the other way. With electron-beam methods, the input of even the simplest unit of information requires a more elaborate and expensive equipment than is needed with light optics. The area of coherent image that can be 'exposed' in one operation will probably be even less than with optical microscope objectives, and an effective process analogous to contact printing from a photographic negative would be difficult to devise. Because of the poor penetrating power of an electron beam, the base for the master negative for 'electron printing' would have to be only a fraction of a micron thick (perhaps $0 \cdot 1$ μ (4 micro-inches) or less). Handling and achieving satisfactory contact and flatness with such a master negative could be a formidable problem.

If the recorded information is to be displayed in a visual form, the processed work-piece would have to be read by an electron microscope: a daunting thought for librarians. Perhaps, most important of all, is the practical experience that has been gained in such fields as graticule production and commercial document microfilming. With each successive stage in the reduction of the size of the images there tended to be introduced extra difficulties. The price of recording and reading devices tended to rise, contamination became an increasingly serious problem, and the need for ever tighter control caused working tolerances to diminish to vanishing point. For such reasons, the author suggested that microfilm users are likely to get the most satisfaction by using the largest images consistent with the designed aim of their process (p. 379). It therefore seems likely that electron-beam methods will supplement rather than replace optical techniques. In the majority of applications, light optics are still likely to provide as great a degree of miniaturization as can be conveniently handled. For very special purposes, such as complete computers operating in super-conductivity conditions in liquid helium (cryatrons), the extra reduction achievable by electron optics can be expected to prove invaluable.

REFERENCES

[1] (a) Eisler, P., *Technology of Printed Circuits*, Heywood and Co. Ltd (London, 1959).

(b) Horsey, E. F. (ed.), *Proceedings of Symposium on Microminiaturization of Electronic Assemblies* (Diamond Ordnance Fuze Laboratories, 1958), Hayden Book, Co. (New York, 1960).

(c) Keonjian, E. (ed.), *Microelectronics, Theory, Design and Fabrication*, McGraw-Hill Book Co. (New York, 1963).

(d) Schlabach, T. D. and Rider, D. K., *Printed and Integrated Circuitry. Materials and Processes*, McGraw-Hill Book Co. (New York, 1963).

(e) *Photosensitive Resists for Industry*, Eastman Kodak Industrial Data Book, P-7. First Issued 1962, reissued when revisions required.

Contains many references, including preparation of metals for photo-etching.

(f) *An Introduction to Photofabrication using Kodak Photosensitive Resists*, Eastman Kodak Publication No. P-79 (Rochester, New York, 1966).

[2] Gresham, D. C., 'The Manufacture of Fine Metal Diaphragms having very accurate Perforations', *Process Engravers Monthly*, 58, 42, 1951 (see also reference [25]).

[3] Loening, E. E. and Gresham, D. C., 'The Manufacture of Fine Metal Grids by a Photomechanical Process', *Process Engravers Monthly*, 57, 359, 1950.

[4] Daeschner, H. W., Seibert, E. E. and Peters, E. D., 'Application of Electroformed Precision Micromesh Sieves to the Determination of Particle Size Distribution', *Symposium on Particle Size Measurement*, American Society for Testing Materials (Philadelphia 1954), p. 26.

[5] Kodak Ltd, *Photosensitive Resist Techniques*, Industrial/Professional Sales Div. Technical Publication 224, 1965.

[6] Van Deusen, W. P., 'Production of Printed Circuits: The Photosensitive Resist Method', *Plating*, 45, 42, February, 1958.

[7] Barditch, I. F., 'Effect of Photo-resist Adhesion on Semi-Conductor Processing', *Electro-technology*, 70 (1), 12, 1962.

[8] Taylor, C. J., 'Electrophoresis-treated Kodak Metal-Etch Resist and Dipropyl Carbonate', in *Kodak Seminar on Microminiaturization*, Eastman Kodak Co. (Rochester, New York, 1966). Pamphlet No. P-77, p. 17.

[9] (a) Martinson, L. E., 'Microresist Technology', *ibid.*, p. 49.
(b) Martinson, L. E., 'The Technology of Microimage Resists', in *Second Kodak Seminar on Microminiaturization* (Rochester, New York, 1967), Pamphlet No. P-89, p. 31.

[10] Bryan, W. Scott, 'General Preparation of Kodak Photoresists and Mixtures of Photoresist and Photosensitive Lacquer', *ibid.*, p. 33.

[11] Kelley, R., 'Relationship between Resist Thickness and Pinholing', *ibid.*, p. 38.

[12] See, for example, leaflets on Photo-Resist Spinners issued by Headway Research Inc. Garland, Texas.

[13] Damon, G. F., 'The Effect of Whirler Acceleration on the Properties of the Photoresist Film' in *Second Kodak Seminar on Microminiaturization* (Rochester, New York, 1967), Pamphlet No. P-89, p. 36.

[14] Schwartz, Mrs G. C., 'Thickness Studies on Exposed Kodak Thin-Film-Resist Films', in *Kodak Seminar on Microminiaturization* (see reference [8]), p. 41.

[15] Sullivan, M. L., 'A Method for the Detection of Pinholes in Resists on SiO_2, and a Method for Stripping Resists', *ibid.*, p. 30.

[16] Donovan, E. P., 'Resist Evaluation', *ibid.*, p. 27.

[17] Bates, T. R., 'Physical Properties of Photoresist', *ibid.*, p. 58.

[18] (a) Easley, J. A., 'A New Chemical Method for Etching Magnesium Printing Plates', *6th Meeting T.A.G.A.*, 76, 1954.
(b) Easley, J. A., 'Combination Plate Etching with the Dow Etch Process', *9th Meeting T.A.G.A.*, 7, 1957.

[19] (a) Borth, P. F., and Rogers, M.C., 'Powderless Etching of Copper', *13th Meeting T.A.G.A.*, 1, 1961.
(b) Borth, P. F., 'Stabilization and Control of Powderless Copper Etching Baths', *16th Meeting T.A.G.A.*, 172, 1964.

[20] Peacock, F., 'Production of Molybdenum Foil Masks by a Photo-selective Etching Process', private communication, *by courtesy of the Director, British Scientific Instrument Research Association.*

[21] Mears, N. B., *Lecture to American Metal Stamping Association*, Spring Technical Meeting, March, 1964.

[22] Buckbee Mears Co., 'Masks with Graded Size Holes', British Patent No. 1,046,686.

[23] Buckbee Mears Co., 'Process for Preparing Photographic Plates', British Patent No. 1,076,410.

[24] Brown, S. A. (assigned to Buckbee Mears Co.), 'Photoprinting Apparatus', British Patent No. 1,050,326.

[25] Buckbee Mears Co., 'Automatic Photoprinting Apparatus', British Patent No. 1,064, 213.

[26] (a) Stookey, S. D., *Ind. Eng. Chem.*, **45**, 115, 1953 (see reference [38(b)], Chapter 2).
(b) Byer, M., 'Chemical Machining Photosensitive Glass', *Materials and Methods*, June, 1956.

[27] Corning Glass Co. Corning, New York. Serial Publications.
(a) Corning Fluidics Forum, first issue, November, 1966.
(b) Corning Fluidic Devices, data sheets issued at intervals.

[28] (a) British Compressed Air Society *and* Trade and Technical Press Ltd, *Pneumatic Handbook*, Trade and Technical Press Ltd (Morden, Surrey, England), 2nd edition, 1966, p. 227.
(b) Engineering Outlines No. 38, 'Fluidics', *Engineering*, 563, 1966.

[29] Lohse, J. M. and Bruins, P. F., *Phot. Sci. Eng.*, **7**, 238, 1963 (see reference [38] Chapter 2).

[30] E. I. Du Pont de Nemours and Co., *'Templex' Industrial Bulletins* (Wilmington, Delaware), first issue, April, 1965.

[31] Planer, G. V., 'Metal and Oxide Film Potentiometers', *J. Brit. Inst. Radio. Eng.*, **18**, 177, 1958.

[32] (a) Dummer, G. W. A. and Granville, J. W., *Miniature and Micro-miniature Electronics*, Sir Isaac Pitman and Sons Ltd (London, 1961), Chapters 6 and 7.
(b) Reference [1(d)] Schlabach, T. D. and Rider, D. K., p. 325 et. seq.
(c) Reference [1(c)] Keonjian, E., p. 173 et. seq.
(d) Holland, L., *Thin Film Microelectronics*, Chapman and Hall Ltd (London, 1965).

[33] Strauss, W. A., Jr, 'Applications of Photo-Etching in the Manufacture, Interconnection and Packaging of Micro-Circuits', *SCP and Solid State Technology*, **9**, 15 February, 1966.

[34] Atherton, D. L. and Peck, A. A., 'The Production of Precision Masks for Vacuum Deposition of Thin Films', *SCP and Solid State Technology*, **8**, 30, July, 1965.

[35] Thornton, C. G., 'New Trends in Microelectronics Fabrication Technology 1965–66, Part II', *SCP and Solid State Technology*, **9**, 28, April, 1966.

[36] Thornton, C. G., as reference [35], Part I, *SCP and Solid State Technology*, **9**, 42, March, 1966.

[37] Payne, P. D., 'Technology of Transistor Mask Fabrication', *Semiconductor Products*, **5**, 33, May, 1962.

[38] Schuetze, H. J. and Hennings, K. E., 'Large-Area Masking with Patterns of Micron and Sub-micron Size', *SCP and Solid State Technology*, **9**, 31, July, 1966.

[39] Novotny, J., Chapter 3 in reference [1(d)], (see also reference [20], Chapter 9).

[40] Pentecost, S., 'The Process Camera', *T.I.C. Bulletin*, No. 2, Section G.; R. W. Borrowdale Co. (Chicago, 1962).

[41] Murray, J. E. and Maurer, R. E., 'Arrays of Microphotographs for Microelectronic Componenets', *Semiconductor Products*, **5**, February, 1962.

[42] Rudge, W. E., Harding, W. E. and Mutter, W. E., 'Fly's-Eye Lens Technique for Generating Semiconductor Device Fabrication Masks', *I.B.M. Journal*, 146, April, 1963.

[43] Anon, 'Yale Precision Micro-module Photo System', Trade Leaflet, Burke and James Inc. (Chicago).

[44] (a) Hellmers, T. C. Jr, and Nall, J. R., 'Microphotographs for Electronics', *Semiconductor Products*, **4**, January, 1961. *Reprinted* as Eastman Kodak Pamphlet No. P-45.
(b) A similar article with the same title was published later. *Society of Photographic Scientists and Engineers. News*, October–December, 1962, p. 35.

[45] From Trade Leaflets issued by David W. Mann Co., Lincoln, Massachusetts.

[46] Walker, R. I., Freestone, R. and Haigh, P. M., in S. W. Bowler, 'Techniques in Applied Photography', *Brit. J. Phot.*, **113**, 1136, 1965.

[47] Watson Double Microscope for Mask Alignment, *50th Exh. Sci. Inst. Phys. Soc.* (London, 1966), p. 157.

[48] Kulicke and Soffa Manufacturing Co (as reference [7], Chapter 8).

[49] Ables, B. D., 'A Study of Transparent Microphotographic Masks and their Applications Using Lippmann Emulsion', *Phot. Sci. Eng.*, **10**, 229, 1966.

[50] McGinnis, R. W. and Roehr, W. D., 'New Masking Techniques for Micropower Transistors', *Electronics*, p. 76, 22 February, 1965.

[51] (a) Ingraham, R. C., 'Photolithographic Masks for Integrated and Thin Film Circuitry', *S.C.P. and Solid State Technology*, **8**, p. 33, March, 1965.
(b) Castrucci, P. P., Collins, R. H. and Marzinsky, W. R., 'High-Resolution Photolithography and Monolithic-Circuit Fabrication', *Reprographics*, **3**, June, 1966.

[52] Eastman Kodak Co., *Kodak Photosensitive Metal-Clad Plates* (Rochester, N.Y., 1967), Pamphlet No. P-128.

[53] Many sources of original information on silicon are quoted in references [1(c)] and [1(d)].

[54] *Semiconductor Network Report on Reliability*, Texas Instrument Inc. (Dallas, Texas, 1962), p. 15.

[55] Weber, S., 'LSI: The Technologies Converge', *Electronics*, 124,

20 February, 1967. This is the introductory review to several papers on the topic of large scale integration.

[56] Canning, M., Dunn, R. S. and Jeansonne, G., 'Active Memory calls for Discretion', *Electronics*, **124**, 143, 20 February, 1967.

[57] Jackson, T. M., Brisbane, A. D. and Sandbank, C. P., 'Automated Inter-connection Processes for Semiconductor Integrated Circuit Slices', in *Integrated Circuits*, Conference Publication No. 30, Institution of Electrical Engineers (London, 1967), p. 181.

[58] Dean, K. J., *Integrated Electronics*, Chapman and Hall (London, 1967), p. 90. This book is concerned more with the physical principles of semiconductor devices rather than with fabrication, but shows many of the reasons underlying the directions in which microelectronics has developed.

[59] (a) Glendenning, W. B. *et al.*, 'Projection Photolithography for use in Microcircuit Fabrication', U.S.A.E.L. Technical Report 2461, A.D. 607,594. In Great Britain, both this and the following reference are available as Microfiche from the National Lending Library, Boston Spa, Yorks.
(b) Sobottke, M. *et al.*, 'High Resolution Rapidly Programmable Masking for Functional Electronic Blocks', A.D. 609,114.

[60] Crawford, B. K., 'Electron Beam Machining', in Bakish, R., *Introduction to Electron Beam Technology*, J. Wiley and Son (New York, 1962), Chapter 11.

[61] Nixon, W. C., 'Electron Beam Etching in Microminiaturization', in *Solid Circuits and Microminiaturization*, Pergamon Press (Oxford, 1964), p. 257.

[62] Möllenstedt, G. and Speidel, R., 'Elektronoptischer Mikroschreiber unter elektronmikroskopischer Arbeitskontrolle', *Physikalische Blätter*, **4**, 192, 1960.

[63] (a) Buck, D. A. and Shoulders, K. R., *Proc. Eastern Joint Computer Conference*, Special Publication T-114, December, 1958 (see reference [41], Chapter 2).
(b) Shoulders, K. R., *Office of Technical Services (U.S.A.)*, P.B. 171027, 1960.

[64] Wells, O. C., 'Electron Beams in Microelectronics', in Bakish, R., *Introduction to Electron Beam Technology*, J. Wiley and Son (New York, 1962), Chapter 11.

REVIEW PUBLICATIONS

[65] Staubach, H. W., 'Photofabrikation', *Photo-Technik und Wirtschaft*, **17**, 202, 1966.

[66] Fishlock, D., 'Electronics in Miniature', *New Scientist*, 10 March, 1966, p. 640.

[67] Hittinger, W. C. and Sparks, M., 'Microelectronics', *Scientific American*, **213**(5), 57, November, 1965.

[68] Gunston, W. T., 'Microelectronics', *Science Journal*, **2**, 32, December, 1966.

[69] Dummer, G. W. A. (ed.), *Proceedings First Microelectronic Lecture Course, Oxford*, United Trade Press Ltd (London, 1966).

[70] Dwyer, J. L., *Contamination Analysis and Control*, Reinhold Publishing Corp. (New York, 1966), (see reference [27], Chapter 3).

[71] Maple, T. G., 'Integrated Mask Fabrication', *SCP and Solid State Technology*, 9(8), 23, August, 1966. In addition to reviewing the performance of equipment and materials, the article includes a directory of suppliers of the special products used.

[72] Lenard, J. A. and Patzner, E. J., 'Survey of Crystal-growing Processes and Equipment', *ibid.*, p. 35. This lavishly illustrated article describes the subtle procedures employed for producing the silicon rods from which wafers are cut.

[73] Sundean, G. E., 'Review of Test Equipment used in Integrated Circuit Manufacture', *ibid.*, p. 43. Complex procedures used for testing the electrical properties of integrated circuits on the wafer before dicing are essential for microelectronic production.

[74] Numerous authors, 'Symposium on Electron Beam Techniques for Microelectronics', *Microelectronics and Reliability*, 4(1), March, 1965. The entire issue was devoted to papers presented at the Royal Radar Establishment, Malvern.

12 · Microphotographic Reproduction and Manipulation of Documents

The copying of documents at a greatly reduced scale has attracted more public attention than any other application of microphotography. Indeed, for many readers, microphotography will previously have seemed to be exclusively concerned with document copying. In this field the word *microphotography* has acquired a particularly elastic meaning. It has been used to encompass both Sir D. Brewster's suggestion (in 1857) that dispatches could be concealed in a full stop [1], and the use of films as wide as 70 or 105 mm (2·75 or 4·1 in) for reproducing engineering drawings. Since many of the latter are decipherable (or legible) with a simple magnifier, they hardly justify the adjective 'microphotographic'.

It was shown in Chapter 1, that minute writing and printing have been practised for some centuries, and Dancer first produced photographs of truly microscopic proportions more than a century ago. Contemporary scholars soon realized the potentialities of Dancer's method for the compression of information, and in 1853 the astronomer Sir J. Herschel proposed the publication of microphotographic reproductions of reference books [2].

By 1860 the basic problems of making legible images of truly microscopic proportions had been solved, but little use was made of these suggestions during the next sixty years. One exception was the pigeon post operated by Dagron in 1870–1 for sending messages into Paris during the Franco-Prussian War [3]. The cables under the Seine were cut, and the besieged city was completely isolated from the rest of France. The postal service was operated by printing the official dispatches and civilian messages on folio pages, which contained as much information as a newspaper page. Sixteen such pages were mounted on a panel, and were reduced by a single exposure on wet-collodion to give an image measuring only $2\frac{1}{2} \times 1\frac{1}{2}$ in (65 × 35 mm) (Plate 49). The resulting negatives were contact printed also on wet-collodion plates, from which the processed emulsion was stripped as a coherent pellicle. Each pellicle contained about 3,000 messages, but they were so light that eighteen weighed only 8 grains (0·5 grams), and this number was carried by a single pigeon on a quill attached to a tail feather. On receipt, the films were projected by a lantern and the messages copied by hand. The military value of this successful process was considered to be so high that full working details never appear to have been released for publication [4]. Collection of information from the literature of that period and examination of surviving specimens of Dagron's pellicles have, nevertheless, permitted a reasonable reconstruction of his methods to be made [5].

Several reasons can be suggested for the slow adoption of the early proposal for applying document microphotography to practical problems. The production of the first satisfactory specimen images demonstrated the potentiality of the process for document copying, rather than its immediate practicability. Large-scale use demands that cheap and reliable methods must be evolved for making very large numbers of images, and for retrieval of individual images. In this connection it should be noted that important ancillary goods, such as transparent and flexible film base, and convenient illuminants for reading machines, were not developed until much later. The absence of such materials may well have retarded the development of document-copying processes. Moreover, for many years the need for document microphotography was not sufficiently obvious to stimulate the necessary development work.

This situation was radically changed by a New York banker (George L. McCarthy, first President of the Recordak Corporation) who visualized the application of reduced document copies on film in banking and office procedures. His initiative resulted in the development of the 'Recordak' machines for making a photographic record of every cheque passing through a bank [6]. The commercial success and usefulness of this first full-scale application led to an ever-swelling stream of further uses. Four decades later, microfilming (and facilities related thereto) is frequently quoted as one of America's major growth industries.

THE BARE ESSENTIALS

Quite acceptable copies of printed documents can be made at reduction ratios up to 20, by using almost any 35 mm camera with a well corrected lens. A fine-grain negative film such as Kodak Panatomic-X or, better, a film such as Recordak Micro-File Pan designed specifically for this purpose should be used. Many of the early experiments in scholarly applications of microfilm used images made in this way. As described in Chapter 1, specially designed working methods and use of an extreme-resolution emulsion permit copies of truly microscopic dimensions to be made with quite simple cameras. Thus it can be seen that making of a few images is not a difficult matter. Novices should, however, beware. This very simplicity of the preliminary experiments can lure the unwary into unexpectedly expensive commitments. To prevent this misfortune, professional advice should be sought at an early stage.

PROBLEM OF LARGE-SCALE APPLICATION

When large-scale applications are planned, and particularly when ingenious methods are used to exploit the full advantages of micro-film, problems can crowd in thick and fast. For example, complete reliability giving virtually a hundred-per-cent yield of legible images becomes a necessity. To satisfy this requirement the copying process must be very well controlled, and must be able to cope with originals of most variable quality. Much ingenuity has been expended and many types of special equipment have been marketed to cope with this and many other problems. The topic has acquired a voluminous literature, so that the space available in this chapter is quite insufficient for a complete treatment of the subject. It has therefore been decided to present a review concerned more with basic principles, than with detailed descriptions of individual apparatus or systems. It is hoped that this may provide a useful framework for further study.

MICROPHOTOGRAPHY AS AN INFORMATION-STORAGE PROCESS

To get some order into an apparently chaotic subject, it is convenient to consider document microphotography as an information-storage process. Description of how this has been reduced to practice can then be divided into three main sections, into which subsidiary subjects may be arranged:

INPUT OF ORIGINALS
The legal problem.
Types of original, and their properties.
Sorting and Classification (grouping) of Documents.

STORAGE AND MANIPULATION
Primary Microfilm Copying

Emulsions for,
Lenses for,
Reduction ratio,
Cameras for,
Copies in two-dimensional arrays,
Introduction of coded information,

Exposing Technique,
Processing,
Quality Control,
Unitization.

Secondary Copies,

Same-size copies,
Copies in aperture cards,
Copies with further reduction (microscopic copies).

Tertiary and later-generation copies.

OUTPUT
Visual magnifiers,
Projection Reading apparatus,
Reader-printers,
Specialized enlargers,
Continuous enlargement and O-P books,
Output for Systems Applications.

Handling of Microforms for Systems and Information Retrieval
Indexing of roll microfilm,
Magazine-loading readers,
Searching for information content,
Handling of short lengths of film,
Images in Giant Assemblies,
Large numbers on film sheets (microfiches).

Microfilm Output for Computer Systems
As computer input,
As computer output.

Conclusion
Impact on civilization.

Input of Originals

THE LEGAL PROBLEM

Before any programme of microfilming is undertaken, it is prudent to
consider certain legal restraints on this work. As this book is being
written for international use, no attempt will be made to present a
detailed picture of the legal position in any single country.[1] In any

[1] Note, however, that most countries with free-enterprise economies have
signed the International Copyright Convention. This confers the benefits of copy‐
right in all the subscribing countries to authors publishing in any one of the same
countries.

case such an attempt could be frustrated by case decisions or by changes in legislation in any country while this book is in the press. It therefore seemed better to discuss three basic questions, which can pertinently be asked during the planning of any programme. It should be emphasized that the intention of this section is only to alert readers to the possible existence of legal problems. *If in any doubt, legal advice should be sought.*

(1) IS COPYING PERMISSIBLE, OR DOES THE PROPOSED PROJECT INFRINGE GOVERNMENT EMBARGOES OR CIVIL LEGISLATION?

The copying of bank-notes and coins is generally a criminal offence, although it is doubtful whether convincing forgeries could be produced by enlarging an average microfilm negative! The copying of many other documents is forbidden—in the United States of America, for instance, these include Government Bonds, Postage Stamps, automobile licences and naturalization papers, while unauthorized copying of militarily restricted documents in all countries threatens the culprit with the dire penalties of espionage laws.

Copyright. Of more general concern is civil legislation and particularly the question of infringement of copyright. Essentially, copyright is a form of property which consists of the sole right to reproduce a literary or artistic work for a period after its initial publication. When it became apparent that photocopying of scientific and technical journals could be of great use in libraries, copyright restrictions at one time seemed to present a serious barrier.

In the United States of America, however, a number of publishers in 1939 issued an agreement which stated that a non-profit-making organization could make single copies of part of a magazine or volume in lieu of a loan or manual transcription. A number of safeguards to protect the copyright owners were written into this 'gentleman's agreement'. International discussion of this topic followed at the Royal Society Scientific Information Conference of 1948 [7]. The proceedings of this conference stated that:

'Science rests upon its published records, and ready access to public, scientific and technical information is a fundamental need of scientists everywhere. All bars which prevent access to scientific and technical publications hinder the progress of science and should be removed. Making single copies of extracts from books or periodicals is essential to research workers and the production of such single-extract copies by, or on behalf of scientists is necessary for scientific practice'.

N

The Information Services Committee of the Royal Society of London drew up a 'Declaration on Fair Dealing in regard to Copying'. This was based on the American 'gentleman's agreement', and scientific societies were invited to subscribe to the following Declaration:

'We will regard it as fair dealing for the purpose of private study or research when a non-profit making organization such as a library, archives office, museum or information office, owning or handling scientific or technical periodicals published by us, makes and delivers a single reproduction of a part of an issue thereof to a person or his agent representing in writing that he desires such reproduction in lieu of a loan or manual transcription, and that he requires it solely for the purpose of private study, research, criticism or review, and that he undertakes not to sell or reproduce for publication the copy supplied, provided that:

(i) the recipient of the copy is given notice that he is liable for infringement of copyright by misuse of the copy, and that it is illegal to use the copy for any further reproduction,

(ii) the organization making and furnishing the copy does so without profit to itself,

(iii) proper acknowledgement is given to the publication from which the copy is made,

(iv) not more than one copy of any one excerpt shall be furnished to any one person.'

The exemption extended also to the officers of the libraries or organization, but involved the responsibility for ensuring that their employees cautioned those receiving the copies against misuse. The Declaration concluded:

'We reserve the right to take action against any person or organization copying or misusing a part or the whole of the work. We reserve the right to withdraw this Declaration.'

In Great Britain, the main principles of this Declaration were incorporated in the Copyright Act of 1956. One statement declared that infringement was not constituted by 'any fair dealing with any work for the purpose of private study, research, criticism, reviews or newspaper summary'.

The protection given to authors and publishers by copyright legislation served the useful purpose of stimulating publication, but there is a potential source of conflict of interest between the producers of the volumes stored in libraries and the community at large. For instance in Great Britain, public libraries, supported entirely by taxation and making no charge for loans, undertake to supply most of the volumes required for recreational reading or for private study. There has been much public comment about the alleged loss of income to authors resulting from this policy, and methods for righting this supposed injustice have been discussed. Royalty-free production of copies on demand is another policy which might be thought to damage authors' or publishers' interests, and this hazard is being watched by editors of the journals of learned societies. The continuation of their publications often demands a strenuous struggle against rising costs, and any loss of income could be a serious matter.

This conflict of interests concerning conditions of copyright is a most important question and opinions held in the United States of America have been discussed in a book edited by L. H. Hattery and G. P. Bush [8]. The arguments of the two sides run rather like this. Statistical analyses of the use so far made of on-demand photocopying indicate that the loss to publishers and authors has been negligible. Librarians and representatives of the photocopying industry have therefore proposed two relaxations of the Fair Dealing concept. Librarians should be allowed to provide copies of complete journals, and to provide multiple copies.

The publishers object that this relaxation of their copyright safe-guards would be intolerable. Even if no severe loss at first occurred because the extent of photocopying was limited by present cost, future technical developments might remove this barrier.

A number of contributors to this volume discuss the possibility of resolving the conflict by arranging for the levying of a royalty when photocopies are provided. It is suggested that research workers should be willing to bear this cost, in return for a freer access to the literature thereby achieved. The administrative difficulties of operating this system are obviously considerable, but the success of music-recording companies in collecting royalties for the public playing of their records is cited as an example and precedent. One contributor notes that the payment of royalties would be simplified where access to photocopies was gained through a data-processing system using a computer. Information about royalties accruing to publishers and authors would be collected by the computer, and aggregates read out once a year.

(2) IN WHAT CIRCUMSTANCES MAY COPYING BE OBLIGATORY? There are indications that microfilming may become contractually obligatory for certain types of business operation. In the United States of America, for instance, various types of records, particularly those applying to war contracts or taxation, must be retained for a stated number of years. Due to the great bulk of such records, micro-filming conducted with suitable statutory precautions (see below), constitutes the most economic way of fulfilling this requirement. Contractors tendering for the supply of engineering stores to United

States Defence Departments must include complete sets of drawings copied on aperture-card microfilm with each tender. It seems likely that these contractual obligations for microfilming are likely to spread.

(3) WHAT STATUTORY PRECAUTIONS ARE NEEDED TO ENSURE THAT MICROFILMS ARE ACCEPTED AS EVIDENCE?

Courts in various countries have been reluctant to accept photocopied or microfilmed documentary evidence. In Great Britain, for instance, the original document must be produced if at all possible. Photographic copies may be accepted as secondary evidence if they can be shown to be a true copy of the original [9]. No case has yet been decided on the acceptability of photocopies produced in evidence when the originals have been deliberately destroyed, and certainly no original documents or title or of similar significance should be so destroyed.

In the United States of America, this bridge has already been crossed, and Lewis and Offenhauser describe circumstances in which original documents can be destroyed after copying without apparent legal hazard [10]. In general, the microfilmed copies need to be accompanied by appropriately worded declarations concerning the destruction of the originals, and the completeness and authenticity of the copy. The microfilms are therefore usually made to include copies of such declarations, which must be on the headed notepaper of the copying organization with authenticity attested by the copier. If the first copy has some frames spoiled, separate declarations about retakes must be included. It therefore follows that any microfilming of documents that may subsequently be presented in the courts should always be preceded by checks on the statutory requirements. In concluding this section, readers (if in doubt) are again reminded to seek legal advice *before* copying commences.

TYPES OF ORIGINALS, AND THEIR PROPERTIES

Two different approaches have been employed in the photography of documents. In special cases, particularly in forensic work, the extraction of the last scrap of information from one single document may justifiably be regarded as a subject for a special piece of research. Elaborate techniques of illumination, or multiple exposures at different wavelengths or masking procedures may be employed. This is the opposite of the approach which must be employed for large-scale document microphotography. A single exposing and processing régime must be able to cope with the variation of image quality inevitably to be found amongst numerous documents. It is therefore necessary to consider the range of properties likely to be presented by the originals for any particular application.

The first commercial microfilming operations used 'Recordak' machines for the copying of every cheque which passed through the banks. The *cheques* varied in the colour or density of their printed background and the infinite degrees of blackness and clarity of hand-writing. Although it was usual to think of documents as 'line' originals with only black and white tones, the information in a multitude of cheques could only be retained by treating them as continuous-tone subjects. The same was true for *invoices* and other commercial docu-ments. In type-written documents the density can change due to the ageing of the ribbon and variations of 'touch'. When *carbon-copies* have to be dealt with, the sharpness can already be so marginal that any further deterioration produces illegibility.

Printed documents and particularly *newspapers* also vary in quality. The blackness of the ink is not constant, aged newsprint can be very discoloured and the smallest printed letters broken and uneven. In addition, the reduction ratio (up to 16 : 1) required to record a full-size newspaper page on 35 mm film means that the aerial images of the smallest type faces have reduced contrast (see p. 179). In fact, the effective blackness of the letters is reduced progressively with decreased size of type.

Great variation is also found in scholarly material, comprising *scientific journals, doctoral theses, historical documents* and *technical reports*.[1] Technical reports sometimes originally issued for very re-stricted circulation have later been copied for widespread publication. The nth carbon copy often proved an inadequate original for this purpose. In some scientific journals, particularly those dealing with the biological sciences, satisfactory recording of half-tone plates or finely shaded drawings may be essential. For instance, mycological literature needs to be copiously illustrated with detailed drawings required for the identification of fungi responsible for diseases of agricultural plants. For all practical purposes, such illustrations often constitute continuous-tone originals.

The adequate copying of continuous-tone originals is important in other applications. *Hospital records* and *medical-case histories* often include *radiographs* or other photographs demonstrating patients' condition from time to time. Microphotographic copies of *press photo-graphs* allow art editors to gain better access to the photographs in their files. The originals need only be disturbed when suitable photo-graphs have been located in the microfilmed files. There have also been similar proposals for reducing entire stocks of *aerial reconnaissance or survey* photographs on microfilm.

Colour is another 'dimension' which sometimes has to be considered.

---

[1] For illustration of this point, see Chapters 1 and 2 of Hawken's *Copying Methods Manual* [92].

The types of original likely to be concerned are *illuminated manu-scripts, medical and biological specimens, art treasures* and *coloured maps*. So far, no extreme-resolution process of colour photography appears yet to have been worked out. Nevertheless, the resolution provided by motion-picture film stock permits useful reduction ratios to be employed [11].

In the examples so far considered, a substantial proportion of the documents would be originated outside the control of the copying agency. In some applications, the production of all the originals is under control, and more consistent quality can be aimed for. Ex-amples are the copying of specially originated documents for *photo-charging in libraries* and for recording transactions in *betting shops*. In neither case would the intrinsic value of the original appear to justify much effort to improve consistency. With *engineering drawings*, how-ever, the value is undoubtedly high. With the growth of this applica-tion much difficulty was caused by differences in line widths combined with the reduction ratios needed for copying very large originals. The problem was aggravated by the dirty condition of many of the older drawings stored in drawing offices. In fact, satisfactory microfilming of collections of existing engineering drawings has proved a very difficult and sometimes an impossible task. This situation caused the Bell Telephone Company to examine their drawing-office methods, and to issue a series of recommendations for production of drawings of more satisfactory line quality [12]. In addition, drawings were simplified by the eradication of (usually unnecessary) features which made them difficult to copy. The scrapping of entrenched drawing-office traditions was the price which had to be paid to achieve the full advantage of microfilming. Commercial concerns in the United States of America and Great Britain have produced tracings of old drawings, but with the new conventions, as a customer service.

A radically different task is the microfilming of *transient displays*. These may take the form of radar-controlled displays depicting dis-positions of ships or moment-to-moment conditions in the approaches to airports. The task may involve continuous monitoring of cathode-ray tubes, or the direct microfilming of computer output depicted on 'Charactron' and related tubes (see p. 436). This type of work may also be concerned with the condensation of magnetic tape records, or direct electron-recording by passing film through the vacuum of a cathode-ray tube. Special photographic problems can be met in such work [13].

SORTING AND CLASSIFICATION (GROUPING) OF DOCUMENTS

The usefulness of collections of microfilmed documents often depends on the thought given to their sorting and classification (in the widest sense of the word). Sometimes the subject matter will be in forms such as journal-volumes or patents, which are already arranged in continuous series. It may alternatively be only necessary to arrange the input in simple chronological or numerical order, according to factors such as date of issue or account numbers. Unless suitable precautions are taken at the time of copying, however, there is a serious danger of information being buried as the mass of the file increases. The problem is most serious when the documents are needed for an active file, and concern technical or research material requiring frequent cross references. They must then be classified to permit effective searches for subject content to be made.

Classification demands scrutiny of the documents for subject matter and allocation of subject classes, code numbers (such as in the Universal Decimal Classification or Dewey systems) or descriptors. Since all attempts to divide knowledge into completely water-tight departments have merely demonstrated the futility of the exercise, classification is a difficult task requiring specialized skill. Achieving adequate classification of the input to a large document collection can involve a serious staffing problem. The job demands wide background knowledge, alertness and common sense, but to many minds hardly offers the intellectual satisfaction needed to maintain consistent classification of large numbers of documents over a long period. Appropriate personnel selection, training and pecuniary recognition are likely to be required to ensure an adequate classification service.

When the documents have been classified, the most active systems involve the recording of coded marks or signals corresponding to the classification class (or classes) of each document. Coded marks can be recorded optically inside or outside the microfilmed 'frames', or by signals on a magnetic stripe. It should be recognized that the generation of the coded information often forms an essential part of the copying process, and must therefore be arranged before copying starts (see p. 387).

Storage and Manipulation of Information by Microfilming

INITIAL GENERATION OF PRIMARY MICROFILM COPIES

As has been emphasized earlier (p. 196), every reproduction of an image by projection through an optical system inevitably produces some image deterioration. A photographer must accept this physical fact, and choose his conditions so that the deterioration is kept within limits tolerable for the intended use of the copies. Before starting a new project, therefore, he would be well advised to consider the quality requirement of the ultimate user *right from the start*. Appropriate selection of the components needed for any job can then be made on a logical basis. The importance of this approach will increase as employment of microfilm becomes integrated into more and more elaborate (and demanding) systems.

It may be found that the demands of the ultimate user are relatively modest, such as when legible copies of cheques are mainly required for reading by direct projection. With many applications, the production of enlargements (so-called 'hard copies') is an important constituent of the system. As explained later, this demands the production of negatives to a more exacting specification, particularly when large numbers of images have to be automatically enlarged.

As users of microfilm output become increasingly experienced, there has been a tendency for details of quality specifications to be written into the contracts for microfilming. Background (or line) density, resolution in different parts of the field and positioning of the images in the frames may be specified. Another development influencing the initial quality required is the demand for the production of multi-generation contact copies. It has been assumed that the primary copy needs to be more than 'just legible' if legibility is to be maintained through a series of generations.

A further tendency demanding upgrading of the quality demanded in the first-generation images is the use of microfilm copies for publication of reduced-size or full-scale copies by offset lithography. High quality is also required when the first generation negatives are used as intermediates for a further reduction stage (p. 409).

BASIC DECISIONS

Before commencing work, the microfilmer needs to consider the implications of the large numbers of images likely to be copied. In commercial-scale operation the question of reliability is of paramount importance, and the average standard of reproduction should be set at a sufficiently high level to minimize the need for checking and retaking of images. A high average quality is ensured by choosing operating conditions providing adequate working tolerances: a principle around which successful operation revolves.

In designing a system, the microfilm technician intrinsically makes three basic decisions, namely choice of:

> *Emulsion,*
> *Lens,*
> *Reduction Ratio.*

In many cases, the person responsible for execution of a project merely satisfies himself that commercial equipment and materials will fulfil his quality requirement. In doing so, he is ratifying the decisions made by the technical designer.

EMULSIONS FOR GENERATION OF PRIMARY COPIES

In most of the other applications of microphotography discussed in this book, emulsion speed is of secondary importance, but for primary microfilming a minimum speed value is essential. The reason is that documents are normally opaque originals which must of necessity be copied by reflected light. The proportion of incident light entering the objective in these circumstances is so small, that only emulsions with sufficient speed will permit use of the short exposure times needed for a satisfactory output. In practice, this means that the only sensitive materials usable for this purpose are those whose development gives a large amplification factor. This requirement is met by silver-halide emulsions and xerographic processes, but only the former have been extensively used. The majority of silver-halide emulsions chosen have had average grain diameters in the range 0·1 to 0·4 microns (Plate 5) and have been panchromatically sensitized to allow them to cope with documents on papers of all colours. Most commercial products have similar photographic speed adjusted for convenient use with available equipment. When normal (high) contrast development is employed, use of an ASA speed rating around 5 should indicate the exposure required (but check manufacturers' instructions). At the silver coating-weights needed, these emulsions are fairly transparent, but the majority still scatter light strongly and show considerable image spread. They cannot, therefore, be considered 'extreme-resolution' materials, but nevertheless permit commercially adequate copies to be made at reduction ratios up to about 40.

The limit of reduction ratio which could be used at the primary stage was materially raised by Eastman Kodak work on the Minicard project. An emulsion was, in effect, 'pushed' to increase speed as far as possible without loss of its extreme-resolution. The outcome was a material about eight times faster than Kodak 'High-Resolution' or 'Maximum-Resolution' plates, and with an ASA speed of 0·08. With an F/4 lens, and on illumination with six 375-watt Sylvania R-32 Reflector lamps at full voltage to give 3,000 foot-candles at the copy-board, an exposure time of 1 second was required. On a production basis, this system gave 330 lines/mm on the axis and 270 in the corners, when the specially computed 16 mm lens was used for 60 : 1 reduction of $14 \times 8\frac{1}{2}$ in documents. The initial image quality was so high that third, fourth or fifth generation contact copies at this reduction were still legible.

Although the Minicard film (p. 428) was several hundred times slower than conventional commercial document-copying films, it was still hundreds of times faster than most of the non-silver processes which have little or no built-in amplification factor. Since the copyboard illumination used in the Minicard system was very high (approximately equivalent to the intensity obtained by full sun light), use of appreciably slower emulsions was not likely to prove practicable.

The contrast is another important property, and in copying line originals for photomechanical work, use of extreme-contrast emulsions assists in the production of negatives with very high density gradients at the edge of the images (p. 242). We have, however, already seen that even original copy with no pictorial content can be of most varying quality. Use of excessive contrast then tends to be disastrous, since the latitude of the copying system will be less than the effective luminosity range of the material copied. The consequence is an inevitable loss of information at one or other end of the tonal scale. In commercial practice, emulsions are developed to a gamma around 3, but since relatively little of the straight line part of the characteristic curve is used (see Exposing Technique, p. 388), the effective 'average slope' is much lower than this. The concept of treating document originals as continuous-tone copy was an important design factor in the Minicard system. The lower part of the curve, on which both text and pictorial information were recorded, had an average slope close to one, so that a minimum loss of information would occur both in the initial copying and at subsequent stages. The curve of this material had a high contrast in the shoulder, to assist production of high densities in the coded dots used for document retrieval.

The performance of microfilm materials is markedly influenced by halation (p. 17), and microfilm stock has usually been sold with an anti-halation backing. In 1964, however, the Eastman Kodak Company found that still better results could be obtained by the use of a bleachable *anti-halation undercoat* between the emulsion and the support, and the AHU film incorporating this feature gave materially improved sharpness for fine detail.

LENSES FOR GENERATION OF PRIMARY COPIES

In Chapter 4 (p. 94) it was noted that lenses for document microphotography need to have short focal length and rather a wide angular field of view, so that reduction ratios up to 40 could be obtained with reasonably compact equipment. With flat-bed cameras, the angular field of the lens determines the height of column needed, and hence the height of the ceiling where the camera is used. Maintenance of sharpness right into the corners of the image is also an essential requirement. With the majority of microfilm emulsions having effective speed values around ASA 5 (see p. 375), the toughness of the lens designer's assignment is slightly softened by light scatter in the emulsion. Because light scatter is practically eliminated in the Minicard emulsion, use of this type of material with a reduction ratio of 60 constitutes a particularly drastic test of a lens's capability.

The problem of meeting the increasingly stringent demands of proposed microfilming programmes has been discussed by W. Mandler [14]. Firstly it has to be appreciated that the task of a lens for microfilming is markedly different from that imposed by general photography. Since the originals are flat, design compromises generally made to allow subjects to be photographed simultaneously at a range of distances are unimportant. When the spectral response of a typical microfilm emulsion to tungsten illumination was compared with that of a 'general' emulsion to daylight, the former showed much reduced sensitivity at wavelengths shorter than 5,000 Å. Mandler concluded that microfilm lenses should be achromatized for the F (blue-green) and C (red) spectrum lines, rather than for the G (violet) and C (red) lines considered for general lens computation.

Field flatness is a particularly demanding property, and the radial and tangential image surfaces were considered to be especially significant for predicting performance of a microfilm lens. Since lens designers had not yet found it possible to make these surfaces completely flat, compromise solutions had to be adopted. For instance, a Tessar lens of focal length 63 mm was classified as an anastigmat with flattened image. This description was justified by the radial and tangential fields in one location (21 mm off axis) having a common location. The field was described as 'flat' because both image surfaces required less than 0·01 in (0·25 mm) in depth over the whole format. However, only 0·0012 in (0·03 mm) change in focal plane was needed to give unacceptable results when this lens was critically focused to give 120 lines/mm over the entire Military 'D' Aperture format (nominally $1\frac{3}{4} \times 1\frac{1}{4}$ in). In the same article Mandler discussed alternative methods (such as use of longer focal length, Gauss-type lens constructions and use of a curved image plane) which might be used for improving field flatness. He cited the following lenses as having been used for the 'D' format (Table 14).

Mandler concluded his article by considering the requirement for lenses working at up to 60 diameters reduction. Since the necessary emulsion development work had already been done (e.g. in the Minicard project) this task constitutes a challenge to the lens designer. It will be assisted by greater freedom of design derived from the use of rare-earth glasses, and by the electronic computer allowing the designer to ask intelligent questions instead of feeling crushed by tedious calculations.

Table 14. Objectives used for Microfilming. (Courtesy of W. Mandler and National Microfilm Association)

Lens manufacturer	Lens name	Focal length mm	Maximum aperture	Taking aperture	Lens type	Used on camera
Eastman Kodak Co.	Microfile Ektar	63	F/8	F/8	Heliar	Recordak C, D, E
Ernst Leitz (Canada) Ltd	Elcan	52	F/2	F/6·3	Modified Gauss	Photodevices PD 1088 D
Ernst Leitz (Canada) Ltd	Elcan	65	F/4	F/5·6	Modified Gauss	
Nippon Kogaku	Micro Nikkor	70	F/5		Gauss	
Jos. Schneider & Co.	Componon	60	F/5·6	F/8	Modified Gauss	
Tokyo Kogaku	Topcor M	77	F/8		Gauss	Dea-Graph CA 7 CA 6
Tokyo Kogaku	Tominom	62	F/5·6		Gauss	Dea-Graph CB 11
Carl Zeiss, Oberkochen	S Tessar	75	F/4·5	F/8	Tessar	Lumoprint MTO, MTI
Carl Zeiss, Oberkochen	S Planar	60	F/4		Gauss	

REDUCTION RATIO

When embarking on a microfilming project, the choice of the reduction ratio may be the most crucial decision of all. Although the basic aim of document microphotography is to compress information, various factors limit the reduction ratio which can usefully be employed. When contemplating use of higher ratios, the following trends should be watched.

(1) The greater the ratio, the higher will be the emulsion resolution needed, and the lower may be the speed of the required emulsion. In addition to the consequences already discussed, low emulsion speed may demand use of a larger lens aperture giving reduced depth of field.

(2) The smaller the images, the greater will be the information lost from image blemishes caused by dust or damage. In addition the tendency will be to crowd more images on one unit of film, and the greater will be the effort wasted if any one image is spoilt.

(3) With higher ratios, equipment needs to be made with greater care and smaller overall tolerances, and is likely to cost more. Design of reading and enlarging equipment becomes more difficult, since the total light flux needed at the plane of the enlarged image is independent of the size of the reduced copy. Special attention may therefore be needed with smaller images, to avoid the danger of film damage by overheating.

(4) With a given lens and emulsion, image quality always deteriorates as greater reduction ratios are employed. The microfilmer therefore has to consider how much deterioration the ultimate user will tolerate. It must be remembered that most users have no interest in the ingenuity employed to produce their microfilm copies. They will judge the copies entirely by the final result: in fact by their ability to read them without fatigue or to produce legible enlargements readily. It has been said that a given space containing 25 readily legible pages is preferable to 100 pages which are only decipherable.

Arguments such as these force one to conclude that a microfilming process should be operated with the largest-sized images consistent with the ultimate aims of the system. In this connection, it might be noted that it is only too easy for a salesman to argue that a process reducing 100 cubic feet of documents to half a cubic foot is 'twice as good' as one reducing the same matter to one cubic foot. The user would, however, be wise to ascertain the likely penalties of the use of the greater reduction ratio. With reduced image quality he is also likely to find greater difficulty of contact copying, lesser working tolerances and the risk of a greater proportion of re-takes. When satisfied that a greater reduction ratio is really required for a project, the designer should check that the investment plus over-all operating and maintenance costs—and not merely the price of film and storage space—really is lower when smaller images are employed.

CAMERAS FOR GENERATION OF PRIMARY COPIES

Whilst the choice of emulsion and lens has a critical effect on the quality achievable in microfilm copies, the choice of camera largely influences factors controlling the cost and convenience of the copying operation. Points to be considered are:

 (i) maximum size of document to be copied,
 (ii) single or multi-sheet documents,
 (iii) speed of operation,
 (iv) skill demanded and hence labour cost,
 (v) provision of fixed or variable reduction,
 (vi) space and power requirements of equipment,
 (vii) uniformity of quality of output,
 (viii) ability to stay in adjustment,
 (ix) automatic focusing,
 (x) warnings of film end, lamp burn-out or other malfunction,
 (xi) exposure control by photocell.

For the simpler microfilming tasks, 'miniature' still cameras, or a ciné camera giving single-frame exposures, can be used to produce strips of film bearing a row of document copies. Such instruments are not particularly convenient for this work, and their use is likely to prove uneconomic for more than a very small volume of work. Much ingenuity (often spurred by commercial competition) has gone into the development of specialized equipment. Apart from achieving the necessary image quality, designers have concentrated their attention on three main aims of great commercial significance:

 (i) maximum efficiency in the use of the available area of film,
 (ii) great dependability,
 (iii) simplicity of operation and speed of output.

Their efforts have led to the development of two quite different types of microfilming equipment. One type copies continuously moving single-sheet documents on a moving film, and the second can copy any type of document on stationary film.

FLOW MICROFILMERS

Flow-microfilmers are exemplified by the 'Commercial Recordak': the pioneer instrument in this field. With this type of machine, the documents are fed into a slot, from which they are carried to the exposing station. As soon as the leading edge of the document reaches a certain point in the mechanism, it moves a lightly-loaded trip bar. This actuates a micro-switch, which turns on the lights and operates a clutch driving the film in the opposite direction to the documents, and at a rate reduced in proportion to the degree of reduction. Thus the reduced aerial image remains stationary relative to the film. Reduction ratios of 17 and 23 have been widely employed, with the film moved at one-seventeenth (or one-twenty-third) of the speed of the document respectively. With the higher reduction ratios currently being employed (for example the 'Recordak Reliant Microfilmer' offers kits for ratios of 24 : 1, 32 : 1 or 40 : 1), appropriately adjusted film drives must of course be used.

In this type of equipment, the length of the exposure is determined by the rate of rotation and the width of a slit behind which the film moves. Keeping this slit narrow not only reduces the exposure time, but also shortens the length of travel during which each element of the emulsion surface receives its exposure. The chance of loss of resolution, resulting from small residual errors in the adjustment of projected-image movement to film movement, is thereby reduced. If loss of resolution due to these errors did occur, image lines at right angles to the film movement should be less sharp than lines parallel to this movement. With the assistance of the Recordak Division of Kodak Ltd. the author tested this question with two types of current microfilmer. In both cases, extremely critical focusing of the microfilm reader was needed to observe the smallest images in the reproduced resolution test chart and no apparent astigmatism could be seen. Loss of sharpness or apparent astigmatism due to imperfect synchronizing of image and film movement were just not detectable.

As soon as the end of each document passes beneath the trip bar, the trip bar returns to its original position which stops the film and turns off the lights. The documents continue their travel through the machine and arrive at the exit chute. By this arrangement, film is only moved and exposed while a document is actually in the position for copying. This ensures that the individual images are conveniently spaced, whatever the length of each document happens to be, and also prevents wastage of film.

Flow-microfilmers are very simple to operate, and will accept documents almost as quickly as they can be fed in. Some operators have fed documents alternately with each hand, and copied cheques at the rate of 5,000 per hour. When the documents are all the same shape and size, copying is further simplified by using an automatic feeder into which stacked batches of documents are loaded. For the effective use of this equipment, the documents need to be completely separated from each other. To ensure this, selection devices have been developed which detect when documents cling together, and stop them at the point of entry to the copier. Such a precaution is virtually a necessity for high-speed copying, but precludes the copying of multi-sheet documents on this type of equipment. It is also obvious that copying of both wide and narrow documents on the same machine would waste film, and maximum document widths are specified for different machines.

Because of their predominantly commercial importance, flow-microfilmers are highly developed products. Many refinements have been built into available machines of this type, and the following are some of the features which may be noted.

Machines have been made increasingly compact, and this aim has been promoted by using mirrors to fold the optical path. For example, one portable microfilmer for copying letters or cheques at 20 : 1 reduction ratio measures only $15\frac{1}{2} \times 12\frac{1}{2} \times 6\frac{1}{2}$ in ($39 \times 31 \times 16$ cm), and weighs only 24 pounds (11 kg).

Crumpled documents may be straightened automatically.

By the use of alternative lens kits, the images may be reduced to occupy the full width or only half the width of the film. In the latter case, the film is reversed at the end of the run, and is re-inserted in the camera for the exposure of the second side. In some cases the same lens kit used with a system of mirrors enables both *backs* and *fronts* of cheques to be recorded side-by-side on the same strip of film.

Arrangements are also provided, with any of the above modes of exposing, for splitting the beam so that two films can be exposed simultaneously thus providing a duplicate directly, with each film having the full quality of a first-generation copy.

Accessories have been provided for endorsing each cheque (or other appropriate documents) and for recording the fact that it has been copied.

Although flow-microfilmers can only accept documents of limited width, they can deal with sheets of great length. This has proved valuable for the copying of the printed output from computers. One such machine requires only 27 minutes to copy 4,800 feet of continuous stationery on 200 feet of 16 mm film.

For some applications, such as the computer-output copier, use of interchangeable film units allows all records from a department to be filmed sequentially on the same film, even when the unit length to be copied only requires part of the length of one film reel.

FLAT-BED OR SO-CALLED PLANETARY[1] CAMERAS

The automatic linking of the motion of the film and the document, and the fact that copying can be made a virtually *continuous* process, makes the flow-microfilmers unrivalled for ease and speed of operation. The equipment is, however, necessarily limited in scope and flexibility. In these respects, flat-bed machines readily giving a continuously adjustable reduction ratio clearly have the advantage.

Flat-bed cameras use a stationary film and document, and the camera unit is usually mounted on a vertical (or nearly vertical) pillar, while the document is laid on the flat bed. The camera units are frequently like a ciné camera, which has been modified to allow single frames to be exposed to successive documents or pages of a book with economy of effort and film.

Before discussing the construction of flat-bed cameras, two factors which can restrict the reader's choice should be mentioned. The *size and form* of the film accepted must be compatible with other units such as readers and enlargers. In addition to using 16 mm film, flat-bed cameras have been made to accept film widths of 35 mm, 70 mm and 105 mm. Other cameras used for making 'step-and-repeat' negatives, from which 'Microcards' or microfiches can be printed, employ cut-sheet film. If the copies are required to bear code marks or binary-coded fields for mechanical retrieval or automatic searching, facilities for producing the marks must be arranged for at the copying stage. For some users, the means used for coding may be at least as important as the primary (copying) function of the equipment (see p. 387 et seq.).

An important attribute of any flat-bed microfilmer is the *rigidity of the column* required to maintain the focal plane parallel to the bed and to minimize effects of vibration. With most equipment now available, *focus* is automatically adjusted by a cam mechanism according to the height of the camera unit. Alternative methods are manual focusing by a scale, and focusing by observing on the flat bed an enlarged image of a graticule placed in the focal plane. *Illumination* is normally by the method conventionally used for photographic copying. In order to avoid surface reflections, the documents are illuminated by two or more tungsten lamps in rows on either side of the flat bed, and placed so that the line from the lamps to the centre of the document subtends an angle about 45° to the normal. Since most microfilm equipment is required for making large numbers of copies, employment of relatively high-wattage lamps and under-running them is a good practice. For special types of 'difficult' single-sheet originals, such as engineering

---

[1] Since flat-bed microfilmers have nothing to do with planets, the microfilming industry would be well advised to return to the shorter and more descriptive term *flat-bed*.

drawings, it has been found that separation of the wanted image from background dirt is assisted by equipping the baseboard with an illuminated opal, and balancing the intensities of reflected and transmitted light to give the best visual appearance. Transmitted-light illumination is particularly desirable for the copying of drawings on translucent materials.

Since microfilming practice demands the production of negatives with consistent background density from frame to frame and over the area of each frame, uniformity of illumination is particularly important. The adjustment of flat-bed microfilmers to give uniform illumination over the entire field has been discussed by Nelson [15].

The use of photocells to assist *exposure control* may at one time have been considered a luxury, but is becoming increasingly essential as specifications for density limits are written into microfilming contracts. Moreover, meticulous exposure control is an important factor in the improvement of image quality required by many of the most advanced applications. To compensate for the different reflectivities of papers or for the effect of partial illumination by transmitted light, the light coming from the document is received by the photocell, and lamp voltages are adjusted to give a specified reading on the light meter (see also pp. 388–96).

With flat-bed cameras, adjustment of the *film advance* to the size of the reduced aerial image is essential for economical use of film. In one simple fixed-focus instrument, this is achieved by moving a guide-bar coupled to the film transport in front of each document immediately before exposure. With variable reduction equipment the *reduction ratio* may be required to be adjusted so that the reduced images fill the space available on the film. This can be effected by projecting the image of a graticule placed in the focal plane, and adjusting the camera height until the projected image fits the documents to be copied. When many documents of the same size have to be copied, the film advance has been controlled by the separation between a pair of movable masks just in front of the focal plane. For adjustment, the image of the masks projected on the copy-board is caused to 'frame' a document of the desired width. At the same time, the position of guide lines on the copy-board is adjusted to coincide with the images of the masks. Thus, documents placed between the guide lines will always be imaged between the masks, and the film advance conveniently equals the distance between the masks.

In many microfilmers, the *exposing routine* is almost completely mechanized. Thus with one camera, exposures are made by pressing a foot switch once each document has been placed in position. An electric motor then successively actuates a suction device holding the film flat in the focal plane, operates the shutter, records the exposure on a counter and advances the film. One second is needed for the entire cycle of operations, and both the operator's hands are free for page turning or moving the documents or drawings into position on the copy-board.

The *speed of operation* of flat-bed equipment is largely controlled by the speed with which successive documents can be placed in position with the required accuracy and without damage. With small books having adequate spinal margins it is merely necessary to turn over the pages. Often film economy and speed of operation is improved by copying two pages at a time. With thick books, the departure of the two pages from a single plane may be undesirably large, and information can be lost by curvature of the pages at the spinal margin. Unexpected defects in a proportion of images may be caused by the pages of the book tending to creep back after turning and during exposure (*page-creep*). To combat such problems, equipment such as the 'Recordak' book-holder has been produced. The two sections of the open book are placed on platforms supported as the pans of old-fashioned kitchen scales. A hinged glass cover is then brought down to flatten the pages and prevent page creep.

Speedy operation with some microfilming jobs can be a fairly strenuous operation. Consider, for instance, the filming of a month's run of a daily *newspaper*, so that each sheet is correctly placed and none is torn or crumpled. The mere task of bringing to the microfilmer sufficient *engineering drawings* to keep it reasonably occupied requires considerable thought, care and application. The considerable weight of *bound newspapers* and the fragility of the paper of older issues poses a special problem. Because the large pages and small size of print makes copying of two pages at a time impracticable, the volume has to be moved sideways by the width of the page after each exposure. To minimize the required effort, a 'shuttle' copy-board has been designed to allow the whole volume to be rolled to and fro, so that alternate pages were brought underneath the camera in their correct numerical sequence.

As with flow-microfilmers, the convenience of many flat-bed cameras has been improved by built-in alarms giving warning of possible causes of failures. When further requirements become apparent, there is a tendency for designers to introduce quite radical modifications. For some purposes, the possibility of obtaining an on-demand microfilm copy without having to wait for the film to be sent away for processing seemed very attractive. In the 3M Filmac 1000d Processor-Camera, documents up to 18×24 in (46×61 cm) in size could be copied on a short length of silver-halide film already mounted in an aperture card (Plate 50). After exposure, the film was automatically developed, fixed, washed to the level required for acceptable storage life and dried within less than 1 minute. Another interesting feature of this flat-bed equipment is the use of mirrors to fold the optical path. This, combined with the use of a large number of small lamps placed to secure uniform illumination, permits the apparatus to be made remarkably compact.

PRODUCTION OF COPIES IN TWO-DIMENSIONAL ARRAYS

Our discussion has, so far, been concerned mainly with the production of series of document images on long lengths of film. For some applications, and particularly in libraries, it has proved convenient to use rectangular pieces of film or paper (called sheet microfilm, microfiche, 'Microcard', etc.) filled with several rows of images, each depicting one or two pages of a book, journal or technical report. Typically, a convenient area for handling and postage is occupied by copies of some 50 or 60 or more pages (Plate 3). In principle, it should be possible to produce such two-dimensional arrays of images by pasting the pages to be copied on a board, and copying them with a single lens, as Dagron produced his pigeon-post pellicles [3]. With double-sided documents, however, two copies of the original would be needed, and the separation and laying out of the separate sheets would be most laborious. In any case, the copying of many pages simultaneously requires a lens covering a very large field, and is an unnecessarily difficult optical task.

One method capable of producing two-dimensional arrays was developed by manufacturers of microphotographic curios around 1860. Cameras were built with horizontally movable dark slides allowing a plate to be exposed behind a single lens, with the number of exposing positions controlled by a ratchet [16]. This gave a single row of images, and further rows were made with the lens moved vertically between each row. 'Step-and-repeat' cameras for copying documents have been constructed on the same principles. In some cases, both vertical and horizontal movements of the dark slide is controlled by ratchets. Some apparatus is provided with sets of ratchets of different pitch, so that a range of reduction ratios can be used for documents of different size with equally efficient use of the available film area [17].

If a machine of this type were used for a working day of 8 hours and a modest average rate of 10 exposures per minute,[1] copying two pages at a time would give 9,600 pages per day. With 50 pages per 5 × 3 in side, this corresponds to 24 sheets exposed per hour, or 48 feet of 5 in wide (125 mm) film per day. At this level of output, simple rack and tank processing by a single operator could cope with the work, and

---

[1] Maintenance of this rate throughout a working day might be difficult with some types of original.

cut-sheet film compatible with this system is convenient for the individual scholar or small research unit. For centralized installations with a much larger output, the film would be better kept in roll form, and continuous processing machines used. Two-dimensional arrays of images in roll form have been produced on equipment developed by Cordonnier [17]. Successive exposures produced images side-by-side across the width of 6 in (15 cm) film, and after completion of a row, the film was advanced by the height of one row.

Another method used to copy documents for two-dimensional arrays was developed by Kuipers [18]. The copies were made on unperforated 16 mm film on a standard flat-bed microfilmer. After six exposures corresponding to the copying of 12 pages on $4\frac{3}{4}$ in (12 cm) of film, the film was advanced for three frames without exposure. The processed film was cut into unit lengths which were assembled into the composite image at the printing stage. At one time it seemed likely that this method would be rapidly superseded by step-and-repeat cameras, but its protagonists stoutly maintain its continued viability. Certainly the obvious inconvenience of having to assemble the lengths at the printing stage can be considered to be recompensed by the ready use of normal microfilm exposing and processing equipment, and the ease of up-dating when only a few pages of a document have to be changed.

One feature of all these systems giving two-dimensional arrays of images, is that bibliographical information reproduced at a size legible by the unaided eyes has been printed across the top of the sheet. Thus each sheet can be positively identified without having to remove it from the file and place it in a reader. Since the field width needed for the copying of the bibliographical information is about five times that for each microfilm frame, an additional optical system is needed for its reproduction. The ingenuity used to accomplish this can have a marked effect on the convenience of copying equipment for producing sheet microforms.

INTRODUCTION OF CODED INFORMATION

With microfilm systems incorporating any sort of optically produced coded marks, the method for generating the marks must be considered an integral part of the filming process. It can certainly have a marked effect on the overall copying rate. The marks may be produced by projecting reduced images of illuminated apertures through the normal microfilming lens, or a separate projection unit may be employed. According to the scale of the operation, the marks may occupy just the edge margin of the film, or the thin gap of otherwise unexposed film between the successive frames, or more or less of the area of the frames themselves (Plate 54). When many digits of coded information are copied, the density requirements for unambiguous recognition become more demanding, and Minicard emulsion (see p. 428) was tailored for this purpose to give high contrast at high density values.[1] For satisfactory functioning of searching equipment, it is necessary for the code marks to occupy locations accurately placed with respect to the slits or apertures of the interrogating equipment. Registration of the marks relative to the edge of the film is thus important, and this rather than emulsion/lens performance has tended to limit the compression of coded information. Silverman has described electronic techniques for by-passing this difficulty [19].

EXPOSING TECHNIQUE

By this stage of our argument, it is assumed that the basic decisions on the choice of reduction ratio, emulsion, lens and camera have all been made. We now come to the thorny and crucial question of exposing technque. By what principles should exposures be adjusted to maximize the success of the microfilming operation?

The first point to remember, is that the variety of line quality encountered in practically every bulk microfilming operation can only be dealt with by treating the input as if it were a continuous-tone subject. This immediately precludes the use of high or extreme-contrast emulsions or developers [20]. The next point to consider is that the contrast or density-range of images reproduced by silver-halide emulsions initially increases with exposure. With lesser exposures, the light received by the emulsion corresponds to the low-contrast 'toe' of the characteristic curve, and the density-range is increased with greater exposures as more of the 'straight-line' part of the characteristic curve is employed.

Consider a specific case, in which the lens projects images of heavy and fine lines and background to give relative luminosity values of 1·59, 5 and 20 respectively. At one exposure level, these may correspond to log-relative-exposure values of 0·2, 0·7 and 1·3 respectively, and a four-fold exposure increase will raise these values by 0·6. From the characteristic curve of Fig. 106, the density readings corresponding to these exposure values were read off.

It is reasonable to assume that users of microfilm wish to retain all the information on the original documents, and the *useful density difference* can therefore be defined as background density minus fine-line density. Table 15 shows that the increased exposure raised this *useful density difference* by 24 per cent, but it also increased the *line-*

---

[1] The emulsion developed for the Minicard project was also designed to retain information through several generations of copying and at a 60 : 1 reduction ratio. This material is obtainable from the Eastman Kodak Co. on supports of different widths and types suitable for a number of special applications.

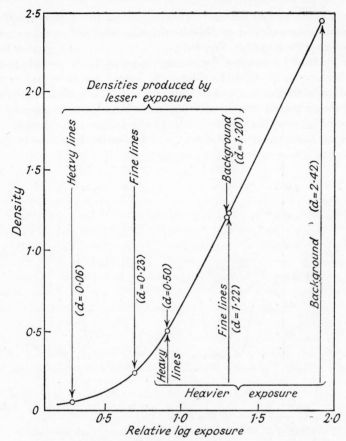

Fig. 106 *Influence of Exposure Level in Document Copying*
Densities produced by different parts of the image at lesser and heavier exposures are shown in brackets.

Table 15. Density dependence on exposure level

	Lesser exposure	Greater exposure
Density of heavy lines	0·06	0·50
,, ,, fine lines	0·23	1·22
,, ,, background	1·20	2·42
Background minus fine lines (*useful density difference*)	0·97	1·20
Fine lines minus heavy lines (*line-density range*)	0·17	0·72

density range by 300 per cent. This increase of *line-density range* by increased exposure was graphically demonstrated with a microdensitometer by Fromm [21] (Fig. 107).

In the use of microfilm, the consequences of the magnitude of the line-density range depend on how the images are used. When the negative microfilm images are viewed directly on a reader, the eyes tend to see mainly the density difference between each line and its adjacent area of background. Differences between the densities of different lines are not obtrusive, and images with relatively high

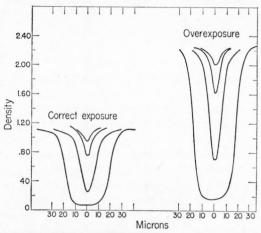

Fig. 107 *Microdensitometer Profile of group of lines with correct and over-exposure*
Lines of width 1, 0·25, 0·06 and 0·015 mm were reduced 30 diameters by an F/8 lens on Recordak Micro-file film (Type 5454).
Courtesy of H. J. Fromm and 'Journal of Photographic Science'.

background density have been used satisfactorily. Note, however, that the density of the fine lines of the heavily exposed image (Table 15) was 0·99 greater than in the lesser exposed image. The brightness of the projected image of the fine lines would therefore be reduced to one-tenth, which indicates that too high a background density should be avoided even with this simplest mode of use.

The consequences of a large line-density range are more serious when the microfilm negatives are designed for subsequent photographic reproduction. This is particularly true when enlarging, because light spread in the projection lens and enlarging paper causes lines to spread rapidly on exposure. It can be shown that the finest reproduction of any line is given by the minimum enlarging exposure producing adequate density or contrast in the print. Thus when the line-density range is large, there will be no single exposure capable of reproducing all lines satisfactorily. The correct enlarging exposure for the heavy lines leaves the fine lines weak (or not recorded at all), and exposures sufficient to reproduce the fine lines coarsen the broad lines. Thus information can be lost at either end of the scale, and this deterioration may continue when further copying stages are used.

On the basis of much practical experience, it has been suggested that microfilm negatives for most purposes should be made with a background density not exceeding 1·2. For example, the United States Military Specification of Requirements for Microfilming of Engineering Documents on 35-mm film (MIL-M-9868. 15 April, 1960) specified background densities between 1·0 and 1·2. For other purposes such as enlargement on xerographic media, background densities as low as 0·9 or less have been suggested. T. Wilson specifically discussed the negative characteristics required for copying engineering drawings to be subsequently re-enlarged at a fixed exposure value on diazo paper after printing on 'Kalvar' film [22]. To produce negatives combining a small line-density range with a large useful-density difference, he extended development of his negative film to 10 minutes at 68° F (20° C) in an X-ray developer (DX. 80) and controlled background density at 1·1. In spite of this forced development, the negatives were neither too fogged nor unduly grainy. This system was stated to retain practically all the information in the drawings: a claim which has been substantiated by some users [23].

For many years it has been the practice to standardize the *background* density of microfilm negatives, in spite of the fact that the images were intended to record the *lines*. This was because only the background presented continuous areas large enough for density measurements by available instruments. A departure from this custom was initiated by Rudd in 1953, while using microfilm as an intermediate for copying and disseminating such originals as technical reports in the Research Laboratories of the Eastman Kodak Co [24]. As his negatives were made only for his own use, he had greater freedom of choice than most commercial microfilming technologists. Since the letters of a document with lightly printed or written text had a higher reflectance than the letters of a document with bold black text, he argued that it was logical to give the former less exposure. Before copying, he suggested that documents be classified into five groups, with each group given an appropriate exposure.

The aim of this system was to produce negatives with approximately constant maximum line density, so that all negatives could be enlarged with the same exposure value. It has been stated that Rudd's method (Table 16) gained wide acceptance [25].

With the increased economic importance of processes for bulk production of enlargements from microfilms, technologists then considered whether instruments could be devised to give objective

Table 16. Rudd's classification of documents for copying

Group	Characteristics of text	Relative exposure	Background density (above base)
1	Dense black printing or writing of moderate size	100	1·42
2	Fine or small print, lightly typed letters, writing with soft pencil	95	1·32
3	Very fine print, somewhat faded print, graphs with thin coloured lines, pencilled engineering drawings	87	1·12
4	Poorly printed faint documents, lightly handwritten manuscripts and drawings	80	0·97
5	'Photostat' and other paper negatives	180	—

measurements instead of the subjective judgements used in Rudd's method. Frey, Nelson and Rubin of the Bell Telephone Laboratories noted that the microfilm industry had operated with an 'upside-down' density standard [26]. Because available equipment had to be used, background densities had been read, rather than the densities of the lines which actually carried the information. Microdensitometers were needed for measuring the densities of lines in both original documents and microfilm copies. For measuring documents (presumably engineering drawings) they recommended a slit 0·003 × 0·0625 in (0·075 × 1·59 mm) and for microfilm negatives these dimensions would be divided by the reduction factor. As a result of their examination of microdensitometer traces of microfilm negatives, they proposed that the negatives should be made with maximum line density 0·25 and background density 1·0.

The reduction of these ideas to practice, and ideas for integrating the measurements into actual microfilming routines, were discussed at the 1962 (11th) Convention of the National Microfilm Association. Jamieson [25] described an instrument called 'Scanalume' which was attached to the input camera for the 'Walnut' system (Fig. 108).[1] This basically consisted of a 1 : 1 camera placed at the side of the copying unit, and employed an F/4·5 10-in (25 cm) lens to image the central portion of the illuminated document on a rotating disc with a circular aperture near its perimeter. The light from the aperture was taken to a photomultiplier through a 0·006 in (150 μ) diameter fibre optic. As the disc rotated, the aperture scanned a circular path corresponding to a 4 in (10 cm) circle on the documents, and a meter recorded the level of background illumination as the intensity of

[1] The 'Walnut' system, developed by International Business Machines Corporation for the United States Central Intelligence Agency, assembled large numbers of images in a mechanized filing system (p. 429).

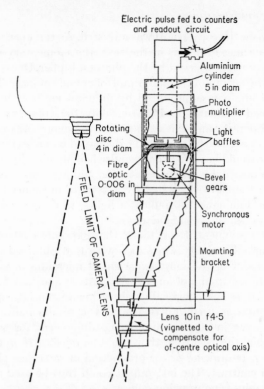

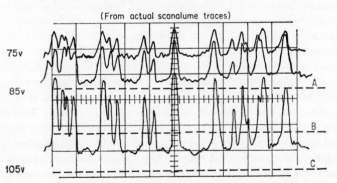

Fig. 108 *Scanalume Unit Monitoring Reflectivities of Detail of Original Documents*
Unit was mounted on microfilmer copying input to Walnut file.
Courtesy of B. Jamieson and National Microfilm Association.

Fig. 109 *Scanalume traces at different illumination levels*

The three traces show relative luminance values for the same area illuminated
with different lamp voltages. The dotted lines show Systems Standards: A for
average line luminance (to give line density 0·35), B and C for minimum and
maximum background luminances (giving background densities of 0·85 and 1·6).
Only at 105 volts was the background density within tolerance.

Courtesy of B. Jamieson and National Microfilm Association of America.

illumination on the copy-board was adjusted. As the aperture crossed the images of lines or letters in the text, the momentary changes of light intensity were observed by the photomultiplier. One could take a trace from the output of the photomultiplier and compare the line and background luminances produced by different lamp voltages with a predetermined standard. In Fig. 109, only 105 volts gave adequate background density and the average line luminance was close to the system standard. The trace could be displayed on an oscilloscope, but the operator would have to average pulse heights visually, and output would be retarded by the necessity for making decisions. Decision making was therefore simplified by a type of pulse-height analyser showing line luminance by indicator lights, while background luminance was shown by a light meter.

With this equipment it was found that exposure control for documents of variable quality was superior to that obtained by the unaided judgement of the most experienced microfilm operators. The system could be used not only for adjusting line and background luminances by reflected light, but also when mixed transmitted and reflected light was used. Furthermore, the results indicated which documents gave insufficient luminance differences for satisfactory copying. When this occurred, they could be rejected from the system for re-typing, re-drawing or for production of same-size photocopies of increased contrast. The instrument could thus be used for quality control in engineering drawing offices.

For the most effective use, the 'Scanalume' used additional devices for predicting the probable consequences not only of changes in line blackness, but also the consequences of changes in line width, line spacing, and the overall contrast of any processes subsequently used for making copies from the microfilm images. However, it only *predicted* the probable result of microfilming, and for effective control, one also needs an instrument for measuring the densities of the images of lines in processed microfilm negatives. The basic requirements seem to have been fulfilled several years previously in the Rapid Scanning Microdensitometer described by Brown of the Eastman Kodak Research Laboratories [27]. A microscope was used to project an enlarged image of a photographic film on a slit in front of a photomultiplier. The mechanical stage of the microscope was automatically traversed, and the resultant changes of current in the photomultiplier were modulated to display density profiles as a trace on an oscilloscope.

Jamieson described the use of a Rapid Scanning Microdensitometer specially built by the Hogan Facsimile Co. of New York, for monitoring microfilm images used in the Walnut project [25]. In this instrument, images of microfilm negatives were projected on the focal plane of a rotating-disc scanner, and the spectral sensitivity of the photo-electric recording system was approximately adjusted to the spectral sensitivity of 'Kalvar' film. The pulses received by the photomultiplier were electronically processed to display the microdensitometer scan across the text on an oscilloscope (Plate 51). This machine was used to inspect microfilm negatives, and any which failed to meet the system specifications for density and contrast were rejected. Measurements on acceptable negatives were used to determine the exposure required on 'Kalvar' film, and tab cards were accordingly punched to indicate one of eight discrete exposure values.

The use of scanning microdensitometers for studying microfilm characteristics has also been discussed by Derr, of the General Aniline and Film Corporation Laboratories [28]. One particularly ambitious instrument employed two matched microdensitometers for comparing the density distribution of different microfilm samples. This caused the traces from the two samples to be alternately displayed on a cathode-ray tube with a high-persistance phosphor, and was used for research on image quality.

In the same paper, Derr described simpler instruments which could prove more suitable for every-day use. An Ozalid Microline Evaluator for measuring engineering drawings comprised a movable optical-measuring head connected by a flexible lead to its amplifier. The head illuminated at 45° the engineering drawing on which it was stood, and light leaving the sample perpendicularly was projected on the photo-multiplier through an aperture corresponding to 0·003 in (76 μ) width at the sample. A reflex mirror on the head permitted its accurate location on any appropriate part of the drawing.

The concept of using a manually moved optical-measuring head would seem well adapted to engineering drawings, in which lines are likely to be inconveniently widely spaced for an automatic scanner such as Scanalume. Manual adjustment of the position of the sample was also used in the Ozalid Microline Evaluator for microfilm. This comprised a simple fixed-position microdensitometer for evaluating processed microfilm images. A reflex mirror was again used for convenient location of the sample. It seems likely that both these instruments could be effectively used for the control of microfilm output. For the sake of simplicity, they attempt neither the scanning nor the decision-making functions discussed by Jamieson, and therefore make greater demands on the operator's skill and judgement.

There seems little doubt that uniformity of image quality can benefit from the employment of microdensitometers, but how widely this will spread in every-day commercial practice is questionable. Their use is likely to slow down the initial microfilming operation, but this loss may be recouped at later stages in the use of the microfilm images. This reasoning suggests that these advanced control methods will be of greatest use when a system demands the critical specification of microfilm quality in the copying of large numbers of varied documents. These conditions are likely to be met when microfilm is used for projects such as Walnut, continuous enlarging, generation of microfiche, 'Microcard' or 'Microprint' and as an intermediate for lithographic printing or further reduction.

PROCESSING OF PRIMARY MICROIMAGES

Microimages have been processed as single images on units of film already mounted in aperture cards, or as plates or cut-sheet film bearing multiple images for 'Microcards' or microfiche, or as film in varying lengths—often as units of 100 feet (approx. 30 metres). A great variety of handling methods can therefore be employed, but these must usually satisfy the requirements of high reproducibility, adequate removal of thiosulphate and freedom from dirt and mechanical damage.

Reproducibility of processing is a crucial requirement, for without it, control of either background or line density is impossible. Fortunately, the principles of maintaining solution temperature, agitation and activity have already been extensively studied for the processing of motion-picture and X-ray films [29].

Since microfilm images are often made to allow destruction of the bulky original documents, the permanence of the processed images is of great importance. A major cause of fading of silver-image photographs has been retention of thiosulphate from the fixing bath. In this connection, the National Bureau of Standards of the United States of America has stated that films for archival storage should not contain more than 0·005 milligrams of thiosulphate per square inch of film [30]. Processing methods designed to achieve satisfactory removal of thiosulphate, and colourimetric analytical procedures for showing the level of residual thiosulphate occupy considerable space in the technical literature [31].

In spite of these Standards, the microfilm industry in the United States of America discovered in 1963 that a small proportion of stored microfilm images were showing chemical attack in the form of microscopic blemishes seen as minute orange or red spots [32]. These were confined to negative silver microfilm, and were most numerous on the blackened leader. The outer turns of image-bearing film were also sometimes affected, and in some instances the films were being subjected to a progressive attack in times of two years (but usually much longer). Although the proportion of films affected was small, the discovery that such an attack *could* occur raised a serious question which merited a major research effort.

In a large proportion of cases, the films could be said to have been exposed in storage to unsuitable atmospheric humidity, temperature or contamination. Because of the long storage times and erratic incidence of the defect, investigation proved extraordinarily difficult. Blemishes of similar appearance could be produced in a few weeks by storage at high humidities and temperatures, or by exposure to hydrogen peroxide vapour. Peroxides formed during the oxidation of drying oils in paint films were already known to be capable of producing rapid fading of prints exposed to the atmosphere.

McCamy of the National Bureau of Standards described researches in which spot formation was promoted by exposure of films to air of moderate to high relative humidity, and which was in contact with organic materials likely to form peroxides during gradual oxidation [33]. In particular, spots were promoted by cardboards of the types used for making the boxes in which processed microfilms had been so widely stored. As a reconstruction of the real course of events, this experiment is extremely plausible.

A variety of methods for combating this attack have been proposed. Since distribution of the spots clearly pointed to atmospheric attack, it was suggested that microfilm should be kept in film cans rather than cardboard boxes. Various processing modifications including addition of iodide to the fixing bath and a final treatment in a gold toning bath have been proposed [34].

It is not yet possible to claim that this trouble has been completely cured. Since, however, such a small proportion of stored film was affected, combination of thorough thiosulphate removal, a processing modification, equilibration to a low relative humidity and storage in cans should give a very high standard of archival permanence (p. 403).

Because the scale of operations can vary so much, many different methods have been used for handling microfilm images. For in-camera processing of single frames of film already mounted in aperture cards (see p. 385), the area to be processed is accurately located over an effective gasket, and developer, fixer and wash-water are in turn applied. At the other extreme come high-capacity continuous-processing machines of the type developed for processing motion-picture film. Other methods used or proposed are:

(i) *Dish (tray) processing*, particularly for 'step-and-repeat' two-dimensional-array negatives,

(ii) *Tank processing* which may be used with nitrogen-burst agitation for optimum uniformity,

(iii) The '*roly-poly*' method, in which film is wound backwards and forwards between two reels under the surface of the solution,

(iv) The *spiral* method, in which the film is loaded into a metal or plastic spiral holding the convolutions apart, and is then developed in tanks as with processing of roll-film or 35 mm film by amateurs,

(v) *Web* processing, in which the film is wound in contact with a porous web bearing the solution,

(vi) *Miniature continuous* processing, in which the film is passed through one or more loops in developing, fixing and washing tanks, at a rate scaled down in proportion to the reduced length of travel.

In continuous-processing machines, much attention has been paid to such questions as film transport, the methods of application and agitation of solutions, the removal of excess solutions between baths, and the maintenance of steady bath activity by controlled bleeding-off of used solution and topping-up with replenisher. The use of deep tanks of solution is normal, but solution application by sprays, or by metering on a viscous solution to the emulsion surface have been considered. For some applications, worth-while mechanical simplification has been derived from the use of 'monobaths' in which the functions of development and fixation are combined in a single solution with minimal loss of desirable image properties.[1]

From what has been said in this section, it will be obvious that processing of microfilm images can either be a matter of passing interest to the reader, who decides to delegate this function to specialists in the field, or it can be a major question for consideration by those deciding to organize their own processing. Factors which may be considered are:

(i) cost,

(ii) the permissible delay between making an exposure and checking the final result,

(iii) commercial or government security,

(iv) steady or sporadic rate of input,

(v) influence of climatic conditions,

(vi) restrictions which may be imposed by 'on location' processing.

Taylor and Kitrosser of Itek Corporation have written a useful survey considering both present practice and possible future developments [36]. They suggest that infra-red monitoring of film density in the developer should be applied to control of microfilm, as has already been used for graphic arts and aerial photography.

---

[1] In some instances, improved sharpness resulting from edge effects has been reported in monobath processing [35].

QUALITY CONTROL OF PRIMARY COPIES

There is only one acceptable rejection rate for large volume micro-filming operations, namely zero. To achieve this standard, quality control at the first-generation copying stage is a most important exercise. The necessity for quality control is indicated not only by the scale of the operation, but also since every single unit image is different and unique. Particularly effective control is required when microfilm is used as an intermediate medium for the generation of further copies at any scale of reproduction. In order to ensure ultimate acceptability of the final output, the images then need a 'reserve of quality' to offset possible degradation during further reproduction.

The adequacy of quality control will be influenced by the choices of emulsion, lens, reduction ratio, camera, exposing technique and processing method. Two different philosophies can be applied to the final checking of results. One approach uses reproducible images such as sensitometric strips, or microfilmed images of resolution test charts to sample the performance of the system at regular intervals during the day's work. Some contracts demand the incorporation of test images in every reel of film. Since test images can be designed to give relatively objective measurements by visual inspection or with a scanning microdensitometer, they are suitable for procedures of statistical control.

The second approach involves subjective judgement of the image quality of document copies passing through the system at any time. For this purpose it is useful to formulate a set of quality descriptions such as the following (see also Binkley [37]).

Table 17. Subjective quality descriptions

Standard	Description of microfilm copy
'Perfect'	Degradation hardly detectable. Copies suitable for typographical scholars.
'Excellent'	Degradation in no way affecting legibility. Copies suitable for prolonged study by scholars or research workers.
'Commercial'	Degradation obvious, but every letter or figure still legible.
'Decipherable'	Severe degradation. Identity of individual letters needs to be checked by their position in words and from the context. This quality often results from inferior input such as poor carbon copies.

Consistency in making such subjective judgements is often assisted by reference to sets of standard images corresponding to the quality descriptions. The setting up of a numerical scale of arbitrary quality values may also be helpful.

Whatever method of inspection is used, achievement of high average quality is the result of continuous care. In this connection Suydom

o

[38] appropriately quoted John Ruskin 'Quality is *never* an accident. It is always the result of intelligent effort. There must be the *will* to produce a superior thing.' In his own article, Suydom discusses four subjects pertinent to quality control. *Equipment* must be kept clean and in good working condition at all times, which requires a continuous programme of preventative maintenance. The cleanliness of the lens is particularly important, and Rudd has described how this can be checked with a pencil torch (flashlight) [24]. Rudd found that lenses could acquire a harmful film overnight by the settling of particles of mineral salt when lake water was used in air-conditioning humidifier sprays. As an essential part of his equipment, Suydom described a 'Universal Target Chart', comprising both grey patches and resolution test images for 'go' and 'no-go' inspection.

In the *monitored operation* of the microfilm programme, inspection of this Universal Target Chart was an integrated part of the routine, and was used to maintain focus, exposure and processing within tolerances. One matter of some concern, is the tendency of microfilm images to show latent-image fading. Results published by Olsen [39] showed that density could fall by around 0·18 if development was delayed over a week-end, and 0·12 in the first 24 hours. These density changes are substantial in relation to the Military Specification of back-ground density between 1·2 and 1·0, and quality control demands suitable allowance for this in the exposing routine.

Suydom's third subject was the *recording* of dates, camera identity, resolution and density figures and processing rates. The filing of such information provides a history, which can be invaluable for rapid detection and correction of any tendency for quality to drift. Finally he discussed *inspection routines*, and the selection and responsibilities of inspectors. Unreliable inspectors can thwart the quality control system. Precautions Suydom recommends are the use of clean cotton gloves at all times by inspectors. Before checking density, the film should be viewed over a light-box for frames out of alignment or documents with folded corners, or with abnormally high or low densities. Densitometers should be given 20 minutes to warm up, and inspectors should be on their guard to offset the effects of astigmatism or reductions of visual efficiency caused by poor health. Finally, the time-consuming test for hypo removal to archival standards should be carried out frequently and on a regularly scheduled basis. Apparatus and procedures were designed for avoiding the risks of poisoning (by the reagents used) and of false results produced by contamination of the solutions.

Fromm [40] reviewed several procedures for monitoring the effective resolution of microfilm copies. When the National Bureau of Standards issued their Microcopy Resolution Test Chart, they included a pamphlet describing a method for estimating the probable quality of reproduction [41]. In effect, it stated that:

$$q = \frac{Re}{r}$$

where q is the quality index,
  R is the measured resolution in l/mm,
  e is the height in millimetres of a lower-case 'e' and
  r is the reduction ratio.

The quality index q is numerically equal to the number of lines just resolvable within the height of the 'e'. Figures of 8, 5, and 3 were suggested as corresponding to excellent, easily legible and just legible qualities respectively.

Since the resolving power should be constant for any given camera/film combination and the minimum acceptable quality index for any application is also constant, Fromm suggested tabulating the maximum permissible reduction ratios against the heights of the smallest lower-case 'e's in the original document. For example, with a required quality index of 5 and a camera giving 130 l/mm, 'e's of height 0·7, 0·9 and 1·1 mm should be copied with reduction ratios not exceeding 18·2 : 1, 23·4 : 1 and 26·8 : 1 respectively.

If this method were consistently applied, it should prevent the production of inferior copies resulting from the use of excessive reduction ratios. Furthermore, by observing the resolution loss occurring during multi-generation printing, he suggested that the original negative can be made with a high enough measured quality index to ensure adequate quality at the final stage.

In the same paper he also discussed the Random-Grain-Pattern step tablet being investigated by J. H. Altman of the Kodak Research Laboratories. This consists of a film containing prints of grain patterns of identical integrated density, but with progressively increasing grain size. When the Step Tablet was laid on a document, the information became progressively less legible as the size of the grain pattern increased. The largest pattern through which the document could be satisfactorily read depended on such factors as the size, sharpness and contrast of the letters or lines. Thus the method might be used to estimate the maximum permissible reduction ratio for the reproduction of the document. By ensuring that unsuitable documents are not copied at all, or that excessive reduction ratios are not used, it was hoped that the method could raise the average quality of microfilm output (see also p. 394).

STORAGE OF MICROFILM
The saving of space achievable by microfilming is by itself an incentive to employ this medium for the storage of records. It is also

natural to contrast the poor storage life of many papers (particularly some samples of newsprint) with the high stability of 'safety' film base and the long life of many photographs. Confidence in the use of microfilm for archival storage has been fortified by many carefully conducted accelerated ageing tests, and this is the type of data on which standards for processing and the properties of film for archival storage have been based.

Recommendations for the storage of microfilm (such as the British Standard 1153 : 1955 and the American (U.S.A.S.I.) Standard PH 5.4–1957 are (as stated in the Foreword of B.S. 1153) 'generally very similar to those necessary for the storage of ordinary paper documents'. Nevertheless, it should be recognized that microfilm is specially vulnerable to high relative humidity and to water. Because of this, unsuitable storage conditions can nullify care lavished on the production and the quality control of the microfilms. If a microfilming operation has been conducted as the only defence against loss of information, accidental destruction of records can be quite disastrous. To avoid this contingency, proper preparations for storage should be made.

For background information, the reader is referred to the two Standards already quoted, and to Eastman Kodak Pamphlet P. 108 *Storage and Preservation of Microfilms* (Rochester, New York, 1965). The topic has also been discussed by Lewis and Offenhauser [10b] and by Hawken [92].

This literature is concerned with the discussion of two main themes. The first deals with protection of the records against foreseeable external disasters such as fire and water (whatever its origin) and physical destruction of buildings. Precautions mentioned include use of fire-resistant cabinets, safes and maximum security vaults specially constructed in the galleries of disused mines. For future historians, storage in 'time capsules' or the cornerstones of buildings has also been discussed. The above methods are largely based on much practical experience in the protection of paper records, money and other valuables.

The second theme is protection of microfilm against the insidious hazards of high humidity, which may cause condensation and possibly sticking, and may permit fungal attack of the emulsion layer to occur.

The American and British Standards agreed in specifying 60 per cent relative humidity as an upper limit for commercial storage (life time up to 25 years). For indefinite (archival) storage, air conditioning to R.H. 40–50 per cent and temperatures in the range 60° to 80° F (16°–27° C) were stipulated. These recommendations seem to be primarily aimed at the control of condensation and fungal attack.

Both the Standards cited above were issued before microscopic spot occurrence (p. 396) had been detected. To deal with this contingency, McCamy and Pope issued recommendations for storage in more closely specified ambient conditions [33b]. For archival storage, a temperature not exceeding 70° F (21° C), and preferably between 50° F (10° C) and 60° F (16° C) was recommended. For active files they recommended a relative humidity of 30–35 per cent and 15–20 per cent for inactive files. Another feature of their recommendations was that microfilm should be stored in closed containers such as cans, rather than in the cardboard boxes previously used. The same recommendations were made in the Eastman Kodak Pamphlet P. 108, which also recommended that commercial records be stored at a relative humidity of 30–35 per cent (50 per cent as a maximum) and below 70° F (21° C) if possible [70–75° F (21–24° C) as a maximum].

The authorities quoted above consider many other aspects of storage, such as:

ventilation;
control of dirt and chemical contaminants;
the risk of conditioning to high humidity during reading and
    before return to store;
protection by lacquering;
periodic inspection;
re-copying if deterioration starts to show.

The treatises so far discussed study the topic mainly from the viewpoint of users in temperate climates and highly developed countries. It is clear that compliance with the recommendations will be far more difficult in less developed territories where electricity for environment control is not freely available and humidities and temperatures are high. Special problems may also arise in storage in libraries and for educational purposes, where some users are more likely to be unaware of the desirable precautions.

To summarize, it is clear that long-term storage of microfilm is a complex subject. In favourable circumstances where continuous air conditioning is already available, or is unnecessary because of ambient conditions, a minimum of special preparation may be necessary. Storage is, however, a topic which should be thought about *before* starting a microfilming operation. The advisability of having a second copy stored in another place should not be overlooked. As with the original conception and planning of a microfilming operation (see pp. 367 and 365), storage is a matter on which it is advisable to seek expert advice. It is also a subject which should be properly understood by suppliers and installers of storage facilities. Disastrous consequences have resulted from their occasional failure to do so.

'UNITIZATION' AND SUB-DIVISION OF MICROFILM

In its earliest commercial applications, the main emphasis of micro-filming was on *storage* of information, and documents were recorded on long lengths of film in roughly chronological order. This involved considerable delay in the finding of any one frame, accompanied by wear and scratching of the films which might have to be wound and rewound many times. Considerable attention was therefore given to the sub-division of microfilm into information packets of convenient size, or even into single frames (unitization).

The sub-division of the copies into two-dimensional arrays such as microfiches and 'Microcards' (p. 386) was one solution to the problem. Another was to cut roll microfilm into conveniently short lengths and store these in suitably indexed jackets or envelopes [42]. Roll micro-film has also been assembled into two-dimensional arrays by sticking short lengths to a transparent plastic sheet (Diebold Corporation 'Cumulative Microfilm'), or by inserting them in pockets in multiple cellulose-acetate or 'Mylar' jackets. In both cases, the optical quality of the assembled product was designed to permit satisfactory reading or enlarging without removal of the individual lengths of film.

For the same purpose, considerable use has been made of prints from microfilm negatives made on long lengths of paper, which were cut into convenient lengths and stuck on a filing card. Different com-mercial forms provided prints with adhesives requiring moistening, or pressure or heat-sensitive adhesives. By this means, libraries with available labour have produced 'do-it-yourself' micro-opaques in-expensively from their own collection of microfilm negatives.

We have already noted the existence of microfilmers giving in-camera processing, and producing strictly 'unitized' microfilm in the form of single frames mounted over an aperture in a punched filing card (aperture card). The majority of systems handling information in this form operate mainly with second or third-generation copies, and are discussed later (p. 408).

PRODUCTION AND USE OF SECONDARY COPIES

Once a satisfactory primary microfilm copy has been made, it is simpler and cheaper to make further copies from the microfilm, than to re-film the original documents. The advantage of easy production of copies for dissemination was early recognized by librarians. Provi-sion of a microfilm copy of research articles was stated to be cheaper than postal loan of the volume in which the article was contained. At first, secondary copies were made by contact printing on film resembling motion-picture positive stock. Once a primary copy is available, it can be illuminated with light of such intensity that emulsions can be used, which are impossibly slow for the copying of the original documents. In particular, by using high-intensity ultra-violet sources and appropriate optical systems, satisfactory copying rates were achieved with materials such as 'Kalvar' giving a negative-positive response, and diazo films giving direct-positive results. Diazo sensitized materials are particularly convenient for card-to-card duplication of aperture cards.

SAME-SIZE SECONDARY COPIES

For many purposes it is convenient to use secondary copies at the same size as the primary copies. Since every optical projection inevitably leads to some image degradation, it is best to make the copies by contact printing. High rates of printing can be obtained by the use of roll-to-roll printers, in which the primary film and the unexposed film or paper stock are brought into close contact by passing them under tension around a cylindrical drum. Exposure is effected by projecting an intense beam of light through a relatively narrow slit behind which the contacted films pass at a uniform rate. Since modern practice is to utilize the largest possible area of the film by employing non-perforated stock, careful design of film-tension and driving mechanisms is needed to avoid film slip. Slip can both scratch the films, and cause local image distortion or decrease of resolution.

When microfilm images are to be widely used as a part of a system ultimately delivering enlarged positive copies on paper ('hard copy'), it is convenient for the disseminated copies to have 'negative' (white-on-black) tone reproduction. Such copies have been made from the original negative film either by two-stage (intermediate positive then dupe negative) contact-copying on silver-halide film, or by reversal processing with bleaching of the first developed negative image, or by single-stage copying on diazo-sensitized film. By the introduction of Recordak Direct Duplicating Film, Type S.O. 156, the Eastman Kodak Co. permitted the archival permanence of silver images to be combined with the convenience and technical advantages of single-stage duplication [43]. If developed without exposure, the Direct Duplicating Film gives a density of about 2. When contact printed in a DePue Printer, modified by using a 300-watt lamp to replace the normal 100-watt lamp, the exposed areas give progressively reduced density with increasing exposure, and the developed image closely duplicates the original negative in tone reproduction and resolution.

The production of prints from two-dimensional arrays of images is more conveniently effected on flat-bed contact printers. With plate, cut-sheet negatives or composite negatives made by jig assembly of short lengths of 35 mm or 16 mm film, roll-to-roll printing is obviously impossible. Since prints of microfiche or opaque cards are often run off in editions of some dozens of images, assembly of the stock from a processed roll of continuously exposed film would be very difficult. Prints have therefore been made on high-speed automatic printers of the type used for the mass-production of D. and P. prints on silver-chloride papers [18]. When a number of duplicates are required, the equipment made possible printing rates in excess of 600 cards per hour.

USE OF PAPER OR FILM FOR TWO-DIMENSIONAL ARRAYS

Whether sheet microforms with two-dimensional arrays of images should be made on paper or film has been the subject of considerable controversy [44]. At first, opaque forms almost entirely were used in the U.S.A., but European practitioners preferred the microfiche. At present both forms are used in libraries, and some organizations offer prints from their negatives in either form. Film support facilitates the production of really sharp images, and images on film are certainly easier to project either for reading or re-enlargement. This is because condenser illumination allows a large proportion of the light transmitted by the film to reach the viewing screen. Opaque images, however, must be illuminated so that no specularly reflected light can enter the projection objective. Solely light diffusely reflected from the paper support can therefore be used, and only a very small proportion of this can enter the objective. The illumination of cards to give a twenty-fold magnified image of adequate brightness is not an easy task, but readers are available which give images of satisfactory brightness by use of specially designed optical systems. Production of 'hard-copy' enlargements from opaque microforms has proved difficult, and the quality obtainable is poor compared with hard copy from microfiche. Even production of further contact copies is more difficult than from film.

It is, however, just this difference in the optical properties of the card, which is closely bound with its main advantage. Because of the conditions required for projection, surface blemishes and scratches are not obtrusive, and the author has carried an unprotected card in a much used pocket for many months without impairing its legibility. By contrast, any marks on either back or front surfaces will show when microfiche are projected, and they really need to be filed in protective envelopes or jackets. A further advantage of cards is that both sides can be filled with images.

In concluding this section, it should be noted that two-dimensional arrays can also be made from the physical assembly of short lengths from prints made on rolls of 35 mm or 16 mm film or paper (p. 404).

DIAZO-SENSITIZED MATERIALS FOR PRODUCTION OF SECONDARY COPIES

As already noted in Chapter 2, layers sensitized with molecularly dispersed diazo salts have the potential for extreme resolution, particularly when they are present as surface layers on an optically structure-free support. Some materials are now marketed with the diazonium compound and coupler incorporated in the surface layer of a cellulose-acetate base, and fine direct-positive copies can be made rapidly by exposing to a mercury-vapour source. The images are developed by ammonia vapour, and since this uses all the remaining photosensitive compound, no extra step is required for fixing or washing. In recent years, much attention has been given to the production of such products to give a stable image of neutral colour, and with an average curve slope of unity for multi-generation copying [45].

Another important application of diazo compounds employs the nitrogen released by photo-decomposition to form the image. For this purpose, the photosensitive compound was coated in a layer of a non-polar thermoplastic colloid. When the layer was exposed at room temperature, only destruction of the diazo compound could be observed, but on heating briefly to a temperature of 70° C (158° F) or above, the softening of the layer allowed the photochemically released nitrogen to form a cloud of minute bubbles.

This phenomenon formed the basis of the 'Kalvar' vesicular or 'bubble-film' process [46]. At the exposing stage, the optical performance of the layer is that of a diazo film, and the bubble size and distribution was controlled to give resolution very adequate for same-size reproduction of the majority of commercial microfilm images. Since the bubbles do not absorb light, but are visible as a result of refraction and scatter, the visible contrast increased with the degree of collimation of the viewing light. Convenient effective contrast values were obtained with the optical systems of projection microfilm readers.

The appeal and usefulness of this material is derived mainly from its ability to be rapidly developed by heat with a completely dry process. Since bubbles will not form until the layer is heated after exposure, there is no absolute need to remove undestroyed diazo compound. According to the user's requirements, the images can either be 'fixed' by flooding with excess ultra-violet and allowing the nitrogen to escape in the cold, or unexposed areas adjacent to exposed and developed images can be used later for recording of 'add-on' images. Since the bubbles look dark by transmitted light, the process is normally negative-working, but positive working can be achieved by exposing image-wise to destroy diazo compound, allowing the nitrogen to disperse, flooding with excess light, and only then developing by heat.

SECONDARY (OR LATER GENERATION) COPIES ON
APERTURE CARDS

For the maintenance of an active and up-to-date file, there is a lot
to be said for the concept of dividing microfilm into single-frame
lengths (unitization). By themselves, such 'unitized' microfilms are
easily damaged or lost and involve a difficult handling problem. Solutions have been to develop mechanisms for handling the so-called film
chips (Filmorex [47], Minicard [48], Magnavox Media [49]) (see pp. 427–
428), or to mount each unit of film over an aperture in a punched card
of the type used in 'Hollerith', I.B.M. and related sorting machines
(Plate 50). Images thus mounted can be used in simple or complex
routines. At the start of a project it may be sufficient to file the cards
by hand-written or typed filing data. The card then constitutes a
'handle' which greatly lessens the risk of loss or damage, and is conveniently compatible with existing filing methods. As the scale of
operations grows, the cards would be punched, and can then be
handled by punched-card systems. The conversion from manual to
automatic filing and searching will be particularly easy if the user
punches cards at their origination, even if manual filing only is first
used.

When images are mounted on punched cards, it must be admitted
that the space in effect occupied by each frame is much increased, and
one of the main purposes of microfilming might thereby seem to be
partially thwarted.[1] If the information content of each frame is
relatively meagre, and if very large numbers of cards have to be
stored, the disadvantage of the increased space requirement could be
really severe. It is therefore interesting that aperture cards have
found especial favour in applications where the information content of
each image tends to be high. Imagine, for example, the number of
pages of text needed for a complete description of an engineering
drawing, architectural plan or map. With such images, the advantages
of aperture cards have been found to outweigh their greater space
requirement. Their use acquired great impetus when the U.S. Government demanded that complete sets of drawings, in the form of microfilm images in aperture cards, should be filed with every tender for
defence contracts.

A special technology has been developed for the production, reproduction and use of microfilmed images mounted on aperture cards.
Various mechanisms and adhesives have been patented for the convenient and secure mounting of single images, with the film held only
by the small margin produced by ordinary camera manipulation.
Minimizing of curvature or buckling of the film is clearly important.

---

[1] The material of the card itself can, however, carry coding, sorting and much
other information.

An alternative method giving maximum protection is to insert the microfilm image in an envelope of very thin 'Mylar' mounted over the aperture.

When series of documents were to be copied (as has generally been the case) the original reductions were made on 35 mm microfilm, and contact copies made from these on silver-halide, diazo or 'Kalvar' materials would be used on the aperture cards. In fact the production of many complete sets of aperture cards from roll film has been used as a method of 'in-house' publication, for dissemination of engineering drawings to satellite factories. For some organizations, this method was not found to be sufficiently flexible, and on-demand production of duplicate cards was required. This can now be done quickly and cheaply by use of blank aperture cards with a piece of diazo or 'Kalvar' film already mounted over it. After copying the microfilm image by contact exposure to an ultra-violet source and developing by ammonia or heat, the original and blank cards are inserted in a small machine which detects the punched holes and reproduces them in the blank.

SECONDARY COPIES WITH FURTHER REDUCTION

When a further reduction is required during making of the secondary copies, a projection system must be used. Because the primary copies are transparent and of a convenient size, there is little difficulty in securing the high levels of exposing illumination required for large output on emulsion of 'print-out' speed such as diazo. In some cases, for instance in the I.B.M. 'Walnut' system (p. 429), only moderate secondary reduction by a factor of 1 : 2·2 was used from an original copy made at 1 : 15·8. Since the primary negatives were photo-electrically sorted for the printing exposure required (see p. 430), the secondary 'Kalvar' copies could be made to have more consistent properties than the original primary images.

MICROSCOPIC DOCUMENT COPIES

When images are required with very high reduction ratios (say 100 : 1 or more), illumination of opaque documents with the brightness required for conveniently brief exposures becomes impracticable. Use of an intermediate negative (such as a primary microfilm) then becomes a necessity. The techniques of making the copies with an extreme-resolution emulsion and a microscope objective are then similar to those described in Chapters 1–8.

The use of microscopic document copies for espionage has acquired considerable notoriety, and these copies have been called by such names as '*punkt*', '*mikrat*' or '*microdots*'. The suggestion of hiding secret information in an ink-blot or full-stop was made by Sir David Brewster, in the *Encyclopaedia Britannica* of 1857 [1]. An early recorded case was their use by the Japanese in the Russo-Japanese War of 1905 [50]. Images were hidden in the ears, nostrils or under the finger nails, or were placed in smooth ivory pellets which were swallowed. A striking case was that described by J. E. Hoover of the United States Federal Bureau of Investigation [51]. The Nazis were found to be hiding microphotographs of espionage documents in the full stops of typescript or telegram forms. The microscopic images on film were cut out with a hypodermic needle, and inserted between the paper fibres, or concealed under a postage stamp.

In mass-production methods for the making of large numbers of microimages from documents, effective working of the system has depended on the production of copies of such dimensions and under such conditions that the probability of any one image proving unsatisfactory is small. Effective quality control can then be secured by close inspection of only a small proportion of the total number of images. With greater reduction ratios this method is less likely to succeed, because working tolerances are reduced, and the probability of loss of information by contamination of the emulsion surface rises steeply. For the production of microscopic images, the work should preferably be organized so that every image is effectively inspected. It is also prudent to arrange matters so that an appreciable proportion of rejected images causes a minimum of inconvenience. It is interesting to note that the necessity for inspection of microscopic images has been repeatedly described in the literature. Commercial workers of the period 1860–75, for instance, customarily made many images on one plate, and discarded those which were unsatisfactory. Goldberg even examined his print-out images at intervals during the exposure (p. 133). A further example is provided by a portable apparatus developed by the Nazis for making microdots [52]. This had a reversible optical train, which used the microphotographic objective to project an enlarged image of the processed film, so that it could be inspected before dispatch.

Another problem in the use of very small images is the degradation resulting from diffraction and refraction while contact printing (p. 217). Even if the optically reduced images are perfect, their commercial usefulness will be severely limited if they cannot be effectively reproduced by contact printing. In connection with their Photochromic Micro Image Memory, the National Cash Register Company state that they are using special refinements to minimize this degradation [96]. Interesting examples of the results they achieved were the mass-produced copies of the Bible sold at the New York World Fair in 1964. Although each page only measured 0.98×0.62 mm (0.04×0.025 in), and the entire Bible only occupied 4.0×3.2 cm (1.56×1.26 in), every image (over 1,200 in all) was legible.

In spite of these difficulties of high-reduction systems, serious attention is being given to their exploitation for special purposes. The AVCO Corporation, for instance, have developed their random-access VERAC system to use a reduction ratio of 1 : 140 to record 10,000 document pages on a 10 × 10 in (25 cm square) film sheet [54]. A number of notable features were built into the system N.C.R. employed for making their Photochromic Micro Image Memory [53]. The original input was recorded with high image quality on 35 mm film with a 10 : 1 reduction ratio. The microimages were then further reduced by 15 : 1 ratio in an air-tight apparatus filled with filtered, dry and clean air. Thus ambient dust at the final reduction stage was effectively under control. Focus was monitored continuously by pneumatic gauging.

Several operational features for overcoming mistakes or malfunction were linked with the properties of the sensitive photochromic plate (p. 47). Since the image was produced directly by light action, it was essentially a print-out process, and the image could therefore be inspected at any time during or immediately after the exposure. Thus the focus, image identity and position could be checked without delay, and faulty images were erased by an infra-red beam. Erasure left the surface ready to receive another image, so that the process made it possible to assemble images of large numbers of pages with checking, and if necessary correction, of every single image before the next image was recorded. By use of the same properties, up-dating of one or more pages in a block of 10,000 images was possible. Carlson, Grafton and Tauber suggested that the resultant ability to avoid scrapping much work should reduce the cost of assembling large numbers of usable images correctly, thereby making the production and use of such assemblies a practical proposition [55].

A complication of the Photochromic Microimage Memory is that the images only had a relatively short life at room temperature, and therefore had to be stored in 'deep-freeze' conditions. For this reason, master positives were printed on a Lippmann-type silver-halide emulsion, from which copies for dissemination were made by further contact printing. Distributed copies were protected by a thick lacquer layer, which also prevented further unlicensed duplication of the whole sheet by contact printing. Reproduction of single frames on a reader-printer was not, however, hindered. One spectacular proposed application of this process was an information file for astronauts. 50,000 pages were copied on 5 ft 2½ in (1·585 m) of 35 mm film and were viewed in a projector 11¾ × 9½ × 2⅛ in (approx 30 × 25 × 5 cm), and weighing less than 6 pounds (under 3 Kg). The unit could be carried on the astronaut's knee.

In the commercial exploitation of this process, high quality microfilm copies of customer's documents are produced at a moderate reduction ratio (around 10 : 1) and these are then further reduced by a factor of 10–15 : 1 on the photochromic layer. From the resultant photochromic images are produced release films containing the images of up to 5,000 pages on a 6 × 4 in (15 × 10 cm) film, at a cost of about $500 for the initial copying, and about $1 for each release film. Fully engineered readers with manual controls for finding any desired frame have been developed and are available on a rental basis. For the execution of this programme, the National Cash Register Company are establishing a number of service stations with clean-room facilities in major commercial centres in the U.S.A. and Europe. The compression of information and the image quality obtainable can be judged from Plate 52.

TERTIARY AND LATER-GENERATIONS OF MICROFILM COPIES

When particularly wide-spread dissemination of microfilmed copies is desired, production of contact-printed images may be continued through two or more generations. As with the production of long runs of graticule images, one reason may be to guard against wear and tear of the original master images, by making secondary working masters. A secondary reason in the Minicard project was that each stage of copying permitted changes to be made in the coded information by which the film chips were to be found.

Loss of information at each printing stage is the major factor to be guarded against when designing microfilming programmes requiring several printing stages. Information may be lost as a result of optical factors causing some loss of image sharpness at each stage (p. 217). These factors may be light scatter in the printing emulsion and diffraction and refraction at the surface of the negative. Of course an additional population of blemishes tends to become apparent at each stage, particularly when printing from a 'positive' image with dark lines on a clear background. Liquid-gate printing [56] (p. 221) is a powerful tool for minimizing this. The high contrast of most silver-halide microfilm emulsions can also cause loss of information during printing and re-printing. With the continuous-tone character of most microfilm images, losses at each end of the tone-scale accumulate at each printing stage. This was the reason for the use of an emulsion giving an effective gamma of approximately one for the Minicard programme (p. 376). Rubin has discussed the use of Unit-Gamma Diazo materials for multi-generation copying [45(a)].

HIGH RESOLUTION LITHOGRAPHY

When long runs of reduced images in sheet form are required, tertiary copying methods of the type evolved by the Readex Microprint Corporation are of special interest [57]. The documents were first microfilmed at moderate reduction, and a two-dimensional array of images was printed on a sensitized surface to give the secondary copy. Processing of this surface gave a plate with ink-accepting letters and an ink-repelling background, and the final long run of tertiary images was printed by offset lithography. This process has been operated by the Readex Corporation for the re-publication of a variety of literature for scholarly use. Their catalogues show that very many items (such as *Hansard's* record of British Parliamentary Debates) and runs of some scientific journals can be supplied from stock.

The production of high-resolution photolithographic plates has been studied at the Central Research Institute of the Dai Nippon Printing Co. Ltd, Tokyo [58]. A grainless aluminium plate was de-greased with a calcium-carbonate paste, and counter-etched for 3 to 5 minutes in 2–3 per cent acetic acid. The rinsed plate was dipped for 10–15 seconds in a 'Brunak' solution (0·35 per cent hydrofluoric acid with 6·25 per cent ammonium dichromate), washed and dried. The treated plates were coated by whirling at 100 r.p.m. with Kodak Photo Resist (2 parts K.P.R. with one part Thinner). A carbon arc was then used to print from a negative image on Kodak High-Resolution plate, so that only the hardened lines of the resist remained after normal development, dyeing and rinsing. After drying at 40–50° C, the plates were cleaned by carefully wiping with alcohol on a soft cloth to remove residual K.P.R., and were baked for 20–30 min at about 150° C. Finally the aluminium surface was etched for 1–3 min in hydrofluoric acid (56 per cent) 25 cc, hydrochloric acid (38 per cent) 25 cc, water to 4,000 cc, and wiped with a gum solution.

With plates prepared in this way, the K.P.R. stencil constituted the ink-accepting image. 4,000 sheets an hour were printed on a Heidel-berg K.O.R. machine using increased pressure and a heavier ink.

A characteristic of lithographic processes is that ink is either effec-tively accepted or is not accepted at all, and there are no intermediate tones. The plate thus acts as a 'go-no-go' gauge for the tones of the negative, and the specification of the line and background densities for such work has to be exceptionally critical.

The Output

By definition, the stored information in microfilmed images cannot be read without optical magnification. The resultant enlarged images are thus quite literally *the output* of the system. Reading aids for use with microfilm may take the form of visual magnifiers, but optical projectors are more commonly used.

VISUAL MAGNIFIERS

If a compound monocular or binocular microscope is already available, an appropriate magnification will give readily legible images. The physical restriction placed on the viewer means, however, that these instruments are better suited for examination of the quality of the images, than for reading more than a short passage.

A simple and inexpensive reader for microfilm at moderate reduction ratios (say 25 : 1 or less) can consist of a frame for holding the microfilm, and a single-stage magnifying lens producing an enlarged virtual image. Quite effective visual magnifiers of this type were made from cardboard and were equipped with a plastic lens. When disguised as matchboxes, they were used by the 'underground' forces in Europe during the Nazi occupation. Somewhat more elaborate magnifiers have been made for students and scholars. All apparatus of this type is more suitable for 'scanning' or for reading for a short time rather than for prolonged study.

In concluding this section, reference should be made to the high magnifications obtainable by the 'Stanhope' lens (p. 3). This principle might conceivably be advantageously applied in appropriate circumstances, possibly with a corrected lens.

PROJECTION READING APPARATUS

For designers of microfilming systems, the convenience, efficiency, durability and cost of the equipment finally used to provide projected images can be important considerations. Photographic enlargers designed for 'miniature' or 'sub-miniature' negatives can be used to read microfilm, but would be found inconvenient for this purpose.

In fact, much thought has been given to the design of projection microfilm equipment, and the following are some of the points that have been considered.

(1) Projection apparatus has been designed for at least four types of task.

   (i) for reading by itself,

   (ii) for reading combined with production of enlarged prints from selected frames. Such 'reader-printers' also contain built-in processing facilities,

   (iii) for optimum-quality or minimum-cost enlargements, especially from microfilm of engineering drawings or from high-reduction microfilm,

(iv) for high-speed or continuous enlargement where the application demands enlargement of every frame.

(2) Whether the microcopies to be read are *opaque* or *transparent* is an important question. Specially developed illumination systems are required to produce projected images of adequate brightness from opaque images such as 'Microcards'. To make the most of the light available, card readers often use only feebly scattering transluscent screens and incorporate a Fresnel lens to give uniform illumination. With this type of equipment the effective viewing angle is rather narrow, and the viewer's head requires to be correctly placed for satisfactory reading.

Although the proportion of new work on cards is probably decreasing in favour of microfiche, readers for cards are likely to remain important

(i) in cases where frequent reference is likely to spoil the legibility of roll microfilm or microfiche,

(ii) when subject matter to be studied comprises substantial collections of literature only available in card form,[1] and

(iii) when users are employing prints on paper strips to assemble their own images on cards.

(3) The *quality of the projected image* comprises factors such as sharpness and brightness. An image with no obvious colour fringes and equally sharp over the entire field is desirable. The brightness determines how easily the reader can be used in a fully-lit room, or whether it is better placed in a dark corner.

(4) Comfort for prolonged reading is markedly affected by the position and type of viewing screen used. *Translucent screens* make more efficient use of the available projected light, and must be placed between the reader and projection system. They are usually mounted approximately vertical in front of the viewer, and are less convenient for tracing or for note taking. Absence of obtrusive structure, 'scintillation', and of 'hot spots' or glare is desirable in translucent-screen readers.

Downwards projection on an *opaque screen* most closely simulates the visual conditions of reading the original document, and is often preferred for scholarly applications.

(5) The *ease of use*, in the sense of providing a correctly oriented image of the desired page with the minimum trouble during loading, is an important consideration. The standard for

---

[1] But the fact that cards *have* been made means that microfiche can be readily printed from the same negatives.

comparison should be the finding of a desired page in a bound book. This property can be resolved into:

(i) the *ease of loading* the microcopy into the reader. In hand-threaded readers for roll microfilm, loading demands time and some care. The process can be especially vexatious for viewers only using the equipment occasionally. Loading of readers for 'Microcards' or microfiche is a less 'fiddly' procedure. Since images on roll microfilm are made with the lines of text running either across or along the film, provision of a swivelling head or a prism for orienting the image is most desirable. The difficulty and delay in loading readers for roll microfilm has been solved by the use of magazine-loading and self-threading readers;

(ii) the *ease of finding the desired page*. With roll microfilm, some readers have allowed the image to go right out of focus during winding, so that the winding must be stopped before page numbers can be read. Even when the film stays in focus, numbers can no longer be read when film is wound at more than a slow speed. With two-dimensional image arrays such as microfiche or 'Microcard', the movements required to find any given page are smaller, and even simple sliding mechanisms are relatively satisfactory.

Self-threading readers with motorized film-winds operating at fast or slow speeds can expedite page finding, and this can be further assisted by various devices for sensing the position on the film as the frames rapidly pass the lens (p. 424). With more complex arrangements, microimages can be automatically scanned on the basis of their indexed content (p. 426);

(iii) the ease of bringing an area requiring special study to the centre of the screen. Even if this capability is not objectively necessary, it is most agreeable to the viewer.

(6) Whether the whole or only part of each sheet or page of the original document can be read at one time is also important. Inability to read a whole line without moving the film can be considered intolerable. With microfilm of newspapers, it is convenient to use a lower magnification for scanning the head-lines, and a higher magnification for such information as market prices.

Even from this summary of requirements, it will be obvious that design and choice of readers is a complex subject. It is also an important subject, since reluctance to use microfilm readers has been a significant factor retarding applications of document microcopies.

Even when the performance of a reader is faultless, the scholar cannot fully employ his skill in the handling of bound books, and is denied satisfactions gained from the feel and the sight and the smell of books.[1] In this situation, an inadequate performance can seem like adding insult to injury. The best performance is most readily obtained by designing specialized apparatus for each frame size, desired magnification and micro-form (roll, fiche or card), but this approach is also the most costly. Much attention has therefore been applied to versatility, so that the widest range of micro-forms can be read with one instrument. Sometimes this has been achieved by compromises, and sometimes by provision of rapidly interchangeable lenses, condensers or film and card-holders.

There are a variety of applications in which other features become important. For some uses, *portability* is important. For expeditions this might be combined with an environment-proof package, and the ability to be operated from a car battery. Hospital patients who cannot hold a book have been provided with specially designed readers for projecting the image on the ceiling [59]. Some film-readers have even been equipped with an automatic 'page-turning' device, so that they could still be operated by action of the lip or neck muscles of severely paralysed patients.

There is an extensive literature on readers. Lewis and Offenhauser [10] devote 46 pages to the subject, and J. Stewart and others have collected much of this information into a specialized book [60].

<h2 style="text-align:center">READER-PRINTERS</h2>

Just the fact that microimages need to be taken to a special place for reading is irksome, and so is the manual copying of details, which cannot be remembered, or of elaborate images such as graphs and engineering drawings. Since readers already produce enlarged images bright enough for recording by sensitized papers, the idea of placing the sensitized paper on the screen of a reader naturally occurred. The experiment was more likely to succeed with readers projecting the image on an opaque screen, but would often show that the uniformity of illumination and sharpness was inadequate for photographic reproduction. This is no reason for condemning an instrument only sold for visual reading, since photographic reproduction requires more uniform illumination than is needed for visual reading.

Convenient production of on-demand enlargements (so-called 'hard copy') has been facilitated by dual purpose instruments, which

---

[1] Nevertheless, while regretting the elimination of these agreeable stimuli, information starvation resulting from the removal of microforms would be intolerable to most scholars.

in their initial mode of operation function as readers. These are called reader-printers, and permit enlargements of selected images to be made rapidly. Having found a frame of interest, the user presses a button, which causes a mirror to pivot so that the image can be projected on the sensitized paper instead of the viewing screen. A typical cycle of operations then automatically exposes the paper, pulls it past a processing station, cuts the copy from the paper web, and delivers the copy to the user in less than one minute. The machine is then switched back to the reading position by pivoting the mirror, and is immediately ready for making of further copies. Although 'projection-speed' papers need to be used in reader-printers, the paper is generally not exposed to room light until it is processed. The machines do not, therefore, need to be operated in a darkened room.

Silver-halide photographic papers and zinc-oxide electrophotographic papers have been widely employed in such apparatus [61]. Techniques, already worked out for the rapid processing of full-scale office-document copies, have been applied to the processing of silver-halide papers in reader-printers. The natural aim was to combine rapid working and adequate contrast and stability with hard copy as nearly dry as possible. For example, the Eastman Kodak Co. market a range of Recordak reader-printers designed for use with silver-halide papers. For simplicity of processing, some of these use a monobath, which accomplishes development and stabilization in a single solution, and processing is completed by removal of excess solution. In another machine, developer-incorporated papers are used, which are processed with separate activator and stabilizer solutions. This equipment can be used with a translucent paper to give full-size intermediates for contact duplication on diazo paper.

In their Thermo-Fax 'Filmac' reader-printers the 3M Company used a zinc-oxide sensitized paper, whose development depended on the fact that the layer remained photoconductive for an appreciable time after exposure. For processing, the sensitized surface was passed over a roller moistened with a metal-salt solution, and application of an electric potential caused electrolytic deposition of a metal image in the exposed areas.

Since the introduction of reader-printers with built-in processing facilities, the growth in their use has been rapid. A natural development, when such use is not restricted by copyright considerations, is the installation of coin-operated reader-printers in libraries, so that copies can be taken back to the workshop or laboratory. Reader-printers form an integral part of some microfilm information-retrieval systems. Each time the searching mechanism registers a 'hit', an enlargement would be made.

Reader-printers can also be used with papers which allow several copies to be made. With a silver-halide emulsion on a translucent base, for example, the enlarged prints can be used for making further copies with a dye-line machine. The enlargements can also be made on a silver-halide material of the type which allows the image to be converted to form a lithographic printing surface, or transferred to the surface of an offset-litho plate, thus permitting runs of hundreds or thousands of copies [62]. In fact the microfilm then becomes the intermediate for a large-scale re-publication of printed texts. Because of the properties of lithographic processes (see p. 413), exceptionally high quality would be demanded of the enlargements. To meet this requirement, the original microfilms should be produced with appropriately decreased reduction factors.

A critical review of reader-printers for use in libraries has been published as a separate volume [61(a)].

SPECIALIZED MICROFILM ENLARGERS

Enlargers adapted to give the large magnifications required for microfilm have been sold for many years. With these, the service of making relatively small numbers of enlargements would form part of a microfilm system, or they could be used in an 'on-demand' basis. A paper describing the design of optics for optimum-quality enlargements is worth noting [63]. With all this type of apparatus, enlargement was essentially a dark-room operation.

Reader-printers took the enlargement process out of the 'dark-room' by building a self-contained dark-room into the equipment, but another approach has been to use diazo-sensitized materials with specially designed optical components. Because the diazo materials are mainly sensitive in the violet and ultra-violet and are of approximately 'print-out' speed, they can be safely handled by tungsten illumination, and with reasonable care in most room-lighting conditions. Their low speed, however, demands the projection of an exceptionally bright and actinic image. For this purpose, enlargers have been marketed with high-pressure mercury-vapour lamps, with specially designed illumination systems and with objectives corrected for the short wavelength light used. An example is the Caps-Jeffree microfilm enlarger, giving enlargements at 16 diameters with typical exposure times of 15–20 s on the fastest diazo paper [64]. Additional advantages claimed for this method of enlarging are the simple processing requirements of diazo materials, and the low cost of diazo papers.

CONTINUOUS ENLARGEMENT AND 'O.P.' (OUT-OF-PRINT) BOOKS

The principle of the continuous microfilmers, in which the film moved in the opposite direction to the documents and at a speed reduced exactly by the reduction factor, can be employed for enlarging, with the sensitive paper taking the place of the documents. The processed microfilm moved past a slit in the film gate, which determined the exposure time. Continuous enlargers of this type have been linked to continuous processing machines and hot-drum driers. The capital cost of such an installation was considerable, and its use was only economic when a large volume of work was available. A noteworthy example of the use of this system was in the 'Airgraph' and 'V-mail' postal services during the Second World War [65]. To reduce the cost and time delays in transmission of Allied service-men's mail, letters were written on special sheets, and were reduced on 16-mm films, which were processed and sent by air to the distant distributing station. After processing the enlargements, the paper was automatically chopped into individual letters, which were distributed as ordinary mail.

A dry system of continuous enlargement was provided by the Rank-Xerox 'Copyflo' machines, using the Xerox principle in which a selenium-coated drum took the place of the drum around which sensitized paper travels in the silver-halide continuous enlargers. As before, the drum rotated in the opposite direction to the microfilm and at a speed exactly increased by the magnification factor. At a series of positions around the drum, it met stations at which the following operations occurred (Fig. 110).

(1) The drum was given an electrostatic charge by passing it under an electrified wire grid.

(2) The charge was dispersed image-wise as the drum passed under the projected images of the microfilm, and the exposure produced a pattern of photoconductivity.

(3) The image was developed by dusting with a powder, which caused pigment to adhere either to the discharged parts (negative/positive reproduction) or the charged parts (direct-positive reproduction).

(4) Paper from a stock-roll was brought into contact with the drum, and the powder was transferred from the drum to the paper by applying a further electrostatic charge.

(5) Most types of plain paper or card could be used, and the powder image was bonded to the paper by heating to fuse the powder.

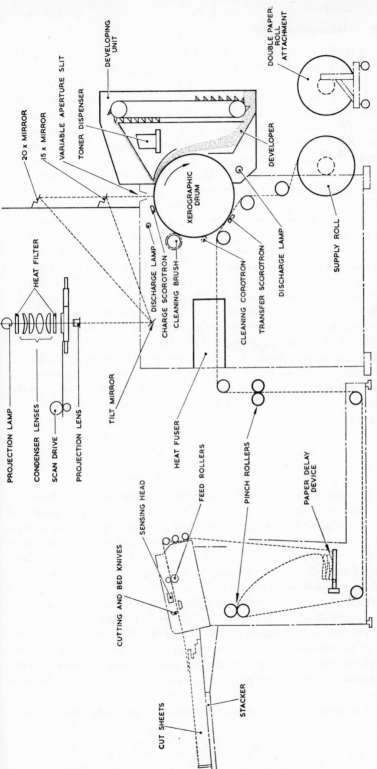

Fig. 110 *Diagram of 'Copyflo' Enlarger*

The scan drive pulls the film to the *left* past the projection lens, and the enlarged image is projected through a slit onto the surface of the selenium drum moving synchronously to the right ×15 or ×20 faster according to the magnification. At successive stations around the drum it is electrostatically *sensitized* (charge scorotron), *exposed* through the slit, *developed* with toner, the image *transferred* to paper and the *drum* cleaned before re-charging.

Courtesy of Rank Xerox Ltd.

(6) Residual powder was dusted from the drum, making it ready for re-use, after it had rotated by less than 360°.

The 'Copyflo' machines were made in various models, for producing copies from roll-microfilm, from unitized microfilm in aperture cards, from half-plate film negatives of engineering drawings and direct from the original documents. Copies were produced at a rate of 1,200 feet of paper per hour.

A remarkable application of the 'Copyflo' system has been the on-demand production of *single copies* of *out-of-print* books [66]. The 'Copyflo' enlargements from a roll microfilm of the entire text were cut into sheets corresponding to the successive pairs of pages seen by the microfilming lens as the pages were turned. The sheets were then folded along the image of the book spine and with the text outwards, and the folded and stacked pages were bound with a special flexible glue-binding. The result was a very usable book, in which the fact that each sheet was a double-ply of paper was not obtrusive (Plate 53). An odd feature was that the page numbers of some books appeared close to the spine and contrary to the convention in printed books, the left-hand pages were the odd numbers.

By this process, copies of out-of-print or disintegrating books can be produced at a cost of a few American cents or British pennies per page. When a new title was asked for, the customer had to wait about three weeks, but additional copies could be supplied in about three days.

OUTPUT FOR SYSTEMS APPLICATIONS

In the earliest applications of microfilm, the central interest dwelt in the saving of storage space combined with ease of transport and security against loss or fraud. However, it was gradually realized that this conversion of information into a compact and easily reproducible form also conferred other useful properties. For example, the successive images could be likened to the cards in an index file, which although closed can never get out of order. Once the film was threaded in the reader, successive images could be rapidly scanned without the annoyance of adjacent cards clinging together. During the making of the microfilm, code marks on the film or signals on a magnetic stripe could be introduced to facilitate rapid manual finding or automatic retrieval. Microfilm frames so devised could demonstrate many of the features of punched or perforated cards, but in a greatly reduced space.

As a result of these inherent possibilities, microfilm has been integrated into 'systems' for the office, laboratory, library, school, vehicle navigation—and so on. Examples are:

The 'Recordak' Single Posting system and the System of Accounting in Retail Stores.

The use of microfilm for recording library loans, and rapidly indicating the borrowers liable to fines for overdue books (Photo-charging) [67].

The use of microfilmed teaching programmes in Teaching Machines [68].

The use of microfilmed maps linked to automatic navigation equipment to give a continuous display of the position of an aircraft or road vehicle [69].

Data-processing and information-retrieval systems ranging in complexity from the personal information file to computer-linked systems for giving access to documents in very large files.

Because of the increasing complexity of manufacture and design associated with technological developments, and the exponential increase in the volume of scientific publications, methods of handling the mass of documents so generated was seen to be of crucial importance. Employment of trained scientists or technologists to re-generate information, while working in ignorance of published results, can be extremely wasteful. Experts with diverse specialized skills have considered the use of microfilm in an active role for systems and data processing, and the subject is rapidly acquiring an impressive literature of its own. Proposals have been made to use microfilm for these purposes in many different ways, and the last ten years have seen the construction of a number of ingenious and costly devices. It may take many more years of trials and development to demonstrate whether some of the larger systems are operationally or economically viable. In the remainder of this chapter, we shall consider mainly the ways of handling microforms which these developments have used. This, after all, is a critical question for the systems designer, who must harmonize the mechanical performance of his mechanisms with the handling properties of a suitable microform to secure fault-less functioning.

HANDLING OF MICROFORMS FOR SYSTEMS APPLICATIONS AND INFORMATION RETRIEVAL

INDEXING OF ROLL MICROFILM

At the instant of exposure, the image of each document projected on the roll-microfilm stock occupies a unique position on the film, and in appropriate circumstances, this by itself may be used to find it. A simple method is to sort the documents before microfilming, and record (on the film-box or cassette) the film footages or frame numbers at which the file sections change. A film-footage indicator on the reader represents an inexpensive and rapid method for finding the appropriate file section. For finding an individual frame, visual counting is slow and tedious, and a reader has been developed which uses a photocell with associated circuitry to count the strips of clear film between frames. With negative microfilm, the photocell signals are not likely to give miscounts, but with positive microfilm, the relays might need to respond to a very weak signal. A method for ensuring strong signals whatever the state of the microfilm images, is to arrange for image-control marks to be photographically recorded on the film on the margin at the side of each frame (Plate 54). With automatic counting and servo-mechanisms actuated by photocell signals, any of 3,000 frames on a 100-ft spool so indexed can be found in less than ten seconds.

Another possibility is to microfilm 'signals' of a type which can be visually counted or seen even when microfilm is being wound through a reader quite fast. Just as 'target' cards can be inserted in a card file to break the file into convenient sections, so can 'target-flash' cards with a bold black-and-white design be inserted at suitable situations in a pile of documents before microfilming commences. The strong visual differentiation of the target-flash cards ensures that they are detected (Plate 54). A powerful method is to expose the microfilm so that signals are recorded on the narrow strips of emulsion between adjacent images ('Kodamatic' Indexing). When film bearing such marks at a constant distance from the edge is wound through a reader at high speed, persistence of vision causes the marks to appear as continuous dark lines running along the film. Several such lines have been used to constitute a code indicating which of 100 sections is in the reader at any instant, and a change from one code combination to the next can be seen even when film is travelling at speed (Plate 54).

MAGAZINE-LOADING OF READERS

When microfilm is used for purposes such as information retrieval, three attributes of the microfilm reader can become especially important.

(1) *Automatic loading and self-threading* When searching rather than reading, delays involved in manual threading and connecting film to a take-up spool can become really serious.

(2) *Damage control* Film used for repeated searching is likely to suffer far more wear than film used for occasional but prolonged study. Refinement of film transport mechanisms is therefore most important.

(3) *Motorized winding* When frequent searches are to be made, motorized winding of the film will save both time and fatigue. Facilities for both rapid and slow winding are of course also necessary.

Great attention has been applied to the incorporation of these attributes in high-speed roll-microfilm readers. For example, in the Recordak range of 'Lodestar' magazine-loading readers, processed 16 mm film was loaded into a plastic magazine, and a short stiff 'Mylar' leader spliced on the leading end. By simply pushing the magazine into a slot on the reader and pressing the 'start' button, rotation of the loaded reel caused the film to thread itself and pass through the reader at 10 feet (3 metres) *per second*. To achieve this performance with minimal damage to the film, recessed rollers have been used, combined with low-friction film guides which control the film-path without touching the image area on either side of the film (Fig. 111). In this group of readers, momentary film tension due to roll-inertia during re-winding has been minimized by dispensing with a take-up spool, and allowing the film to festoon, as in some high-speed motion-picture cameras.

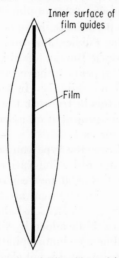

Inner surface of
film guides

Film

Fig. 111 *Cross-section of Film Channel in Lodestar Reader*

Since the film occupies the position of a chord to the two arcs, abrasion can only occur at the extreme edges.

SEARCHING FOR INDIVIDUAL INFORMATION CONTENT

The above-mentioned handling methods all require the documents to to be sorted before microfilming, and the film bears no indication of the contents of the frames. If the documents can be coded before microfilming, their code assignments can be recorded in black-and-white patches forming a binary code across the film. An early version of this technique was the Rapid-Selector initiated by Vannevar Bush at the Library of the U.S. Department of Agriculture [70]. Each frame of the film contained an abstract and a binary reference code consisting of an area of black film with a system of clear rectangles. The film was wound rapidly past a projector, which caused the images of the coded area to be superimposed on an 'interrogating card' bearing the code corresponding to the information being sought. When the photoelectric detector sensed coincidence between a descriptor code on the film and the pattern on the interrogating card, the circuit triggered an electronic flash which caused the image of the desired frame to be printed on unexposed film stock. The space available for coded information allowed documents to be coded by several aspects, and early prototypes were stated to scan film at the rate of 72,000 frames per minute. From a later paper [71] it appears that work on the Rapid-Selector was interrupted for a time, and many mechanical modifications were adopted. In particular, the motion of the image on the moving film was 'stopped' by projecting the image on a slit past which the print film passed at the same speed as the image. More modest scanning speeds of 6 ft of film (2 metres) per second, or about 2,000 coded pages per minute, have been described in a modified system built for the Publications and Information Retrieval Branch of the U.S. Navy's Bureau of Ships. A similar order-of-magnitude of film speed appears to have been used in the Benson-Lehner Corporation's Film Library Instantaneous Presentation (FLIP) System [72]. In this instrument the film was scanned in a reader and selected frames projected on a screen. Probable addition of a hard-copy unit was forecast.

Systems of the Rapid-Selector type can scan large collections of documents recorded on large reels. The National Bureau of Standards modification used 6,000 ft (2,000 metres) rolls with about 33,000 images, and the Benson-Lehner system about double the length of film and the number of images. A Benson-Lehner pamphlet suggested that a second dimension could be added by selecting from any one of a number of reels all held on a common spindle. How much mechanical complication would be involved is not clear.

SEARCHING IN VERY LARGE COLLECTIONS

An alternative approach to the handling of very large document collections on roll microfilm is represented by the Recordak Corporation's Microfilm Information Retrieval Access Code ('Miracode') system [73]. In this, film with any desired number of columns of code information between the frames is used in lengths up to 100 ft (30 metres) (Plate 55). The films are loaded in plastic magazines for rapid insertion in a high-speed motorized reader-printer linked to a selecting system controlled by a push-button key-board. Since only relatively modest numbers of images (2,000 or less according to the depth of indexing) would be stored in each magazine, the documents need to be sorted into broad categories before microfilming. As the mechanism of the self-threading reader accepts properly spliced film, each roll can be added to until its length reaches 100 ft. Several hundreds of rolls can be held in a rack within convenient reach of a seated operator. Once the interrogating code has been set up on the key-board, less than 15 seconds are required to select the appropriate magazine, insert it in the reader and ascertain whether it contains any frame corresponding to the keyed-in code. In this sense, the 15 seconds suffice to ascertain whether the collection of 900,000 or more units contains the desired frame.

Indications of the effectiveness of this system are now appearing in the literature. For example, Daniel of the Tennessee Valley Authority has described its application for information retrieval in the chemical industry [73(c)]. Weil, Emerson and Bolles [73(d)] reported user reactions, operating experience and economics of the use of *Chemical Abstracts* with the years 1907–1964 covered by 253 reels of microfilm with 'Miracode' indexing. Looking up of specific abstracts was materially faster than with the bound volumes.

AUTOMATIC HANDLING OF MICROFILM 'CHIPS'

When images are stored in roll-microfilm form, inter-sorting and purging of individual frames cannot readily be effected, and the systems have to be designed to cope with this fact. This limitation has been overcome in a number of systems employing microfilm cut into very short lengths (unitized—see p. 404). When microfilm frames are mounted on aperture cards, punched-card sorting equipment can subsequently be used to find required cards, but the area employed for the punch-coded information is many times that of the microfilm frame. Higher condensation of information can be achieved by equipment using units of film bearing binary coded marks scanned photo-electrically. This principle has been employed in several systems.

(1) The 'Filmorex' invented by Samain employs film units rather smaller than 3×2 in (72×45 mm) on 0·008 in (200 μ) thick cut-sheet film base [47]. Each unit typically contains an abstract, bibliographical information and the coded information required for automatic searching at 600 frames per minute.

(2) The Eastman Kodak 'Minicard' consisted of units of 16 mm

film rather more than 1 in (32 mm) long [48]. The film 'chips' had a rectangular aperture at one end for threading on a rectangular rod or stick, and the sixty-fold reduction ratio allowed up to twelve pages of text to be carried by each chip. For the automatic sorting and extraction of information, the film chips were automatically 'dealt' from the stick, so that each lay in sequence on a sorting belt. After photoelectric scanning, the chips were directed to their appropriate sticks or collected for reading.

(3) The Magnavox Company responsible for the Minicard sorting mechanism, employed similar principles in their MEDIA system [49]. Images were recorded at thirty-fold reduction on 16 mm film and the binary code was now only used to depict the unit-number of the film chip. The same unit-number with all the information required for sorting and data-processing was also recorded on a magnetic medium for high-speed searching with a computer. From a file of 30,000,000 pages, a hard copy of any page could be obtained in less than a minute.

(4) The Magnavox Company developed still another chip-handling system for the Redstone Arsenal of the United States Army Missile Command [74]. For the DARE (Documentation Automated Retrieval Equipment) system, the primary input consisted of aperture cards containing microfilm images of engineering drawings with Hollerith punchings in the cards. To generate the film chips, the information obtained from read-out of the punchings was transformed into binary-coded form, and printed at one end of a 3 in length of 35 mm diazo film. At the other end of the film, was contact printed a duplicate of the image of the drawing. 3,000 of the resultant film chips were stored in each of 285 magazines. The retrieval mechanism extracted the chips and selected individuals by scanning of the coded information at a rate of 70 chips per second.

By a method such as this, it would seem possible for an aperture-card system that had grown too large for effective retrieval to have its capacity increased by one or more orders of magnitude. To be able to do this by a system accepting aperture cards as its normal method of input is an idea of considerable interest.

COLLECTION OF IMAGES INTO GIANT ASSEMBLIES

There have been developed a number of systems, which employ microphotographic images collected into giant assemblies. One example is the Command Retrieval Information System (CRIS) developed by the Information Retrieval Corporation [75]. Images were first microfilmed at thirty-fold reduction on 35 mm or 16 mm film. The sub-frame size was 0.583×0.416 in (14.6×10.4 mm) containing a pair of microfilmed pages, and nine of these were assembled into a frame of size 1.75×1.25 in (44×31 mm). By step-and-repeat printing on diazo or 'Kalvar' film, eleven of these frames and a twelfth frame containing coded information were assembled into a column $1\frac{3}{4}$ in wide and 17 in (43.2 cm) high. By assembly of images in this fashion on 17 in wide film, there was obtained a scroll which could hold half a million sub-frames on a 400-ft (120 metres) length. Automatic handling of the scroll in the CRIS machine allowed any desired sub-frame to be found in 17 seconds.

Mechanical assembly rather than photographic assembly by step-and-repeat was used in the 'Walnut' system. The following operations were involved [76].

(1) On receipt of a document

  (i) a unique number was assigned,
  (ii) the number of pages was recorded,
  (iii) an index record including an abstract was punched on paper tape,
  (iv) the document was microfilmed with 15.8 reduction ratio and with the line-density control procedure discussed previously (p. 392),
  (v) an input control card was punched with the document number and page count.

(2) An 'image converter' then reduced the processed microfilm images by a further 2.2 ratio (35 ratio overall) on 'Kalvar' film. For this purpose, 50 lengths of the film of the dimensions shown in Fig. 112, had been previously loaded in an Image File Cell.

The image converter accomplished a number of interlocking operations:

  (i) it assigned an 'address' consisting of file-module, cell, strip and strip-position numbers to each document, and punched these addresses into the input control cards;
  (ii) a tweezer-like device then moved to the appropriate one of 50 strip positions, and withdrew the unexposed 'Kalvar' film from its cell by an amount corresponding to the strip-position number designated in the address on the input control card. At the same time, the optical system shifted to the appropriate one of three image columns (Fig. 112);
  (iii) when the 'Kalvar' film was correctly positioned, it was exposed to the reduced image from the microfilm frame.

According to density measurements previously made on the microfilm (see p. 395), exposure times between 0·2 and 1 second were given. The film was then moved to a second station, in which the image was developed by

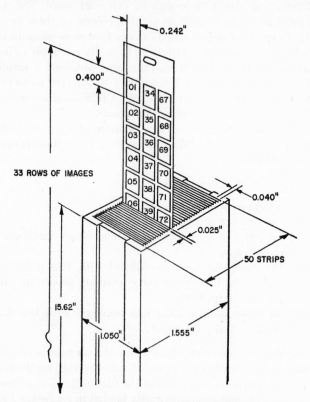

Fig. 112 *Image-file Cell of 'Walnut' System*
Partly withdrawn film strip shows image configuration.
Courtesy of I.B.M. and 'American Documentation', official publication of the American Documentation Institute, 2000 P St, Washington, D.C. 20036

pressing it for 0·35 seconds in contact with a hot platen at 235° F (113° C). In a third station, the film was chilled and submitted to an intense overall ultra-violet exposure, which fixed the image by destroying the remainder of the diazo sensitizer.

When complete, each Image File Cell could contain 4,950 images reduced from 14 × 8 in (35 × 20 cm) pages, and 200 such Cells were loaded into a circular bin (Fig. 113). While the photocopying was proceeding, the data from the paper tape was loaded into a magnetic digital-memory index, which could search 1,000 records averaging 250 characters in length in two seconds. Retrieval from the file was achieved by a sub-system adapted from the I.B.M. Random Access Method of Accounting and Control Computer. When an address was located by the computer, movement of the circular bin presented the appropriate cell, from which the appropriate strip was withdrawn to present the designated image from a collection of 990,000. The images were then printed on a Kalvar-sensitized aperture card, from which they could be read on a reader or enlarged xerographically.

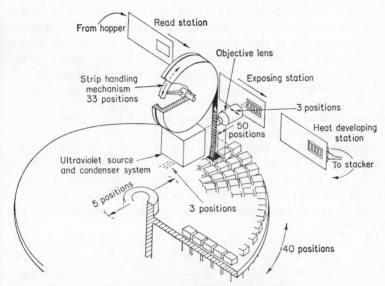

Fig. 113 *Image-file of 'Walnut' System*
Diagram shows bin, and arrangement for withdrawing film strips and projecting required images on Kalvar loaded aperture cards.
Courtesy of I.B.M. and 'American Documentation', official publication of the American Documentation Institute, 2000 P St, Washington, D.C. 20036.

The above outline of the photographic method of building up the Walnut file demonstrates some interesting features. The mechanism allows images to be printed into any one of 990,000 positions without taking the 'Kalvar' film strips out of the system. Likewise, no film is taken out of the system during the retrieval operation, so that the file remains complete. Because of the dry-working properties of the 'Kalvar' layer, the developing and fixing treatments can be applied to discrete areas corresponding to the individual exposed frames. Any strip need, therefore, only be partially loaded with images and placed in the file, and more images may be added later. Advantages with

P

respect to speed of response, efficiency and flexibility of search and avoidance of film wear have been claimed for the principle of separating the functions of indexing the documents and finding them [49], [76(b)]. To realize these advantages, however, it is probably necessary to install a high-speed computer.

MECHANICAL FILING OF SHORT LENGTHS OF 16 MM FILM
The Walnut system resembles a gigantic collection of 'pigeon-holes', in which records of required documents were found by their position. A simpler form of the same concept has been applied in the Recordak Microstrip System [77]. 12 in (30 cm) lengths of 16 mm microfilm had plastic eyelets inserted in one end, and were loaded into holders consisting of rigid plastic sleeves. These holders had colour-coded end-tabs to index subject content and identify image groups, and the positions of individual images were indicated by precise tell-tale symbols on the top of each holder. When a holder was inserted in a slot in the reader, the eyelet was engaged by a stud on the index selector, so that any desired frame was rapidly found (without looking at the image projected on the screen) by moving the selector to the appropriate tell-tale index (Plate 56). According to the intended application the frames would just be read, or hard copies would be made on a printer attachment. Collections of one hundred holders were in turn held in Access Files 12 in (30 cm) wide and rather less than 6 in (15 cm) deep, and these files conveniently nested together in larger blocks.

The Microstrip System was designed to deal with active and frequently amended files of a type in which the basic index would already be generated by an existing business system. Intended applications were directories, inventory lists, credit cards and account-verification procedures.

In its first form, the Microstrip System sacrificed storage capacity to achieve rapid access at low capital cost. Thus each Access File occupied a space of $12 \times 12 \times 6$ in ($30 \times 30 \times 15$ cm) but held only about 100 feet of film. In a later version, this capacity has been much increased by modifying the holders and selector mechanisms to permit 10 strips to be held in each holder.

COLLECTION OF LARGE NUMBERS OF IMAGES ON FILM SHEETS
Designers of systems for storage and retrieval of documents have been interested in an advantage of two-dimensional arrays of images. If 100 1-inch square images are recorded on a 10 inch square film, a movement of less than 15 inches is needed to move from page 1 to page 100. On roll microfilm, 100 inches is needed. There have there-

fore been a number of proposals for storing thousands of reference numbers, abstracts or complete document copies on a single sheet of film.

An early example of this approach was the Automatic Microimage File, developed by Kuder at the National Bureau of Standards [78]. Information from a master random file was assembled in a predetermined sequence in the form of 0·1 in (2·5 mm) square images filling a 10 in (25 cm) square film. Location of desired images was effected by keying in a 20-bit binary code which actuated servo-mechanisms adjusting the relative positions of the film and projection head on x and y axes. Another proposal was to combine the use of film sheets bearing large numbers of images, with the 'Peek-a-boo' perforated-card system for finding the required position. Perforated cards, in which the x and y co-ordinates of the punched holes constitute the code, were super-imposed on the film sheet. The 'Microcite' films for this purpose bore 1,000 abstracts on a film $7\frac{3}{8} \times 3\frac{1}{4}$ in ($18\cdot4 \times 7\cdot6$ cm), corresponding to 42 abstracts per square inch, or an image size of about $\frac{1}{6} \times \frac{1}{7}$ in ($4\cdot2 \times 3\cdot6$ mm) [79]. On this area was reduced the contents of a 5×3 in (125×75 mm) filing card. Those areas of the Microcite film visible through perforations in the Peek-a-boo card were read by projection.

Both these examples used modest reduction ratios around 30 : 1, but there are being developed systems employing higher ratios, so that thousands of complete document pages could be recorded on a single manageable sheet of film. Some of the problems of assembling thousands of high-reduction images on a single sheet, and the adaptation of photochromic layers for this purpose, are discussed on p. 411. When sheet films have been filled with thousands of regularly placed images, it is relatively simple to provide manually operated mechanisms allowing any image to be found by its co-ordinates in a few seconds. For example, the N.C.R. Miniaturized Microimage viewer (Model ED.MRII) used manual row and column drives. With 9,600 images arranged in 25 lines across the width of each foot of 35 mm film, less than 5·5 seconds access time was needed per foot of film. This reader was designed to be used on an astronaut's knee.

It seems likely that high-reduction two-dimensional arrays will be used in circumstances where the user has a good idea of what he wants to find and where to find it. An example was the N.C.R. project for recording 72 columns and 35 rows on $\frac{1}{16}$ in (1·6 mm) centres on a 5×3 in (127×76 mm) film. These were used for an Allowance Parts List for the U.S. Navy [80]. Automobile spare-parts lists, trade directories, mail-order catalogues and telephone directories are other probable applications for the process described on p. 47. Plate 52 demonstrates the application of this process for scholarly purposes, and illustrates a transparency containing 31 rows and 91 columns (over 2,800 pages) of the Catalogue of the London Library.

MICROFILM OUTPUT ANCILLARY TO COMPUTER SYSTEMS

In the preceding section, computers were considered in the ancillary rôle of finding information stored on microfilm. Output from processed microfilm can, however, provide valuable services for computer input or output.

MICROFILM INPUT FOR COMPUTERS

A major problem in many computer applications is the extraction of information from documents for input to computers, at a rate commensurate with the speed of computer operation. For this purpose, much attention is being given to automatic character recognition, but the methods mainly used so far have started with human operators reading documents and keying the information into punches generating punched cards or perforated tape. Information from the cards or tape would then be fed directly into the computer, or transcribed on magnetic tape. The possibility of short-circuiting this process by appropriate control of the form of the original documents was demonstrated by Greenough, Cook and Martens and associates of the U.S. National Bureau of Standards [81].

At the request of the U.S. Bureau of the Census, the National Bureau of Standards developed the Film Optical Sensing Device for Input to Computers. For this purpose, the census forms to be filled in by the public were provided with ovals or rectangles, and questions were answered by filling in these spaces in pencil at the appropriate places. Index marks were also printed on the side of the forms, and these were used to trigger the scanning operation and compensate for small inaccuracies in the positioning of the papers when their images were electronically scanned. The collected census forms were microfilmed at an appropriate reduction ratio on 16 mm film. Since the quality required for ultimate electronic read-out corresponded to ready visual legibility, the forms could be discarded once microfilmed.

The condensed information in the form of processed microfilm was then passed through the FOSDIC machine, in which the image of a flying spot producing a raster on a cathode-ray tube was projected in succession on each microfilm frame. The resultant momentary changes in light intensity caused by the detail in the microfilm image were recorded by a photomultiplier. The principle resembled that used in the flying-spot (television) microscope. As soon as the scan detected an index mark, the length of scan was momentarily extended to search the adjacent column of ovals (Plate 57), and the information was read out on magnetic tape. By this means, the images of census forms were automatically read at approximately 2,880 per hour. With good marking and filming conditions, the error rate was found to be less than 1 in 100,000 [82]. This was mainly due to film blemishes, but did not appreciably add to other sources of error in the enumeration process.

For the United States 1960 census, a later version of FOSDIC was operated on a gigantic scale [82]. Nearly 50 million forms were collected from the public, and their information was collected at 28 : 1 reduction ratio on 57,500 hundred-foot rolls of microfilm. Four FOSDIC machines were used to extract the information and the entire process after the collection of the forms required 28,000 man days, with a peak of 100 camera and machine operators. In the previous 1950 census, manual card-punching was done by a peak of 3,000 operators, and the operation required 200,000 man days.

It seems likely that this sort of method could be applied in many other cases in which 'yes' or 'no' answers or simple choices of alternatives can be indicated on printed forms. The conducting of at least elementary examinations and of market surveys by this means can be imagined. A modified FOSDIC machine was constructed for interrogating microfilmed images of punched cards from a collection of 300 million cards at the Weather Records Center in Asheville, N.C. The FOSDIC machine was used to search for images to match previously programmed information at a rate of 4,000 cards per minute. When appropriate images were found, their information was read to generate new punched cards at a rate of 100 per minute. Substantially higher searching speeds and operational flexibility was believed possible [83].

In a later form (FOSDIC IV), the cards were photographed with an anamorphic lens reducing by factors of 24 : 1 horizontally and 43 : 1 vertically. By this means, the images were compressed so that the rectangular punched apertures were recorded as 60 μ (0·0024 in) squares and 11 images were recorded per inch of the 16-mm film. The interrogation system, as before, read and selected appropriate cards, but then also performed logical operations and selected certain data which was recorded on magnetic tape for input to digital computers. The aim was to study long-range weather patterns and thereby improve the reliability of weather forecasts [83(b)].

MICROFILM OUTPUT FROM COMPUTERS

Another requirement of computer operations is the translation and physical condensation of information stored on magnetic tape. Often, the information may also require further processing, before it can

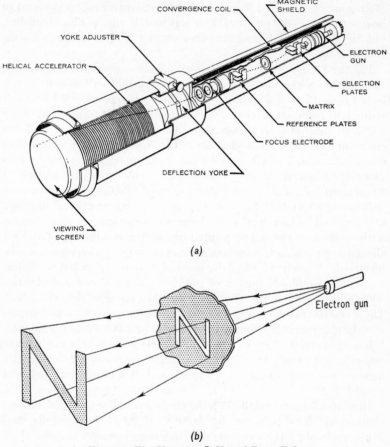

(a)

(b)

Fig. 114 *The Charactron*[R] *Shaped-Beam Tube*

A narrow electron beam is caused to impinge on the desired character in the etched metal matrix plate (*a*), and the extruded beam (*b*) is directed to the appropriate position on the viewing screen.

Courtesy of Stromberg-Carlson Division of General Dynamics Corporation and National Microfilm Association

be interpreted by scientists and engineers. One method of achieving these objectives is demonstrated by the General Dynamics/Electronics S-C 4020 and S-C 4400 High-Speed Recorders [84]. The heart of these devices is the 'Charactron' Shaped-Beam Tube (Fig. 114), which causes images from an etched-metal matrix plate to be projected at appropriate places on the screen of the cathode-ray tube.

The circuitry associated with the 'Charactron' tube accepts coded digital data directly from a computer, or more usually from magnetic

```
BEGIN    INTEGER  NOP, JT, I;    REAL  XARG, XLO, XUP, FLAG, AVINT;          00000020
NAME INIT=NOP, JT, XARG, XLO, XUP, FLAG;                                     00000030
     FORMAT F1 '(2I12,4E12.8)';                                             00000040
EXIT:  INPUT (F1,INIT);                                                     00000050
     BEGIN OWN ARRAY XA[1:NOP],  YA[1:NOP];                                 00000060
NAME XANDY=FOR  I=1 STEP 1 UNTIL  NOP  DO  (XA[I],YA[I]);                    00000070
     FORMAT F2 '(6E12.8)';                                                  00000080
BEGIN      REAL  CA, CB, CC, A, B, C, SYL, SYU, TERM1, TERM2, TERM3, DA     00000090
     , DIF, SUM;                                                            00000100
          INTEGER  JM, JS, JUL, IA, IB;                                     00000110
          SWITCH ALPHA=L1, L1, L12;                                        00000112
          SWITCH GAMMA=L10, L11;          SWITCH BETA=L9, L5, L6;           00000112
                                          SWITCH DELTA=L8, L8, L13;         00000114
NAME OUTLIST=NOP, JT, XARG, XLO, XUP, AVINT;                                 00000120
     FORMAT F3 '(5H-NOP=I6,2X,3HJT=I2,2X,5HXARG=1E14.6,2X,4HXLO=1E14.6       00000130
     ,2X,4HXUP=1E14.6,2X,6HAVINT=1E14.6)';                                  00000140
     IF FLAG#0 THEN INPUT (F2;XANDY);                                       00000150
     GOTO ALPHA[JT];                                                       00000160
COMMENT  FOR INTERPOLATION, DIFFERENTIATION,vINTEGRATION; SET JT=1,         00000180
     2,v3 RESPECTIVELY;                                                     00000190
L1: IF XARG=XA [NOP] THEN GOTO  L2;                                         00000210
    IF XARG=XA [NOP-1] THEN GOTO L2;                                        00000220
    IF XARG=XA [1] THEN GOTO L3;                                            00000230
    IF XARG=XA [2] THEN GOTO L3;              GOTO L4;                      00000240
L2: JM=NOP-1;     JS=1;      GOTO TERM;                                     00000250
L3: JM=2;        JS=1;      GOTO TERM;                                      00000260
COMMENT   LOCATE ARGUMENT;                                                  00000270
L4: FOR IA=2 STEP 1 UNTIL NOP DO BEGIN   IF XA[IA]>XARG THEN GOTO           00000280
     L7;   JM=IA         END ;                                             00000290
COMMENT   BEFORE LOOP IS COMPLETE XARG=XA [IA];                             00000300
L5: CA=A;    CB=B;     CC=C;     JS=3;     JM=JM+1;   GOTO TERM;            00000310
L6: A=(CA+A)/2;  B=(CB+B)/2;  C=(CC+C)/2;     GOTO L9;                      00000320
L7: JS=2;    GOTO TERM;                                                     00000330
L8: GOTO BETA [JS];                                                        00000340
L9: GOTO GAMMA [JT];                                                       00000350
COMMENT    INTERPOLATION, JT=1;                                            00000360
L10:DA=A×XARG×XARG+B×XARG+C;               GOTO EXIT1;                      00000370
COMMENT    DIFFERENTIATION, JT=2;                                          00000380
L11:DIF=2×A×XARG+B;          GOTO EXIT2;                                    00000390
COMMENT    INTEGRATION, JT=3;                                              00000400
L12:SUM=0;   SYL=XLO;   JUL=NOP-1;   IB=2;                                 00000410
COMMENT    LAGRANGE FORMULAE;                                               00000415
```

Fig. 115 *Typescript Output from S-C 4020 High-Speed Recorder*
Such images can be generated at six frames per second.
Courtesy of Stromberg-Carlson Division of General Dynamics Corporation.

tape, and rearranges this to the form used by the computer. The information is then converted to drive signals for the 'Charactron'. An electron beam is either moved in the normal controlled way to produce a desired pattern, or is positioned to pass through the appropriate part of the matrix. The 'extruded' beam is then focused on the phosphor layer of the tube, and the x and y co-ordinates of its position are controlled to any one of 1,024 positions on each co-ordinate. The image on the phosphor is projected on 16 mm or 35 mm microfilm, or on full-size photorecording paper.

The equipment is very flexible, for according to the signals on the tape it will produce series of exposures as points, line segments or alphanumeric characters (letters or figures), and a half-silvered mirror allows these to be superimposed on standard overlay information presented by a slide projector. In one mode of operation, it can simulate an automatic typewriter, filling pages line by line and character by character. The end of a line or page can be ended automatically at a margin, or the frame change can be actuated by a signal from a computer. A speed of 17,500 characters a second, nearly 2,000 times faster than an automatic typewriter was achieved. This corresponds to six pages (such as that shown in Fig. 115) per second, or a capacity equalling that of flow-camera filming of continuous stationery. The expense of generating the continuous stationery is also eliminated.

Other modes of operation have been used to display the output from Tiros weather satellites, calculated orbits of satellites, multiple graphs such as spectrophotometer or oscillograph data, or the data contained by the magnetic tape used for the computer control of machine tools (p. 298). In these applications, data points and notations can be positioned at more than 12,000 operations per second, and line segments at 2,500 per second. The reason for processing machine-tool-control tape, was to check for control errors or design miscalculations, and show the designer and programmer that the instructions were as intended, without use of expensive machine time in operations on a metal work-piece. Fig. 116 shows a drawing produced by the S-C 4020 High Speed Recorder in two seconds.

Such equipment as the S-C 4020 is clearly only economic if the volume of work available ensures reasonably full exploitation of its high working speed. One method of coping with this organizational problem is indicated by the announcement in 1963 that the General Dynamics and Recordak Corporations were offering a service, in which the S-C 4020 was used to convert tapes from computer centres in Government and Industry to a more usable form. The service included programming and consultation assistance, and was offered on an hourly or a job basis.

By the time this volume is in print, more examples of the integration of microfilm in computer operation are likely to be published. Nevertheless, the FOSDIC and S-C 4020 concepts provide striking demonstrations of these trends.

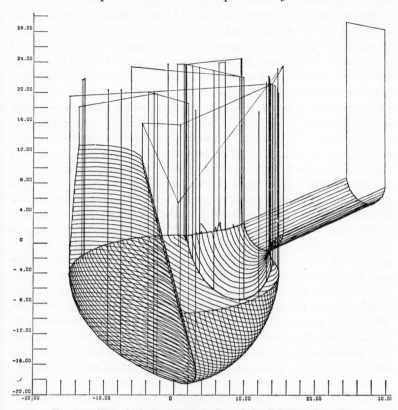

Fig. 116 '*Drawing*' *generated in* 2 *Seconds by S-C* 4020 *Recorder*

The drawing depicts the programme stored by a machine-tool-control tape, and allows the programme to be checked visually.

Courtesy of Stromberg-Carlson Division of General Dynamics Corporation and National Microfilm Association

Conclusion

Because of the length and complexity of this chapter, it seemed desirable to conclude with a brief summary indicating the broad significance of microfilm operations for modern civilization.

A critical stage in the development of civilization was reached when men invented notations for recording ideas or speech in writing. Prior to this, the store of knowledge was limited by the memories of tribal elders. The invention of writing permitted a large increase in the possible accumulation of corporate knowledge and skills. In the recording and dissemination of information, the invention of paper to provide a cheap and plentiful substitute for parchment was a landmark; and so was the development of the printing press to supersede the laborious manual copying of books.

During the last century the rate of accumulation of records has increased at an exponential rate: approximately doubling every fifteen years. In time, this accumulation of records began to thwart its purpose by reason of its sheer volume. Today, it has been calculated that a scientist would need a century to read the output of original papers published in a single year. For a few decades, the problems were *alleviated* by the publication of abstract journals, containing brief summaries of papers published in connection with specific fields of knowledge, but even these invaluable aids have not *solved* the problem. The research worker or development engineer finds it increasingly difficult to ascertain whether a proposed project has been examined before. In so far as they are unable to find published records of earlier work, they tend to be reduced to the condition of primitive tribal life, in which only verbal information was available.

The inability to find appropriate published references can be both frustrating and expensive. For a professional scholar, exposure of an apparently inadequate knowledge of the literature can be exasperating and humiliating. The matter is even worse when lack of information permits futile repetition of work involving the construction of expensive apparatus or the operation of intricate production processes. These embarrassments are especially keenly felt in connection with patent applications, for the applicants have to be able to demonstrate the 'novelty' of an invention as one of the requirements for upholding the validity of a patent. It is therefore interesting to note that the United States Department of Commerce has awarded a contract for the microfilming of $3\frac{1}{4}$ million U.S. patents to the Recordak Division of the Eastman Kodak Company [85]. The copies will be incorporated in aperture cards containing copies of up to eight pages, and hard-copy enlargements from these will be used to meet the 25,000 daily orders for patent copies demanded by commercial workers and scientists. Whereas the Patent Office's Search Room in the Department of Commerce was the *only* place where a complete classified collection could be found, the microfilm system makes this facility possible in other locations.

Another facet of the 'lost-information' problem is that titles of original articles (or even abstracts) may not mention parts of the subject matter which can be of crucial interest to other investigators. This can be particularly vexatious for an investigator needing to develop an *apparatus* or *technique*, for it has become a wide-spread custom to index scientific papers mainly by the *results* obtained. Unless an article is specifically concerned with a new method, how the results were obtained is often not apparent from the index or abstract.

With conventional indexing and filing methods of scholarly literature, attempts to deal with this information loss by multiple and cross indexing may be self-frustrating, for many indexes are already too large for convenient searching. Increasing the size of the hay-stack in proportion to the number of needles sought is no solution. In fact, this is the sort of problem that it is hoped to solve by the use of microphotographic images and handling procedures such as are mentioned in this Chapter. Some authorities believe that effective command of such methods is essential for political and economic survival in an increasingly competitive world.

REFERENCES

[1] Brewster, Sir D., 'The Microscope', *Encyclopaedia Britannica* (8th edition, 1857), **14**, Chapter 9, p. 801.

[2] (a) Herschel, Sir J., Letter to *The Athenaeum*, July, 1853. *See*
(b) Luther, F., *Microfilm: A History 1839–1900*, Barre Publishing Co. (Barre, Massachusetts, 1959), p. 25.

[3] (a) Dagron, R. P. P., *Bull. Soc. Franc. Phot.*, **17**, 12, 1871 and *La Post par Pigeons Voyageurs Tours-Bordeaux, 1870–71*.
(b) Luther, F. (as above).
(c) de la Follye, *Memoir on the Photographic and Administrative Section on the Servicing of Dispatching by Carrier Pigeons, 1870–71*. English Translation published by G. W. Angers (Springfield, Massachusetts, 1952). The author of this most informative account was Inspector of Telegraphs and administrated the service.
(d) Tissandier, G., *History and Handbook of Photography*, Sampson, Low, Marston, Searle and Rivington (London, 2nd edition, 1878), Chapter 6, 'Microscopic Dispatches during the Siege of Paris'.

[4] Fabre, C., *Traité Encyclopédique de Photographie* (Paris), 1890, **4**, p. 76.

[5] Stevens, G. W. W., 'Microscopical Examination of Some Pigeon Post Pellicles', *The National Micro News*, November, 1959, p. 47.

[6] Stokes, D., *Men behind Victory*, Hutchinson (London, 1944), p. 75.

[7] Anon., 'Copying from Journals of Scientific Papers', *Nature*, **164**, 289, 1949.

[8] Hattery, L. H. (Ed.) and Bush, G. P. (Ed.), *Reprography and Copyright Law*, American Institute of Biological Sciences (Washington, 1964), see also Appendix C of Hawken, W. R., *Copying Methods Manual* (reference [92]).

[9] Verry, H. R., *Microcopying Methods*, Focal Press (London, 1963), p. 147. 'Appendix IV. Use of Microfilm in Evidence' (see also reference [10]).

[10] Lewis, C. M. and Offenhauser, W. H., *Microrecording, Industrial and Library Applications*, Interscience Publishers Inc. (New York, 1956), p. 350. Appendix A, Section: 'Protection of Business Records, Supplemental Data'.

[11] Rudd, R. G., 'Colour Reprographic Methods', in *Reprographie, 1st Internationalen Kongress*, Verlag O. Helwich (Darmstadt, 1964), p. 256.

[12] Gallacher, W. J., 'Drafting Standards for Microfilmed Engineering Drawings', *Proc. Ann. Conv. Nat. Microfilm. Assoc.*, **7**, 77, 1958.

[13] Tarnowski, A. A. and Evans, C. H., 'Photographic Recording by Direct Exposure with Electrons', *J. Soc. Mot. Pic. Tel. Eng.*, **71**, 765, 1962.

[14] Mandler, W., 'Survey of Microfilm Lenses', *Proc. Ann. Conv., Nat. Microfilm, Assoc.*, **12**, 23, 1963.

[15] Nelson, C. E., *Microfilm Technology (Engineering and Related Fields)*, McGraw-Hill Book Co. (New York, 1965), p. 51, et seq.

[16] Willemin, H., *B. J. Phot.*, **12**, 152, 1865 (see Fig. 36, p. 158).

[17] Wolk, L. J. v.d. and Tonnon, J. C., 'The Microcopy on Flat Film as an Aid to Documentation', *Rev. Doc.*, **17**, 134, 1950.

[18] Kuipers, J. W., 'Microcards and Microfilm for a Central Reference File', *Ind. Eng. Chem.*, **42**, 1463, 1950.

[19] Silverman, D., 'The Micro-Digital Film', *The National Micro-News*, **65**, 1, August, 1963.

[20] Fromm, H. J., 'The Quality of Microfilm Images', *Proc. Ann. Conv. Nat. Microfilm. Assoc.*, **12**, 175, 1963.

[21] Fromm, H. J., 'Factors influencing Microimage Quality', *J. Phot. Sci.*, **10**, 147, 1962.

[22] Wilson, T., 'Microfilm Negatives for Modern Print-out Processes', *Brit. J. Phot.*, **110**, 480, 1963.

[23] Hampshire, T., 'Microfilming and Re-enlarging of Engineering Drawings', in *Reprographie, 1st Internationalen Kongress*, Verlag O. Helwich (Darmstadt, 1964), p. 270.

[24] Rudd, R. G., 'Some Factors Influencing the Quality of Microfilm Images', *Proc. Ann. Conv. Nat. Microfilm. Assoc.*, **2**, 44, 1953.

[25] Jamieson, B., 'New Techniques for Microfilm Exposure Control', *Proc. Ann. Conv. Nat. Microfilm. Assoc.*, **11**, 69, 1962.

[26] (a) Frey, H. C., Nelson, C. E. and Rubin, H. E., 'A Line Density Standard to Replace Background Density', *Proc. Ann. Conv. Nat. Microfilm. Assoc.*, **11**, 103, 1962.
(b) Rubin, J., 'An Historical Survey of Line Density Approach to Exposure Control', *Reproduction Methods*, April, 1964.

[27] Brown, W. R. J., 'A Rapid-Scanning Microdensitometer', *J. Soc. Mot. Pict. Tel. Eng.*, **63**, 147, 1954.

[28] Derr, A. J., 'Instrumentation for Microfilming Processes', *Proc. Ann. Conv. Nat. Microfilm. Assoc.*, **12**, 47, 1963.

[29] (a) Levenson, G. I. P., 'Maintaining Developer Activity', *Functional Photography*, 5 and 6, April–October, 1954.
(b) Society of Motion Picture and Television Engineers, *Control Techniques in Film Processing*, Published by the Society (New York, 1960).

[30] American Standard *Specification for Films for Permanent Records* (Z.38.3.2.–1945). Now replaced by PH.1–28.–1957.

[31] American Standard, *Determining the Thiosulphate Content of Processed Black-and-White Photographic Film* (PH.4.8.-1958).

[32] (a) Henn, R. W. and Wiest, D. G., 'Microscopic Spots in Processed Microfilm: Their Nature and Prevention', *Phot. Sci. Eng.*, **7**, 253, 1963.
(b) McCamy, C. S., 'Inspection of Processed Record Films for

Aging Blemishes', *U.S. National Bureau of Standards Handbook*, No. 96, 1964.

[33] (a) McCamy, C. S. and Pope, C. I., 'Current Research on Preservation of Archival Records on Silver-Gelatin Type Microfilm in Roll Form', *J. Research National Bureau of Standards, A, Phys. and Chem.*, 69A, 385, 1965.
(b) McCamy, C. S., 'Current Research on Archival Microfilm', *Proc. Ann. Conv. Nat. Microfilm. Assoc.*, 14, 61, 1965.

[34] Henn, R. W. and Mack, Bernadette D., 'A Gold Protective Treatment for Microfilm', *Phot. Sci. Eng.*, 9, 378, 1965.

[35] Barnes, J. C., Johnson, G. J. and Moretti, W. J., 'Effect of Thiosulphate Ion Upon Image Structure', *Phot. Sci. Eng.*, 8, 312, 1964.

[36] Taylor, J. B. and Kitrosser, S., 'Survey of Microfilm Processing Technology', *Proc. Ann. Conv. Nat. Microfilm. Assoc.*, 12, 164, 1963.

[37] Binkley, R. C., *Manual on Methods of Reproducing Research Materials*, Edwards (Ann Arbor, Michigan, 1936).

[38] Suydam, W. S., 'High Quality Microfilm through Inspection Control Techniques', *Proc. Ann. Conv. Nat. Microfilm. Assoc.*, 12, 185, 1963.

[39] Olson, O. G., 'A Technical Evaluation of the High Capacity Processing Laboratory', *Proc. Ann. Conv. Nat. Microfilm Assoc.*, 10, 238, 1961.

[40] Fromm, H. J., 'Methods for Controlling the Quality of Microimages in Microreproduction Systems', *Proc. Ann. Conv. Nat. Microfilm. Assoc.*, 14, 103, 1965.

[41] Photographic Research Section, National Bureau of Standards, *Instructions for the Use of the National Bureau of Standards Microcopy Resolution Test Chart*, USCOM-NBS-DC, 6th edition, July, 1962.

[42] Engelstein, S., 'Microfilm Jackets in Unitized Microfilm Systems', in *Reprographie, 1st Internationalen Kongress*, Verlag O. Helwich (Darmstadt, 1964), p. 245.

[43] Fromm, H. J. and Insalaco, S. C., 'A New Direct Duplicating Silver-Halide Film', *The National Micronews*, No. 83, 1966.

[44] (a) Ardern, L. L., 'Microfiche', *Libr. Assoc. Record.*, 60, 150, 1958.
(b) de Mink, H. L., ' "Microfiche" or "Microcard" in Micro-publishing', *Reprographie, 1st Internationalen Kongress*, Verlag O. Helwich (Darmstadt, 1964), p. 320.

[45] (a) Rubin, H. E., 'Sensitometry of New Diazo Films as related to Specific Microfilm Applications', *Proc. Ann. Conv. Nat. Microfilm. Assoc.*, 10, 202, 1961.
(b) Alfaya, R., 'Diazotype Systems for High-Acuity Continuous-Tone Reproduction', *Phot. Sci. Eng.*, 6, 258, 1962.

[46] (a) Nieset, R. T., 'The Basis of the Kalvar System of Photography', *Proc. Ann. Conv. Nat. Microfilm. Assoc.*, 10, 177, 1961.
(b) Anderson, M. G. and Sandlin, E. E., 'Vesicular Systems for High-Resolution Generation Printing', *Proc. Ann. Conv. Nat. Microfilm. Assoc.*, 13, 189, 1964.

[47] (a) Samain, J., 'Une Nouvelle Technique de Classement et de Sélection de Documents', *L'Onde Electrique*, 36, 671, 1956.

(b) Samain, J., 'Filmorex', *F.I.D. Manual on Document Reproduction and Selection*, April, 1956, p. 753.E.1.

[48] Kuipers, J. W., Tyler, A. W. and Myers, W. L., 'A Minicard System for Documentary Information', *Am. Documentation*, 8, 246, 1957.

[49] Jenkins, D. D., 'Magnetic Indexing, Microfilm Storage and Information Retrieval', *Proc. Ann. Conv. Nat. Microfilm. Assoc.*, 11, 205, 1962.

[50] Anon., 'Photography in the Russo-Japanese War', *Brit. J. Phot.*, 52, 22, 1905.

[51] Hoover, J. E., 'The Enemy's Masterpiece of Espionage', *Reader's Digest (London Edition)*, 48, 49, May, 1946.

[52] Editors of *Look*, *The Story of the F.B.I.*, E. P. Dutton (New York, 1947).

[53] Tauber, A. S. and Myers, W. C., *Proc. Ann. Conv. Nat. Microfilm. Assoc.*, 11, 256, 1962 (see reference [31], Chapter 2).

[54] (a) Bowker, K., Martin, L. H., Lucas, E. J. and Phaneuf, C., *Technical Investigations of Elements of a Mechanized Library System*, Electronics Research Laboratories, Crosley Division, AVCO Corporation (Boston, 1960). Final Report No. EW-6680.
(b) Clapp, V. W., *The Future of the Research Library*, University of Illinois Press (Urbana, 1964), pp. 20 and 68.

[55] Carlson, C. O., Grafton, A. and Tauber, A. S., 'The Photochromic Micro-image Memory', *NCR-ED. Tech. Publications*, May, 1961, also in Yovits, M. C. (Ed.), *Large Capacity Memory Techniques for Computing Systems*, The Macmillan Co. (New York, 1962), p. 385.

[56] Stott, J. G., Cummins, G. E. and Breton, H. E., *J. Soc. Mot. Pict. Tel. Eng.*, 66, 607, 1957 (see reference [9(a)], Chapter 8).

[57] Boni, A., 'Microprint', *Am. Doc.*, 2, 150, 1951.

[58] (a) Anon., 'How many books can you put on the head of a pin?', *Modern Lithography*, 33 (4), 24, 1965.
(b) Private communication from Dr K. K. Koseki.

[59] Forsdyke, Sir J., 'Microfilms for the Disabled', *Aslib, Proc.*, 4, 39, 1952.

[60] Stewart, J. and D. Hickey, *Reading Devices for Micro-Images*, Rutgers University Press (New Brunswick, N.J., 1960).

[61] (a) Hawken, W. R., *Enlarged Prints from Library Microforms*, American Library Association (Chicago, 1963).
(b) Nelson, C. E., as reference [15], p. 163 et seq.

[62] Scott, M. L., Abbott, T. I., Yackel, E. C. and Connolly, L. T., 'New Direct and Indirect Offset Plates by Photography', in *Reprography, 1st Internationalen Kongress*, Verlag O. Helwich (Darmstadt, 1964), p. 256.

[63] Pickering, R. D., 'The 20 × Precision Enlarger', *Phot. Sci., Eng.*, 4, 213, 1960.

[64] (a) Anon., 'Put your Drawings on Active Microfilm', *Engineering*, 200, 358, 1964.
(b) Caps Consultants Ltd, *Microreproduction*, a series of Technical Leaflets concerned mainly with ultra-violet enlarging.

[65] (a) Smith, K. Stuart, 'The Airgraph Service', *Proc. Brit. Soc. Int. Bibl.*, 4, 31, 1942.

(b) Paul, W. A. J., 'Microgram Service', *Phot. J.*, **85B**, 70, 1945 (refers to military applications).

[66] Power, E., 'O.-P. Books; A Library Breakthrough', *Am. Doc.*, **9**, 273, 1958.

[67] Corbett, E. V., *Photo-Charging*, J. Clarke and Co. (London, 1957).

[68] (a) Whitaker, G. C., 'The Rôle of Microfilm in the Teaching Machine', *Proc. Ann. Conv. Nat. Microfilm. Assoc.*, **11**, 143, 1962.
(b) Taks, J. J., 'Microfiche Data Storage in Teaching Machines', *Reprographie, 1st Internationalen Kongress*, O. Helwich (Darmstadt, 1964), p. 353.

[69] (a) Brown, R., 'Navigating in land Vehicles', *New Scientist*, **29**, 711, 1966. (b) Honick, K. R., 'Developments in Pictorial Navigation Displays', *Phot. J.*, **107**, 97, 1967.

[70] (a) Bush, V., 'As We May Think', *Atlantic Monthly*, **176**, 101, 1945.
(b) Green, J. C., 'The Rapid Selector: an Automatic Library', *Rev. Doc.*, **17**, 66, 1950.

[71] Pike, J. L., and Bagg, T. C., 'The Rapid Selector and other N.B.S. Document Retrieval Studies', *Proc. Ann. Conv. Nat. Microfilm. Assoc.*, **11**, 213, 1962.

[72] Anon., 'Film Library Instantaneous Presentation', *Am. Doc.*, **8**, 330, 1957.

[73] (a) Tydings, K., 'Miracode: A New System of Automated Information Retrieval', *Brit. J. Phot.*, **111**, 1098, 1963.
(b) Recordak Miracode System, Recordak Corp. Leaflet.
(c) Daniel, E. S., 'Solving Information Storage and Retrieval Problems with Miracode', *J. Chem. Documentation*, **6**, 147, August, 1966.
(d) Weil, B. H., Emerson, W. G., and Bolles, S. W., 'Esso Research Experiences with *Chemical Abstracts* on Microfilm', *J. Chem. Documentation*, **5**, 193, 1965.

[74] Patterson, H. D., 'Automation of Engineering Documentation Files', *Proc. Ann. Conv. Nat. Microfilm. Assoc.*, **14**, 129, 1965.

[75] Larsen, P. W., 'The Command Retrieval Information System', *Proc. Ann. Conv. Nat. Microfilm. Assoc.*, **11**, 41, 1962.

[76] (a) Bradshaw, P. D., 'The Walnut System. A Large Capacity Document Storage and Retrieval System', *Am. Doc.*, **13**, 270, 1962.
(b) Vogel, N. A., 'Walnut Document Storage and Retrieval System', *Proc. Ann. Conv. Nat. Microfilm. Assoc.*, **11**, 27, 1962.

[77] Recordak Corporation Leaflets on Products Nos 3405, 5570, 5571, 5572, 5575.

[78] Kuder, M. L., 'An Automatic Microimage File', *Nat. Bur. Standards Tech. News Bull.*, **40**, 88, 1956.

[79] (a) Stern, J., 'Microcite, An Aid to More Effective Referencing', *Nat. Bur. Standards Tech. News Bull.*, **41**, 141, 1957.
(b) Stern, J., 'A New Microcite Machine', *Nat. Bur. Standards Tech. News Bull.*, **45**, 113, 1961.

[80] Myers, W. C., 'P.C.M.I. Technology and Applications', *National Cash Register Co. Technical Publication*, No. 4605, 1964, p. 23. Also Ref. 39 quotes work on Navy Contract Nonr-3865(00).

[81] Greenough, M. L., Cook, H. D. and Martens, M., 'FOSDIC—A Film Optical Sensing Device for Input to Computers', *Nat. Bur. Standards Tech. News Bull.*, **38**, 24, 1954.

[82] McPherson, J. L. and Volk, M., 'FOSDIC Microfilm Problems and Their Solution', *Proc. Ann. Conv. Nat. Microfilm. Assoc.*, **11**, 193, 1962.

[83] Greenough, M. L. and Palasky, E. C., 'FOSDIC II—Reads Microfilmed Punched Cards', *Nat. Bur. Standards Tech. News Bull.*, **41**, 72, 1957; see also,
Palasky, E. C., 'FOSDIC IV Reads Microfilmed Weather Data for Computer', *Nat. Bur. Standards Tech. News Bull.*, **51**, 63, 1967.

[84] Jones, W. H., 'Microfilm. An output Medium for Digital Computers', *Proc. Ann. Conv. Nat. Microfilm. Assoc.*, **12**, 331, 1963.

[85] Anon., 'Patent Copy Document System Contract Awarded', *The National MICRO-NEWS No. 82*, 278, June, 1966.

SUPPLEMENTARY REFERENCES

For more general study, readers are recommended to consult references [2(a)], [7], [8], [9], [13], [33], [47(b)], [53] and [54]. Attention should also be directed to the following works:

[86] Ballou, H. W., *Guide to Microreproduction Equipment*, National Microfilm Association (Annapolis, 1st edition, 1959). Further editions and supplements have since appeared. An essential work for study of equipment.

[87] International Federation for Documentation, *Manual on Document Reproduction and Selection*. A serial publication oriented to library and scholarly applications.

[88] Hawkins, R., *Production of Micro-forms*, Rutgers University Press (New Brunswick, N.J., 1960).

[89] Frank, O., *Die Mikrofilmtechnik*, Dorotheen-Verlag (Stuttgart, 1961).

[90] Bagg, T. C. and Stevens, M. E., *Information Selection Systems Retrieving Replica Copies*, Natural Bureau of Standards Technical Note, 157, 1961. This work not only describes available and proposed systems with an extensive bibliography, but also discusses systems design, operation and evaluation.

[91] Alexander, S. N. and Rose, F. C., 'The Current Status of Graphic Storage Techniques: Their Potential Application to Library Mechanization', in *Libraries and Automation*, Council on Library Resources (Washington, D.C., 1964), p. 111. This chapter effectively updates Bagg and Stevens (above), and the whole work represents a later discussion of this topic.

[92] Hawken, W. R., *Copying Methods Manual*, Library Technology Program, American Library Association (Chicago), 1966. This book deals with *all* methods of copying. Attention is directed particularly to illustrations of the variability of documents (Chapters 1 and 2), and to the discussion of copyright problems in Appendix C.

[93] Cuadra, C. A. (Ed.), *Annual Review of Information Science and Technology*, Vol. 1, Interscience Publishers (New York), 1966. This first volume regards information processing and retrieval as a technology in its own right. Since its thirteen chapters take the

form of review articles (mostly with 100 or more references) it should prove invaluable for following further developments.

[94] Verry, H. R., and Wright, G. H., *Microcopying Methods*, Focal Press, London, 1967. Revised edition of reference [9].

[95] Williams, B. J. S., *Evaluation of Microrecording Techniques for Information and Data Storage and Retrieval*, HERTIS (Hertfordshire Information Service), Hatfield, 1967.

[96] Carlson, C. O., Scherr, B. F. and Rondas, I. V., *Contact Printer*, U.S. Patent 3,316,825 (see reference [14], Chapter 8).

13 · Microphotography as a Research Tool

Microphotographic techniques, emulsions and products from their earliest days have constituted potentially useful tools for scientific research. Examples illustrating this statement have multiplied in the last quarter century, since commercial extreme-resolution plates were first marketed, and many have been described in earlier chapters of this book. Microphotography can, for instance, play its part:

(a) In the literature search which should precede a research project.
Microphotographic document copies may not only give the research worker more ready access to world-wide literature collections, but also assist the search by information-retrieval systems. The importance of suit-case reference libraries for field workers should not be overlooked.

(b) In the production of many of the physical tools and components required for the collection of data.
The first (and still very important) example is the production of graticules and instrument scales. From this stemmed the production of binary-coded scales used in some types of digitized instruments. These are important for the automated extraction of data from many types of records, for telemetry, and for collection of data at very high speeds. Photographically produced moiré-fringe gratings overlap the functions of binary-coded scales, and are used for measurements of small changes in length. From this has been derived methods for checking the accuracy (or controlling the output of) machine tools, testing the straightness of lathe beds and studying vibration.
Microphotographic techniques for fabrication of components for mechanical and electronic devices are increasingly employed. Examples are precision springs and wire meshes, and microelectronic components and circuits on which the electronics industry has been spending a large proportion of its research effort.

(c) In the processing of data, and its reduction to concepts and statements simple enough for communication to workshops or other laboratories.

448

Digitized scales and moiré-fringe equipment are also important at this stage, since the information they collect can be fed
directly into a computer without any need for human intervention. Development of the computers themselves depends
increasingly on the perfection of photographically produced
microelectronic components. Systems such as FOSDIC are
employed for processing information for the United States
Weather Bureau, and the SC-4020 and 'Charactron' tube for
visual display of computer output, facilitate the interpretation
of large masses of data, whose significance would remain hidden
without their aid (see pp. 436 and 438).

No doubt their users find these applications of microphotography
most valuable, but there have been some research projects in which
microphotographic techniques or materials were still more directly
involved. Such researches fall into three classes.

(1) The study and improvement of detail recognition.
(2) The recording of material shifts.
(3) Recording the field patterns of light and X-rays.

Study and Improvement of Detail Recognition

PHOTOGRAPHIC EMULSIONS AND LENSES

Detail recognition[1] by photographic lenses and emulsions has engaged
the attention of many scientists and technologists during the last
century. Their efforts have improved the performance obtainable in
most applications of photography, but have been of special benefit
in cinematography, in permitting reduction in the size and weight of
hand-held cameras, in the graphic arts, in aerial photography and in
the manifold applications of microphotography itself.

The basic principle of the experimental work is simple, and consists in studying changes in the visibility or contrast of a pattern reproduced by the optical system or emulsion under test. For fundamental work, and for mathematical analysis of performance, the
present tendency is to measure modulation-transfer functions (see
pp. 37 and 107). For testing lenses, for instance, equipment has now
been built which uses a photoelectric system to display the modulation-transfer function *immediately* as a curve on an oscilloscope [1].
The results are particularly suitable for predicting the performance
to be expected from a number of components combined into a system.
This method involves no photographic stage at all.

---

[1] This general term includes such concepts as resolving power, acutance and
optical transfer functions (see also [47], on p. 63).

Because of the application of such methods, the concept of resolving power as an *absolute quantity* has lost much of its attractiveness. This change in the climate of technical opinion should not, however, be allowed to conceal the usefulness of resolution tests for demonstrating and recording optical performance. Their special virtue is that the results obtained can be so easily related to our specific tasks.

All resolution tests employ a test chart in which a simple pattern is reproduced at various sizes usually graduated in a geometrical progression (see p. 257 and Plate 58). For testing lenses, it is usual to combine a number of complete test-chart images on a single slide, so that performance in different parts of the field can be conveniently observed. In the practical execution of the tests, observations are made on the legibility or line quality of images of sizes down to and below the performance limit of the component under test. According to the circumstances, performance of lenses may be assessed either by direct inspection of the projected image, or by first recording the image on an appropriate photographic material. In their turn, photographic materials may be assessed by their reproduction of images impressed on them either by projection or by contact printing. It is axiomatic that the testing conditions (whenever possible) should closely simulate the intended conditions of use.

VISUAL RESOLUTION TESTING

Direct visual inspection of lens performance is most appropriate for lenses designed primarily to project enlarged images for direct viewing. Examples are lenses used in slide, ciné and profile projectors and in microfilm readers. For such instruments, inspection of fine microphotographic resolution-test images enlarged into the normal viewing plane provides a very practical test. When the projection lens is used for making enlargements, the enlarged images can be recorded on a suitable paper. In this application, the modulation-transfer function of the recording emulsion is likely to be high at line frequencies corresponding to the lens's resolution limit, and the choice of emulsion for this purpose is not so critical.

A microscope can be used to inspect the aerial image given by lenses normally employed for photographic recording of reduced images, but factors such as differences of spectral response and tone and edge discrimination tend to render the test less significant for this application. In fact, opticians often prefer to inspect the spread pattern in the reduced aerial image of a 'star' or illuminated pinhole. Considerable skill is required for interpreting the results of this test [1].

PHOTOGRAPHIC RESOLUTION TESTING BY PROJECTION

When lenses have been designed for photographic reduction, inspection of images recorded on an appropriate emulsion is the ultimate test, but it must be realized that a simple photographic test can only indicate the image quality produced at one focus position. This is radically different from the situation in visual testing, where image quality can be watched continuously as the focus setting is moved through the optimum position. For photographic resolution testing of lenses, therefore, it is essential to be able to change the focus controllably and reproducibly with increments small enough to ensure that the optimum position can be observed (see p. 134). For this reason, resolution-test cameras have frequently been built with a precision adequate for microphotographic work with extreme-resolution emulsions [2]. In fact, essentially microphotographic registration and focusing techniques are used in this work. The tests must also be made with finely graded series of exposures (Appendix III) to ensure optimum performance.

In specifying an 'appropriate' emulsion for recording resolution tests of lenses, due regard should be given to the designed application for the lens. Results given by an aero lens on microfilm may have little relevance for the intended application of either component. With photographic objectives, use of extreme-resolution emulsions tends to demonstrate the visual resolution limit, which may have little significance for the practical situation. The effective spectral distribution of the illuminant and the spectral sensitivity of the recording emulsion should also be deliberately adjusted according to the designed application.

The ultimate test for photographic materials designed for recording projected images is also inspection of images recorded on them by a lens of the type intended to be used in practice. Criteria of relevance again tell us that tests with a radically different optical system have rather slight practical significance. Thus use of a microscope objective for projecting an image on a high-speed emulsion, or use of interference patterns with extreme-resolution emulsions will certainly allow differences of *potentiality* to be observed. Whether the observed potential differences of performance have any significance for the designed conditions of use can only be decided by actual practical tests. It must, therefore, always be remembered that the results of a resolution test are the consequence of the *interaction* between the energy distribution in the image and the properties of the emulsion under test.

Differences between the performance of all but extreme-resolution emulsions can be demonstrated by contact printing from microphotographic images previously made on an extreme-resolution emulsion (Plate 58). For convenience, the test charts are usually made with a row of images, and the exposure in contact printing is increased progressively from one end of the chart. A convenient method for giving a series of exposures is to use a non-scattering optical wedge.

For general photographic laboratory work, contact-resolution tests are rather out of favour. Production of satisfactory multiple-image charts is relatively time-consuming and expensive, and the pressures needed to secure satisfactory contact can soon damage them (Plate 19).[1] When photographic materials are primarily intended for contact copying, however, this method of testing is by far the most relevant. Examples are papers used for contact copying of aero negatives and documents, films used for duplication of motion-pictures and microfilm and plates used for multi-stage production of graticules and photo-fabrication masks. In all such cases, the test charts are preferably made on the support carrying the images to be copied in commercial practice.

Contact-resolution tests are also useful for testing the ability of photographic materials to produce images from which further satisfactory contact copies can be made. When the printing medium is potentially an extreme-resolution material, prints can appear very different from the visual appearance of the negative (Plates 18 and 21). The ability of a negative to transfer its information to a contact print is important for half-tone block production, for photoresist work (especially in microelectronics) and for microfilm applications requiring multi-generation printing.

Special Applications of Microphotographic Resolution Images

THE FINE DETAIL OF PHOTOGRAPHIC PROCESSING REACTIONS

In some photographic processes, the final image is the result of the deposition of coloured material depending on the image-wise formation of a soluble reaction product. For example, many processes for toning (or intensification) of photographic prints depend on the formation of ferrocyanide ions during bleaching of a silver image, followed by precipitation of insoluble ferrocyanides by metal salts also present in the solution. Another example of great technical im-

---

[1] Resolution-test images made by photo-etching chromium mirrors on glass should be much more durable (p. 343).

portance is the formation of dye images by the reaction of couplers with soluble developer-oxidation products, which is a keystone of modern colour photography. In processes of this type, resolution can be strongly influenced by any tendency of the image-wise reaction product to diffuse sideways before precipitation occurs. Resolution-test images in a concentrated Lippmann emulsion represent a most sensitive means for studying these tendencies. Experiments of this type would assist the evolution of an extreme-resolution colour process.

RESOLUTION TESTING FOR RADIOGRAPHY

Because of the difficulty of focusing X-rays, detail-recognition tests have necessarily been made by a process resembling contact printing. The penetrating property of X-rays, however, makes it difficult to obtain test objects opaque enough to give radiographs with useful contrast, but fine enough to demonstrate limits of emulsion performance. Small bones or diatoms or wire meshes or analogous structures are useful for sharpness comparisons, but are less suitable for measuring the resolution limit. It was found that resolution test images with properties adequate for some tests could be prepared from Maximum-Resolution emulsion [3]. We have already seen that the mass of the images could be greatly increased by physical development, because the chemically developed image consisted of a very finely divided silver deposit. By itself this increase in mass raised the opacity to X-rays, but a further substantial increase was obtained by depositing a metal of higher atomic number than silver. Lumiére and Seyewetz's physical developer [4] allowed mercury (atomic no. 80) to be deposited in the same way as silver (atomic no. 47) is deposited from more conventional physical developers. Several hours processing with constant agitation and hourly renewal of the solution deposited a layer corresponding to 25 μ (0·001 in) thickness of liquid mercury. This was several times the thickness of the original emulsion layer, and the mercury was chemically equivalent to fifty times the silver content of the coated emulsion.

In using these test charts, the conflicting claims of resolution and image spread resulting from heavy deposition of metal for high opacity had to be considered. It was therefore decided to employ the minimum degree of intensification needed to give a useful visible contrast on the radiograph at the kilovoltage used in any particular test. For example, a short intensification produced test charts having an opacity of 4 to the soft (8 kV) X-rays used for microradiography, and with the finest group (320 lines/mm) satisfactorily resolved. Tests on different emulsions showed that the resolution limit was easily measured on X-ray and process-type photomechanical films, but a fine-grain nuclear-particle emulsion resolved the last group. This chart was thus useful for measuring the resolution of emulsions designed for making microradiographs intended for viewing at moderate magnifications—up to 50 diameters. There seemed little hope of using this method for measuring the microradiographic resolution of extreme-resolution emulsions. Since their resolution to soft X-rays should be higher than their resolution to light, there was no possibility of forming sufficiently fine images for this purpose by optical projection.

Heavily intensified images were also made with an opacity of 1·5 to X-rays of the quality used for chest radiography (55 kV with 0·2 mm copper filtration). Now two different standards of resolution can be achieved according to the exposure conditions used for medical radiography. Whenever possible, X-ray films are used with fluorescent screens, which reduce the exposure and consequent X-ray dosage to the patient by a factor of about forty. In these conditions, the test-chart was found to have adequate resolution, and limiting values between 10 and 20 lines/mm were measured on high-speed X-ray film (Plate 59). When the same films were given the increased exposure required to produce the same density with direct X-rays, much sharper images were produced, but the spread of the intensified images in the test chart now determined the limit (Plate 59).

These experiments amounted to a partially successful feasibility trial. For better results, it would be necessary to make the test charts by methods offering positive control of the image spread. Possibilities are:

(i) production of a pattern on thin sheets of lead or gold by photoetching. If 'powderless' etching could be modified to deal with these metals, resultant control of undercut could give test charts with improved opacity and resolution.

(ii) electroplating of a metal of high atomic number through a stencil made from photosensitive nylon. The published evidence [5] suggests that exceptionally thick and sharp metal stencils could be made by this route.

In fact methods of the type used for refined production of metallic components for mechanical or electronic use (Chapter 11), could be extended to the production of radiographic resolution-test charts.

RESOLUTION TESTING IN AUTORADIOGRAPHY

Any specimen containing radioactive material can be considered as a 'self-luminous' object, from which a record of the distribution of the radioactive material can potentially be obtained by allowing the radiation to enter a photographic emulsion. The developed record is an *autoradiograph*. Since the radiation is emitted in every direction, the emulsion needs to be brought as close as possible to the sources, and the image-forming process is a type of contact printing. The specimens examined are usually smears, 'squashes', histological sections or solid objects with at least one flat surface. For different purposes specimens have just been contacted with X-ray film, immersed in or coated with liquid emulsion, or coated with a stripped emulsion layer [6]. In Pelc's stripping-emulsion technique, a piece of dry photographic emulsion stripped from a specially prepared plate is laid on a clean water surface [7]. The emulsion layer first 'puckers' as it swells, but within a minute or two stretches out quite flat on the water surface. It can then be lifted out on the specimen, and on drying follows all the undulations of the specimen so that substantially perfect contact is achieved.

For medical research, autoradiography has been employed for studying biochemical and metabolic phenomena in studies of the function of specific organs and of cell growth and division. For example, administration of sodium iodide labelled with I^{131} to a rat, followed by autoradiography of the thyroid gland, demonstrated the connection between the structure of the gland and the distribution of the iodide uptake (Plate 60). In such applications the autoradiographs were viewed with a microscope, and good resolution was required to demonstrate which group of cells or even what part of a single cell contained the radioactivity.

Much progress towards selecting conditions for high resolution was achieved by theoretical calculations, but it was desirable to check the underlying assumptions by objective and reproducible tests. Estimates of resolution made from autoradiographs of biological specimens were of limited use. Each histological section had its own unique three-dimensional uptake of radioactive material, and the distribution could never be precisely known or reproduced. What was obviously needed was a radioactive resolution-test chart.

Now developed photographic silver images can be submitted to a variety of chemical reactions, many of which lead to the quantitative deposition of elements with available radioactive isotopes. Such *toning* reactions could be used to make ordinary resolution-test images radioactive. The iodine isotope I^{131} was first chosen, since it could readily be used for this purpose, and was (at the time) of great medical interest. A silver image could be converted by bleaching first to silver bromide, and then changing to labelled silver iodide by double decomposition:

$$Ag + KBr + K_3Fe(CN)_6 \rightarrow AgBr + K_4Fe(CN)_6$$
$$AgBr_{\text{a}} + NaI^* \rightarrow AgI^* + NaBr$$

Preliminary experiments showed that a resolution-test image on Maximum-Resolution emulsion could be converted in this way and then blackened by converting to silver sulphide

$$2AgI^* + Na_2S \rightarrow Ag_2S + 2NaI^*$$

and still resolve over 1,000 lines/mm. This was good evidence that the distribution of the silver iodide and its associated radioactive isotope had followed the pattern of the silver image faithfully.

We have already noted that the autoradiographic emulsion needs to be very close to the specimen, and calculations suggested that separations of even a few microns could influence the results. It was therefore desirable that the test-chart images should be confined to the very surface of the emulsion, and this was accomplished by Kowaliski's technique of dyeing the gelatin heavily to restrict light penetration [8]. Not only did this method confine the images to the top quarter of a Maximum-Resolution emulsion layer (Plate 61), but it also greatly eased the problem of producing adequate quality with a wide range of line widths (see p. 258). In addition, when they were made radioactive, these images corresponded to the most favourable histological preparation with all the radioactivity concentrated right in the surface.

These radioactive test charts were employed for a systematic study of the emulsion factors operating in the stripping-film technique [9]. Experimental products were applied to the test charts, and were stored in the dark for a range of times to obtain an optimum exposure value. Although the normal practice is to process autoradiographs in contact with the specimen, for this purpose it seemed better to remove the autoradiographic emulsion before processing, to prevent chemical interference during development. In the resultant study of the influence of emulsion-type and coating thickness, it was concluded that a four-micron layer of a fine-grain nuclear-track emulsion was close to the optimum [10]. Plate 62 shows the resolution obtained on Kodak A.R.10 Autoradiographic plates which resulted from this work.

The potentiality of this testing method was explored further by super-coating the processed test charts with quantities of dilute gelatin solution giving layers of clear gelatin of known thickness when dry. Autoradiographs then showed that 3 μ separation (0·0001 in) seriously decreased the sharpness, while 10 μ (0·0004 in) resulted in gross blurring of the images (Plate 63). The same testing method was subsequently used by Lamerton and Harriss [11] to demonstrate that the stripping-film technique gave important improvements of resolution even with images recorded on large-grain high-speed X-ray emulsions. This testing method is not restricted to iodine, and test charts have also been toned with other radioactive isotopes such as sulphur [12] and phosphorus [13].

At the time this work was done, a microphotographic procedure seemed the only practicable method for making such images. Since a moderate number of images is required for this type of investigation, it still seems the most suitable approach. Radioactive test charts consist of precisely defined patterns in a very thin layer of radioactive material. The range of elements used could be extended by employing photo-resist stencils to control image-wise etching or deposition of radioactive layers. By the use of radioactive test charts, it can be fairly claimed that assessment of emulsion experiments proceeded with a speed and sureness that would have been impossible with histological samples. It also seems likely that publication of photographs, such as Plate 62, must have generated confidence in the physical validity of autoradiographic methods, and thereby encouraged research workers to adopt these procedures.

RECORDING OF MATERIAL SHIFTS

For the better understanding of the processes of metal fabrication or fracture tests, details of the movement of the surface have been studied by observing a fine grid printed or etched on the specimen [14]. The resolution obtainable by extreme-resolution emulsions permits very small material shifts to be detected. The potentiality of this method has been demonstrated by an investigation of the glazing of photographic prints [15].

When allowed to dry with the emulsion open to the air, the surface of prints on 'glossy' photographic papers have a definite texture which causes the emulsion to give a somewhat diffuse rather than specular reflection of light. If prints on the same papers, however, are allowed to dry with the emulsion pressed into contact with a highly polished surface, the dried emulsion becomes glass-smooth and reflects light specularly. It seemed likely that the details of this glazing process could be studied by observing the behaviour of a sufficiently fine grid printed on paper coated with an extreme-resolution emulsion. For this purpose Maximum-Resolution emulsion was used heavily dyed to prevent halation from spoiling the definition (Chapter 3), and was coated at the thickness and with the hardeners normally used for paper emulsions. The images were obtained by direct projection, using a $\frac{2}{3}$ in (16 mm) achromat with a 'salt-cellar' distance piece (Fig. 31). The resultant grid had lines about 0·0001 in (2–4 μ) wide and 0·0005 in (12 μ) apart, with satisfactory sharpness over a circle of 0·04 in (1 mm) diameter.

When these images were dried open to the air, the lines showed hardly any distortion, even when the underlying structure of the paper showed that the emulsion surface must have been quite uneven. Similar prints cold-glazed by drying in contact with a 'ferrotype' sheet, or hot-glazed on a commercial glazing machine, showed definite distortion of the grid. The size of the emulsion shifts varied greatly over the surface of the prints, being greatest over prominent paper fibres (Plate 64), but no significant difference between hotglazed and cold-glazed prints could be detected. In the worst cases the distortion corresponded to about half a division of the grid (0·00025 in, or 6 μ), which is about one eighth of the least separation

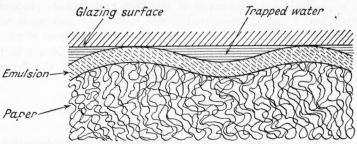

Fig. 117 *Wet Paper Emulsion before Glazing*

When the emulsion is squeegeed to the glazing surface, pockets of water are trapped in the hollows of the emulsion surface.

(about 0·002 in or 50 μ) which can be seen by the naked eye. Such small distortions of the emulsion were thus unlikely to influence the image sharpness of ordinary photographic prints.

The reason for these distortions can be deduced from a detailed consideration of the nature of the glazing process. The surface of a freshly processed and wet print is quite rough, and can be likened to mountainous country with hills and valleys. When the wet emulsion is applied to the glazing surface, air and the gross excess of water are removed by a roller or a squeegee. At this stage only the hills can actually be touching the glazing surface, and the valleys must still be filled with water (Fig. 117). The glazing sheet is quite impervious, and the emulsion can, therefore, only dry as a result of water evaporating through the paper base. It obviously will not be dry until all the water filling the valleys has also evaporated. Forces exerted during this stage of the drying must be sufficient to draw the floors of the valleys in the still plastic emulsion layer right up to the glazing surface. The final stages of drying then take place with the whole emulsion surface in practically molecular contact with the glazing sheet, so that the emulsion acquires the polished finish of the glazing surface. It is thus evident that different areas of the emulsion surface must suffer vertical movements relative to each other, and it is most probable that these vertical movements will be accompanied by lateral shifts. On this hypothesis the lateral distortions are likely to be greatest where the emulsion surface is most uneven, and the correspondence between the largest lateral shifts and prominent paper fibres is thus only to be expected.

It would be foolish to claim that this experiment on glazing is itself of much intrinsic importance, or that it is likely to facilitate technical improvement of photographic products. It does, however, demonstrate a type of investigational technique which has other applications. Grid patterns have, for example, been applied to the surface of metal sheets before shaping, so that the movements of material occurring during stamping could be followed. The ease with which thin layers of photosensitive resin can be applied to many substrates makes this type of product very convenient for the application of the grid patterns. By this method, Bell and Langdon showed that grain-boundary sliding in metals was revealed by sharp offsetting of the grid lines [16].

The analytical power of such procedures can be increased by comparing the distorted grid with a transparency of the original pattern, and observing the moiré fringes so formed. Dally and Riley have shown how this procedure can be used to observe displacements of models under stress [17]. Changes in shape were indicated in great detail, and visual observation located regions of high strain and provided information on the nature of the stress distribution. With high-speed recording of the moiré fringes, the method provided full dynamic strain information.

Recording the Field Patterns of Light and X-rays

In Chapter 8, it was shown that extraordinary results could sometimes be obtained by the contact printing of fine images on extreme-resolution emulsions (Plates 18 and 21). These were the result of sideways spread of light from different elements of the image by refraction or diffraction, which was sometimes accompanied by interference. The structures observed were too fine to have been detected by faster and light-scattering emulsions, but the extreme-resolution emulsion was able to provide a detailed picture of the distribution of electromagnetic energy at the moment of exposure. This principle can be applied in several ways.

LIGHT DISTRIBUTION IN PROJECTED IMAGES

In the same Chapter, we saw that projection of a fine grid pattern in the lower layers of an extreme-resolution emulsion produced a strong image, accompanied by a weaker image showing spurious resolution with staggered lines in the emulsion surface (Plate 17). With a lesser exposure, only the image in the depth of the emulsion would have been recorded, as a result of optical sectioning. The ability of such an emulsion to record optical sectioning can be demonstrated even more clearly by imaging an array of dots. Plate 65 shows the result of using a 4 mm microscope objective (N.A. 0·65) to project an image in the emulsion surface, followed by re-focusing, turning the negative through a right angle, and projecting the array in the depths of the emulsion. Both images were recorded quite separately within the depth of the emulsion. This technique could be used for the production of test objects for measuring the depth of focus of microscope objectives.

Emulsion properties which enable images like this to be obtained could be used in other ways. The field curvature in the image plane of microscope objectives, on their own or with suitable oculars, could be measured by projecting a reduced image of a negative with rows of dots into a microphotographic emulsion. A transverse section of the resultant developed image should permit the field curvature to be observed directly, and to be measured with fair precision. The usefulness of this method might also be extended by employing thicker emulsion coatings, with the necessary transparency preserved by the use of lower silver concentrations combined with the ultra-fine grain of a true Lippmann emulsion (Chapter 2). Knowledge about the processing of thick emulsion layers obtained in nuclear research suggests that coatings of thicknesses of 0·004 in (100 μ), or more, could be used for this purpose. Such a depth is sufficient to record the changes of light distribution for a useful distance on either side of the focal plane, even with objectives of quite moderate aperture.

X-RAY FIELD PATTERNS IN MICRORADIOGRAPHY

Experiments on the use of fine-grain emulsions for the production of radiographs of delicate structures which could be subsequently enlarged optically date from early in this century. Applications of this technique derived considerable impetus from the commercial introduction of Lippmann-type emulsions, and contact radiographs have been made with detail justifying inspection at several hundred diameters magnification.

Since the microradiographs depict the field pattern of X-rays resulting from attenuation of the beam by the entire thickness of the specimen, thin sections hinder blurring by geometrical factors or confusion by overlapping of structure. Geometrical blurring is also hindered by the use of a small focal spot. For example, Ehrenberg and

White [18] used a 40 μ (0·0016 in) spot at a focus-specimen distance of 27·5 cm (11 in). The thickness of the specimen had to exceed 10 μ (0·0004 in) before the blur on the film exceeded 0·1 μ (0·000004 in).

The results obtainable are also strongly dependent on the kilo-voltage of the X-rays. Values of 8 kV and less are used to obtain adequate contrast from thin specimens and to avoid loss of resolution by the fogging effect of secondary electrons scattered in the emulsion layer. In appropriate cases, extra detail can be revealed by injection or 'staining' of the samples with reagents containing strongly absorbing elements of high atomic number.

Whereas powerful light sources and condenser illumination allow emulsions of 'print-out' speed to be used for optical microphotography, such insensitive materials, if employed for microradiography, would require very long exposure times or massive and expensive electrical equipment.[1] The relatively high sensitivity of the silver-halide materials is therefore valuable in keeping exposure times down to the order of a minute. This sensitivity is derived from two factors. For the recording of any electro-magnetic radiation it is firstly essential that the radiation be *absorbed* by the emulsion. The stopping power for X-rays resulting from the relatively high atomic numbers of silver and bromine confers an immediate advantage over organic sensitive compounds mainly comprising elements of low atomic number. Stopping power and sensitivity are also directly proportional to the total mass of sensitive material in the layer at the instant of exposure. It is therefore advantageous to use layers containing all the metal salt subsequently required for image formation. For fixed radiographic and development conditions, the contrast will also be directly proportional to coating weight. The second factor conferring sensitivity is the amplification provided by development (see p. 30).

Since beams of sufficiently soft X-rays will be neither scattered nor refracted to any significant extent by emulsion constituents, image spread from these causes in microradiography is negligible. Micro-radiographs are, however, continuous-tone images, in which graini-ness is particularly easily seen (see p. 35). Because of this, the enlargement of grain size which can result from physical intensification in chemical developers needs to be closely watched (p. 73). Developers such as Kodak D.8 or D.178 produce rapid physical intensification, and because of this are less suitable than less solvent developers such as Kodak D.158 for microradiography. Because of the very fine grain of the emulsions used, however, even D.158 produces detectable grain-size growth, and Dr G. C. Blake of the Eastman Dental Hospital,

---

[1] In fact, microradiographs have been made with organic compounds producing a strong colour on direct X-ray exposure, but the image was contained in a layer too thick for subsequent high-resolution photomicrography.

London, has used a minimum solvent, ferrous-oxalate developer [19] with advantage when the finest possible grain was required.

Since X-ray stopping power and speed and contrast are all directly proportional to silver-halide coating weight, increasing the silver/gelatin ratio should produce a superior product. The effective resolution of a microradiograph, however, is also determined by the suitability of the image for subsequent enlargement by a microscope. A number of authorities [20] noted that the thickness of conventional emulsion coatings was several times the depth of focus of high-aperture microscope objectives (see also p. 99). The solution to this problem [18] was to employ an emulsion of substantially higher silver/gelatin ratio to give acceptable speed when coated to give a dry layer about 1 μ thick. Plate 66 demonstrates the performance obtained by Ehrenberg and White by using Kodak Experimental Scientific Film V.6028 evolved by Berriman of the Kodak Research Laboratories, Harrow.

Microradiography is a widely used research technique for collecting otherwise inaccessible data [21], and has been applied particularly intensively in medical research and in the investigation of light alloys.[1] The evolution of the technique gained a great deal from the availability of emulsions developed for microphotography.

Field Patterns Produced by Interference and Diffraction of Light

RECORDING OF STANDING LIGHT WAVES

When a regular series of transverse waves is reflected by a suitable surface, interference occurs between the incident and reflected waves. In the simple case of plane waves parallel to and moving towards a plane reflector, interference causes the establishment of stationary bands of maximum disturbance (anti-nodes) and minimum disturbance (nodes). These bands are parallel to the reflector, and successive nodes are separated by half the wavelength of the waves. The resultant system is known as *stationary* or *standing waves*, and can be easily observed on the surface of liquids. They should also be formed when light is reflected from a mirror, and in 1890 Wiener demonstrated these photographically [23]. For this purpose, he required an emulsion which was transparent and non-scattering, and he obtained a suitable product from commercially available collodion-silver-nitrate and collodion-chloride solutions. Before mixing the two solutions, he diluted each nineteen-fold with ether-alcohol mixture, and the

---

[1] Radiographs with substantial primary magnification can also be made by using special equipment to give a microscopic focal spot. Magnification is achieved by making the emulsion-to-specimen distance many times the emulsion-to-target distance [22].

resultant photosensitive mixture was quite clear even when observed in the flask. Very thin coatings were obtained by allowing three drops to spread by capillarity between a pair of plates 7 × 5 cm (3 × 2 in), separating rapidly, spinning and then laying flat to dry. From the liquid coating weight and the solid content of the solution, he calculated that the layer was about 0·03 μ (0·0000012 in) thick. This order of magnitude was confirmed interferometrically, and represents possibly the thinnest photosensitive layer ever used.

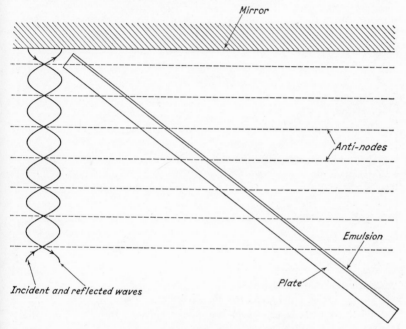

Fig. 118 *Recording of Stationary Light Waves*
Wiener's experiment. A very thin transparent emulsion was placed at an angle close to a mirror.

When dry, the emulsion was wiped from part of a plate, which was then pressed against a surface-silvered mirror. The plate thus lay at a small angle to the mirror, and when illuminated by a normal beam of parallel monochromatic light, the emulsion intersected the resultant system of waves (Fig. 118). The exposed plates were physically developed in a silver-pyrogallol solution, and showed parallel bands between 0·5 and 2 mm (0·02 and 0·08 in) apart. This seems to have been the first recorded case of the use of microphotographic emulsions for recording light-field patterns.

The success of the experiment depended on the very low light scatter and absorption of the emulsion used. Scatter would have

Q

spoiled the coherence of the light, and appreciable absorption would have decreased the amplitude of the reflected train of waves and thereby would have decreased interference at the nodes. In a variation of the experiment, Wiener used polarized light incident at 45°. The results confirmed that the photochemical change was produced by the electrical vector but not by the magnetic vector of electromagnetic vibration. This was a result of fundamental interest in all photochemical reactions, including all those employed in photography.

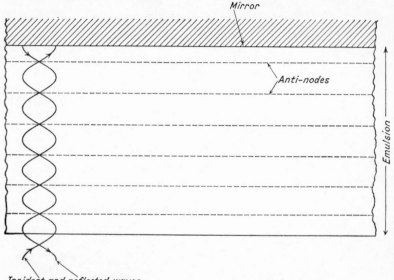

Fig. 119 *Lippmann's Process of Colour Photography*

A relatively thick layer of very transparent emulsion was placed in optical contact with a mirror.

Experiments of a similar type were performed in 1891 by Lippmann [24], but with a dye-sensitized gelatin–silver-bromide emulsion many wavelengths thick coated on a surface-silvered mirror, or with a pool of mercury placed behind it. In either case the emulsion was thus in optical contact with a mirror during the exposure, and with normally incident light the greater emulsion thickness allowed many anti-nodes to be formed inside the emulsion itself (Fig. 119). This caused the emulsion grains to blacken in a series of planes parallel to the surface of the mirror, and the separation of these planes depended on the wavelength (and hence on the colour) of the exposing light. If the developed emulsion layer was illuminated by white light, this periodic structure imposed its own modulation on the train of waves, with consequent selective transmission or reflection of the same wavelengths as those used for exposure. Lippmann employed this phenomenon as the basis for a process of colour photography. When the image projected from a camera lens fell on the back of the colour-sensitized plate with the emulsion in contact with mercury, the plate not only recorded the spatial and tonal information projected in the emulsion, but also the colour as depicted by the lamellae of developed grains within the emulsion thickness. With appropriate conditions of illumination, Lippmann colour photographs showed very brilliant colours of reputedly unparalleled accuracy. Unfortunately the lengthy exposures required (minutes in full sunlight) prevented extensive use of this beautiful and elegant process.

An interesting feature of Lippmann's colour photographs was that they constituted a three-dimensional record of the field pattern, since many lamellae were imaged within the emulsion thickness. The ability to provide such a record depends on the optical clarity which permits equally sharp images to be formed at all levels, and from the low absorption per unit thickness which allows grains at any level to receive a light intensity that has not been significantly attenuated by the layers above. An example of the potentiality of concentrated Lippmann emulsions for three-dimensional recording was Wolfe and Eisen's photograph of Lloyd's fringes projected in an Eastman 548 G.H. plate [25]. Sections cut through the processed emulsion confirmed that the images of the fringes formed thin vertical layers of grains passing throughout the depth of the emulsion.

Lippmann's experiment made even greater demands on the emulsion used. The increased thickness of the layer meant that the transparency and clarity of unit thickness of the emulsion needed to be even more perfect than in Wiener's experiment. Moreover, in Wiener's work the separation of the images of the anti-nodes was greatly increased by inclining the emulsion at a small angle from the mirror, whereas in Lippmann's process the emulsion had to record the separation of successive fringes formed within its own depth. When allowance is made for the refractive index of the emulsion, the recording of blue light of wavelength 4,500 Å corresponds to a line width of 0·000003 in (0·075 μ), or a resolution of about 6,000 lines/mm. Such photographs, in fact, probably display the highest photographic resolution (for light exposures) which has ever been achieved.

For the arts of microphotography, Lippmann's crowning achievement was his proof that such resolution figures could be combined with the development-amplification factor of his emulsion. This fact is of crucial importance for many of the applications described in this book.

RECORDING OF FRESNEL DIFFRACTION PATTERNS AND RESEARCH ON RECONSTRUCTED WAVEFRONTS

In spite of the magnificent results achieved by microscopy, investigators have for long realized that specimens might contain detail of a fineness beyond the reach of their equipment. With microscopy by light, the limit was set by visible wavelengths, which are about a thousand inter-atomic distances. The range of structures which could be studied was greatly extended by the invention of the electron microscope, since effective wavelengths were 100,000 times smaller, but the practically achieved resolution only increased a hundredfold. The 'lenses' used in electron microscopes suffered from spherical aberration, and since only very narrow bundles can be focused to a point, their working aperture (and the resolution associated therewith) was severely restricted. In addition, resolution was also limited by astigmatism resulting from residual errors of roundness (ellipticity) found in the products of the best workshops [26].

For considerations such as these, D. Gabor in 1948 examined the possibility of producing photographs allowing accidental errors to be compensated subsequently when they were viewed or printed [27]. For this purpose the photograph would have to record the full information in the radiation from the object, even if in a distorted form. As he pointed out, there is no way of correcting an out-of-focus holiday snapshot, since the information required for subsequent correction is irretrievably lost. Gabor demonstrated the principles of a process he called 'diffraction microscopy'. He allowed coherent light[1] from a monochromatic source focused on a pinhole to strike a transparency, and after travelling a further distance, the light fell on an extreme-resolution plate. Because the transparency had narrow black lines on a clear background, most of the area of the plate was flooded with freely transmitted background light. At any point on the plate, however, the amplitude was modulated by interference between the background light and the diffracted wavelets coming from different points of the transparency. When developed, the plate showed numerous systems of fringes, which only bore slight resemblance to the original appearance of the transparency. In fact it constituted a photograph of the Fresnel Diffraction field pattern, which he called a *hologram*, because it contained the whole information on the object.

When the hologram was suitably illuminated with 'coherent' light, it imposed its modulation on the incident beam, and in effect *reconstructed the wavefronts* present at the instant of exposure, and a reconstructed image of the transparency could be seen as a result of the

---

[1] Monochromatic light, which is all in phase as a result of emission from a sufficiently small source, is described as *coherent*.

consequent interference phenomena. The reconstructed images published by Gabor showed that the principle worked, but there was
clearly room for improvement. In his series of papers on the subject,
Gabor proposed that holograms should be made by an electron beam,
and subsequently viewed by light [25]. In this case, the image would
be magnified by the ratio of the wavelength of the reconstructing
light to the wavelength of the recording electron beam.

During the next fifteen years, the potentialities of holograms were
extended by the invention of lasers, which provided parallel light of

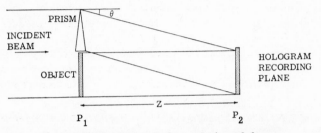

Fig. 120 *Wedge Technique for producing a hologram*
The object is placed in the lower part of plane P_1; the hologram is recorded at
plane P_2.
Courtesy of E. N. Leith, J. Upatnieks and 'Journal of the Optical Society of America'.

high spectral purity and much greater intensity than previously
available beams of coherent light. With this too, much attention has
been given to the refinement of Gabor's methods. Leith and Upatnieks
at the University of Michigan [28], noted that Gabor needed to use
transparencies with narrow dark lines and large transparent areas to
flood the plate with undiffracted background light. To overcome this
limitation, they employed a prism to deflect undiffracted light to the
plate (Fig. 120). In the absence of an object, this superimposition of
the upper part of the beam on the lower part formed a fringe pattern.
With the object in place, the Fresnel diffraction pattern from the
object was superimposed on and modulated these fringes, and the
plate recorded the entire complicated field pattern. When illuminated
as in Fig. 121, the fine structure of the fringe patterns caused the
hologram to act like a diffraction grating, and the first-order real
images showed good reconstruction of transparencies with narrow
clear lines on a dark background or with continuous tones (Plate 67).
In fact, their results showed both improved image quality in the
reconstructions, and avoidance of restriction as to subject characteristics necessitated by Gabor's method. For the production of their
holograms, Leith and Upatnieks employed a Kodak High Contrast
Copy plate and the extreme-resolution Kodak Spectroscopic Plate,

Type 649-F. The latter is a concentrated-Lippmann emulsion with its spectral sensitivity extended for use with red light emitted by a helium-neon or ruby laser.

G. W. Stroke described an extension of this type of method to the

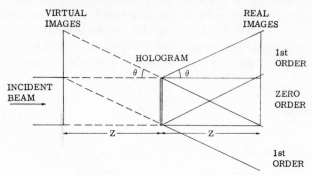

Fig. 121 *Wavefront reconstruction from Hologram*
Courtesy of E. N. Leith, J. Upatnieks and 'Journal of the Optical Society of America'.

'lensless photography' of solid objects [29]. Laser light diffracted from the surface of the object was allowed to interfere with a 'carrier wave' reflected from the surface of a plane mirror. The reconstructed image from a hologram produced in these conditions was three-dimensional. To observe parallax when viewing such a reconstruction produced from a flat plate without any refracting elements is quite an eerie experience.

EMULSIONS FOR HOLOGRAPHY

The design and choice of emulsions for holography is a crucial question for many investigators. In view of the demands which may be introduced by new applications and new lasers, it could take some time for opinions on this matter to become stabilized. Nevertheless, some basic facts are already clear. It is obviously necessary that the emulsion should be adequately sensitized for the wavelength (or wavelengths) emitted by the chosen laser, and chemical sensitization should be compatible with the anticipated exposure durations.

As with so many topics discussed in this book, we again encounter the conflict between photographic speed and resolution. The photographic speed limits the effective volume in space that can be illuminated by a given laser, and influences the exposure duration required, and hence the precautions needed to control the effects of vibration [30]. The resolution limits the fringe frequency which can be adequately recorded, and the fringe frequency is determined by the 'design angle' between the 'reference' and 'information' beams.

These interactions between emulsion properties, equipment requirements and the demands of particular experiments have been discussed by Rogers [30]. He concluded that design angles up to 3° could be recorded on most silver-halide emulsions, and angles of 10–25° could be recorded on fine-grain photomechanical plates. At angles greater than 25°, use of an extreme-resolution emulsion is obligatory.

It is significant that most investigators make their holograms on extreme-resolution emulsions. The following seem to be the properties they are seeking. Since holograms are, by definition, required to record *all* the information from the object, degradation of the recorded pattern by light scatter during exposure would appear no more tolerable than in other applications of microphotographic emulsions. Development conditions permitting excessive enlargement of the grain by physical development (p. 73) should be avoided. Degradation of the reconstructing beam by light scatter in the developed image is also damaging, and this problem is noticed especially when silver images are converted to a white image to improve the brightness of reconstruction (see also p. 292). The desirability of processing the emulsion so as to exaggerate the image-wise lenticules at the emulsion surface (p. 217) is debatable. Some investigators have used the lenticules as the sole information-carrying medium, by aluminizing the surface of the processed emulsion and re-constructing wavefronts by reflected light. It is, however, now evident that surface lenticules are largely a consequence of minute gelatin shifts resulting from processing (p. 293). Since the unexposed emulsion surface had no such lenticules, these shifts must necessarily be accompanied by small distortions of the fringe pattern. The distortions may be disadvantageous, particularly when information is contributed by the distribution of Lippmann-type laminae *within* the emulsion thickness.

Special requirements are introduced when holograms are produced with the information beam entering the front of the plate and the reference beam entering the back. In these conditions, no effective interference between the beams can occur if light absorption by the unprocessed emulsion is excessive, and the processed emulsion may not record the fringe structure constituting the hologram. In fact, Lin and LoBianco [31] reported that absorption by the emulsion of Kodak Spectroscopic Plates (Type 649-F) was undesirably high when used in this way. They showed that improved diffraction efficiency in these exposure conditions was obtained with a modified emulsion of similar layer thickness but lower silver content.

The structure of the processed image in these so-called 'volume' holograms resembles that of Lippmann colour photographs in that it contains laminar layers of developed grains within the depth of the emulsion. By reason of the frequency of these laminae, the monochromatic wavelength required for re-construction is automatically selected on illumination by white light. Because of vertical shrinkage of the emulsion during processing, the laminae tend to be closer than during exposure, and the selected wavelength correspondingly shorter. To counteract this tendency, Lin and LoBianco [31] bathed the processed holograms in a triethanolamine solution just before drying.

APPLICATIONS OF PHOTOGRAPHIC HOLOGRAMS

The publication of Leith and Upatnieks' paper [28] was rapidly followed by an increasing stream of communications. These demonstrated that the possibilities had excited the imagination of many physicists and engineers. The subject is being examined in more than a hundred laboratories, and many ingenious variations in the production and applications of holograms have been explored. Sources for more detailed introductions are review papers [29] [32] [33] [34], an extensive bibliography up to 1966 [38], and specialist text books by Stroke [35], and DeVelis [36]. Which of the many suggested applications will blossom from laboratory curiosities into techniques of major scientific or industrial importance is a most interesting question. While no attempt at a prediction is intended in the following section, some of the suggestions having the merit of producing results difficult to acquire in any other way are described below.

Ennos discussed the following applications [33].

With different reference-beam directions, a single hologram plate can store ten or more separate (and separable) images. This facility might be used in systems for pattern recognition and automatic reading of alphabetic or numerical symbols.

Separate images can also be stored in a single plate by exposing with different types of laser (or with different wavelengths from the same laser) and with the reference beams entering the back of the plate. Three-dimensional colour re-constructions from such holograms have been made with white light [31].

In addition to giving images permitting three-dimensional re-constructions, holography gains advantages from the formation of high-resolution images without use of an imaging lens. As a result, both the area recorded and the depth of focus obtained are increased in comparison with images made with lenses. In exploiting these properties, holograms have been used for determining the size distribution of particles in a fog cloud, and have been suggested for recording nuclear tracks in a 'bubble' chamber. Some remarkable results have been obtained by using a pulsed laser to arrest motion in a suspension of freely swimming plankton organisms. When the re-constructed image was subsequently inspected with a microscope, sharp images were seen in planes separated by distances of up to 26 mm (1 in) along the axis.

Holograms can be used for creating beams of light with special distributions of intensity and directionality, and in so doing can function as optical elements. For example, a hologram, made in an appropriate manner from the light distribution given by a lens with aberration, can be used in combination with the lens as an aberration-free system capable of forming sharp images.

Holograms have been applied in a number of novel interferometric procedures. The hologram provides a permanent record of the shape of an object at one instant, and this can be compared with the shape later, when the object is under stress or has been submitted to potentially distorting treatments. Such changes of shape can be observed by interference fringes formed between the re-constructed image and:

(i) the same object under load or after treatment;
(ii) the reconstructed image from a second hologram recorded on the same plate; or
(iii) another ostensibly identical object placed in the same position as the first object.

Analogous principles have been applied to the recording of vibration modes and flow patterns. A fascinating example is the recording of flow patterns in the gas of an incandescent lamp by combining holograms produced by the lamp when cold and when lit. In this method, optical errors produced by striations in the glass envelope are cancelled out.

Holography can also be used in cases where normal imaging by lenses or mirrors is impractical. Ennos [33] cited the possibility of imaging down to atomic dimensions with X-rays and the development of techniques for mapping out terrain by holographic processing of information obtained by 'side-looking' radar.

Further indications of the scope of interferometric applications have been given in a beautifully illustrated paper by Brooks [37]. He noted that holograms can do many of the tasks of conventional interferometers in measuring small displacements and changes of refractive index, but with lower quality components and at lower cost. The savings were expected to be particularly important when the subject of the interferometric study was large.

In addition to discussion of several of the applications mentioned above, a review by Stroke [32] described the synthesis of holograms of imaginary objects corresponding to sets of computed image-point co-ordinates in space. Hologram images were built up by programmed movements of a digitally movable microscope lens and pinhole system illuminated by a laser beam. In effect, the concept is analogous to the generation of computed microelectronic masks by programmed movements of plate or lens (p. 352). Holograms of ultrasonic fields have also been made by photographing the patterns of ripples in the surface of a tank of water in which a test sample was irradiated with an ultrasonic beam.

In conclusion, it may be noted that publications on holography (and topics related thereto) have for several years formed a substantial proportion of the total output of journals accepting optical papers. There is every indication that this trend will continue. In this situation, readers wishing to keep abreast are advised to watch later issues of the journals cited in this section.

Conclusion

This chapter confirms a truth already repeatedly demonstrated in earlier chapters of this book. It is that useful and sometimes quite wonderful results can accrue from microphotography's ability to record highly condensed information. Superficially, some of the results do not always seem to contain condensed information. A single narrow and sharp straight line, for instance, would seem to contain little information. Because it is sharp, however, it must be made by a process potentially capable of greatly condensing information. Moreover, many digits are needed to describe the exact positions of the edges, and just there, information can be considered to be highly condensed.

Photographic materials capable of producing very high condensation rates have only been freely available for the last quarter of a century. Their existence seems to have stimulated certain types of creative imagination, and facilitated refinements needed by science and industry. These would seem to be the reasons for microphotography's essential rôle at many of the growth points in science and industry. Present trends suggest that exciting further developments are forthcoming. For this reason, the author believes that microphotography merits much further study. It is hoped that this book will help others on their way.

REFERENCES

[1] Baker, L. R., *Perspective*, 6, 133, 1964 (see reference [12], Chapter 4).
[2] (a) Narath, A., 'La Limite de Résolution des Couches Sensible et sa Mesure', *9th Int., Congress. Phot.*, Paris, 1935, 297.
(b) Perrin, F. H. and J. H. Altman, *J. Opt. Soc. Am.*, 41, 265, 1951 (see reference [7], Chapter 5).

Microphotography as a Research Tool · 473

[3] Smith, E. T. and Stevens, G. W. W., 'Photographic Images for Resolution Testing in Radiography', in *Science and Applications of Photography*, Proceedings of Royal Photographic Society Centenary Conference (London, 1955), p. 412.

[4] Lumière, A. and L. and Seyewetz, A., 'Development of Photographic Plates after Fixing', *Brit. J. Phot.*, 58, 643, 1911.

[5] Lohse, J. M. and Bruins, P. F., *Phot. Sci. Eng.*, 7, 238, 1963 (see reference [39(a)], Chapter 2).

[6] Boyd, G. A., *Autoradiography in Biology and Medicine*, Academic Press (New York, 1955).

[7] Pelc, S. R., 'Autoradiographic Technique', *Nature*, 160, 749, 1947.

[8] Kowaliski, P., *Versuche zur Verbesserung des Auflösungsvermögens Photographischer Schichten*; Effingerhof (Brugg, 1944).

[9] Berriman, R. W., Herz, R. H. and Stevens, G. W. W., 'A New Photographic Material: A High-Resolution Emulsion for Autoradiography', *Brit. J. Radiol.*, 23, 472, 1950.

[10] Stevens, G. W. W., 'Radioactive Microphotographs for Resolution Testing in Autoradiography', *Brit. J. Radiol.*, 23, 723, 1950.

[11] Lamerton, L. F. and Harriss, E. B., 'Resolution and Sensitivity Considerations in Autoradiography', *J. Phot. Sci.*, 2, 135, 1954.

[12] Oka, S., Mukaibo, T., Suzuki, S., Nagae, H., Yamada, K., Adachi, K. and Osakada, A., 'Preparation of Test Chart Used for Measuring the Resolving Power of Nuclear Emulsions on Irradiation by β-rays of S^{35}', *Ann. Rep. Res. Comm. Appl. Artif. Radioactive Isotopes Japan*, 3, 56, 1956.

[13] Bleecken, S., *Atompraxis*, 'The Determination of Autoradiographic Resolution with ^{32}p-Toned Test Images,' 13, 190, 1967.

[14] Anon., 'Photo-Grid Techniques for Measuring Distortion', *Iron Age*, 156, 8 November, p. 78, 1945.

[15] Stevens, G. W. W., 'Microphotography as a Research Tool', as reference [3], p. 493.

[16] Bell, R. L. and Langdon, T. G., 'A Method of Printing Grids on to Metal Surfaces for Deformation Studies', *J. Sci. Instruments*, 42, 896, 1965.

[17] Dally, J. W. and Riley, W. F., 'Experimental Stress Analysis with the Moiré Fringe Method', *Product Engineering*, 36, 41, 24 May, 1965.

[18] Ehrenberg, W. and White, M., 'Resolution in Contact Microradiography', *Brit. J. Radiol.*, 32, 558, 1959.

[19] (a) Blake, G. C. Private communication, *see also*
(b) Blake, G. C., 'An Experimental Investigation into the Permeability of Enamel and Dentine with Reference to its Relation to Dental Cavities', *Proc. Roy. Soc. Medicine*, 57, 678, 1958.

[20] (a) Combée, B., Houtman, J. and Recourt, A., 'A Sealed-off X-ray Tube for Contact Microradiography', *Brit. J. Radiol.*, 28, 537, 1955.
(b) Blackett, N. M., 'The Resolution Obtainable with a Commercially Available Microradiography Unit', *Brit. J. Radiol.*, 31, 368, 1958.
(c) Ehrenberg, W. and White, M., as reference [18].

[21] (a) Cosslett, V. E. and Nixon, W. C., *X-ray Microscopy*, Cambridge University Press (Cambridge, 1960).
(b) Cosslett, V. E., Engström, A. and Pattee, H. H., Jr, (Editors),

474 · *Microphotography*

X-ray Microscopy and Microradiography, Academic Press (New York, 1957).

(c) Engström, A., Cosslett, V. E. and Pattee, H. H., Jr, (Editors), *X-ray Microscopy and X-ray Microanalysis*, Elsevier Publishing Co. (Amsterdam, 1960).

[22] Cosslett, V. E. and Nixon, W. C., 'The X-ray Shadow Microscope', (a) *Nature*, **168**, 24, 1951.
(b) *J. Applied. Physics*, **24**, 616, 1953.

[23] Wiener, O., 'Stehende Lichtwellen und die Schwingungsrichtung polarisierten Lichtes', *Wied. Ann.*, **40**, 203, 1890.

[24] Lippmann, G., 'La Photographie des Couleurs', *Bul. Soc. Franc. Phot.*, **7** (Series II), 74, 1891.

[25] Wolfe, R. N. and Eisen, F. C., 'The Spatial Photographic Recording of Fine Interference Phenomena', *J. Opt. Soc. Am.*, **40**, 143, 1950.

[26] Gabor, D., 'Diffraction Microscopy', *Research*, **4**, 107, 1951.

[27] (a) Gabor, D., 'A New Microscopic Principle', *Nature*, **161**, 777, 1948.
(b) Gabor, D., 'Microscopy by Reconstructed Wavefronts', *Proc. Roy. Soc.*, A.**197**, 454, 1949.

[28] Leith, E. N. and Upatnieks, J., 'Wavefront Reconstruction with Continuous-Tone Objects', *J. Opt. Soc. Am.*, **53**, 1377, 1963.

[29] Stroke, G. W., 'Lensless Photography', *International Science and Technology*, 52, May, 1965.

[30] Rogers, G. L., 'The Design of Experiments for Recording and Reconstructing Three-dimensional Objects in Coherent Light (Holography)', *J. Sci. Inst.*, **43**, 677, 1966.

[31] Lin, L. H. and LoBianco, C. V., 'Experimental Techniques in making Multicolor White Light Reconstructed Holograms', *Applied Optics*, **6**, 1255, 1967.

[32] Stroke, G. W., 'Holography Steps into New Fields', *Scientific Research*, **2**, 41, 1967.

[33] Ennos, A. E., 'Holography and its Applications', *Contemporary Physics*, **8**, 153, 1967.

[34] Burch, J. M., 'The Applications of Lasers in Production Engineering', *The Production Engineer*, **44**, 431, 1965.

[35] Stroke, G. W., *An Introduction to Coherent Optics and Holography*, Academic Press (New York, 1966).

[36] DeVelis, J. B., *Theory and Applications of Holography*, Addison-Wesley (Reading, Massachusetts, 1967).

[37] Brooks, R. E., 'New Dimensions for Interferometry', *Electronics*, **124**, 15 May, 88, 1967.

[38] Chamber, R. P. and Courtney-Pratt, J. S., 'Bibliography on Holograms', *J. Soc. Mot. Pict. Tel. Eng.*, **75**, 373–434 and 759–808, 1966. Includes précis of most references cited.

Appendix I · Processing Formulae

The formulae given in the following pages are those which the author has found particularly useful for the production of high quality images on extreme-resolution emulsions, and for the making of intermediate transparencies. American readers should note that some of the formulae published by Kodak Ltd in Great Britain are not included in the lists printed by the Eastman Kodak Company, but equivalent figures in American units are included for their convenience. These recommendations are in the main based on experience with sensitive materials commercially available in Great Britain. It is not likely that they will be found unsuitable for plates manufactured in other countries, but if in doubt the reader should use the formulae recommended by the manufacturer of the material he is using. In the American versions 28 per cent acetic acid has been substituted for the 'glacial', and 'desiccated' sulphite and carbonate should be used where 'anhydrous' is given.

(A) Developers

High-contrast negative developer. 'Kodak' formula D.19b

	Avoirdupois (British)	Metric	Avoirdupois (American)
'Elon'[1]	77 grains	2·2 grams	32 grains
Sodium sulphite (anhyd.)	5 ounces 330 grains	72·0 grams	2 ounces 180 grains
Hydroquinone	310 grains	8·8 grams	125 grains
Sodium carbonate (anhyd.)	3 ounces 370 grains	48·0 grams	1 ounce 260 grains
Potassium bromide	140 grains	4·0 grams	58 grains
Water to make	80 ounces	1,000 cc	32 ounces

When used at full strength, this developer is useful for obtaining high contrast on photomechanical or high-speed negative materials, without the use of caustic solutions. May be used for developing master negatives with development times up to 10 minutes at 20° C (68° F).

[1] Monomethyl paraminophenol sulphate, also known as 'Metol', 'Genol', etc.

Physical developer

(Formula due to Lüppo-Cramer, *Photographische Industrie* (1921), p. 797)

STOCK SOLUTION A

	Avoirdupois (British)	Metric	Avoirdupois (American)
'Elon'	175 grains	20 grams	290 grains
Citric acid	350 grains	40 grams	1 ounce 150 grains
Gum arabic (20% solution)	380 minims	40 cc	1¼ ounces
Distilled water to make	20 ounces	1,000 cc	32 ounces

STOCK SOLUTION B

Silver nitrate. 10 per cent solution in distilled water

Solution A should be kept for only about one week after making up.
Solution B will keep indefinitely in a brown bottle.

As with other physical developers, all vessels should be cleaned before use, preferably with concentrated nitric acid. (*Caution*—very corrosive!)

For use, add 1 part of solution B to 25 parts of A *just* before starting development, and develop for up to 5 minutes at 20° C (68° F). This developer may be used for developing latent images in various emulsions (Lippmann, wet-collodion, silver-albumen), and also for intensifying chemically developed images in Lippmann or extreme-resolution emulsions.

High-contrast developer for Extreme-Resolution emulsions.
'Kodak' formula D.178

STOCK SOLUTION

	Avoirdupois (British)	Metric	Avoirdupois (American)
Sodium sulphite (anhyd.)	7 ounces 90 grains	90 grams	3 ounces
Hydroquinone	3 ounces 265 grains	45 grams	1½ ounces
Sodium hydroxide (caustic soda)	1 ounce 190 grains	18 grams	260 grains
Potassium bromide	2 ounces 175 grains	30 grams	1 ounce
Water to make	80 ounces	1,000 cc	32 ounces

Note. The hydroquinone will not dissolve completely until the sodium hydroxide is added.

Use 2 parts Stock Solution to 1 part of water, and develop Maximum-Resolution plates for 3–4 minutes at 20° C (68° F). This solution can also be used for high-contrast development of photomechanical materials, when making line negatives. It gives appreciably higher contrast than 'Kodak' Formula D.19b. For this latter purpose it is better to increase the sodium hydroxide content to 3 ounces (British), 37·5 grams (Metric) or

1¼ ounces (American). This gives 'Kodak' Formula D.8, which for many years was recommended for use with Eastman Kodak High-Resolution Plates.

READY MIXED HIGH-CONTRAST DEVELOPERS FOR EXTREME-RESOLUTION EMULSIONS

To avoid the dust hazard of preparing solutions from dry chemicals and to facilitate obtaining reproducible results, industrial users of extreme-resolution emulsions are tending to prefer to use ready mixed developer solutions. To meet this demand, the Eastman Kodak Co. introduced the H.R.P. (High-Resolution Plate) developer, and Kodak Ltd recommend D.G.10 for use with Maximum-Resolution Plates.

Normal-contrast developer for photomechanical or extreme-resolution emulsions. 'Kodak' formula D.158

STOCK SOLUTION

	Avoirdupois (British)		Metric	Avoirdupois (American)	
'Elon'		110 grains	3·2 grams		47 grains
Sodium sulphite (anhyd.)	4 ounces		50·0 grams	1 ounce	280 grains
Hydroquinone	1 ounce	40 grains	13·3 grams		195 grains
Sodium carbonate (anhyd.)	5 ounces	220 grains	69·0 grams	2 ounces	130 grains
Potassium bromide		32 grains	0·9 grams		13 grains
Water to make	80 ounces		1,000 cc	32 ounces	

For use, dilute with an equal volume of water, and develop for up to 4 minutes at 20° C (68° F). This developer is recommended for Maximum-Resolution plates in applications where preservation of fine-grain structure is more important than high contrast, e.g. for microradiography.

Low-contrast developer for making transparencies. 'Kodak' formula D.165

STOCK SOLUTION

	Avoirdupois (British)		Metric	Avoirdupois (American)	
'Elon'		210 grains	6 grams		90 grains
Sodium sulphite (anhyd.)	2 ounces		25 grams		365 grains
Sodium carbonate (anhyd.)	3 ounces		37 grams	1 ounce	100 grains
Potassium bromide		35 grains	1 gram		15 grains
Water to make	80 ounces		1,000 cc	32 ounces	

Dilute 1 part of Stock Solution with 3 parts of water, and develop for up to 4 minutes at 20° C (68° F). When used with photogravure plates, this developer can be used to make continuous-tone transparencies with a low density range, for use with extreme-resolution emulsions having high contrast and a short exposure scale.

Reversal processing for extreme-resolution emulsions.
'Kodak' formula R.21

STOCK SOLUTION A. BLEACHING BATH

	Avoirdupois (British)	Metric	Avoirdupois (American)
Water	80 ounces	1,000 cc	32 ounces
Potassium dichromate	4 ounces	50 grams	1½ ounces
Sulphuric acid (concentrated)	4 fluid ounces	50 cc	1½ fluid ounces

Dissolve the dichromate in the water, then add the sulphuric acid *slowly*, with constant stirring, to the cold solution. For use dilute one part of Stock Solution with nine parts of water.

STOCK SOLUTION B. CLEARING BATH

	Avoirdupois (British)	Metric	Avoirdupois (American)
Water	80 ounces	1,000 cc	32 ounces
Sodium sulphite (anhyd.)	4 ounces	50 grams	1½ ounces
Sodium hydroxide (caustic soda)	35 grains	1 gram	15 grains

REVERSAL PROCESS

Develop 3 minutes in D.178 (see Appendix I, A),
Wash 2 minutes in running water,
Bleach in R.21A. (diluted 1 + 9) for about 45 seconds,
Turn on room lights,
Clear for 30 seconds in undiluted R.21B,
Wash in running water for 2 minutes,
Expose for 15 seconds close to a 100-watt bulb,
Re-develop in D.178 for 3 minutes at 68° F,
Wash for 5 minutes, and bathe 2 minutes in clean industrial spirit to remove sensitizing dye.

Note. For reasons discussed on p. 90, the quality of fine lines obtainable by reversal processing always tends to be worse than that given by direct development.

PREVENTION OF LIME SCUM IN DEVELOPERS

If developer solutions cannot be conveniently compounded with distilled, de-mineralized or soft water, scum due to precipitation of lime and magnesium salts in the developer may be prevented in two ways:

(a) The complete solution diluted to working strength may be left for the precipitate to settle. After several hours the clear supernatant liquor can be decanted and used.

(b) Scum formation can be inhibited by adding sequestering agents such as 'calgon' (sodium hexametaphosphate) to the developer. One source [1] suggests addition of from 1 to 5 grams per litre (35 to 175 grains per 80 ounces), and another [2] recommends 0·5 grams per litre for developers containing borax, and 2 grams per litre for developers containing carbonate.

REFERENCES

[1] Data booklet GN.5 (p. 16), (published by Kodak Ltd, England).
[2] Clerc, L. P., *Photography. Theory and Practice*, 3rd edition, Pitman (London, 1954), p. 197.

(B) Stop Baths

Non-hardening stop bath. 'Kodak' formula SB. 1a

	Avoirdupois (British)	Metric	Avoirdupois (American)
Water	80 ounces	1,000 cc	32 ounces
Acetic acid (glacial)	4 ounces	50 cc	—
or Acetic acid (28% solution)	—	125 cc	4 ounces

A short immersion of extreme-resolution emulsions, after development in a caustic-hydroquinone developer, greatly reduces the risk of stain.

Tropical hardening stop bath. 'Kodak' formula SB.4

	Avoirdupois (British)	Metric	Avoirdupois (American)
Water	80 ounces	1,000 cc	32 ounces
Potassium Chrome alum	2 ounces 175 grains	30 grams	1 ounce
Sodium sulphate (cryst.)	11 ounces 90 grains	140 grams	—
or Sodium sulphate (anhyd.)	4 ounces 350 grains	60 grams	2 ounces

The freshly made bath is a violet-blue colour and keeps indefinitely while unused. It is unwise to store a partially used bath, and the solution should in any case be discarded after the equivalent of twenty 10 × 8 in plates per gallon have been treated.

Agitate the plates for 30–45 seconds to avoid unevenness when they are first transferred from the developer, and leave them for 3 minutes. The use of this solution counteracts the tendency of the emulsion to swell very rapidly when rinsing after development. Its use is likely to prove beneficial when exact preservation of image size is required.

R

(C) Fixing Bath

Acid hardening-fixing bath. 'Kodak' formula F.5

	Avoirdupois (British)	Metric	Avoirdupois (American)
Warm water (52° C, 125° F)	48 ounces	600 cc	80 ounces
Sodium thiosulphate (hypo. cryst.)	19 ounces, 90 grains	240 grams	2 pounds
Sodium sulphite (anhyd.)	1 ounce, 90 grains	15 grams	2 ounces
Acetic acid (28% pure)	—	47·5 cc	6 fluid ounces
or ,, ,, (glacial)	1 fluid ounce, 120 minims	17 cc	—
Boric acid (cryst.)	260 grains	7·5 grams	1 ounce
Potassium alum	1 ounce, 90 grains	15 grams	2 ounces
Water to make	80 ounces	1,000 cc	1 gallon

This bath will fix most plate emulsions in a few minutes, but ten minutes' treatment at 20° C (68° F), is recommended to ensure satisfactory hardening of gelatin emulsions. Prolonged immersion of fine-grain silver images is to be avoided, since it is likely to result in a reduction of density.

(D) Miscellaneous Formulae

Ammonium-Thiosulphate reducer and stain remover
(R. W. Henn, J. I. Crabtree and H. D. Russell,
J. Phot. Soc. Am. (Phot. Sci. and Tech.), **17B**, 1951, 110)

Stock hardener solution. 'Kodak' formula F.5a

	Avoirdupois (British)	Metric	Avoirdupois (American)
Water (52° C, 125° F)	50 ounces	625 cc	21 ounces
Sodium sulphite (anhyd.)	6 ounces 110 grains	75 grams	2 ounces 220 grains
Acetic acid (glacial)	5 ounces 120 minims	66 cc	—
or Acetic acid (28% solution)	—	236 cc	9 ounces
Boric acid (cryst.)	3 ounces 55 grains	37·5 grams	1 ounce 110 grains
Potassium alum	6 ounces 110 grains	75 grams	2 ounces 220 grains
Water to make	80 ounces	1,000 cc	32 ounces

To prepare reducer mix together:

	Avoirdupois (British)		Metric	Avoirdupois (American)
Ammonium thiosulphate	3 ounces		150 grams	5 ounces
F.5a Stock Solution	4 ounces		200 cc	6½ ounces
Citric acid (for slow-working solution)		130 grains	15 grams	½ ounce
Citric acid (for fast-working solution)		260 grains	30 grams	1 ounce
Water to make	20 ounces		1,000 cc	32 ounces

The authors describe the use of these solutions for selectively removing stain with a minimum of attack on the chemically developed image. When used with microphotographic images the necessary time of treatment (up to 20 minutes at 20° C; 68° F), should be found by preliminary tests; or the treatment should be interrupted at intervals to permit its progress to be assessed.

Farmer's 'cutting' reducer. 'Kodak' formula R.4a

STOCK SOLUTION A

	Avoirdupois (British)	Metric	Avoirdupois (American)
Potassium ferricyanide	6 ounces	75 grams	2¼ ounces
Water to make	80 ounces	1,000 cc	32 ounces

STOCK SOLUTION B

	Avoirdupois (British)	Metric	Avoirdupois (American)
Sodium thiosulphate (hypo. cryst.)	19 ounces	240 grams	8 ounces
Water to make	80 ounces	1,000 cc	32 ounces

For use, take 1 part of Solution A, 4 parts of Solution B and add 27 parts of water. Pour the mixed solution at once over the negative to be reduced. Watch closely, and remove the negative as soon as sufficient reduction has occurred. Wash thoroughly before drying. This solution is suitable for making line 'master' negatives on 'process' plates, but is likely to prove too drastic for truly microscopic images. (See appropriate sections of Chapter 4.)

Mercury intensifier. 'Kodak' formula IN.1

	Avoirdupois (British)		Metric	Avoirdupois (American
Potassium bromide	1 ounce	350 grains	22·5 grams	¾ ounce
Mercuric chloride[1]	1 ounce	350 grains	22·5 grams	¾ ounce
Water to make	80 ounces		1,000 cc	32 ounces

[1] See footnote on p. 482.

Bleach the developed image in the above solution until it is white, and wash thoroughly. Blacken in a developer such as D.19b or D.154 (see Appendix I, A). The process can be repeated.

The same intensifier is useful for increasing the density and contrast of 'line' negatives, particularly if they have first been treated in a 'cutting' reducer. For this application it is often more convenient to blacken in the following solution:

	Avoirdupois (*British*)		*Metric*	*Avoirdupois* (*American*)	
Sodium or potassium cyanide[1]	1 ounce	90 grains	15·0 grams	½	ounce
Silver nitrate	1 ounce	350 grains	22·5 grams	¾	ounce
Distilled water	80 ounces		1,000 cc	32	ounces

· Dissolve the cyanide and silver nitrate separately each in half of the water, and add the silver nitrate to the cyanide until a permanent precipitate is *just* formed. Allow the mixture to stand for some time and filter.

Etch-bleach bath. 'Kodak' formula EB.2

STOCK SOLUTION A

	Avoirdupois (*British*)		*Metric*	*Avoirdupois* (*American*)	
Water (52° C, 125° F)	60 ounces		750 cc	24 ounces	
Copper sulphate (cryst.)	9 ounces	220 grains	120 grams	4 ounces	
Citric acid	12 ounces		150 grams	5 ounces	
Potassium bromide		260 grains	7·5 grams		110 grains
Water to make	80 ounces		1,000 cc	32 ounces	

SOLUTION B

Hydrogen peroxide 3 per cent solution.
('10 volume' solution, as purchased.)

For use, mix equal parts of A and B Solutions. The bleaching of the silver image should be accompanied by rapid disintegration of the gelatin in the blackened areas. Hydrogen peroxide solutions tend to decompose on storage. If the peroxide is too weak, the proportion of Solution B may be increased. The bleaching action will then be somewhat slower, but the final result should be quite satisfactory.

[1] *Warning*

In appropriate cases, these solutions are very effective, but it is unfortunate that both mercuric salts and cyanides are scheduled poisons. Cyanide should be handled with special care, since it can evolve a deadly gas, particularly if allowed to mix with acid solutions. To combat this hazard, run the cold tap fast for 15 seconds before pouring a discarded cyanide solution slowly down the drain. Continue running the water to flush out the drain. Never use cyanide solutions in poorly ventilated rooms.

Appendix II · Lens Calculations

(A) Approximate Relationship between *u* and *v*

When focusing an objective for microphotography it is often useful to know the mutual relationship between changes in the distance of the object plane (*u*), and the corresponding changes in the objective-image distance (*v*).

Changes in one quantity resulting from a change in the other can be calculated exactly from the lens formula (Chapter 4, p. 96), but it is usually only necessary to know the approximate magnitude of these quantities. Values sufficiently accurate for most practical purposes can be found from Table 17, which has been computed for objectives of nominal focal length.

Table 17. Changes in *v* (objective-image distance) produced by changes in *u* (distance of object plane)

Change in u	Corresponding changes in v for focal length value of						
	4 mm	8 mm	12·5 mm	16 mm	25 mm	50 mm	100 mm
mm							
∞–10,000	0·0016	0·006	0·016	0·026	0·063	0·251	1·010
10,000– 5,000	0·0016	0·007	0·015	0·025	0·063	0·254	1·031
5,000– 2,000	0·0048	0·019	0·048	0·078	0·191	0·777	3·222
2,000– 1,000	0·0081	0·033	0·079	0·131	0·324	1·350	5·848
1,000– 900	0·0018	0·007	0·018	0·030	0·073	0·309	1·389
900– 800	0·0022	0·009	0·022	0·037	0·093	0·392	1·786
800– 700	0·0029	0·011	0·029	0·047	0·119	0·513	2·381
700– 600	0·0039	0·016	0·039	0·064	0·161	0·699	3·333
600– 500	0·0054	0·022	0·054	0·091	0·229	1·011	5·000
500– 400	0·0081	0·033	0·083	0·138	0·351	1·587	8·333
400– 300	0·0137	0·056	0·141	0·234	0·606	2·857	16·667
300– 200	0·0275	0·114	0·289	0·490	1·298	6·667	50·0

TO USE THE TABLE

All the distances in the table are given in millimetres, and can be converted to inches by using the factor 0·001 in equals 0·025 mm (to be exact 0·0254 mm). It should be remembered that the changes of *u* and *v* are of opposite sign. Thus a *decrease* in *u* is accompanied by an *increase* in *v*, and conversely.

Figures for larger changes than those tabulated can be calculated by adding the changes in the vertical columns, and approximate values for smaller changes can be found by dividing the appropriate figures by the factor needed. In practice this table is likely to be used in two ways.

(i) In the focusing of distance pieces (see p. 145) it is necessary to know by how much the distance piece should be shortened (i.e. decrease in v), to move the object plane out by a required amount. For instance, with a 16-mm objective a movement of the object plane from 700 to 800 mm should result from shortening the distance piece by 0·047 mm. Similarly a movement from 500 to 800 mm would need the removal of 0·091 plus 0·064 plus 0·047 mm or 0·202 mm in all.

(ii) This table can also be used to show the magnitude of the changes in the distance (u) needed to produce small changes in v; for instance, when fine focusing is performed by changing the camera-to-object-plane distance. Thus with a 4-mm objective a decrease of u from 700 to 600 mm will increase the objective-image distance (v) by 0·0039 mm.

(B) Precise Relationship between u and v

When the figures given in Table 18 are not sufficiently precise, it is necessary to make allowance for the difference between the actual and the nominal focal lengths of the objective. This can be simply done by tabulating related values of u and v for an objective whose focal length is unity. As shown in Chapter 4 (p. 97), this simplifies their relationship to the form

$$v = \frac{u}{u - 1}.$$

Moreover, the reduction factor is found by dividing u by v, hence

$$R = \frac{u}{v} = \frac{u}{\dfrac{u}{u - 1}} = u - 1.$$

A useful table can be constructed by tabulating a suitable range of reductions, and related values of u and calculating v from this formula.

Table 18. Relation between u and v for a focal length of unity

Reduction factor	u	v	Reduction factor	u	v
10	11	1·1000	56	57	1·0179
12	13	1·0833	68	69	1·0147
14	15	1·0714	80	81	1·0125
17	18	1·0588	96	97	1·0104
20	21	1·0500	112	113	1·0089
24	25	1·0417	136	137	1·0074
28	29	1·0357	160	161	1·0063
34	35	1·0294	192	193	1·0052
40	41	1·0250	224	225	1·0045
48	49	1·0208			

Figures for u and v for any given objective can then be found by multiplying the values in this table by the actual focal length of the objective. The precision obtained is likely to be limited by the accuracy with which the focal length can be measured.

If many calculations of this type have to be made with varying degrees of reduction, it is convenient to plot u against v on single logarithmic paper. v is plotted on the linear scale and u on the logarithmic scale. Now if R is the required reduction, R plus 1 is the value of u; and with the aid of this graph the value of v corresponding to R plus 1 is read off. The result can be checked by dividing u by v, which should equal R within about 0·1 per cent. Since this method provides values for both u and v, the object-plane-to-image-plane distance D, which equals their sum, is also directly obtainable. This is convenient, since the distance D can be measured more readily than either u or v separately.

(C) Depth of Field and Depth of Focus

It is apparent from Chapter 8 that sharp images can be obtained in some cases at different levels in a microphotographic emulsion. In fact, the depth of focus is not determined only by the performance of the objective, but is also influenced by the thickness and transparency of the emulsion.

With some extreme-resolution emulsions, in particular, the phenomenon of optical sectioning permits sharp images of fine black lines to be obtained at all levels in the emulsion. In fact, the thickness of the emulsion effectively supplements the depth of focus and necessarily also the depth of field. The depth of field which should for this reason be obtained under different conditions with an emulsion layer $5\,\mu$ thick is shown in the following table.

Table 19. Depth of field equivalent to $5\,\mu$ depth of focus

Distance of object plane (*millimetres*)	Depth of field (*in millimetres*) equivalent to 5 μ depth of focus for objectives of focal length						
	4 *mm*	8 *mm*	12·5 *mm*	16 *mm*	25 *mm*	50 *mm*	100 *mm*
200	12	2·88	1·13	0·66	0·25	0·045	0·005
300	27·4	6·7	2·65	1·58	0·61	0·100	0·020
400	49	12	4·8	2·88	1·13	0·25	0·045
500	77	19	7·6	4·58	1·81	0·41	0·080
600	111	27·4	11·0	6·67	2·65	0·61	0·100
700	—	37·4	15·1	9·14	3·65	0·85	0·18
800	—	49	19·9	12·0	4·81	1·13	0·25
900	—	62	25·2	15·3	6·13	1·45	0·32
1,000	—	77	31·2	18·9	7·62	1·81	0·41
2,000	—	310	126	77	31·2	7·61	1·81
5,000	—	—	—	485	198	49	12
10,000	—	—	—	—	—	198	49

These figures form a useful basis for deciding the magnitude of the changes in u which should be made in different conditions, when focusing by changing the camera-object-plane distance.

In interpreting this table it should be noted that these figures were calculated from a formula which is only accurate when the changes in object distance are relatively small.

The figures in *italics* should, therefore, be considered as approximate since the changes exceed 5 per cent of the total distance.

Appendix III · Series of Exposure Times

The response of the human eye, or the density produced by a silver-halide emulsion, are approximately proportional to the logarithm of the light intensity falling on them; and for this reason it is generally recommended that photographic exposure-tests should be made with a geometrical series of intensities or times. This results in the production of images showing approximately equal density increases with each increase of exposure, and also having equal increases of visual blackness. Other advantages of geometrical series are that they are consistent with the system used for marking lens diaphragms, and permit any desired accuracy to be obtained over a given exposure range with a minimum number of tests.

An important factor in designing exposure tests is the magnitude of the increment by which the exposures are increased. This depends firstly on how nearly the correct exposure is already known, and secondly on how closely the exposure must be controlled to ensure the photographic quality required.

If the conditions are completely unfamiliar, time can often be saved by making a test with a large factor such as 4 or 10. With the factor 4, a range of 1,000 : 1 can be covered with only 6 test exposures (i.e. 1, 4, 16, 64, 256 and 1,012 seconds), and if the correct exposure falls within the range of times given, one or other of the images will be incorrectly exposed by a factor of not more than 2. A second test with a total range of 2 : 1 will then enable the correct exposure to be determined precisely.

Photographers making contact prints or enlargements are often advised to make exposure tests using a factor of 2 (i.e. using times such as 5, 10, 20, 40 . . . seconds), but this factor is too large to secure the highest possible print quality with fixed development conditions. In practice the prints are often inspected during development, which is curtailed or prolonged to compensate for a slightly incorrect exposure. The disadvantage of such a large factor really becomes apparent when making prints from small-density-range negatives on high-contrast papers, or when making microphotographs on high-contrast emulsions. In the latter instance particularly, the problem is aggravated by the impracticability of developing by inspection.

A more sensitive control is obtained by using exposure times selected from the series:

$$10, 14, 20, 28, 40, 56, 80 \ldots \text{seconds}$$

Each time is approximately $\sqrt{2}$ greater than the preceding one[1] and the factor by which the exposure increases is equivalent to half a 'stop'. When the lamp intensity and development conditions are carefully controlled, it is sometimes useful to use an even finer series:

10, 12, 14, 17, 20, 24, 28, 34, 40, 48, 56, 68, 80 . . . seconds

The factor is approximately $\sqrt[4]{2}$, corresponding to a quarter of a stop.

When making exposure tests for microphotography, the surest practice is to expose a complete image at each exposure time. With this method and exposure times of ten seconds or longer, manual timing with the aid of a large-dial dark-room clock is sufficiently accurate even for the very fine $\sqrt[4]{2}$ series of times.

If these fine exposure series are used when enlarging, the $\sqrt{2}$ series may be built up by covering successive strips of one sheet of paper as each exposure time elapses. Thus the whole sheet could be exposed for 10 seconds, and further times of 4, 6, 8, 12, 16 and 24 seconds given with an opaque card moved farther over the paper between each exposure. Thus neighbouring strips of the emulsion are exposed respectively for 10, 14, 20, 28, 40, 56 and 80 seconds. With the finest ($\sqrt[4]{2}$) series, however, errors in the timing of the increments, or in the response of the emulsion to intermittent exposures, may make this cumulative-exposure technique unsatisfactory. The rest should, therefore, preferably be made with separate strips of paper, each exposed for a single time from this series.

[1] In fact, $\sqrt{2}$ is 1·4141. . . (recurring), so that 14 is 1 per cent less than $\sqrt{2} \times 10$, and 20 is 1 per cent more than $\sqrt{2} \times 14$.

Indexes

Subject Index

Name and Author Index

505